Visit classzone.com and get connected

Online resources for students and parents

ClassZone resources provide instruction, practice, and learning support.

eEdition Plus ONLINE

This interactive version of the text encourages students to explore science.

Content Review Online

Interactive review reinforces the big idea and key concepts of each chapter.

SciLinks

NSTA-selected links provide relevant Web resources correlated to the text.

Chapter–Based Support

Math tutorials, news, resources, test practice, and a misconceptions database help students succeed.

Now it all clicks!™

CLASSZONE.COM

McDougal Littell

McDougal Littell

CALIFORNIA

Science

FOCUS ON LIFE SCIENCES

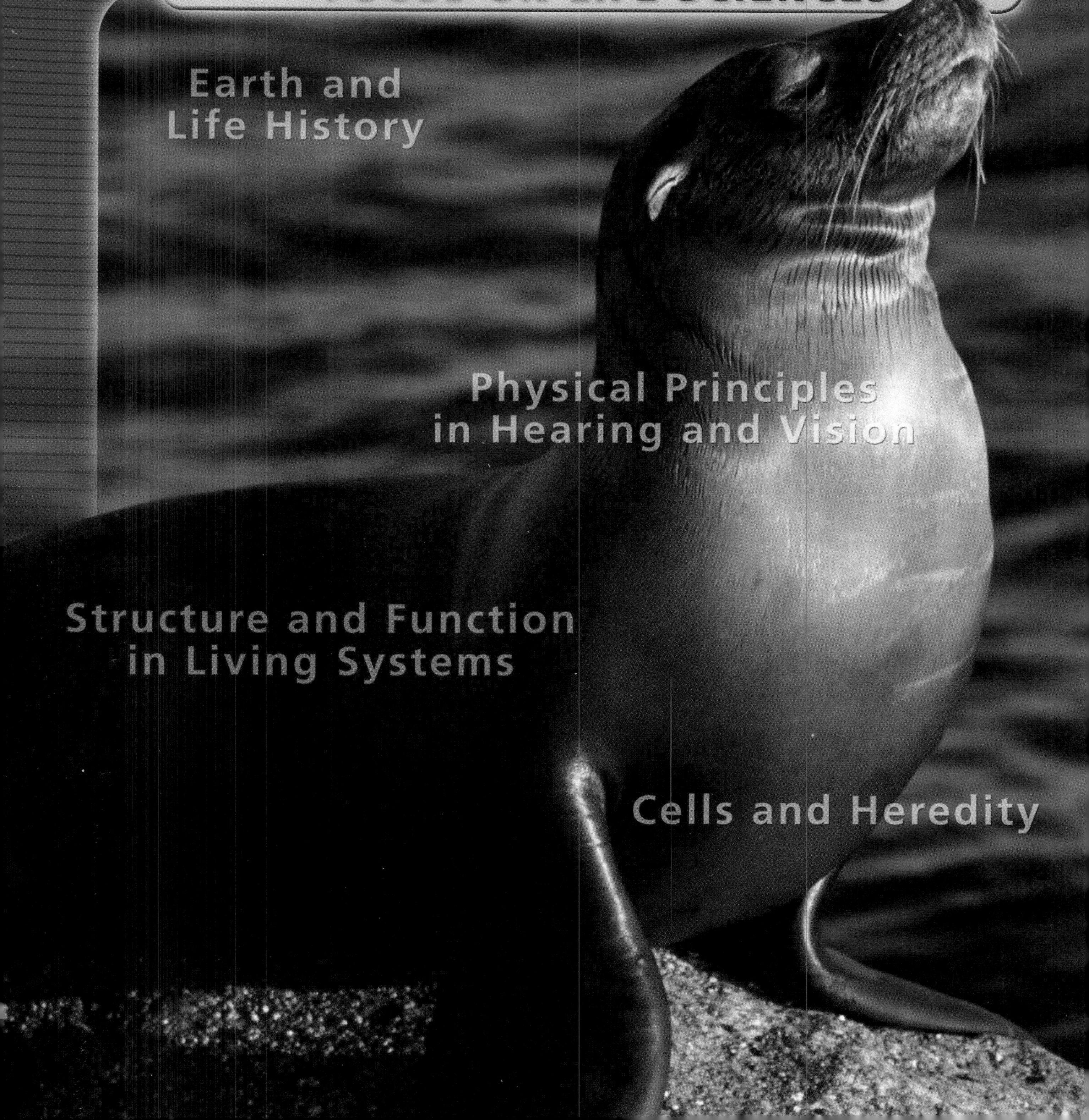

Earth and
Life History

Physical Principles
in Hearing and Vision

Structure and Function
in Living Systems

Cells and Heredity

Science Content Standards for California Public Schools reproduced by permission, California Department of Education, CDE Press, 1430 N Street, Suite 3207, Sacramento, CA 95814.

Copyright © 2007 by McDougal Littell, a division of Houghton Mifflin Company.

No part of this work may be reproduced or transmitted in any form or by any means, electronic or mechanical, including photocopy and recording, or by any information storage or retrieval system without the prior written permission of McDougal Littell unless such copying is expressly permitted by federal copyright law. Address inquiries to Supervisor, Rights and Permissions, McDougal Littell, P.O. Box 1667, Evanston, IL 60204.

Printed in the U.S.A.

ISBN 13: 978-0-618-64095-9
ISBN 10: 0-618-64095-9   3 4 5 6 7 8 VJM 09 08 07

Internet Web Site: http://www.mcdougallittell.com

Science Consultants

Chief Science Consultant

James Trefil, Ph.D. is the Clarence J. Robinson Professor of Physics at George Mason University. He is the author or co-author of more than 25 books, including *Science Matters* and *The Nature of Science.* Dr. Trefil is a member of the American Association for the Advancement of Science's Committee on the Public Understanding of Science and Technology. He is also a fellow of the World Economic Forum and a frequent contributor to *Smithsonian* magazine.

Rita Ann Calvo, Ph.D. is Senior Lecturer in Molecular Biology and Genetics at Cornell University, where for 12 years she also directed the Cornell Institute for Biology Teachers. Dr. Calvo is the 1999 recipient of the College and University Teaching Award from the National Association of Biology Teachers.

Kenneth Cutler, M.S. is the Education Coordinator for the Julius L. Chambers Biomedical Biotechnology Research Institute at North Carolina Central University. A former middle school and high school science teacher, he received a 1999 Presidential Award for Excellence in Science Teaching.

Instructional Design Consultants

Douglas Carnine, Ph.D. is Professor of Education and Director of the National Center for Improving the Tools of Educators at the University of Oregon. He is the author of seven books and over 100 other scholarly publications, primarily in the areas of instructional design and effective instructional strategies and tools for diverse learners. Dr. Carnine also serves as a member of the National Institute for Literacy Advisory Board.

Linda Carnine, Ph.D. consults with school districts on curriculum development and effective instruction for students struggling academically. A former teacher and school administrator, Dr. Carnine also co-authored a popular remedial reading program.

Donald Steely, Ph.D. serves as principal investigator at the Oregon Center for Applied Science (ORCAS) on federal grants for science and language arts programs. His background also includes teaching and authoring of print and multimedia programs in science, mathematics, history, and spelling.

Sam Miller, Ph.D. is a middle school science teacher and the Teacher Development Liaison for the Eugene, Oregon, Public Schools. He is the author of curricula for teaching science, mathematics, computer skills, and language arts.

Vicky Vachon, Ph.D. consults with school districts throughout the United States and Canada on improving overall academic achievement with a focus on literacy. She is also co-author of a widely used program for remedial readers.

Content Reviewers

John Beaver, Ph.D.
Ecology
Professor, Director of Science Education Center
College of Education and Human Services
Western Illinois University
Macomb, IL

Donald J. DeCoste, Ph.D.
Matter and Energy, Chemical Interactions
Chemistry Instructor
University of Illinois
Urbana-Champaign, IL

Dorothy Ann Fallows, Ph.D., MSc
Diversity of Living Things, Microbiology
Partners in Health
Boston, MA

Michael Foote, Ph.D.
The Changing Earth, Life Over Time
Associate Professor
Department of the Geophysical Sciences
The University of Chicago
Chicago, IL

Lucy Fortson, Ph.D.
Space Science
Director of Astronomy
Adler Planetarium and Astronomy Museum
Chicago, IL

Elizabeth Godrick, Ph.D.
Human Biology
Professor, CAS Biology
Boston University
Boston, MA

Isabelle Sacramento Grilo, M.S.
The Changing Earth
Lecturer, Department of the Geological Sciences
San Diego State University
San Diego, CA

David Harbster, MSc
Diversity of Living Things
Professor of Biology
Paradise Valley Community College
Phoenix, AZ

Richard D. Norris, Ph.D.
Earth's Waters
Professor of Paleobiology
Scripps Institution of Oceanography
University of California, San Diego
La Jolla, CA

Donald B. Peck, M.S.
*Motion and Forces; Waves, Sound, and Light;
Electricity and Magnetism*
Director of the Center for Science Education (retired)
Fairleigh Dickinson University
Madison, NJ

Javier Penalosa, Ph.D.
Diversity of Living Things, Plants
Associate Professor, Biology Department
Buffalo State College
Buffalo, NY

Raymond T. Pierrehumbert, Ph.D.
Earth's Atmosphere
Professor in Geophysical Sciences (Atmospheric Science)
The University of Chicago
Chicago, IL

Brian J. Skinner, Ph.D.
Earth's Surface
Eugene Higgins Professor of Geology and Geophysics
Yale University
New Haven, CT

Nancy E. Spaulding, M.S.
Earth's Surface, The Changing Earth, Earth's Waters
Earth Science Teacher (retired)
Elmira Free Academy
Elmira, NY

Steven S. Zumdahl, Ph.D.
Matter and Energy, Chemical Interactions
Professor Emeritus of Chemistry
University of Illinois
Urbana-Champaign, IL

Susan L. Zumdahl, M.S.
Matter and Energy, Chemical Interactions
Chemistry Education Specialist
University of Illinois
Urbana-Champaign, IL

Safety Consultant

Juliana Texley, Ph.D.
Former K–12 Science Teacher and School Superintendent
Boca Raton, FL

English Language Advisor

Judy Lewis, M.A.
Director, State and Federal Programs for reading proficiency
and high risk populations
Rancho Cordova, CA

California Teacher Reviewers

Bill Bruce
Tenaya Middle School
Fresno, CA

Mark J. Handwerker, Ph.D.
Erle Stanley Gardner Middle School
Temecula, CA

Jack Castro
William Sheppard Middle School
San Jose, CA

Sandy Steinburg
Winston Churchill Middle School
Carmichael, CA

Bernice Filerman, Ph.D.
Bell Gardens High School
Bell Gardens, CA

California Panel Members and Lab Evaluators

Al Brofman
Tehipite Middle School,
Fresno, CA

Jenifer Cox
Sylvan Middle School,
Citrus Heights, CA

Ann Marie Lynn
Amelia Earhart Middle School,
Riverside, CA

Barbara Newell
Charles Evans Hughes Middle School,
Long Beach, CA

Greg Pirolo
Golden Valley Middle School,
San Bernardino, CA

Nancy Stubbs
Sweetwater Union Unified
School District,
Chula Vista, CA

Lori Walker
Audubon Middle School &
Magnet Center,
Los Angeles, CA

Teacher Panel Members

Carol Arbour
Tallmadge Middle School,
Tallmadge, OH

Patty Belcher
Goodrich Middle School,
Akron, OH

Gwen Broestl
Luis Munoz Marin Middle School,
Cleveland, OH

John Cockrell
Clinton Middle School,
Columbus, OH

Linda Culpepper
Martin Middle School,
Charlotte, NC

Melvin Figueroa
New River Middle School,
Ft. Lauderdale, FL

Doretha Grier
Kannapolis Middle School,
Kannapolis, NC

Robert Hood
Alexander Hamilton Middle School,
Cleveland, OH

Scott Hudson
Covedale Elementary School,
Cincinnati, OH

Loretta Langdon
Princeton Middle School,
Princeton, NC

Carlyn Little
Glades Middle School,
Miami, FL

James Minogue
Lowe's Grove Middle School,
Durham, NC

Kathleen Montagnino-DeMatteo
Jefferson Davis Middle School,
West Palm Beach, FL

Joann Myers
Buchanan Middle School,
Tampa, FL

Anita Parker
Kannapolis Middle School,
Kannapolis, NC

Laura Pottmyer
Apex Middle School,
Apex, NC

Lynn Prichard
Williams Middle Magnet School,
Tampa, FL

Jacque Quick
Walter Williams High School,
Burlington, NC

Robert Glenn Reynolds
Hillman Middle School,
Youngstown, OH

Stacy Rinehart
Lufkin Road Middle School,
Apex, NC

Theresa Short
Abbott Middle School,
Fayetteville, NC

Rita Slivka
Alexander Hamilton Middle School,
Cleveland, OH

Marie Sofsak
B F Stanton Middle School,
Alliance, OH

Sharon Stull
Quail Hollow Middle School,
Charlotte, NC

Donna Taylor
Bak Middle School of the Arts,
West Palm Beach, FL

Sandi Thompson
Harding Middle School,
Lakewood, OH

Teacher Lab Evaluators

Andrew Boy
W.E.B. DuBois Academy,
Cincinnati, OH

Jill Brimm-Byrne
Albany Park Academy,
Chicago, IL

Gwen Broestl
Luis Munoz Marin Middle School,
Cleveland, OH

Michael A. Burstein
The Rashi School,
Newton, MA

Trudi Coutts
Madison Middle School,
Naperville, IL

Larry Cwik
Madison Middle School,
Naperville, IL

Esther Dabagyan
Le Conte Middle School,
Los Angeles, CA

Jennifer Donatelli
Kennedy Junior High School,
Lisle, IL

Melissa Dupree
Lakeside Middle School,
Evans, GA

Carl Fechko
Luis Munoz Marin Middle School,
Cleveland, OH

Paige Fullhart
Highland Middle School,
Libertyville, IL

Sue Hood
Glen Crest Middle School,
Glen Ellyn, IL

William Luzader
Plymouth Community Intermediate School,
Plymouth, MA

Ann Min
Beardsley Middle School,
Crystal Lake, IL

Aileen Mueller
Kennedy Junior High School,
Lisle, IL

Nancy Nega
Churchville Middle School,
Elmhurst, IL

Oscar Newman
Sumner Math and Science Academy,
Chicago, IL

Lynn Prichard
Willimas Middle Magnet School,
Tampa, FL

Jacque Quick
Walter Williams High School,
Burlington, NC

Stacy Rinehart
Lufkin Road Middle School,
Apex, NC

Seth Robey
Gwendolyn Brooks Middle School,
Oak Park, IL

Kevin Steele
Grissom Middle School,
Tinley Park, IL

MCDOUGAL LITTELL SCIENCE
Focus on Life Sciences

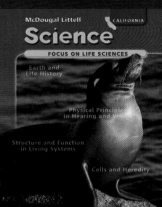

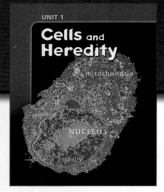

UNIT 1
Cells and
Heredity

eEdition

UNIT 1
Cells and Heredity

Unit Features

1 The Cell   6

the **BIG** idea

All living things are
made up of cells.

2 How Cells Function   38

the **BIG** idea

All cells need energy and
materials for life processes.

*How do plants like
these sunflowers
change energy
from sunlight?
p. 38*

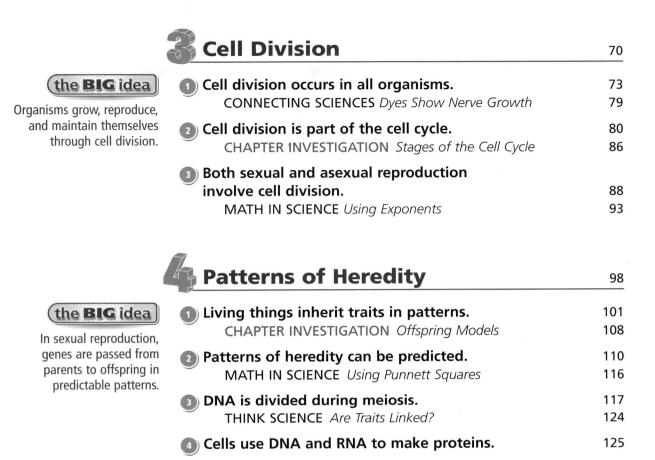
Visual Highlights

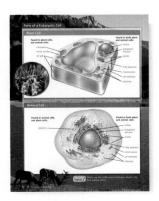

UNIT 2
Earth
and Life
History

classification

FOSSIL

species

preserved
remains

UNIT 2
Earth and Life History

eEdition

Unit Features

the **BIG** idea

Rocks, fossils, and other types of natural evidence tell Earth's story.

5 Views of Earth's Past

How do scientists learn about the evolution of living things? p. 182

Visual Highlights

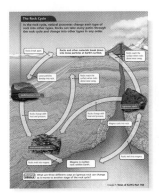

eEdition

Unit Features

Systems in Organisms   268

the **BIG** idea

Organisms are made of different parts that work together to perform life functions.

What do these people have in common with this giant sequoia? p. 268

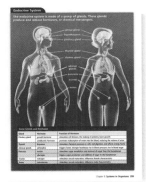

Visual Highlights

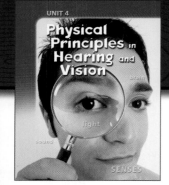

UNIT 4
Physical Principles in Hearing and Vision

eEdition

Unit Features

How does the sound of the guitar get to your ears? p. 420

Visual Highlights

Features

Math in Science

Think Science

Connecting Sciences

Science on the Job

California Close-Up

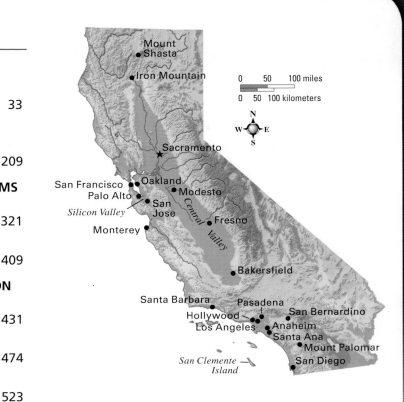

Frontiers in Science

Timelines in Science

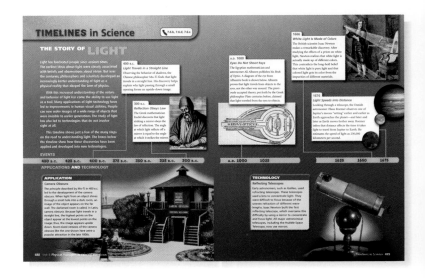

Internet Resources @ ClassZone.com

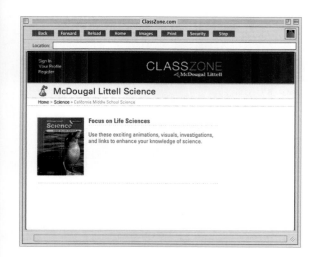

Simulations

Visualizations

Career Centers

Resource Centers

CELLS AND HEREDITY
Resources for the following topics may be found at ClassZone.com: *Cell Structures, Unicellular Organisms, Macromolecules, Diffusion, Nerve Cell Regeneration, Cell Cycle, Asexual Reproduction, Sexual Reproduction, Meiosis, DNA Genetics Research.*

EARTH AND LIFE HISTORY
Resources for the following topics may be found at ClassZone.com: *Evidence of an Event in Earth's Past, Finding the Age of Rocks, Fossils, Mass Extinctions, Natural Selection, Evidence for Evolution, Carolus Linnaeus, Taxonomy, Modern Classification.*

STRUCTURE AND FUNCTION IN LIVING SYSTEMS
Resources for the following topics may be found at ClassZone.com: *Shackleton's Expedition, Plant Systems, Endocrine System, Advances in Medical Imaging, Flowers and Fruit, Muscular System, Artificial Limbs, Joints as Levers, Fluids and Pressure, Circulatory System, Balance.*

PHYSICAL PRINCIPLES IN HEARING AND VISION
Resources for the following topics may be found at ClassZone.com: *Waves, Wave Speed, Sound Safety, The Electromagnetic Spectrum, Visible Light, Light Research, Optics, Microscopes and Telescopes.*

Math Tutorials

NSTA SciLinks

Codes for use with the NSTA SciLinks site may be found on every chapter opener.

Content Reviews

There is content review for every chapter at ClassZone.com.

Test Practice

There is test practice for every chapter at ClassZone.com.

Explore the Big Idea

Chapter Opening Inquiry

Each chapter opens with hands-on explorations that introduce the chapter's Big Idea.

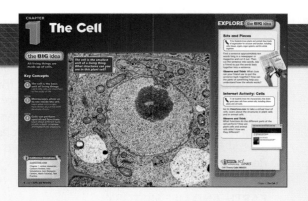

Cells and Heredity

Earth and Life History

Structure and Function in Living Systems

Physical Principles in Hearing and Vision

Chapter Investigations

Full-Period Labs

The Chapter Investigations are in-depth labs that let you form and test a hypothesis, build a model, or sometimes design your own investigation.

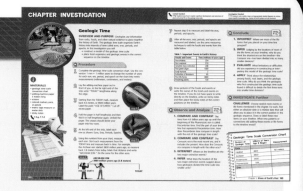

Explore

Introductory Inquiry Activities

Most sections begin with a simple activity that lets you explore the Key Concept before you read the section.

Investigate

Skill Labs

Each Investigate activity gives you a chance to practice a specific science skill related to the content that you're studying.

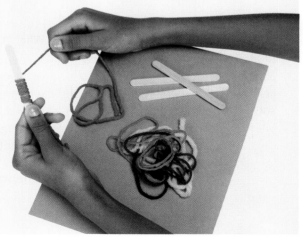

As you read and study your science book this year, you'll be learning many of the ideas described in the California Science Standards. The standards that you will concentrate on are listed here.

Following each standard is an explanation of what it means and how you will learn about it. References to chapters tell you where you'll begin to study the content in the standard. Many standards refer to several chapters. That's because you will read and study information presented in several chapters in order to understand a standard fully. By the end of the year, you will have learned the content of these California Science Standards.

Focus on Life Sciences

Cell Biology

Standard 7.1: All living organisms are composed of cells, from just one to many trillions, whose details usually are visible only through a microscope.

Standard 7.1.a	What It Means to You
Students know cells function similarly in all living organisms.	You will learn that the basic unit of living things is the cell. Some organisms consist of one cell each, whereas other organisms consist of many cells. You will learn about some of the functions that all cells share. **(Chapters 1, 2, 3, and 4)**

Standard 7.1.b	What It Means to You
Students know the characteristics that distinguish plant cells from animal cells, including chloroplasts and cell walls.	You will learn about differences between plant cells and animal cells that can be seen under a microscope. A plant cell contains chloroplasts, which are essential to the process of photosynthesis. A plant cell is also surrounded by a cell wall. An animal cell does not have a cell wall, but it contains lysosomes, which are not found in most plant cells. **(Chapter 2)**

Standard 7.1.c	What It Means to You
Students know the nucleus is the repository for genetic information in plant and animal cells.	When you use a microscope to examine plant cells or animal cells, you will see a structure called the nucleus. The nucleus contains DNA (deoxyribonucleic acid), which stores genetic information. A cell uses this information to make molecules that carry out the cell's functions. You will learn what happens to DNA in the cycle of cell growth and division. **(Chapters 1 and 4)**

Standard 7.1.d	What It Means to You
Students know that mitochondria liberate energy for the work that cells do and that chloroplasts capture sunlight energy for photosynthesis.	You will learn how energy is released in both plant cells and animal cells. Energy is released by the process of cellular respiration, which takes place in the mitochondria. Plant and animal cells both have mitochondria. In plants, a process known as photosynthesis occurs inside chloroplasts. The chloroplasts absorb energy from sunlight and store some of the energy in sugar molecules. The sugar molecules can be later broken down for energy. **(Chapter 2)**

Standard 7.1.e	What It Means to You
Students know cells divide to increase their numbers through a process of mitosis, which results in two daughter cells with identical sets of chromosomes.	You will learn about the cell cycle of growth and division in cells with nuclei. Before dividing, a cell's DNA is copied. Other structures are also doubled. The DNA is divided in a process called mitosis. Most of the rest of the material of the cell is divided in a process called cytokinesis. The result of this division is two cells, each of which has the same genetic information as the original, or parent, cell. **(Chapter 3)**

Standard 7.1.f	What It Means to You
Students know that as multicellular organisms develop, their cells differentiate.	You will learn that cells in most multicellular organisms become different from one another, or differentiated. The different types of cells have different functions. For example, the cells in your brain are different than the cells that make up your muscles. Most differentiated cells can only perform their own specific functions. **(Chapters 1 and 8)**

Genetics
Standard 7.2: A typical cell of any organism contains genetic instructions that specify its traits. Those traits may be modified by environmental influences.

Standard 7.2.a	What It Means to You
Students know the differences between the life cycles and reproduction methods of sexual and asexual organisms.	Organisms can produce offspring, or reproduce, in two main ways. In asexual reproduction, only one parent is needed. Sexual reproduction involves two parents. Some organisms reproduce in both ways. You will learn about the different ways offspring are produced and the advantages of each. **(Chapters 4 and 9)**

Standard 7.2.b	What It Means to You
Students know sexual reproduction produces offspring that inherit half their genes from each parent.	In sexual reproduction, an offspring gets about half its genetic material from each of the two parents. You will learn how the genetic material is divided and combined and how this process affects the offspring and the species. **(Chapters 4 and 9)**

Standard 7.2.c	What It Means to You
Students know an inherited trait can be determined by one or more genes.	A trait is an observable characteristic that can range from appearance to the chemical functioning of cells. Inherited traits are passed from parents to offspring during both asexual reproduction and sexual reproduction. You will learn how genes carry the information that produces inherited traits. **(Chapters 4 and 9)**

Standard 7.2.d	What It Means to You
Students know plant and animal cells contain many thousands of different genes and typically have two copies of every gene. The two copies (or alleles) of the gene may or may not be identical, and one may be dominant in determining the phenotype while the other is recessive.	You will learn how the genes from two parents can end up in many possible combinations during sexual reproduction, and how this results in offspring that are not identical to their parents. A gene is a specific piece of genetic material (DNA), such as the gene for hair texture. An allele is a particular variation of a gene, such as the allele for curly hair. You have a unique combination of alleles. You will learn how different pairs of alleles can produce different traits. **(Chapter 4)**

Standard 7.2.e	What It Means to You
Students know DNA (deoxyribonucleic acid) is the genetic material of living organisms and is located in the chromosomes of each cell.	Genes are segments of DNA, or deoxyribonucleic acid, a long molecule shaped like a twisted ladder. You will learn how DNA contains the information to produce the molecules—proteins—that result in traits. You will learn how DNA is copied before cells divide. You will also learn how a special form of cell division is needed for sexual reproduction. **(Chapters 3 and 4)**

Evolution

Standard 7.3: Biological evolution accounts for the diversity of species developed through gradual processes over many generations.

Standard 7.3.a	What It Means to You
Students know both genetic variation and environmental factors are causes of evolution and diversity of organisms.	Within a species, there are small variations of traits. Within a species that uses sexual reproduction, there are more variations. You will learn how some traits give a species advantages in some environments but are a disadvantage in other environments. You will also learn how the variety of traits and the changes in environmental conditions can cause some species to die out and new species to develop. **(Chapters 5, 6, and 7)**

Standard 7.3.b	What It Means to You
Students know the reasoning used by Charles Darwin in reaching his conclusion that natural selection is the mechanism of evolution.	Charles Darwin, a naturalist, observed the similarities and differences in species around the world. He found species with traits that allowed them to survive and reproduce in a particular environment. He concluded that conditions in the environment make it more likely for organisms with useful traits to survive and reproduce. You will learn about how this natural selection works. **(Chapters 5, 6, and 9)**

Standard 7.3.c	What It Means to You
Students know how independent lines of evidence from geology, fossils, and comparative anatomy provide the bases for the theory of evolution.	You will learn about the evidence that shows how organisms changed over time, or evolved. New species arose at different times and many species became extinct. Different types of evidence show how species arose from other species, and how the species that survived were adapted to their environments. You will learn how the theory of natural selection explains the observations. **(Chapters 5, 6, and 7)**

Standard 7.3.d	What It Means to You
Students know how to construct a simple branching diagram to classify living groups of organisms by shared derived characteristics and how to expand the diagram to include fossil organisms.	Species—both living and extinct—are classified according to shared ancestors. You will learn about branching diagrams called cladograms that are similar to family trees. Cladograms help scientists make and test hypotheses about the ways species are related. **(Chapter 7)**

Standard 7.3.e	What It Means to You
Students know that extinction of a species occurs when the environment changes and the adaptive characteristics of a species are insufficient for its survival.	The theory of natural selection explains how species survive and why most species become extinct over time. As Earth changes, environments change. A species that had useful traits for one environment may not be able to survive as well in the changed environment. You will learn how species with a greater variety of traits are more likely to be able to survive slow changes, and how sudden changes may wipe out many species at once. **(Chapter 6)**

Earth and Life History (Earth Sciences)
Standard 7.4: Evidence from rocks allows us to understand the evolution of life on Earth.

Standard 7.4.a	What It Means to You
Students know Earth processes today are similar to those that occurred in the past and slow geologic processes have large cumulative effects over long periods of time.	Rocks and fossils provide us with information about Earth's past. You will learn that very slow changes over time can cause huge changes in Earth's landscape. You will learn about plate tectonics—the movement of the lithospheric plates—and about how rocks and fossils show Earth's history. **(Chapters 5 and 6)**

Standard 7.4.b	What It Means to You
Students know the history of life on Earth has been disrupted by major catastrophic events, such as major volcanic eruptions or the impacts of asteroids.	You will learn that sudden, widespread events in Earth's history changed the development of organisms on Earth. The eruption of volcanoes, the impact of at least one large object from space, and other events caused changes in the climates and species on Earth. **(Chapters 5 and 6)**

Standard 7.4.c	What It Means to You
Students know that the rock cycle includes the formation of new sediment and rocks and that rocks are often found in layers, with the oldest generally on the bottom.	You will learn how the three main types of rock—sedimentary, metamorphic, and igneous—move through a cycle of breaking down and re-forming. Sedimentary rock forms in layers that become a record of organisms and conditions at the time each layer was formed. The layers on the top are usually younger than the layers on the bottom. **(Chapter 5)**

Standard 7.4.d	What It Means to You
Students know that evidence from geologic layers and radioactive dating indicates Earth is approximately 4.6 billion years old and that life on this planet has existed for more than 3 billion years.	Scientists have used different techniques to determine the ages of rock layers and fossils. You will learn that Earth is more than 4 billion years old. Relative dating tells us which of several rock layers or objects is oldest. Absolute dating determines the actual age of an object or layer. You will learn how both types of dating make use of the way radioactive elements change over time. **(Chapter 5)**

Standard 7.4.e	What It Means to You
Students know fossils provide evidence of how life and environmental conditions have changed.	You will learn about the information determined from fossils, which are traces of past organisms. Fossils can provide evidence about the organisms, their environment, and their relationships to other organisms. Fossils show how species evolved over time. **(Chapters 5, 6, and 7)**

Standard 7.4.f	What It Means to You
Students know how movements of Earth's continental and oceanic plates through time, with associated changes in climate and geographic connections, have affected the past and present distribution of organisms.	You will learn how changes in Earth's surface resulted in the development of species over time. The movement in Earth's plates resulted in changes in the landscape—such as new barriers—and climate changes. As conditions changed, species with different traits evolved. You will learn how Darwin and others used the locations of different species and fossils to develop the theory of natural selection. **(Chapters 5 and 6)**

Standard 7.4.g	What It Means to You
Students know how to explain significant developments and extinctions of plant and animal life on the geologic time scale.	In the history of the Earth many species have developed and many, such as most dinosaurs, have become extinct. You will learn how slow changes in the environment can cause species to die out. You will also learn how rapid changes can cause many species to go extinct at once. Such a mass extinction also leaves opportunities for many new species to develop. You will learn about these changes and how they are organized on the geologic time scale. **(Chapters 5 and 6)**

Structure and Function in Living Systems
Standard 7.5: The anatomy and physiology of plants and animals illustrate the complementary nature of structure and function.

Standard 7.5.a	What It Means to You
Students know plants and animals have levels of organization for structure and function, including cells, tissues, organs, organ systems, and the whole organism.	You will learn how there are different types of cells in most multicellular organisms. Cells make up tissues, tissues make up organs, and organs make up organ systems. Different organ systems serve different functions in an organism. **(Chapters 1 and 8)**

Standard 7.5.b	What It Means to You
Students know organ systems function because of the contributions of individual organs, tissues, and cells. The failure of any part can affect the entire system.	You will learn about important organ systems in plants and animals. The parts of these systems function separately but also work together as a system. By studying human organ systems, you will learn what happens when part of a system fails. **(Chapter 8)**

Standard 7.5.c	What It Means to You
Students know how bones and muscles work together to provide a structural framework for movement.	You will learn about the skeletal and muscular systems in organisms. You will learn how these systems work together to allow movement. **(Chapters 8 and 10)**

Standard 7.5.d	What It Means to You
Students know how the reproductive organs of the human female and male generate eggs and sperm and how sexual activity may lead to fertilization and pregnancy.	You will learn how sexual activity between a human female and a human male can produce a baby. Humans reproduce sexually. You will learn about the female and male reproductive systems and the stages of pregnancy. **(Chapter 9)**

Standard 7.5.e	What It Means to You
Students know the function of the umbilicus and placenta during pregnancy.	You will learn how the developing human offspring is carried in the mother's body. Special tissues carry nutrients from the mother's blood to the developing offspring and carry wastes back to the mother's blood, where they can be removed. **(Chapter 9)**

Standard 7.5.f	What It Means to You
Students know the structures and processes by which flowering plants generate pollen, ovules, seeds, and fruit.	Some plants produce flowers, seeds, and fruit in one specific form of sexual reproduction. You will learn how different parts of these plants function in the process of reproduction. Plant reproduction is important for food crops. It will also help you understand some aspects of human reproduction. **(Chapter 9)**

Standard 7.5.g	What It Means to You
Students know how to relate the structures of the eye and ear to their functions.	The eye focuses and detects light waves, while the ear detects sound waves. Then electrical impulses are sent to the brain. The eye and the brain are both needed for vision. The ear and the brain are both needed for hearing. Both eyes and ears are limited to a certain range of frequencies of the waves they detect. You will learn about the structures of the eye and the ear, including how the ear affects balance. **(Chapters 11, 12, 13, and 14)**

Physical Principles in Living Systems (Physical Science)
Standard 7.6: Physical principles underlie biological structures and functions.

Standard 7.6.a	What It Means to You
Students know visible light is a small band within a very broad electromagnetic spectrum.	The electromagnetic spectrum includes radio waves, microwaves, infrared light, visible light, ultraviolet light, x-rays, and gamma rays. These are all electromagnetic waves that vary only in frequency and wavelength. Humans see only a short range of the frequencies. When the waves are spread out by frequency, as in a rainbow, they form a spectrum. **(Chapter 13)**

Standard 7.6.b	What It Means to You
Students know that for an object to be seen, light emitted by or scattered from it must be detected by the eye.	Unlike your fingers, your eyes don't reach out to sense objects. Light must enter your eyes before you can see. The light must first be produced by matter. You can see a glowing object. Other objects you can see because light from another source bounces off of them. You will learn how light is produced and how it enables you to see. **(Chapters 13 and 14)**

Standard 7.6.c	What It Means to You
Students know light travels in straight lines if the medium it travels through does not change.	You will learn how light travels in straight lines except when something changes. A change in the light's medium can cause the light to change direction—to bend or to bounce. **(Chapters 13 and 14)**

Standard 7.6.d	What It Means to You
Students know how simple lenses are used in a magnifying glass, the eye, a camera, a telescope, and a microscope.	A lens, such as a magnifying glass, is a clear optical tool. You will learn how lenses can focus light or change the path of light in useful ways. You will also see how lenses and other optical tools can be combined to form cameras, telescopes and binoculars, and microscopes. **(Chapter 14)**

Standard 7.6.e	What It Means to You
Students know that white light is a mixture of many wavelengths (colors) and that retinal cells react differently to different wavelengths.	White sunlight can be spread out by frequency into a spectrum of colors. You will learn how frequency is a property of light, but the colors you perceive depend on the way your body reacts to different frequencies and combinations of frequencies. Cells inside your eyes absorb certain frequencies of light. The electrical signals from these cells are sent to your brain, which interprets the result as different colors. **(Chapter 13)**

Standard 7.6.f	What It Means to You
Students know light can be reflected, refracted, transmitted, and absorbed by matter.	Matter can reflect light, or cause it to bounce. Matter can transmit light, or allow the light to pass through. When a transmitting medium changes, the change can cause light to refract, or bend. Matter can also absorb light, or take up the light, which then ceases to exist. You will learn about the different ways that matter can interact with light and the different results. **(Chapters 13 and 14)**

Standard 7.6.g	What It Means to You
Students know the angle of reflection of a light beam is equal to the angle of incidence.	When light reflects, or bounces, off a surface, the path is predictable. The incoming angle and outgoing angle are equal. You will learn how these angles are measured and how to predict the path of light. **(Chapter 14)**

Standard 7.6.h	What It Means to You
Students know how to compare joints in the body (wrist, shoulder, thigh) with structures used in machines and simple devices (hinge, ball-and-socket, and sliding joints).	You will learn about how bones meet to form different types of joints in the human body. The joints in the body allow different types of movement. You will learn that the structures for different types of movement can be modeled using simple machines, such as the lever. **(Chapter 10)**

Standard 7.6.i	What It Means to You
Students know how levers confer mechanical advantage and how the application of this principle applies to the musculoskeletal system.	The skeletal system and the muscular system together make up the musculoskeletal system. Most levers in the body are third-class levers, which allow for small motions of muscles to produce larger motions. You will learn about mechanical advantage, which is the ratio of output force to the applied input force. **(Chapter 10)**

Standard 7.6.j	What It Means to You
Students know that contractions of the heart generate blood pressure and that heart valves prevent back-flow of blood in the circulatory system.	Pressure is a force spread over an area. You will learn about fluids and fluid pressure. You will learn about blood pressure in your heart and blood vessels, and the different structures of your circulatory system. You will also learn about fluid pressure in other organ systems. **(Chapter 11)**

Investigation and Experimentation

Standard 7.7: Scientific progress is made by asking meaningful questions and conducting careful investigations. As a basis for understanding this concept and addressing the content in the other three strands, students should develop their own questions and perform investigations.

Standard 7.7.a	What It Means to You
Select and use appropriate tools and technology (including calculators, computers, balances, spring scales, microscopes, and binoculars) to perform tests, collect data, and display data.	As you carry out investigations, you will need to decide which tools will work best for the tasks that you need to perform. For example, a hand lens can help you to see small details of an onion's root, but a microscope can help you to see the root's individual cells and how they fit together. You will also learn about some of the tools that scientists use and have used in the past. **(Chapters and investigations throughout)**

Standard 7.7.b	What It Means to You
Use a variety of print and electronic resources (including the World Wide Web) to collect information and evidence as part of a research project.	Throughout the year, you may find you have questions that go beyond the material in your textbook. You may also be given assignments that require you to do research. Some questions can be answered by other people, but you should also know how best to use other resources, such as those in libraries. Throughout the book, you will find references to resources available through the World Wide Web. **(Chapters and investigations throughout)**

Standard 7.7.c	What It Means to You
Communicate the logical connection among hypotheses, science concepts, tests conducted, data collected, and conclusions drawn from the scientific evidence.	A hypothesis is a tentative explanation for something you observe, while a theory is broader and has already been tested many times. You will read about evidence and theories. In some of your investigations, you will use what you have already learned or observed to develop hypotheses. Then you will develop ways to test your explanations. In other investigations, you will apply your knowledge to predict an outcome. You will record your measurements and other observations, and use these to try to draw conclusions. Most investigations are limited, so you can often draw only limited conclusions from a single investigation. Often, you will write a conclusion in the form of an answer to a problem statement. **(Chapters and investigations throughout)**

Standard 7.7.d	What It Means to You
Construct scale models, maps, and appropriately labeled diagrams to communicate scientific knowledge (e.g., motion of Earth's plates and cell structure).	A scale model, such as a scale map, shows the relative sizes of the parts of something. For example, a scale map relates the distances on the map to actual distances on Earth's surface. Models can also show how the parts of something function without showing relative sizes. Diagrams can also show sizes and how things work or fit together. The labels on a diagram often supply important information. You will use models and diagrams to help you understand and communicate science concepts. **(Chapters and investigations throughout)**

Standard 7.7.e	What It Means to You
Communicate the steps and results from an investigation in written reports and oral presentations.	The process of science only works when scientists communicate what they have done and learned. Scientists must communicate the steps they took, the data they collected, and the way they analyzed their data. Only then are other people in a position to decide whether to accept the scientists' results and explanations. Unit projects, investigations, and other activities will help you practice different ways to communicate the steps that you take and the results that you get. **(Chapters and investigations throughout)**

Introducing Science

Scientists are curious. Since ancient times, they have been asking and answering questions about the world around them. Scientists are also very skeptical of the answers they get. They carefully collect evidence and test their answers many times before accepting an idea as correct.

In this book you will see how scientific knowledge keeps growing and changing as scientists ask new questions and rethink what was known before. The following sections will help you get started.

What Is Science?

Science is the systematic study of all of nature, from particles too small to see to the human body to the entire universe. However, no individual scientist can study all of nature. Therefore science is divided into many different fields. For example, some scientists are biologists, others are geologists, and still others are chemists or astronomers.

All the different scientific fields can be grouped into three broad categories: life science, physical science, and earth science.

- Life science focuses on the study of living things; it includes the fields of cell biology, botany, ecology, zoology, and human biology.
- Physical science focuses on the study of what things are made of and how they change; it includes the fields of chemistry and physics.
- Earth science focuses on the study of our planet and its place in the universe; it includes the fields of geology, oceanography, meteorology, and astronomy.

McDougal Littell Science, Focus on Life Sciences

McDougal Littell Science, Focus on Life Sciences, explores the living things in your world, from the tiniest cells to your own body. It includes some physical science and earth science as well. In this book, you will begin with the study of cells, the smallest units of life, and learn how they live, grow, divide, and reproduce. Then you will learn how they have evolved from the earliest times on Earth, and how people have learned about this history of life. You will learn about how modern living things—plants and animals—have evolved and how they survive and reproduce. Finally, you will learn about humans, and how physical principles operate in the human body to enable our hearts to beat and our lungs to breathe, to enable us to move and to grow and to reproduce, and to enable us to see and to hear.

Unifying Principles

As you learn, it helps to have a big picture of science as a framework for new information. *McDougal Littell Science* has identified unifying principles from each of the three broad categories of science: life science, physical science, and earth science. These unifying principles are described on the following pages. However, keep in mind that the broad categories of science do not have fixed borders. Life science shades into physical science, which shades into earth science, which shades back into life science.

On the next few pages, look for the four unifying principles of life science:

- All living things share common charactertistics.
- All living things share common needs.
- Living things meet their needs through interactions with the environment.
- The types and numbers of living things change over time.

> **the BIG idea**
>
> Each chapter begins with a big idea. Keep in mind that each big idea relates to one or more of the unifying principles.

What Is Life Science?

Life science is the study of living things. As you study life science, you will observe and read about a variety of organisms, from huge redwood trees to the tiny bacteria that cause sore throats. But life science is not simply about learning the names of millions of organisms. It includes big ideas to help us understand how all these living things interact with their environment. Life science is the study of characteristics and needs that all living things have in common. It's also a study of changes, both daily changes and changes that take place over millions of years. It's the study of how living things depend on Earth and its resources.

Living things, such as these birds, have certain characteristics that distinguish them from non-living things. One important characteristic is the ability to grow. If all goes well, these warbler chicks will grow to become adult birds that can feed and take care of themselves.

UNIFYING PRINCIPLES of Life Science

All living things share common characteristics.

Despite the variety of living things on Earth, there are certain characteristics common to all. The basic unit of life is the **cell**. Any living thing, whether it has one cell or many, is described as an **organism**. Four characteristics distinguish living things from nonliving things, and help answer the question, "What is life?" All organisms are characterized by

- **organization**—the way that an organism's body is arranged. The largest level of organization in any living thing is the organism itself. The smallest level of organization capable of performing all the activities of life is the cell. Every organism is made up of cells.
- **growth**—the way that an organism grows and develops over its lifetime. Most living things grow and develop. Growth often involves not only an increase in size, but also an increase in complexity. An example is a tadpole growing into a frog.
- **reproduction**—the way an organism produces offspring. Most living things produce offspring like themselves. Those offspring are also usually able to reproduce.
- **response**—the ways an organism interacts with its surroundings. You know that your own body adjusts to changes in your surroundings. On a very hot day, you may sweat; on a very cold day, you may shiver. Sweating and shivering are examples of a response.

All living things share common needs.

Inside every living thing, chemical reactions constantly change materials into new materials. For these reactions to occur, an organism needs energy, water and other materials, and living space.

- **Energy** enables an organism to carry out all the activities of life. Movement, growth, and sleep all require energy, which you get from food. Plants use the energy of sunlight to make sugars for energy. Almost all animals get their energy by eating either plants or other animals that eat plants.
- **Water** is essential in the cells of all living things. The chemical reactions inside cells take place in water. Water plays an important part in moving materials within organisms. **Other materials** are also essential for life. For example, plants must have carbon dioxide from the air to make sugars. Plants and animals both use oxygen to release the energy stored in sugars.
- **Living space** is the environment in which an organism gets the energy and materials it needs. Living space is like a home; it protects you from external conditions and is a place where you can get materials such as water and air.

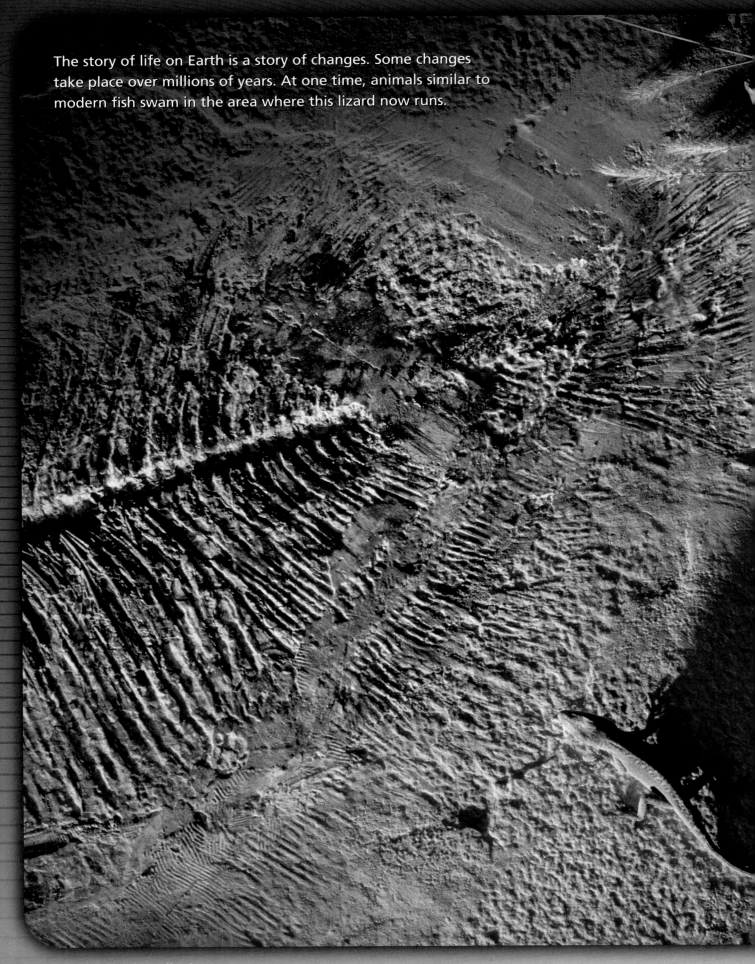

The story of life on Earth is a story of changes. Some changes take place over millions of years. At one time, animals similar to modern fish swam in the area where this lizard now runs.

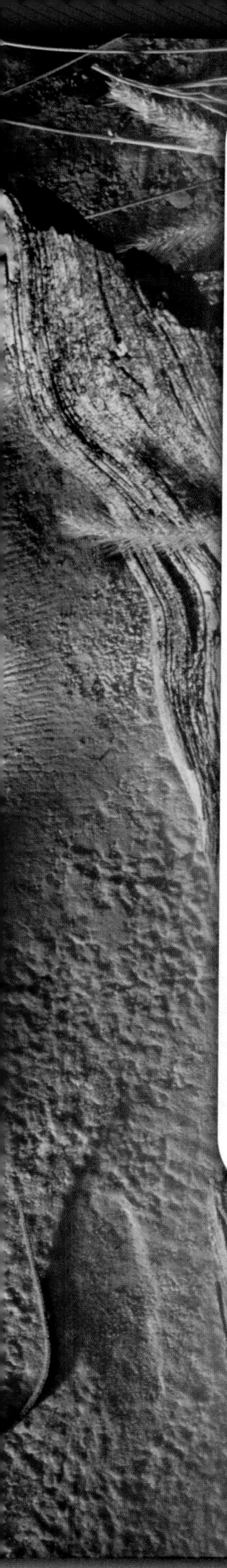

UNIFYING PRINCIPLES of Life Science, continued

Living things meet their needs through interactions with the environment.

The **environment** is everything that surrounds a living thing. An environment is made up of both living and nonliving factors. Living factors include any other organisms, and nonliving factors include rainfall, sunlight, and soil.

All living things in an environment meet their needs through interactions. An **interaction** occurs when two or more things act in ways that affect one another. Plants interact with the environment by capturing energy from the Sun and changing that energy into chemical energy that is stored in sugar. Animals can interact with plants by eating the plants and getting energy from the sugars that plants have made. Animals interact with other animals in a variety of ways.

The types and numbers of living things change over time.

A **species** is a group of living things so closely related that they can produce offspring together that can also reproduce. Scientists have named about 1.4 million different species. There are even more species that haven't been named. The great variety of species on Earth today is called **biodiversity**.

Over the millions of years that life has existed on Earth, new species have come into being and others have disappeared. The disappearance of a species is called **extinction**. Studying fossils of extinct organisms is one way that scientists have of seeing how living things have changed over time.

Different species have different characteristics, or **adaptations**, that allow the members of that species to survive in a particular environment. Adaptations are related to needs. For example, a lizard's legs are an adaptation that allows it to move on land. Over time, species either develop adaptations to changing environments or they become extinct.

What Is Physical Science?

Physical science is the study of what things are made of and how they change. It combines the studies of both physics and chemistry. Physics is the science of matter, energy, and forces. It includes the study of topics such as motion, light, and electricity and magnetism. Chemistry is the study of the structure and properties of matter. It especially focuses on how substances change into different substances.

Forces make the world go round. Forces allow you to walk across a room, and forces keep the stars together in galaxies. Consider the forces acting on the rafts in this picture. The rushing water is pushing the rafts forward. The force from the people paddling helps to steer the rafts.

UNIFYING PRINCIPLES of Physical Science

Matter is made of particles too small to see.

The tiny particles that make up all matter are called **atoms**. Atoms are so tiny that they are far too small to see even through a powerful microscope. In fact, an atom is more than a million times smaller than the period at the end of this sentence. There are more than 100 basic kinds of matter called **elements**. The atoms of any element are all alike but different from the atoms of any other element.

Matter changes form and moves from place to place.

You see objects moving and changing all around you. All changes in matter are results of atoms moving and combining in different ways. Regardless of how much matter may change, however, under ordinary conditions it is never created or destroyed. Matter that seems to disappear merely changes into another form of matter.

Energy changes from one form to another, but it cannot be created or destroyed.

All the changes you see around you depend on energy. **Energy**, in fact, means the ability to cause change. Using energy means changing energy. But energy is never created or destroyed, no matter how often it changes form. This fact is known as the **law of conservation of energy**. The energy you may think you've lost when a match has burned out has only been changed into other forms of energy.

Physical forces affect the movement of all matter on Earth and throughout the universe.

A **force** is a push or a pull. Every time you push or pull an object, you are applying a force to that object, whether or not the object moves. There are several forces—several pushes or pulls—acting on you right now. All these forces are necessary for you to do the things you do, even sitting and reading. **Gravity** keeps you on the ground. Gravity also keeps the Moon moving around Earth, and Earth moving around the Sun. **Friction** is the force that opposes motion. The friction between the bottoms of your shoes and the floor makes it possible for you to walk without slipping. Too much friction between a heavy box and the floor makes it hard to push the box across the floor.

What Is Earth Science?

Earth science is the study of Earth's interior, its rocks and soil, its atmosphere, its oceans, and outer space. For many years scientists studied each of these topics separately. Recently, however, they have started to look more and more at the connections among the different parts of Earth—its oceans, atmosphere, living things, rocks and soil, even other planets in the solar system and stars and galaxies far away. Through these studies scientists have learned more about Earth and its place in the universe.

When a wolf eats a rabbit, matter and energy move from one living thing into another. When a wolf drinks water warmed by sunlight, matter and energy move from Earth's waters into one of its living things. Energy and matter move among different parts of the Earth system.

UNIFYING PRINCIPLES of Earth Science

Heat energy inside Earth and radiation from the Sun provide energy for Earth's processes.

Energy is the ability to cause change. All of Earth's processes need energy to occur. Earth's interior is very hot. This heat energy moves up to Earth's surface, where it provides the energy to build mountains, cause earthquakes, and make volcanoes erupt. Earth also receives energy from the Sun as **radiation**—energy that travels across distances in the form of certain types of waves. Energy from the Sun causes winds to blow, ocean currents to flow, and water to move from the ground to the atmosphere and back again.

Physical forces, such as gravity, affect the movement of all matter on Earth and throughout the universe.

What do the stars in a galaxy, the planet Earth, and your body have in common? For one thing, they are all made of matter. **Matter** is anything that has mass and takes up space. Rocks are matter. You are matter. Even the air around you is matter. Everything in the universe is also affected by the same physical forces. A **force** is a push or a pull. Forces affect how matter moves everywhere in the universe.

Matter and energy move among Earth's rocks and soil, atmosphere, waters, and living things.

Think of Earth as a huge system, or an organized group of parts that work together. Within this system, matter and energy move among the different parts. The four major parts of Earth's system are the

- **atmosphere**, which includes all the air surrounding the solid planet
- **geosphere**, which includes all of Earth's rocks and minerals, as well as Earth's interior
- **hydrosphere**, which includes oceans, rivers, lakes, and every drop of water on or under Earth's surface
- **biosphere**, which includes all the living things on Earth

Earth has changed over time and continues to change.

Events are always changing Earth's surface. Some events, such as the building or wearing away of mountains, occur over millions of years. Others, such as earthquakes, occur within seconds. A change can affect a small area or an entire continent, such as North America.

The Nature of Science

You may think of science as a body of knowledge or a collection of facts. More important, however, science is an active process that involves certain ways of looking at the world.

Scientific Habits of Mind

Scientists are curious. They are always asking questions. A scientist who observes that the number of plants in a forest preserve has decreased might ask questions such as, "Are more animals eating the plants?" or "Has the way the land is used affected the numbers of plants?" Scientists around the world investigate these and other important questions.

Scientists are observant. They are always looking closely at the world around them. A scientist who studies plants often sees details such as the height of a plant, its flowers, and how many plants live in a particular area.

Scientists are creative. They draw on what they know to form a possible explanation for a pattern, an event, or a behavior that they have observed. Then scientists create a plan for testing their ideas.

Scientists are skeptical. Scientists don't accept an explanation or answer unless it is based on evidence and logical reasoning. They continually question their own conclusions as well as conclusions suggested by other scientists. Scientists trust only evidence that is confirmed by other people or methods.

A white-tailed deer feeds on many plants, including the trillium shown here.

By measuring the growth of this tree, a scientist can study interactions in the ecosystem.

Science Processes at Work

You can think of science as a continuous cycle of asking and seeking answers to questions about the world. Although there are many processes that scientists use, scientists typically do each of the following:

- Observe and ask a question
- Determine what is known
- Investigate
- Interpret results
- Share results

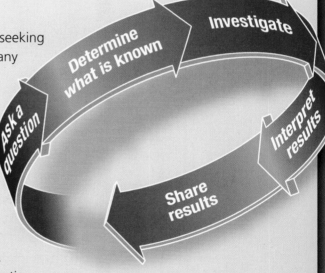

Ask a question
Determine what is known
Investigate
Interpret results
Share results

Observe and Ask a Question

It may surprise you that asking questions is an important skill. A scientific investigation may start when a scientist asks a question. Perhaps scientists observe an event or a process that they don't understand, or perhaps answering one question leads to another.

Determine What Is Known

When beginning an inquiry, scientists find out what is already known about a question. They study results from other scientific investigations, read journals, and talk with other scientists. A biologist who is trying to understand how the change in the number of deer in an area affects plants will study reports of censuses taken for both plants and animals.

Investigate

Investigating is the process of collecting evidence. Two important ways of collecting evidence are observing and experimenting.

Observing is the act of noting and recording an event, a characteristic, a behavior, or anything else detected with an instrument or with the senses. For example, a scientist notices that plants in one part of the forest are not thriving. She sees broken plants and compares the height of the plants in one area with the height of those in another.

An **experiment** is an organized procedure during which all factors but the one being studied are controlled. For example, the scientist thinks the reason some plants in the forest are not thriving may be that deer are eating the flowers off the plants. An experiment she might try is to mark two similar parts of an area where the plants grow and then build a fence around one part so the deer can't get to the plants there. The fence must be constructed so the same amounts of light, air, and water reach the plants. The only factor that changes is contact between plants and the deer.

Close observation of the Colorado potato beetle led scientists to a biological pesticide that can help farmers control this insect pest.

Forming hypotheses and making predictions are two other skills involved in scientific investigations. A **hypothesis** is a tentative explanation for an observation or a scientific problem that can be tested by further investigation. For example, since at least 1900, Colorado potato beetles were known to be resistant to chemical insecticides. Yet the numbers of beetles were not as large as expected. It was hypothesized that bacteria living in the beetles' environment were killing many beetles. A **prediction** is an expectation of what will be observed or what will happen and can be used to test a hypothesis. It was predicted that certain bacteria would kill Colorado potato beetles. This prediction was confirmed when a bacterium called *Bt* was discovered to kill Colorado potato beetles and other insect pests.

Interpret Results

As scientists investigate, they analyze their evidence, or data, and begin to draw conclusions. **Analyzing data** involves looking at the evidence gathered through observations or experiments and trying to identify any patterns that might exist in the data. Often scientists need to make additional observations or perform more experiments before they are sure of their conclusions. Many times scientists make new predictions or revise their hypotheses.

Computers help scientists analyze the sequence of base pairs in the DNA molecule.

Share Results

An important part of scientific investigation is sharing results of experiments. Scientists read and publish in journals and attend conferences to communicate with other scientists around the world. Sharing data and procedures gives them a way to test one another's results. They also share results with the public through newspapers, television, and other media.

Living things contain complex molecules such as RNA and DNA. To study them, scientists often use models like the one shown here.

The Nature of Technology

Imagine what life would be like without cars, computers, and cell phones. Imagine having no refrigerator or radio. It's difficult to think of a world without these items we call technology. Technology, however, is more than just machines that make our daily activities easier. Like science, technology is also a process. The process of technology uses scientific knowledge to design solutions to real-world problems.

Science and Technology

Science and technology go hand in hand. Each depends upon the other. Even designing a device as simple as a toaster requires knowledge of how heat flows and which materials are the best conductors of heat. Scientists also use a number of devices to help them collect data. Microscopes, telescopes, spectrographs, and computers are just a few of the tools that help scientists learn more about the world. The more information these tools provide, the more devices can be developed to aid scientific research and to improve modern lives.

The Process of Technological Design

Heart disease is among the leading causes of death today. Doctors have successfully replaced damaged hearts with hearts from donors. Medical engineers have developed pacemakers that improve the ability of a damaged heart to pump blood. But none of these solutions is perfect. Although it is very complex, the heart is really a pump for blood; thus, using technology to build a better replacement pump should be possible. The process of technological design involves many choices. In the case of an artificial heart, choices about how and what to develop involve cost, safety, and patient preference. What kind of technology will result in the best quality of life for the patient?

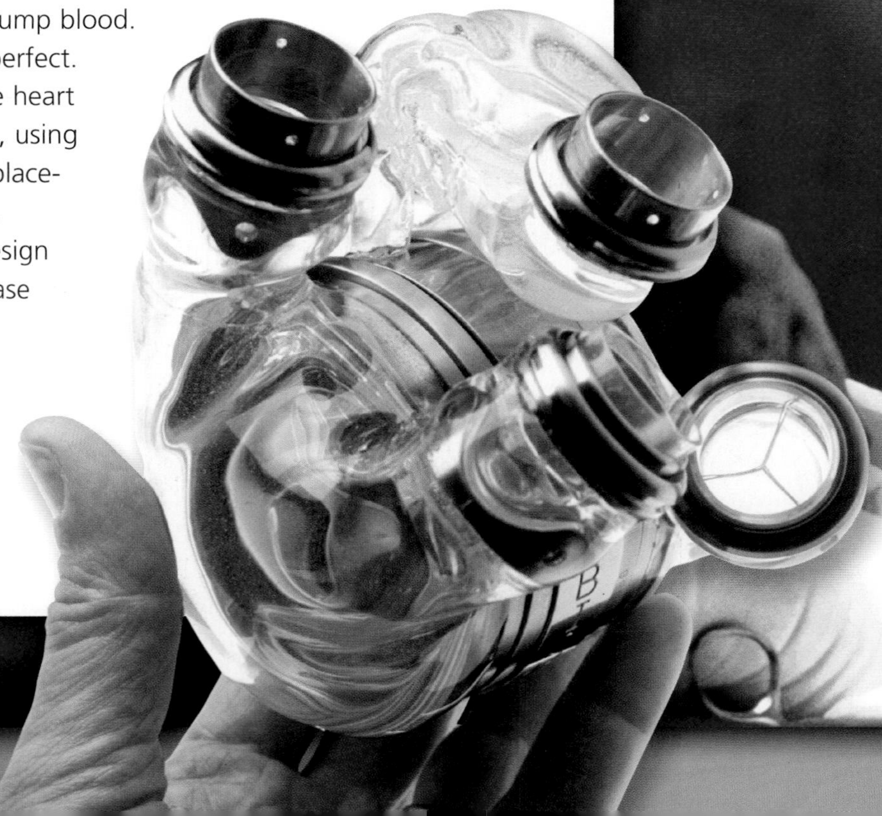

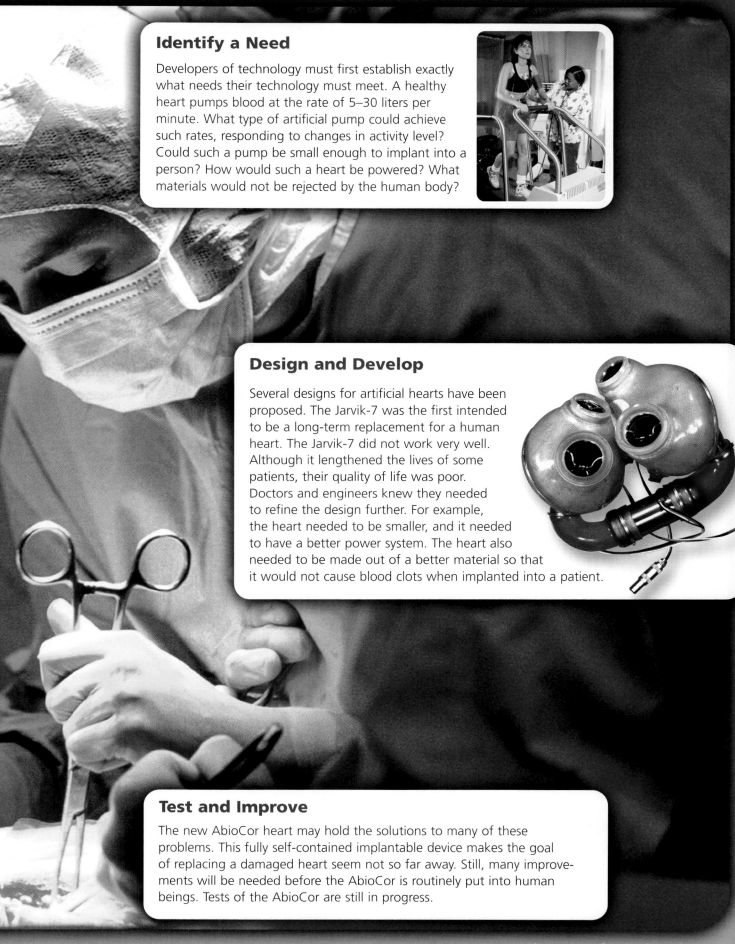

Identify a Need

Developers of technology must first establish exactly what needs their technology must meet. A healthy heart pumps blood at the rate of 5–30 liters per minute. What type of artificial pump could achieve such rates, responding to changes in activity level? Could such a pump be small enough to implant into a person? How would such a heart be powered? What materials would not be rejected by the human body?

Design and Develop

Several designs for artificial hearts have been proposed. The Jarvik-7 was the first intended to be a long-term replacement for a human heart. The Jarvik-7 did not work very well. Although it lengthened the lives of some patients, their quality of life was poor. Doctors and engineers knew they needed to refine the design further. For example, the heart needed to be smaller, and it needed to have a better power system. The heart also needed to be made out of a better material so that it would not cause blood clots when implanted into a patient.

Test and Improve

The new AbioCor heart may hold the solutions to many of these problems. This fully self-contained implantable device makes the goal of replacing a damaged heart seem not so far away. Still, many improvements will be needed before the AbioCor is routinely put into human beings. Tests of the AbioCor are still in progress.

Using the Tools of Science

You can learn about science by doing it. Doing science includes trying experiments or making observations so that you see for yourself what happens. For example, activities such as growing plants, measuring acid in rainwater, looking at live cells under a microscope, and trying to make an object fly are the exciting parts of science. These are the reasons people become scientists.

Safety First!

 apron
 goggles
 disposal
 electrical safety
 chemical safety
 fire safety
 sharp objects
 heating safety
fumes
 poison
 gloves

To do any experiments, think safety first! You may think it is unnecessary to wear goggles or plastic gloves—and sometimes it is unnecessary. But beakers break and spill, even if the materials are not dangerous. Why take a chance? You can prevent injuries or ruined clothes by taking simple precautions. Remember, we never plan for things to go wrong, but accidents happen!

The investigations and explorations in this book have safety symbols next to them when needed. Some have to do with what you wear—goggles, apron, gloves. Some warn of fire and heat dangers; some concern safety when working with electricity. Others caution you about chemicals, sharp objects, disposing of materials, or working with animals. Look at the safety rules and symbols on page R10. Become familiar with them. Look for them before you do an activity, and take the necessary precautions.

Measuring

Scientists use the International System (SI) for measurements of length, volume, mass, and temperature. The units in the SI system are metric, based on multiples of ten. These are different from the units we use in the United States, but most countries and all scientists use them. Once you learn the SI system, you will become part of the international community.

Measuring Length In science, meters and centimeters, not yards, feet, and inches, are used to measure length. A meter is about a yard. Within the metric system you change units by multiplying or dividing by powers of 10. For example,

1 centimeter (cm) = .01 meter (m), or 1/100 of a meter

1 millimeter (mm) = .001 meter (m), or 1/1000 of a meter

The prefix tells you how large or small each measurement is. You can easily change units to and from the SI units. See page R20 for help in changing units of the metric system.

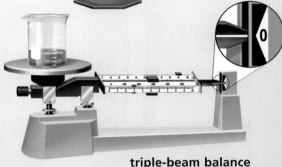
graduated cylinder

Measuring Volume The metric system measures volume in liters, not gallons. If you buy a 2 liter bottle of soda, it is about half a gallon in U.S. units. In a lab, it is more precise to measure 20 milliliters than to measure 1 teaspoon. Remember that 1 liter (L) = 1000 milliliters (mL). The prefix *milli-* means "one thousandth." When you measure the volume of a liquid, use a graduated cylinder and read the volume in mL, or milliliters. Each milliliter equals 1 cm^3.

Measuring Mass Mass is measured in grams, not pounds. By now you can guess that 1 kilogram (kg) = 1000 grams (g). A pound is a measure of weight, and weight is not the same as mass. In SI units, weight is measured in newtons. To measure mass, you use a double-pan balance or a triple-beam balance.

triple-beam balance

Measuring Temperature There are three systems of temperature measurement in the International System: Kelvin, Celsius, and Fahrenheit. Usually in science class you will use Celsius, not Fahrenheit or Kelvin. The Celsius system uses one hundred degrees between the freezing and the boiling point of water, 0–100° C. The Fahrenheit system, which we commonly use in the United States, goes from 32° to 212° F freezing to boiling point. Again, since it's based on 10's, the Celsius scale is easier to use.

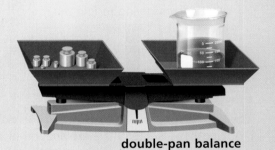
double-pan balance

Why Bother?

Why do all scientists need to use standard tools and measurements? They do this so that others can reproduce their experiments. Remember that scientists are a skeptical bunch—they don't believe what they hear until they try it themselves. To try an experiment that someone else has done, you have to have exact measurements. One drop more of a solution can make a huge difference in the results! One temperature degree higher and the whole experiment might fail!

Reproducibility is the only way scientists accept each other's work. Hypotheses have to be tested over and over again. If the results are different every time the experiment is done, then the hypothesis is not supported.

You need to use the scientific method every time you do an investigation. The scientific method varies according to the kind of investigation you're doing. The next two pages walk you through a lab. How do you make a hypothesis? How do you set up a test for it? How do you interpret your results? **Turn the page to find out.**

Conducting an Investigation

The fun part of science is "doing" science. You "do" science when you conduct your own investigations, collect your own data, and reach your own conclusions. You will practice using scientific methods whenever you do an investigation. Your method will change depending on what you are investigating. Sometimes you will observe and collect data. Sometimes you will make a model to see how things work. Sometimes you will conduct an experiment.

CHAPTER INVESTIGATION

Problem

Make sure you understand the purpose of your investigation. What are you trying to find out?

Diffusion

OVERVIEW AND PURPOSE The cell membrane controls what diffuses into and out of a cell. What factors affect the diffusion of substances across the cell membrane? In this investigation, you will

- observe the diffusion of a solution through plastic wrap
- determine how the concentration of iodine affects the amount of diffusion in a given time

▶ Problem `Write It Up`

How does the concentration of a substance affect its diffusion through a membrane?

▶ Hypothesize `Write It Up`

After step 4, write a hypothesis to explain how the concentration of iodine will affect the amount of diffusion in 20 minutes. Your hypothesis should be in the form of an "if . . . , then . . . , because . . . " statement.

Hypothesis

A hypothesis is a tentative explanation of what will happen and why it may happen. You base your hypothesis on what you know and a bit of educated guessing. You might not be right, but you test it to see. Set it up as a 3-part **if-then-because** statement:

1. **If** the strongest iodine solution diffuses into the cornstarch for 20 minutes, (What you'll do)
2. **then** the cornstarch will turn the darkest color, (Your prediction)
3. **because** the strongest solution has the most molecules to diffuse. (Your reason)

▶ Procedure

1. Make a data table like the one shown on the sample notebook page.

2. Use one eyedropper to put several drops of cornstarch solution on the lid of the jar. With another eyedropper, add a few drops of Lugol's iodine to the solution on the lid. Observe and record what happens when iodine mixes into water and starch.
   `step 2`

3. Fill the jar about three-fourths full with the cornstarch solution. Place the plastic wrap loosely over the jar. Adjust it so that the center of the plastic dips a little into the cornstarch solution.
   `step 4`

Procedure

Read the entire procedure before you begin. This procedure is what makes the experiment reproducible. Then follow it step by step, recording data accurately as you go.

4. Pour 10 mL of the iodine solution that you are given (A, B, or C) on the plastic wrap membrane. Solution A is the most concentrated and C is the least. Record your observations. Now write your hypothesis.

The **independent variable** is the factor you change in an experiment. You keep all other things the same—they are the **constants** (or controlled parameters). The **dependent variable** is what you measure—it depends on the independent variable.

Content Standard
7.1.a Students know cells function similarly in all living organisms.

Investigation Standard
7.7.c Communicate the logical connection among hypotheses, science concepts, tests conducted, data collected, and conclusions drawn from the scientific evidence.

5 Examine the solutions above and below the membrane after 20 minutes. Record any color changes, as well as the intensity of any changes, that you observe. Also look at your classmates' solutions, noting which solution (A, B, or C) each used.

▶ Observe and Analyze   Write It Up

1. **IDENTIFY VARIABLES** Identify the constants. What is the same in the experiment for all groups?

   Identify the independent variable. What is being changed between groups?

   Identify the dependent variable. What is being observed?

2. **RECORD OBSERVATIONS** Draw before-and-after pictures of your setup and label each drawing. Be sure to show the colors of the solutions on both sides of the membrane in each drawing.

3. **INFER** Make a drawing to show the direction in which molecules diffused through the membrane in your experiment.

4. **COMPARE AND CONTRAST** Compare the observations you made about your iodine solution with the observations made by your classmates. Be sure to record which iodine solution (A, B, or C) produced which changes.

▶ Conclude   Write It Up

1. **ANALYZE** Which iodine solution (A, B, or C) produced the greatest color change?

2. **INTERPRET** Do the class's results support your hypothesis? Explain.

3. **IDENTIFY LIMITS** Describe anything that might have varied from group to group. How might these variations affect your results?

4. **INTERPRET** Did starch diffuse through the membrane into the iodine solution? How do you know? Did iodine diffuse through the membrane into the cornstarch solution? How do you know?

5. **INFER** Which solution do you think contains larger molecules, cornstarch or iodine? Why weren't the larger molecules able to diffuse through the membrane?

6. **APPLY** Identify two real-life situations in which diffusion occurs.

▶ INVESTIGATE Further

CHALLENGE Investigate the role of temperature in diffusion. Predict how changes in the temperature of the iodine solution will affect the diffusion process. Explain.

Identify Limits

Evaluate how accurate your measurements were. If others reproduced this experiment, would they get the results you got? Are all people measuring the same way?

Diffusion

Table 1. Color Changes

Solution	Color at 0 min		Color at 20 min	
	cornstarch solution	iodine solution	cornstarch solution	iodine solution
A				
B				
C				

Chapter 2: **How Cells Function 65**

Analyze

Look again at the problem and your hypothesis. Do your results support your hypothesis? What did you learn by doing this experiment?

UNIT 1

Cells and Heredity

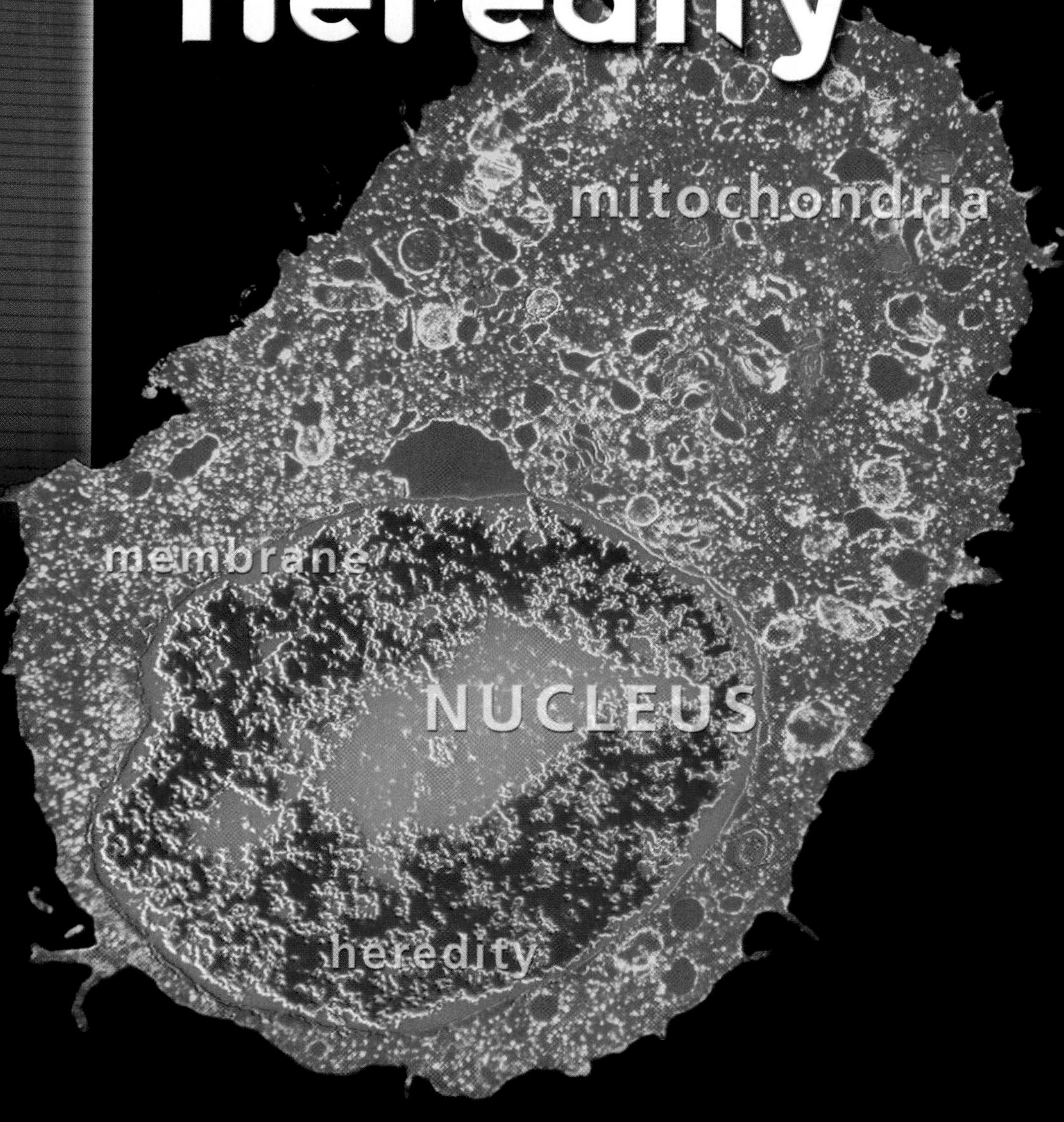

mitochondria

membrane

NUCLEUS

heredity

Contents Overview

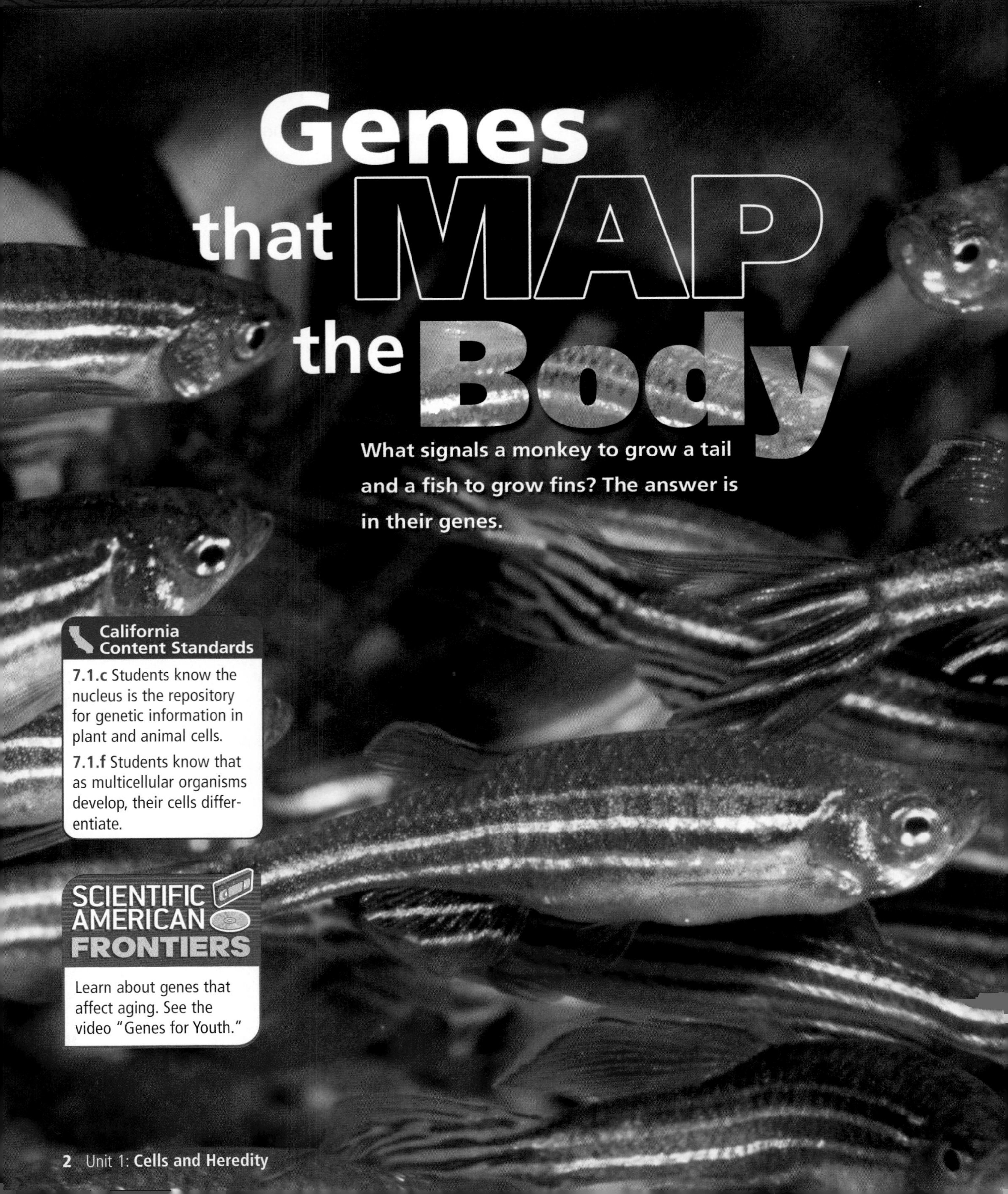

Genes that MAP the Body

What signals a monkey to grow a tail and a fish to grow fins? The answer is in their genes.

California Content Standards

7.1.c Students know the nucleus is the repository for genetic information in plant and animal cells.

7.1.f Students know that as multicellular organisms develop, their cells differentiate.

SCIENTIFIC AMERICAN FRONTIERS

Learn about genes that affect aging. See the video "Genes for Youth."

What's in a Gene?

Humans and fish are about as different as one animal can be from another. Yet both organisms have a similar body pattern: front and back, top and bottom, left side and right side. The head is at one end and limbs extend from the body—fins in a fish, arms and legs in a human. Inside are similar structures—brains, hearts, and stomachs—and cells that function in similar ways.

DNA is the genetic material found in all living things. DNA determines how cells grow, develop, and function. Within the DNA are genes, segments of DNA, that determine whether a cell becomes a brain cell or a heart cell. Both a fish and a human start out life as a single cell. As the cell divides again and again, each organism grows into its familiar shape. Scientists are studying what it is that maps out the head-to-tail development that gets every part of a body in the right place.

One group of genes, called *Hox* genes, are critical in the early development of an animal's body. These genes are found in the DNA of every animal—from humans to fruit flies. The position of *Hox* genes, from top to bottom along the DNA, matches up to the particular parts they control of an organism's body.

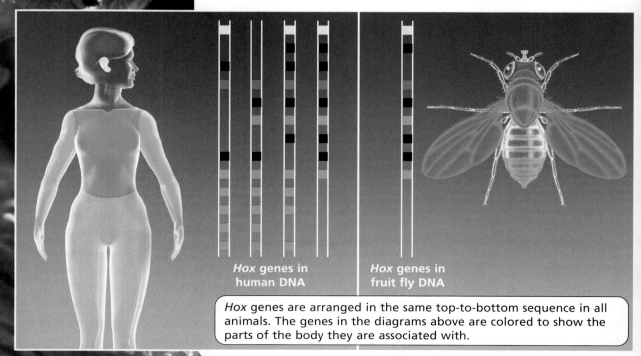

Hox genes in human DNA

Hox genes in fruit fly DNA

Hox genes are arranged in the same top-to-bottom sequence in all animals. The genes in the diagrams above are colored to show the parts of the body they are associated with.

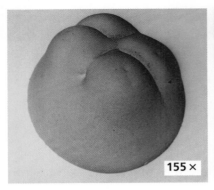

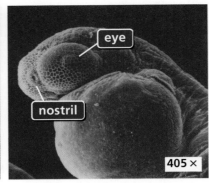

The egg of a zebrafish starts to divide after fertilization.
SOURCE for three images, Dr. Richard Kessel and Dr. Gene Shih/Visuals Unlimited

The egg now has 16 cells, all of which are similar in size and shape.

Many hours later, the cells have started to develop into different parts of the body.

How *Hox* Genes Work

Hox genes act like switches. A particular *Hox* gene turns on the development of a particular structure in an animal's body. One type of *Hox* gene switches on the development of structures in the head—for example, eyes and ears. Another switches on the development of limbs—the arms, legs, fins, or wings of an animal. The position of the genes within an animal's DNA matches to the part of the body it controls. *Hox* genes at the top control development of parts of the head. Those toward the middle control development of the main part of the body and the limbs.

How a Limb Develops

What happens if a *Hox* gene gets out of position? If the *Hox* gene that controls the development of legs in a fruit fly is placed in with the *Hox* genes that control development of the head, the fruit fly will grow legs from its head. The gene functions as it should; it just isn't doing its job in the right place.

Another interesting thing about *Hox* genes is that they are active only for a certain period of time. They "switch off" when the part of the body they control has developed. Studies of the zebrafish have provided clues as to how this happens.

SCIENTIFIC AMERICAN FRONTIERS

View the "Genes for Youth" segment of your Scientific American Frontiers video to learn about the role of genes in aging.

IN THIS SCENE FROM THE VIDEO biologist Cynthia Kenyon observes the activity level of some unusual worms that remain active much longer than other worms.

Kenyon is interested in what controls aging in worms. She studies how the genes in long-living worms affect the activity of their cells. She looks for differences between the cells of unusual worms and those of normal worms.

Because cells of animals function in similar ways, Kenyon is interested in

UNDERSTANDING AGING A multicellular organism starts life as a single cell. As an organism grows, it goes through different stages of development. Think of the differences between a baby, a teenager, a young adult, and an older person.

how what she learns about aging in worms might apply to other animals. Even though a worm is far less complex an animal than a human, studying these worms may provide clues about how humans age.

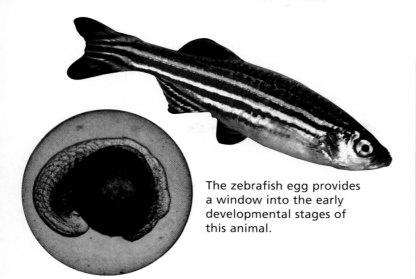

The zebrafish egg provides a window into the early developmental stages of this animal.

A Window on Development

Zebrafish are tiny fish that hatch in about three days. Scientists can actually see through the fish egg to watch its body develop. Working with the *Hox* genes of zebrafish, one researcher studied the amount of time the *Hox* gene that controls fin development was active. The gene "turned on" for a short period of time, the fin developed, and then the gene "turned off."

This research led scientists to think about the length of time the same *Hox* gene is active in other animals. It's possible that limbs are longer in larger animals because their *Hox* genes are active for a longer period of time. Researchers are excited because what they learn about the *Hox* genes of a simple animal can provide clues about the development of larger, more complex animals.

UNANSWERED Questions

There are many unanswered questions about the role *Hox* genes play in the development of body plans:

- Which *Hox* genes control which stages of development and how long are the genes active?

- What is it that signals the genes to "turn on and off"?

- How can research on *Hox* genes be used by medical researchers to help them treat genetic diseases or disorders that affect how a body develops?

UNIT PROJECTS

As you study this unit, work alone or with a group on one of the projects below.

Design an Experiment (7.1.f)

Use fast-growing plants to observe differences among plants.

- Follow directions for growing the plants.

- Observe the plants as they grow and identify different characteristics.

- Use your observations to form a question about genes and plant characteristics.

- Design an experiment to answer your question.

Living Cell (7.1.a, 7.1.b)

Work cooperatively to present a "living cell" demonstration. Model cell processes, such as photosynthesis and cellular respiration.

- Design a model that shows parts of the cell at work.

- Include structures such as membranes, the nucleus, chloroplasts, and mitochondria. Represent energy and materials that move into and out of a cell.

- Choose one student to narrate each process.

DNA Detective Work (7.2.e)

Prepare an oral presentation about how DNA technology is used to solve crimes.

Explain the science behind police and detective work.

CAREER CENTER
CLASSZONE.COM

Learn more about careers in molecular biology.

The Cell

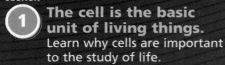

All living things are made up of cells.

Key Concepts

SECTION

1 **The cell is the basic unit of living things.** Learn why cells are important to the study of life.

SECTION

2 **Microscopes allow us to see inside the cell.** Learn what microscopes have shown about the inner structure of cells.

SECTION

3 **Cells can perform specialized functions.** Learn about different types of cells in both unicellular and multicellular organisms.

California ClassZone

CLASSZONE.COM

Chapter 1 online resources: Content Review, two Simulations, two Resource Centers, Math Tutorial, Test Practice

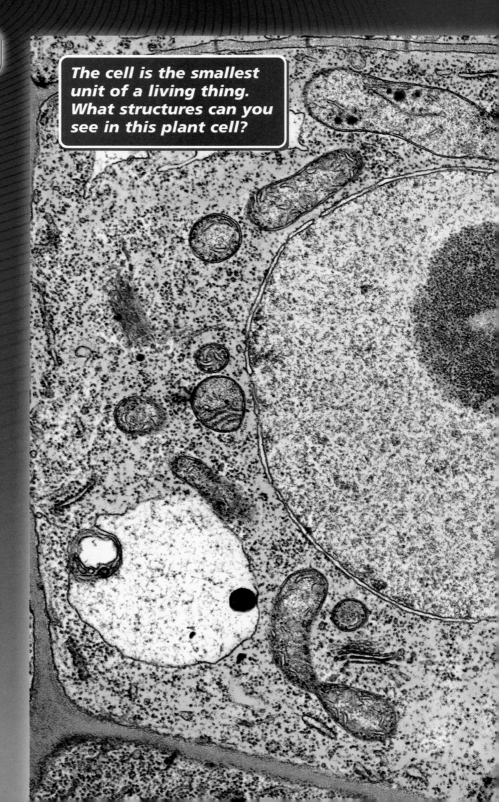

The cell is the smallest unit of a living thing. What structures can you see in this plant cell?

Bits and Pieces

7.5.a Students know plants and animals have levels of organization for structure and function, including cells, tissues, organs, organ systems, and the whole organism.

Find a sentence approximately ten words long in a newspaper or magazine and cut it out. Then cut the sentence into words. Ask a friend to put the words back together into a sentence.

Observe and Think What clues can your friend use to put the sentence back together? How can the parts of something help you understand how the whole works?

Internet Activity: Cells

7.1.b Students know the characteristics that distinguish plant cells from animal cells, including chloroplasts and cell walls.

Go to **ClassZone.com** to take a virtual tour of cells. Learn about the structures in plant cells and in animal cells.

Observe and Think
What functions do the different parts of the cell perform? How are plant cells and animal cells alike? How are they different?

Cell Theory **Code: MDL031**

Getting Ready to Learn

◀ CONCEPT REVIEW

- Living things share certain characteristics that distinguish them from nonliving things.
- Living things have common needs, including energy, materials from the environment, and living space.

◀ VOCABULARY REVIEW

See Glossary for definitions.

cell

genetic material

organism

theory

CONTENT REVIEW
CLASSZONE.COM

Review concepts and vocabulary.

▶ TAKING NOTES

MAIN IDEA WEB

Write each new blue heading, or main idea, in the top box. In the boxes around it, take notes about important terms and details that relate to the main idea.

VOCABULARY STRATEGY

Write each new vocabulary term in the center of a **four square** diagram. Write notes in the squares around each term. Include a definition, some characteristics, and some possible examples of the term. If possible, write some things that are not examples of the term.

See the Note-Taking Handbook on pages R45–R51.

SCIENCE NOTEBOOK

Multicellular organisms have different types of cells working together.

All living things are made of cells.

The cell is the smallest unit that performs the activities of life.

In a unicellular organism a single cell carries out all the activities of life.

Definition	Characteristics
an organism made of a single cell	performs all the functions of a living thing

UNICELLULAR

Example	Nonexamples
bacteria	animal, plant

The cell is the basic unit of living things.

1.1

CALIFORNIA
Content Standards

7.1.a Students know cells function similarly in all living organisms.

7.1.f Students know that as multicellular organisms develop, their cells differentiate.

BEFORE, you learned

- Living things have common characteristics
- Living things have common needs
- A theory is a well-tested explanation of many observations

NOW, you will learn

- How living things are different from nonliving things
- How the microscope led to the discovery of cells
- About the cell theory

VOCABULARY

unicellular p. 11
multicellular p. 11
microscope p. 12
cell theory p. 13
bacteria p. 14

THINK ABOUT

Are the flames of a fire alive?

Think about the flames of a campfire or of a lit candle. You can watch the flames jump and move. The flames are hot—they give off energy. They can grow and spread. They can change color. The flames consume materials that they come in contact

with. Despite all of these characteristics, flames are not alive. How can you determine if something is living or nonliving?

MAIN IDEA WEB
Make a main idea web about living things, including how they differ from nonliving things.

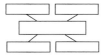

Living things are different from nonliving things.

You know life when you see it. Perhaps your class takes a field trip to a local state park to collect water samples. You are surrounded by trees. There is a stream, with rocks covered with moss and green algae. There are fish and frogs; there are birds and insects. You are surrounded by life. But how would you define it?

One way to answer the question is to think about what makes a living thing different from a nonliving thing. You might ask if a thing uses energy. Or maybe you would observe it to see if it moves. You could investigate whether it consumes food and water. These are characteristics of living things, or organisms. Any individual form of life that uses energy to carry out its activities is an organism. All organisms get water and other materials from the environment.

Characteristics of Life

Living things have these characteristics:

- organization
- the ability to develop and grow
- the ability to respond to the environment
- the ability to reproduce

An organism's body must be organized in a way that enables it to meet its needs. Some organisms, such as bacteria, are very simple. A more complex organism, such as the kingfisher shown in the photograph below, is organized so that different parts of its body perform different jobs, called functions. For example, a kingfisher has wings for flying, a heart for pumping blood, and eyes for seeing.

Another characteristic of organisms is that they grow and usually develop into adult forms. Some organisms change a great deal in size and appearance during their lifetimes, while others grow and change very little. Organisms also respond to the world outside them. Think of how the pupils of your eyes get smaller in bright light. Finally, organisms can reproduce, or make new organisms that are similar to themselves.

 CHECK YOUR READING What four characteristics are common to living things?

Needs of Life

Organisms cannot carry out life activities without energy, materials, and living space. What does it mean to need energy? You know that if you want to run a race, you need energy. But did you know that your body also needs energy to sleep and breathe and think? All organisms require a steady supply of energy to stay alive. Where does this energy come from? How does an organism get it?

APPLY Identify three living things in this photograph. How do they meet their needs?

Food is a source of **energy** and **materials**.

Water provides **materials** and **living space**.

The energy used by almost all forms of life on Earth comes from sunlight. Plants and some bacteria are able to capture this energy to make food. Your body, like the bodies of other animals, uses this food as a source of energy. The food animals eat comes from plants or from organisms that eat plants. Food provides the materials needed for growth and reproduction. These materials include carbon, nitrogen, oxygen, and water. All organisms also need space to live and grow. If any one of these requirements is missing, an organism will die.

All living things are made of cells.

The cell is the smallest unit of a living thing. Some organisms are made of a single cell. These organisms are **unicellular** and usually too small for you to see directly. Pond water is full of tiny unicellular organisms. Most of the organisms you can see, such as a frog or a water lily, are made up of many cells. Organisms made up of many cells are called **multicellular** organisms.

Unicellular organisms have the same needs and characteristics of life as multicellular organisms. Each tiny single-celled organism in a drop of pond water performs all the activities that characterize life. Multicellular organisms, such as a frog or a water lily, have bodies that are more complex. Different body parts of a multicellular organism perform different functions. For example, a water lily's roots hold it in the soil. Its leaves capture energy from sunlight. A frog moves with its legs and eats with its mouth.

Multicellular organisms have different types of cells. Roots are made of root cells, which are different from leaf cells. Muscle cells have special parts that allow them to move. In a multicellular organism, many cells work together to carry out the basic activities of life.

VOCABULARY
Add four square diagrams for *unicellular* and *multicellular* to your notebook. You may want to add more characteristics and examples as you read through the chapter.

Multicellular and Unicellular Organisms

Both multicellular and unicellular organisms live in this pond.

There are many **unicellular organisms** in this drop of pond water, magnified 75×.

The frog and water lilies are **multicellular organisms**.

READING VISUALS What are some differences between the multicellular and unicellular organisms in this photograph? some similarities?

The microscope led to the discovery of cells.

READING TiP

The word *microscopic* is an adjective form of the noun *microscope*. Things that are microscopic are too small to see without the use of a microscope.

Most cells are microscopic, too small to see without the aid of a microscope. A **microscope** is an instrument that makes an object appear bigger than it is. The invention of this tool led to the discovery of cells. In the 1660s, Robert Hooke began using microscopes to look at all sorts of materials. Anton van Leeuwenhoek (LAY-vuhn-HOOK) took up similar work in the 1670s. They were among the first people to describe cells.

Robert Hooke gave the cell its name. He was looking at a sample of cork, a layer of bark taken from the cork oak tree. He saw a group of similarly shaped compartments that looked to him like tiny empty rooms, or cells. You can see from his drawing, shown at right, how well these cells fit Hooke's description. Hooke used a microscope that magnified objects 30 times (30 ✕). In other words, objects appeared 30 times larger than their actual size.

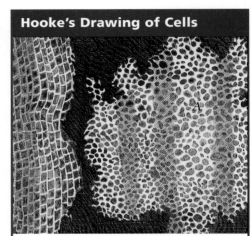

Hooke's Drawing of Cells

Robert Hooke published this drawing of dead cork cells in 1665. The microscope he used, shown at left, has two lenses.

The cork cells Hooke saw were actually dead cells, which is why they appeared empty. Leeuwenhoek was one of the first people to describe living cells. He looked at a drop of pond water under a microscope. Imagine his surprise when he saw that a drop of water was full of living things! Using lenses that could magnify an object almost 300✕, he observed tiny unicellular organisms like those shown on page 11.

CHECK YOUR READING How did the invention of the microscope change the study of biology?

Microscopes make small things look larger, and more powerful microscopes make things look many times larger. When objects look larger, you can see more detail. Think about a penny, which is 19 millimeters (0.75 in.) across. If you magnified it 30 times (30 ✕), it would appear about 570 millimeters (22 in.) across, or slightly bigger than the tire of a ten-speed bicycle. The writing on the penny would be large enough to trace with your finger. If you magnified the penny 300 ✕, it would appear to be about 5700 millimeters across. That's almost 6 meters (19 ft). The building shown on the penny would be taller than most people.

Cells come from other cells.

The studies of Hooke and Leeuwenhoek made people ask if all living things have cells. People continued to observe samples taken from many types of living matter. They continued to find cells, although often these cells looked very different from one another. Still, it was clear that all living matter was made of cells.

There was another important question scientists were trying to answer: Where do cells come from? By the 1860s, the answer to this question was settled. People studying all types of living cells observed the same thing—that cells divide. One living cell divides into two living cells. Here, under the microscope, was evidence of where cells come from. Life comes from life—that is, a cell must come from another cell.

 What do scientists mean when they say that life comes from life? Your answer should include the word *cells*.

The observations and evidence gathered over a long time by many scientists are summarized in the three concepts of the **cell theory:**

1. Every living thing is made of one or more cells.

2. Cells carry out the functions needed to support life.

3. Cells come only from other living cells.

The Cell Theory

The importance of the cell to life is summarized in the cell theory.

1. **Every living thing is made up of one or more cells.** A polar bear is a multicellular organism.

2. **Cells carry out the functions needed to support life.** Fat cells are animal cells that provide energy as well as insulation.

400 ×

3. **Cells come only from other living cells.** Each polar bear cub began as a single cell.

The cell theory is important to the study of biology.

The three ideas on page 13 are grouped together using the word *theory*. A scientific theory is a widely accepted explanation of things observed in nature. A theory must be supported by evidence, including experimental evidence and other observations. A theory is valuable when it explains new discoveries and observations.

CHECK YOUR READING What are two characteristics of a scientific theory?

Theories are important for a number of reasons. They satisfy scientists' desire to understand the natural world. They serve as the basis of further research and study. Theories can also lead to research that has practical benefits for society.

Louis Pasteur

The work of the French scientist Louis Pasteur shows how an understanding of cell theory can have practical uses. Pasteur lived in the 1800s, when there were no refrigerators in homes. People were used to having foods spoil, as when milk goes sour. During this time, many people died from diseases such as typhoid fever, tuberculosis, and diphtheria. Pasteur's work showed that microscopic organisms were involved both in the spoiling of food and in disease.

Pasteur observed that milk that turned sour contained large numbers of tiny single-celled organisms called **bacteria** (bak-TEER-ee-uh). He developed a process called pasteurization, in which heat is used to kill bacteria. Killing the bacteria keeps milk fresh longer. Because bacteria caused milk to sour, Pasteur wondered whether microscopic organisms—microorganisms—could also cause sickness in humans and other animals.

The milk that you get from the school cafeteria has been pasteurized so that it will stay fresh longer.

The Source of Bacteria

Using a microscope to study air, water, and soil, Pasteur found microorganisms everywhere. He found bacteria in the blood of animals. He found them in people who were sick. Pasteur referred to the microorganisms he observed as "germs." He realized that an understanding of germs might help prevent disease. Pasteur's work led to the first animal vaccinations for cholera and anthrax and to a treatment for rabies in humans.

At the time that Pasteur was doing his research, some scientists thought that bacteria grew from nonliving materials. Their idea was called spontaneous generation.

READING TIP

Spontaneous generation is the outdated idea that cells can grow from nonliving matter.

Pasteur's Experiments

Pasteur's experiments showed that bacteria are present in the air. They do not appear spontaneously.

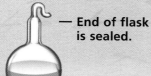 — End of flask is sealed.

1 Broth is boiled to destroy any living bacteria, and the flask is sealed.

2 A few days pass, and the broth is clear. No bacteria have grown.

3 More days pass, and the broth is still clear. No bacteria have grown.

 — End of flask is sealed.

 — End of flask is broken. Exposure to air is the variable.

1 Broth is boiled to destroy any living bacteria, and the flask is sealed.

2 A few days pass, and the broth is clear. The end of the flask is then broken to expose the broth to air.

3 Two to three days pass, and the broth is cloudy because of the growth of bacteria.

Pasteur conducted a series of experiments that showed that bacteria could not be formed by spontaneous generation. He showed that cells come only from other cells. Two of Pasteur's experiments are shown above. Both began with a sealed flask containing boiled broth. In the first experiment, the flask remained sealed. In the second experiment, the top of the flask was broken to expose the contents to air. Bacteria grew only in the second flask. Pasteur concluded that the bacteria must have come from bacteria in the air.

 Review

KEY CONCEPTS

1. Name four characteristics of living things. (7.1.a)

2. How did the microscope change human understanding of life? (7.1.a)

3. Explain the three concepts that make up the cell theory. (7.1.a)

CRITICAL THINKING

4. **Analyze** Relate the characteristics of a scientific theory to the cell theory.

5. **Compare and Contrast** Draw a Venn diagram to compare and contrast multicellular and unicellular organisms.

◯ CHALLENGE

6. **Synthesize** Explain how Pasteur's experiment supported the idea that cells come only from other cells. Explain how it failed to support the idea of spontaneous generation.

CHAPTER INVESTIGATION

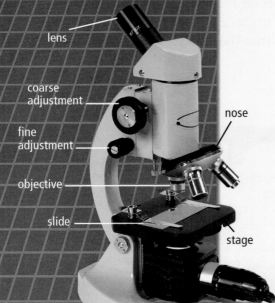

Using a Microscope

OVERVIEW AND PURPOSE The smallest forms of life are not visible to the human eye. In this investigation, you will use a light microscope as a tool to observe very small unicellular and multicellular organisms. Then you will compare the organisms you see under the microscope to the Identification Key. Refer to pages R14 and R15 of the Lab Handbook for more information about using a microscope and preparing a slide.

▶ Procedure

1. Make a data table like the one shown on page 17. To observe the microscopic organisms, you need to make a wet-mount slide. Obtain a slide and use the eyedropper to place 2–3 drops of pond water in the center of the slide.

2. Obtain a cover slip for your slide. Place one edge of the cover slip on the slide, at the left edge of the pond water. Slowly lower the cover slip as if you were closing the cover of a book. The cover slip should lie flat on the slide. If you see air bubbles, pick up the cover slip and lower it again.

   step 2

3. Clean the lenses of the microscope with lens paper. Choose the lowest magnification, and then place the slide on the stage. Start with the objective at its lowest point and raise the objective to focus. First focus with the coarse adjustment, which is usually the larger knob. Begin your search for living organisms. Use the fine adjustment to make the image clearer. Be patient when looking for life on your slide. It may take some time.

4. When you find something interesting, carefully switch to a higher magnification. Turn the nose of the microscope until another objective snaps into place. Use only the fine adjustment when viewing at high power, to avoid scratching the microscope or the slide. Move the slide gently from side to side as you look through the microscope. Search different parts of the sample for different organisms.

   step 4

MATERIALS
- slides
- eyedropper
- pond water
- cover slip
- light microscope
- lens paper
- Identification Key

  7.1.a, 7.7.d

lens

coarse adjustment

fine adjustment

objective

slide

nose

stage

Content Standard
7.1.a Students know cells function similarly in all living organisms.

Investigation Standard
7.7.d Construct scale models, maps, and appropriately labeled diagrams to communicate scientific knowledge (e.g., motion of Earth's plates and cell structure).

Identification Key

Euglena (unicellular) **Paramecium** (unicellular) **Stentor** (unicellular) **Desmid** (unicellular) **Water flea** (multicellular) **Hydra** (multicellular) **Copepod** (multicellular) **Volvox** (group of unicellular)

5 Make a sketch of each of the different organisms that you see. Record any movement or behavior you observe. Include the magnification of the objective lens that you used.

▶ Observe and Analyze   Write It Up

1. **CLASSIFY** Use the Identification Key above to identify the organism. If you cannot make an identification, write *unknown*.

▶ Conclude   Write It Up

1. **COLLECT DATA** Compare your sketches with those of your classmates. How many different organisms in total did your class find? How many were identified as unicellular? How many were identified as multicellular?

2. **COMMUNICATE** Why is the microscope an important tool for studying cells and entire organisms?

3. **INTERPRET** Using what you learned in this chapter and in this investigation, explain the ways in which you would use the different objectives on a microscope.

4. **APPLY** Many diseases, such as strep throat, are caused by microscopic organisms. Why might a microscope be an important tool for a doctor?

5. **APPLY** How might the way a biologist uses a microscope be different from the way a doctor uses a microscope?

▶ INVESTIGATE Further

Collect a small sample of soil from outside the school or your home. Mix the soil with enough tap water to make it liquid. Then take a sample of the soil mixture and examine it under the microscope. Sketch some of the organisms you see. Are they similar to those in the pond-water sample? Why do you think different types of organisms live in different environments?

Using a Microscope

Table 1. Identifying Microorganisms

Organism 1
  Magnification used:
  Movement/behavior:
  Sketch:

  Name:

Organism 2
  Magnification used:
  Movement/behavior:
  Sketch:

  Name:

1.2 Microscopes allow us to see inside the cell.

CALIFORNIA
Content Standards

7.1.b Students know the characteristics that distinguish plant cells from animal cells, including chloroplasts and cell walls.

7.1.c Students know the nucleus is the repository for genetic information in plant and animal cells.

7.1.d Students know that mitochondria liberate energy for the work that cells do and that chloroplasts capture sunlight energy for photosynthesis.

VOCABULARY

cell membrane p. 20
cytoplasm p. 20
prokaryotic cell p. 20
eukaryotic cell p. 20
organelle p. 20
nucleus p. 20
cell wall p. 21
chloroplast p. 23
mitochondria p. 23

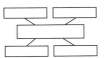

MAIN IDEA WEB
Make a main idea web that explains the importance of the microscope.

BEFORE, you learned

- Some organisms are unicellular, and some are multicellular
- A microscope is necessary to study most cells
- The cell theory describes the cell as the fundamental unit of life

NOW, you will learn

- About different types of microscopes
- About prokaryotic and eukaryotic cells
- How plant and animal cells are similar and different

THINK ABOUT

How small are cells?

Because cells are so small, describing them requires a very small unit of measure: the micrometer (μm). A micrometer is one millionth of a meter. Cells can range in size from about 1 micrometer (some bacteria) to 1000 micrometers (some plant and animal cells). To get a sense of the sizes of cells, consider that it would take about 17,000 tiny bacterial cells lined up to reach across a dime. How many of these cells might fit on your fingertip?

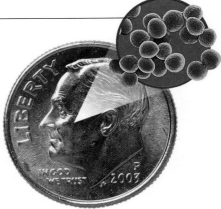

The microscope is an important tool.

The invention of the light microscope led to the discovery of cells and to the development of the cell theory. In light microscopes, lenses bend the light to make objects appear bigger than they are. Modern light microscopes can magnify objects up to 1000 times.

The light microscope is still used today to study cells. Over many years scientists have found ways to make light microscopes more useful. Cell samples are treated with dyes to make structures in the cells easier to see. Scientists use microscopes with video cameras and computers to observe the movement of cell parts and materials within cells. Light microscopes allow scientists to observe living cells.

Two other types of microscopes are important in the study of cells. The light microscope can be used for objects as small as 0.2 micrometers. The scanning electron microscope (SEM) and the transmission electron microscope (TEM) can produce images of objects as small as 0.00002 micrometers. A light microscope can be used to see some parts of a cell, but only the SEM and TEM can be used for looking at the details of those parts.

In both the SEM and the TEM, tiny particles called electrons, not light, are used to produce images. The advantage of these microscopes is that they can magnify objects up to a million times. The disadvantage is that they cannot be used to study live cells.

SIMULATION
CLASSZONE.COM
View cells through different types of microscopes.

CHECK YOUR READING Compare light microscopes with electron microscopes. What are the advantages and disadvantages of each?

To be viewed with an SEM, a cell sample must be coated in a heavy metal, such as gold. Then a beam of electrons is run back and forth over the surface of the cell. The electrons bounce off the coating. They are read by a detector that produces a three-dimensional image of the surface.

A cell viewed with a TEM is sliced extremely thin. Electrons pass through a thin section. Images produced by a TEM appear two-dimensional, like a picture on a flat page.

Electron Microscopes

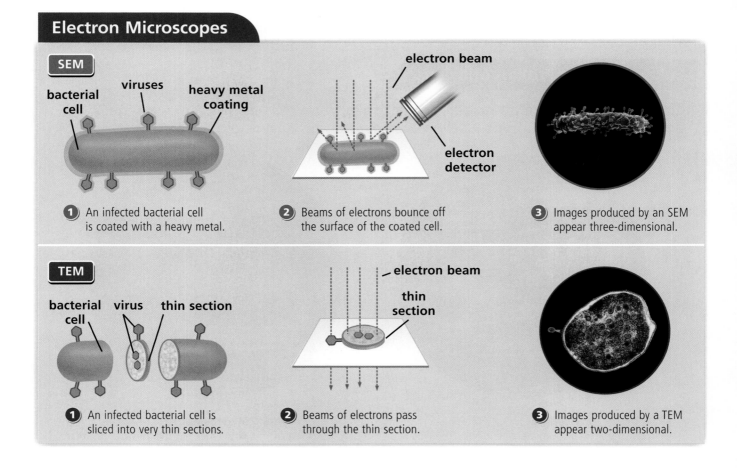

SEM

bacterial cell   viruses   heavy metal coating

electron beam

electron detector

1. An infected bacterial cell is coated with a heavy metal.

2. Beams of electrons bounce off the surface of the coated cell.

3. Images produced by an SEM appear three-dimensional.

TEM

bacterial cell   virus   thin section

electron beam

thin section

1. An infected bacterial cell is sliced into very thin sections.

2. Beams of electrons pass through the thin section.

3. Images produced by a TEM appear two-dimensional.

Cells are diverse.

When scientists used early microscopes to study cells, they saw that cells differ in size and shape. As microscopes were improved, scientists could see more and more details of cells. They saw that the inside of one cell can be very different from that of another cell.

A covering called a **cell membrane** encloses the inside of each cell and protects it. Any material moving into or out of the cell must pass through the cell membrane. Inside the cell membrane is a gelatin-like material called **cytoplasm** (SY-tuh-PLAZ-uhm). Most of the work of the cell is carried out in the cytoplasm.

Cells have genetic material that allows the cell to reproduce and function. Scientists classify cells into two categories based on the location of the genetic material. In a **prokaryotic cell** (proh-KAR-ee-AWT-ihk), the genetic material is in the cytoplasm.

In a **eukaryotic cell** (yoo-KAR-ee-AHT-ihk), the genetic material is separated from the cytoplasm by a membrane. Scientists use the word **organelle** (AWR-guh-NEHL) to describe any part of a cell that is enclosed by a membrane. The organelle that contains most of the genetic material is called the **nucleus** (NOO-klee-uhs). Most unicellular organisms are prokaryotic cells. Almost all multicellular organisms are eukaryotic.

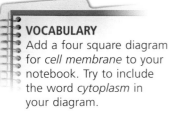

VOCABULARY
Add a four square diagram for *cell membrane* to your notebook. Try to include the word *cytoplasm* in your diagram.

Eukaryotic and Prokaryotic Cells

Eukaryotic cells have a nucleus, while prokaryotic cells do not. On average, eukaryotic cells are about 10 times larger than prokaryotic cells.

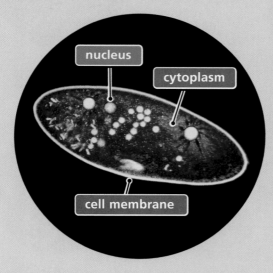

A **eukaryotic cell** has a nucleus. The paramecium shown here is magnified 133×.

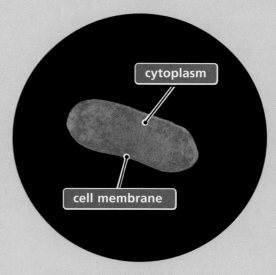

A **prokaryotic cell** does not have a nucleus. The bacterium shown here is magnified 12,000×.

INVESTIGATE Plant and Animal Cells

How do plant and animal cells compare?

PROCEDURE

1. Choose the objective lens with the lowest magnification. Place the plant-cell slide on the stage and turn on the light source. Handle the slide carefully.

2. Observe the cells at low magnification. Make a drawing of one of the cells.

3. Observe the cells at high magnification. Fill in details. Return to the low-magnification lens before removing the slide.

4. Repeat steps 1–3 with the animal-cell slide.

WHAT DO YOU THINK?

- Compare the drawings you made. How are the plant and animal cells alike? How are they different?

- Compare the thickness of the plant cell's cell membrane and cell wall with the thickness of the animal cell's cell membrane.

CHALLENGE Placing a ruler on top of the slides, view each slide at low power. Estimate and compare the sizes of the two cells.

SKILL FOCUS
Observing (7.1.b)

MATERIALS
- prepared slides
- microscope
for Challenge:
- millimeter ruler

TIME
30 minutes

Plants and animals have eukaryotic cells.

Plant and animal cells are eukaryotic cells. The nucleus is usually the largest organelle in the cell. It is the compartment that stores the instructions a cell needs to function.

Surrounding the nucleus is the cytoplasm. The cell membrane is the boundary between the cytoplasm and the outside of the cell. Plant cells also have cell walls. A **cell wall** is a tough outer covering that lies just outside the cell membrane. The cell wall supports and protects the cell. Having a cell wall is one important way in which plant cells differ from animal cells.

RESOURCE CENTER
CLASSZONE.COM

Find out more about cell structures.

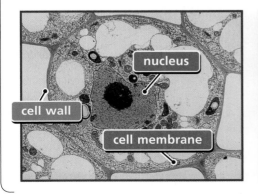

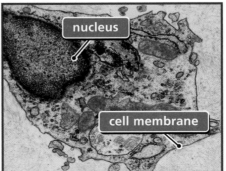

Both a plant cell (shown at left magnified 1750×) and an animal cell (shown at right magnified 12,000×) have a nucleus and a cell membrane. Plant cells also have a cell wall.

Parts of a Eukaryotic Cell

Plant Cell

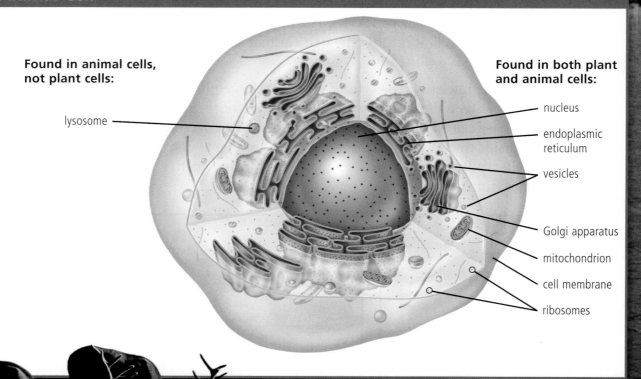

Found in plant cells, not animal cells:

- chloroplast
- central vacuole
- cell wall

Found in both plant and animal cells:

- nucleus
- endoplasmic reticulum
- vesicles
- Golgi apparatus
- mitochondrion
- cell membrane
- ribosomes

Animal Cell

Found in animal cells, not plant cells:

- lysosome

Found in both plant and animal cells:

- nucleus
- endoplasmic reticulum
- vesicles
- Golgi apparatus
- mitochondrion
- cell membrane
- ribosomes

READING VISUALS What are the differences between plant cells and animal cells?

Structures That Process Information

The nucleus is often the largest organelle in a cell. It contains information a cell needs to function. Some of the information is translated by ribosomes. These tiny structures are located throughout the cytoplasm and the structure called the endoplasmic reticulum. They are shown in the illustration on page 22 as tiny dots. Ribosomes use the information to build important molecules called proteins.

Organelles That Provide Energy

No cell can stay alive without energy. Cells need energy to perform all the activities of life. Plants absorb energy from sunlight. Within plant cells are **chloroplasts** (KLAWR-uh-PLASTS), organelles in which the energy from sunlight is used to make sugars. Plants use some of the sugar immediately, to keep their cells functioning. The rest of the sugar is stored in the cells.

Animal cells do not contain chloroplasts. As a result, animals are not able to use energy from sunlight. Instead, animals get their energy from food. Much of the food an animal uses for energy comes from the sugars that plant cells have stored. Animals can get this energy by eating plants or by eating animals that have eaten plants.

This plant cell is magnified 6000×.

 CHECK YOUR READING — How can a chloroplast, a structure found in plant cells but not in animal cells, provide energy for both plants and animals?

Both plant cells and animal cells must be able to use energy to do work. The energy is made available by organelles found in all eukaryotic cells. **Mitochondria** (MY-tuh-KAHN-dree-uh) are the organelles that use oxygen to get energy from processing food.

READING TiP

Mitochondria is plural. The singular form is *mitochondrion*.

Organelles That Process and Transport

You know that plant and animal cells get their energy from the sugars that the organisms make or consume. Sugars are also part of the starting materials that cells use to maintain themselves and grow. Many structures in the cytoplasm contribute to the making of cell parts from the starting materials.

In the illustrations on page 22, you can see that the endoplasmic reticulum is a system of twisting and winding membranes. Some of the endoplasmic reticulum contains ribosomes, which build proteins. The endoplasmic reticulum makes parts of the cell membrane.

The endoplasmic reticulum is also part of the cellular transport system. Pieces of endoplasmic reticulum break off to form small packages called vesicles. The vesicles carry processed materials to an organelle called the Golgi apparatus. The folded membranes of the Golgi apparatus make it look like a stack of pancakes. The Golgi apparatus takes the materials made by the endoplasmic reticulum and finishes processing them.

Organelles for Storage, Recycling, and Waste

Cells store water, sugar, and other materials, which they use to function. Cells must also store waste materials until they can be removed. Inside plant and fungus cells are sacs called vacuoles. Vacuoles are enclosed by a membrane. They can hold water, waste, and other materials. Vacuoles function with the cell membrane to move materials into or out of the cell. A plant cell has a large central vacuole in which water and other materials can be stored. Water in the vacuole provides support for smaller plants.

Inside animal cells are sacs called lysosomes. Like vacuoles, lysosomes are enclosed by a membrane and can hold materials. Lysosomes contain chemicals that break down nutrients taken into the cell. The chemicals also break down old cell parts and other waste.

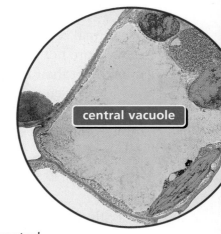
central vacuole

 Compare and contrast lysosomes and central vacuoles.

1.2 Review

KEY CONCEPTS

1. What advantages and disadvantages does a light microscope have compared with an electron microscope? (7.7.a)

2. What is the difference between a eukaryotic cell and a prokaryotic cell? (7.1.c)

3. List three structures found in plant cells that are not in animal cells. (7.1.b)

CRITICAL THINKING

4. **Synthesize** How might some organelles in a cell be compared to an assembly line? Explain.

5. **Compare and Contrast** Make a Venn diagram comparing and contrasting plant and animal cells.

CHALLENGE

6. **Synthesize** Identify the type of microscope used to capture the image at the right, and indicate whether the cell is a plant cell or an animal cell. How do you know?

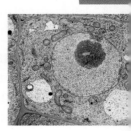

 MATH TUTORIAL
CLASSZONE.COM
Click on Math Tutorial
for more help with
scientific notation.
Math 7.NS.1.1

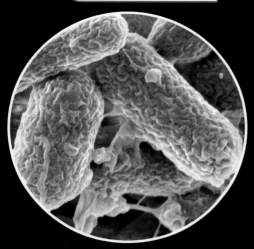

How many bacteria can fit on
the head of a pin? The bacteria
are magnified 50,000 × in this
photograph. The head of the
pin below is
magnified 7 ×.

Comparing Sizes

Measuring the sizes of very small things such as atoms or very large
things such as planets requires numbers with many places. For
example, the diameter of the nucleus of a cell is around 1/100,000
of a meter, while the diameter of Earth is 12,756,000 meters. How
can you compare these sizes?

Example

(1) Express a large
number as a
number between
1 and 10
multiplied by a
power of 10.

$12,756,000 \text{ m} = 1.2756 \times 10^7 \text{ m}$

The exponent is the number of
places following the first place.

$\dfrac{1}{100,000} \text{ m} = 0.00001 \text{ m} = 1 \times 10^{-5} \text{ m}$

(2) Express any
number smaller
than 1 as a
negative power of 10.

The exponent is the number of
places following the decimal point.

(3) Compare -5 and 7 to see that 7 is 12 more than -5.

ANSWER Earth's diameter is roughly 10^{12} times bigger than the
diameter of a cell's nucleus.

Answer the following questions.

1. An oxygen atom measures 60/100,000,000,000 of a meter
across. Write the width of the oxygen atom as a decimal.

2. Write the width of the oxygen atom in scientific notation.

3. A chloroplast measures 5 millionths of a meter across. Write its
width in standard form and in scientific notation.

4. A redwood tree stands 100 meters tall. There are 1000 millimeters in a meter. Express the height of the redwood tree in
millimeters. Write the number in scientific notation.

5. A typical plant cell measures 1 millionth of a meter in width.
Express the width in standard form and in scientific notation.

CHALLENGE The yolk of an ostrich egg is about 8 centimeters in diameter. A full-grown male ostrich is about
2.4 meters tall. Write each of these lengths in the same unit,
and express them in scientific notation. Then tell how many
times taller an average ostrich is than an average yolk.

KEY CONCEPT

1.3 Cells can perform specialized functions.

CALIFORNIA Content Standards

7.1.f Students know that as multicellular organisms develop, their cells differentiate.

7.5.a Students know plants and animals have levels of organization for structure and function, including cells, tissues, organs, organ systems, and the whole organism.

7.5.b Students know organ systems function because of the contributions of individual organs, tissues, and cells. The failure of any part can affect the entire system.

VOCABULARY

specialization p. 28
tissue p. 29
organ p. 30

BEFORE, you learned

• Modern microscopes reveal details of cell structures
• Some cells are prokaryotic, and some are eukaryotic
• Plant and animal cells have similarities and differences

NOW, you will learn

• How organisms are classified into three domains
• About specialization in multicellular organisms
• How cells, tissues, and organs are organized

EXPLORE Specialization (7.1.f)

How do roots differ from leaves?

PROCEDURE

1. Separate a grass plant from the bunch and soak it in a cup of water to clean away any dirt.

2. Compare the color of the roots with the color of the blades or leaves. Record your observations.

3. Wash your hands when you have finished.

WHAT DO YOU THINK?

• How does the color of the grass roots compare with that of the grass blades?
• Chloroplasts contain a chemical that gives leaves their green color. What does this suggest to you about the functions of the grass blades and roots?

MATERIALS
• grass plant
• cup
• water

Organisms can be classified by their cell type.

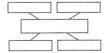

MAIN IDEA WEB
Make a web of the important terms and details about the main idea: *Organisms can be classified by their cell type.*

Look around you at this moment. The living organisms you see may number 10, 20, 100, or 1000, depending on where you are. What you are not seeing, but what is also there, is a huge number of unicellular organisms. For example, there can be as many as 10 million bacteria living on each square centimeter of your skin. Most of the organisms alive on Earth today are made of a single cell.

In 1977 scientists discovered organisms living without the energy from sunlight and in conditions that seemed too harsh for life. This led scientists to look for life in other places that were thought too harsh.

Archaea and Bacteria

Scientists continue to discover unicellular organisms living in other very harsh environments. Some live at thermal vents, deep in the ocean, where there is extreme heat and little oxygen. Others live in the salty waters of the Great Salt Lake. Still others live in the hot sulfur springs of Yellowstone Park.

At first, these organisms were referred to as archaebacteria. The organisms looked like bacteria. The prefix *archae* comes from a Greek word that means "ancient." Many of these organisms live in environments that scientists think are like the environments of ancient Earth.

▼ **REMINDER**

The genetic material in a prokaryotic cell is not enclosed in a nucleus. In eukaryotic cells, genetic material is stored in a nucleus.

thermal vent

archaea

Archaea are prokaryotic organisms that can live in extreme environments such as these thermal vents. In a thermal vent, temperatures can reach 400 degrees Celsius (750°F). Some archaea can survive in temperatures above 100 degrees Celsius (212°F).

It took a while for scientists to realize that these organisms that looked like bacteria were genetically very different from bacteria. Scientists decided to establish a separate category for them, a domain called Archaea (AHR-kee-uh). A domain is a broad category of living things that is based on characteristics of their cells. Scientists have identified three domains. Bacteria are classified in the domain Bacteria. A third domain includes organisms with eukaryotic cells.

Bacteria and archaea are both types of organisms that consist of a prokaryotic cell. Therefore, they are called prokaryotes. Their cytoplasm contains ribosomes but no nucleus or other organelles. The structure of a prokaryote is simple. Most prokaryotes have a tough cell wall that protects the organism.

RESOURCE CENTER
CLASSZONE.COM

Learn more about unicellular organisms.

 CHECK YOUR READING Why did scientists decide to establish separate domains for archaea and bacteria?

Eukarya

The third domain is Eukarya. Organisms in this domain have cells with a nucleus. Eukarya includes almost all the multicellular organisms on Earth: plants, animals, and fungi. It also includes many unicellular organisms called protists. The cells of unicellular eukaryotes are more complex in structure and larger than the cells of prokaryotes.

 CHECK YOUR READING How are eukaryotes different from prokaryotes?

The paramecium is one of the most complex of all unicellular eukaryotes. It is lined with hairlike strands, called cilia (SIHL-ee-uh), that allow it to move. It has dartlike structures that carry a substance used in healing and, perhaps, defense. Along the outside of the cell is a long oral groove lined with cilia that leads to a mouth pore. The paramecium has a nucleus. It also has other organelles that enable it to digest food and remove water and wastes. The paramecium has all it needs to live as a single cell.

paramecium 1000×

mouth pore

oral groove

cilia

Cells in multicellular organisms specialize.

VOCABULARY
Remember to add a four square diagram for *specialization* to your notebook.

Most multicellular organisms consist of many different types of cells that do different jobs. For example, most animals have blood cells, nerve cells, and muscle cells. The cells are specialized. **Specialization** of cells means that specific types of cells perform specific functions. This specialization is why a single cell from a multicellular organism cannot survive on its own. One type of blood cell can help you fight infection. Another type of blood cell can deliver oxygen to your muscles. However, neither type of blood cell can cause your body to move as a muscle cell can. Plants have cells that make sugars through photosynthesis. Other plant cells draw water from the soil, and still others support the plant's weight.

CHECK YOUR READING What does it mean for a cell to be specialized?

A fully grown salamander has many specialized cells.

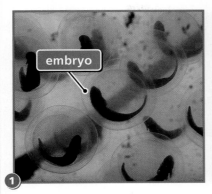

① A salamander, which is a multi-cellular organism, begins life as a single cell. The single cell divides and develops into an embryo.

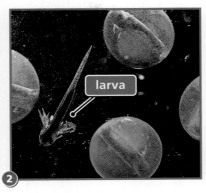

② As the cells divide, they begin to specialize. The amount of specialization depends on the complexity of the organism.

③ A salamander's body has many specialized cells. These include skin cells, blood cells, bone cells, muscle cells, and nerve cells.

A multicellular organism is a community of cells.

Cells in most multicellular organisms are specialized. The ways in which the cells work together depend on the organism. You can think of the cells of an organism as members of a community. The size and nature of the community differ from organism to organism.

A sponge is an animal that is fairly simple in its organization. It may spend its life attached to the ocean floor, filtering food and other nutrients from the water. The sponge's different types of cells perform different functions. For example, certain cells take in food, and other cells digest it. However, cells in a sponge are not very highly specialized. A piece broken from a living sponge will actually grow into an entirely new sponge. New cells replace the ones that were lost.

In more complex plants and animals, cells are not only specialized but grouped together in tissues. A **tissue** is a group of similar cells that are organized to do a specific job. If you look at your hand, you will see the top layer of tissue in your skin. You also have other tissues below this. Together these tissues provide protection and support.

CALIFORNIA Focus

California's state fish is the golden trout (*Oncorhynchus mykiss aguabonita*). The golden trout is a multicellular organism with specialized cells. Cells in its skin become specialized to produce its beautiful golden colors.

 In what way is a tissue an organization of cells?

Levels of Organization

Levels of organization in multicellular organisms include cells, tissues, organs, organ systems, and the organism itself.

Plant cell

Tissue

Organ: leaf

Organ system: leaves, stems

Organism: lilac tree

Animal cell

Tissue

Organ: eye

Organ system: eyes, brain, nerves

Organism: tarsier

An **organ** is made of different tissues working together to perform a particular function. Organs represent another level of organization. The eye is an organ that functions with an animal's brain to allow sight. A leaf is an organ that provides a plant with energy and materials. It has tissue that brings water and nutrients from other parts of the plant, tissue that uses sunlight to make sugars, and tissue that moves sugars to other parts of the plant.

CHECK YOUR READING What is the relationship between tissues and organs?

Different organs and tissues working together form an organ system. An organism may have only a few organ systems. One organ system of plants includes stems and leaves. Other organisms have many organ systems. Humans have about 40 organs that are usually grouped into about 10 named systems. The human nervous system, for example, includes the brain, spinal cord, nerves, and sensory receptors in organs, such as the ears and eyes.

An organism represents the highest level of organization. The organism has all the characteristics we associate with life. If an organism is a complex organism—a human, for example—it will consist of trillions of cells grouped into tissues, organs, and organ systems. However, a simple organism, such as a sponge, meets its needs with a body made up of only a few types of specialized cells.

 CHECK YOUR READING What level of organization is an organism? What do we see at this level of organization?

INVESTIGATE Cell Models

What are some of the limitations of using a model to represent a cell?

PROCEDURE

1. Work with a partner to choose a type of cell to model and to determine the types of organelles to include.

2. Using the poster board as a base, construct the model from available supplies. Make the model as accurate as you can.

3. Use a marker to label each organelle, and include a description of its function.

4. Compare your cell model with those made by your classmates.

WHAT DO YOU THINK?

- What are some of the limitations of using a model to represent a cell?

- What are some of the benefits of making a three-dimensional model of a cell?

CHALLENGE Think of something to which you might compare the activities of a cell—perhaps the activities of a factory or a school. Add labels to your model to show how the comparison applies to each of the cell's structures.

SKILL FOCUS
Making models
(7.1.a, 7.1.b)

MATERIALS
- craft supplies
- scissors
- glue
- poster board
- markers

TIME
30 minutes

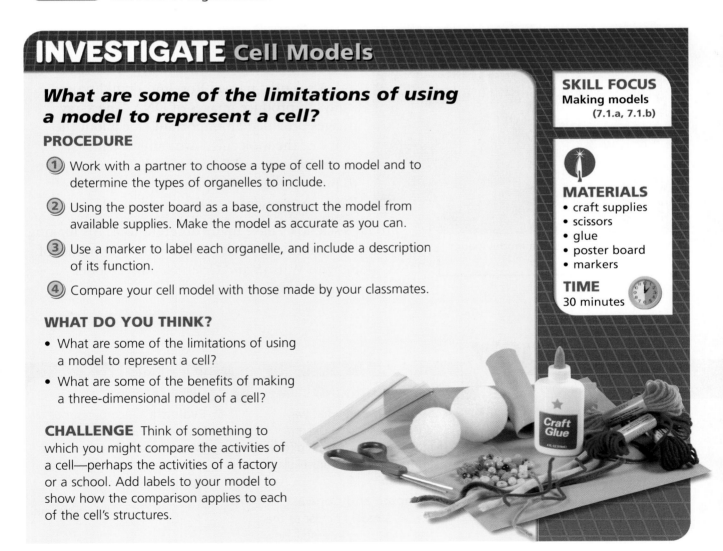

Scientists use models to study cells.

If you look at plant or animal cells under a microscope, you will notice some differences between real cells and the diagrams on page 22. Any drawing or photograph on a flat page is two-dimensional. In addition, diagrams of cells are often simplified to make them easier to understand. In order to study cell structures and their functions, scientists use many types of models, including three-dimensional models. One of the most important discoveries in science involved the use of models.

DNA is the genetic material common to all cells. You will read more about the structure and function of DNA later in this unit. By the early 1950s, scientists had a good idea about what DNA was made of. However, they could not figure out how all the pieces of the molecule fit together.

A scientist named Rosalind Franklin used x-rays to produce images of DNA. The x-ray images provided an important clue about the shape of the molecule. Two other scientists, James Watson and Francis Crick, were then able to put together a three-dimensional model of DNA and present it to the world in 1953.

Today's scientists have many different tools for making models. The images at the left show a computer model of DNA, along with Watson and Crick's famous model.

Scientific Models

Scientists use several different types of models.

Watson and Crick used a model made from wire and tin.

1.3 Review

KEY CONCEPTS

1. What are the three domains, and what type of cells do the organisms in each domain have? (7.1.f)

2. Define specialization in your own words. (7.5.a)

3. Describe the levels of organization in a tree. (7.5.a)

CRITICAL THINKING

4. **Synthesize** In what way does a specialized cell in a multicellular organism differ from the cell of a unicellular organism?

5. **Compare and Contrast** How is a model similar to the real object it represents? How is it different?

◯ CHALLENGE

6. **Evaluate** The organism below is called *Chlamydomonas*. What domain does it belong to, and what do the internal structures tell you about it?

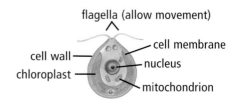

flagella (allow movement)

cell wall —
chloroplast —
— cell membrane
— nucleus
— mitochondrion

EXTREMOPHILES

Living in Hot Acid

7.1.a Students know cells function similarly in all living organisms.

Iron Mountain Mine, an abandoned mine near Redding in northern California, contains water that is the most acidic on Earth. A century of mining exposed rocks to air. The rocks contaminated underground water with sulfuric acid and heavy metals. The water is so acidic that scientists who go into the mine must wear protective clothing. In addition, the water is also quite hot—50°C (120°F).

A Slime Community

While Iron Mountain Mine is an unfriendly environment for people, certain microorganisms thrive there. These microorganisms live in extreme conditions where most forms of life could not survive. So, scientists call these microorganisms extremophiles. These tiny organisms live on the surface of the water. They stay on the surface by coating themselves in floating pink slime.

The slime contains a community of five types of microorganisms that work together to produce what they need to live. For example, one type makes the slime. Another converts nitrogen gas from the air into a form the community can use. The microorganisms get their energy from iron. In the process, they cause iron pyrite (fool's gold) to dissolve quickly. The iron pyrite reacts with water and oxygen to form sulfuric acid. In this way, the microorganisms continue to have the acidic environment that they need to live.

No Cell Wall

Researchers used to think that cells needed a thick cell wall to survive in harsh conditions. But some microorganisms at Iron Mountain have no cell wall. They have a very thin cell membrane. Yet the membrane can shield the cytoplasm from sulfuric acid and high amounts of metals in the surrounding water. Scientists are trying to figure out how this membrane works.

Despite the heat, scientists at Iron Mountain Mine must wear plastic coveralls, safety glasses, rubber boots, rubber gloves, and hardhats.

The water from the mine carries iron, which can produce reddish deposits.

The pink slime being collected in the photograph contains a community of extremophiles.

WRITING ABOUT SCIENCE

Think of another organism that lives in an extreme environment, such as a cactus or a penguin. Write a paragraph that compares this organism with an extremophile.

Chapter Review

the **BIG** idea

All living things are made up of cells.

CONTENT REVIEW
CLASSZONE.COM

◀ KEY CONCEPTS SUMMARY

1 ## The cell is the basic unit of living things.

All living things are made up of one or more cells. **Organisms** share the following characteristics:

• organization
• ability to grow and develop
• ability to respond
• ability to reproduce

Multicellular organisms include this frog and these water-lily plants.

Many unicellular organisms live in pond water.

VOCABULARY
unicellular p. 11
multicellular p. 11
microscope p. 12
cell theory p. 13
bacteria p. 14

---

2 ## Microscopes allow us to see inside the cell.

A **prokaryotic cell** is relatively simple in structure, with no nucleus or other organelles. A **eukaryotic cell** is more complex, with many different organelles inside it.

bacterium

plant cell

animal cell

A bacterium consists of a single prokaryotic cell.

Plants and animals are made up of many eukaryotic cells.

VOCABULARY
cell membrane p. 20
cytoplasm p. 20
prokaryotic cell p. 20
eukaryotic cell p. 20
organelle p. 20
nucleus p. 20
cell wall p. 21
chloroplast p. 23
mitochondria p. 23

---

3 ## Cells can perform specialized functions.

• The single cell of a unicellular organism does all that is necessary for the organism to survive.

• A multicellular organism is a community of **specialized** cells.

• Scientific models make it easier to understand cells.

The tarsier has many levels of organization in its body.

VOCABULARY
specialization p. 28
tissue p. 29
organ p. 30

Reviewing Vocabulary

1–5. *Use a vocabulary term to identify each numbered part of this plant cell.*

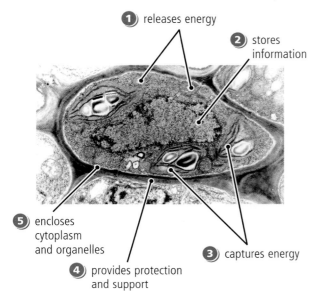

1 releases energy

2 stores information

5 encloses cytoplasm and organelles

4 provides protection and support

3 captures energy

In one or two sentences, describe how the terms in each of the following pairs are related. Underline each term in your answer.

6. unicellular, multicellular

7. cell, organelle

8. prokaryotic cell, eukaryotic cell

9. tissue, organ

Reviewing Key Concepts

Multiple Choice *Choose the letter of the best answer.*

10. Which statement about cells is part of the cell theory? (7.1.a)
   a. Cells are found in most living things.
   b. Cells with cell walls do not have cell membranes.
   c. All cells capture energy from sunlight.
   d. Cells come only from other living cells.

11. What structure does a plant cell have that is not found in an animal cell and that allows a plant cell to capture energy from sunlight? (7.1.b)
   a. cell wall
   b. chloroplast
   c. mitochondrion
   d. central vacuole

12. Which technology was important to the development of the cell theory? (7.7.a)
   a. computer
   b. scientific model
   c. microscope
   d. refrigeration

13. Organisms can be divided into domains on the basis of the characteristics of their cells. What are these domains? (7.1.f)
   a. Archaea, Bacteria, and Eukarya
   b. prokaryotes and eukaryotes
   c. plants, animals, and bacteria
   d. unicellular and multicellular

14. A complex multicellular organism has different levels of organization. What is the order of these levels? (7.5.a)
   a. cell membrane, cytoplasm, nucleus
   b. tissues, organs, organ systems
   c. tissues, organs, specialized cells
   d. cell membrane, organelles, nucleus

15. What is the function of the genetic material in a cell? (7.1.c)
   a. provides transport of materials from the nucleus to the cell membrane
   b. breaks down materials brought into the cell
   c. provides information a cell needs to reproduce and function
   d. controls what comes into a cell and what goes out

Short Answer *Write a short answer to each question.*

16. What are four characteristics common to all living things? (7.1.a)

17. What are three needs common to all living things? (7.1.a)

Thinking Critically

The next three questions refer to polar bears and their cells as examples of animals and animal cells.

18. **PREDICT** Some polar bears go through long periods of sleep during the cold winter months. In what two ways might their fat cells help the bears survive during these periods? (7.5.a)

19. **PROVIDE EXAMPLES** Animals do not get energy directly from sunlight as plants do. Give one or two examples of body systems in a polar bear that help it obtain and process food. (7.1.d)

20. **COMPARE AND CONTRAST** Consider the fat cells in a polar bear and compare them with the single cell of a bacterium. How are the cells alike, and how are they different? (7.1.f)

21. **CONNECT** The cell theory applies to all organisms, including you. State the three parts of the cell theory and describe briefly how they relate to you. (7.1.a)

22. **ANALYZE** Louis Pasteur designed the swan-necked flask to use in his experiments. In one experiment, he used two sealed flasks of nutrient broth. He heated one flask and left the other untouched. Bacteria grew in the untouched flask. Nothing grew in the flask that had been heated, or sterilized. How did this experiment provide evidence against the idea of spontaneous generation? (7.7.d)

23. **PREDICT** What would happen if the neck of the sterilized flask in question 22 were broken? (7.7.d)

24. **IDENTIFY CAUSE** Why might pasteurized milk eventually spoil?

25. **COMPARE AND CONTRAST** A plant cell has a number of structures and organelles that an animal cell does not. Copy the table below and place a check in the appropriate box of each row. The first two are done for you. (7.1.b)

	Animal Cell	Plant Cell
Cell wall		✓
Cell membrane	✓	✓
Cytoplasm		
Nucleus		
Central vacuole		
Chloroplast		
Mitochondrion		

the BIG idea

26. **CLASSIFY** Look again at the photograph on pages 6–7. Can you identify any of the structures shown? Can you identify the type of microscope used to make the photograph? How do you know? (7.1.a)

27. **CONNECT** What are three ways that an understanding of cells has changed the way people live? **Hint:** Think about Pasteur and his work.

UNIT PROJECTS

If you are doing a unit project, make a folder for your project. Include in your folder a list of the resources you will need, the date on which the project is due, and a schedule to track your progress. Begin gathering data.

Analyzing Hypotheses

7.1.b, 7.1.f

Read the following description of euglenas and how scientists classify them. Then answer the questions below.

Plants and animals are typically multicellular organisms. For a long time, scientists tried to classify any unicellular organism that had a nucleus as either a single-celled plant or a single-celled animal. One group of unicellular organisms, of the genus *Euglena*, was particularly difficult to classify. These tiny organisms can be found living in most ponds. What is puzzling about euglenas is that they have characteristics of both plants and animals.

Some scientists wanted to classify euglenas as a type of plant because euglenas have chloroplasts. Chloroplasts are structures that allow both plant cells and euglenas to capture energy from sunlight. Other scientists wanted to classify euglenas as animals because euglenas can take in food particles from water. Euglenas also have flagella, or tail-like structures, that allow them to swim. Euglenas even have an eyespot for sensing light.

1. What cellular structures enable plant cells and euglenas to capture energy from sunlight?
  a. flagella   **c.** nuclei
  b. chloroplasts   **d.** eyespots

2. What cellular structures are common to plant cells, animal cells, and euglenas?
  a. flagella   **c.** nuclei
  b. chloroplasts   **d.** eyespots

3. In what way are euglenas different from both plants and animals?
  a. They have no nuclei.
  b. They are unicellular.
  c. They live in ponds.
  d. They get energy from food.

4. What does an eyespot do?
  a. senses light   **c.** provides energy
  b. captures food   **d.** senses movement

5. Compare euglenas with an animal. What animal behavior does a flagellum help euglenas do?
  a. eat food   **c.** sense light
  b. get energy   **d.** move about

Extended Response

Answer the following questions in detail. Include some of the terms in the word box. In your answers, underline each term you use.

sunlight	energy	food
eyespot	flagellum	move

6. A jar of water containing euglenas is placed in a sunny window. After a while, a noticeable cloud forms in the water, near where the light shines into the water. Over the course of the day, the position of the Sun changes. As it does, the cloud keeps moving toward the light. On the basis of your reading, what do you think is happening and why?

7. Suppose there is a small pond near your school. The pond is surrounded by many tall trees that tend to block sunlight around the edges of the pond. In this situation, explain why it is an advantage for euglenas to have the characteristics they do. Which of these characteristics do you associate with plants? with animals?

How Cells Function

the **BIG** idea

All cells need energy and materials for life processes.

How do plants like these sunflowers change energy from sunlight?

Key Concepts

SECTION

1 **Chemical reactions take place inside cells.**
Learn why water and four types of large molecules are important for cell functions.

SECTION

2 **Cells capture and release energy.**
Learn about the process of photosynthesis and the two ways cells release energy.

SECTION

3 **Materials move across the cell's membranes.**
Learn about the different ways materials move through cells.

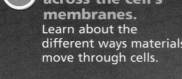

California ClassZone

CLASSZONE.COM

Chapter 2 online resources: Content Review, two Visualizations, two Resource Centers, Math Tutorial, and Test Practice

EXPLORE (the BIG idea)

Just a Spoonful of Sugar

> **7.1.a** Students know cells function similarly in all living organisms.

Pour a little warm water into each of two cups. Stir eight spoonfuls of sugar into one of the cups. Drop several raisins into each cup and wait for six hours. After six hours, compare the raisins in each cup.

Observe and Think How are the raisins different? How would you explain your observation?

Internet Activity: Photosynthesis

> **7.1.b** Students know the characteristics that distinguish plant cells from animal cells, including chloroplasts and cell walls.

Go to **ClassZone.com** to examine how plants use energy from sunlight to make sugar molecules. This process takes place in chloroplasts inside plant cells.

Observe and Think What are the starting materials of photosynthesis? What are the products?

Photosynthesis **Code: MDL032**

Getting Ready to Learn

◀ CONCEPT REVIEW

- Cells are the basic units of living things.
- Some cells have organelles that perform special functions for the cell.
- Animal cells and plant cells have similar structures, but plant cells have cell walls and chloroplasts.

◀ VOCABULARY REVIEW

cell membrane, p. 20

organelle, p. 20

chloroplast, p. 23

mitochondria, p. 23

molecule *See Glossary.*

CONTENT REVIEW
CLASSZONE.COM

Review concepts and vocabulary.

▶ TAKING NOTES

OUTLINE

As you read, copy the headings on your paper in the form of an outline. Then add notes in your own words that summarize what you read.

VOCABULARY STRATEGY

Draw a **word triangle** diagram for each new vocabulary term. On the bottom line, write and define the term. Above that, write a sentence that uses the term correctly. At the top, draw a small picture to show what the term looks like.

See the Note-Taking Handbook on pages R45–R51.

SCIENCE NOTEBOOK

I. Chemical reactions take place inside cells.

  A. All cells are made of the same elements.

  B. Large molecules support cell function.

    1. Carbohydrates
      a.
      b.

    2. Lipids
      a.
      b.

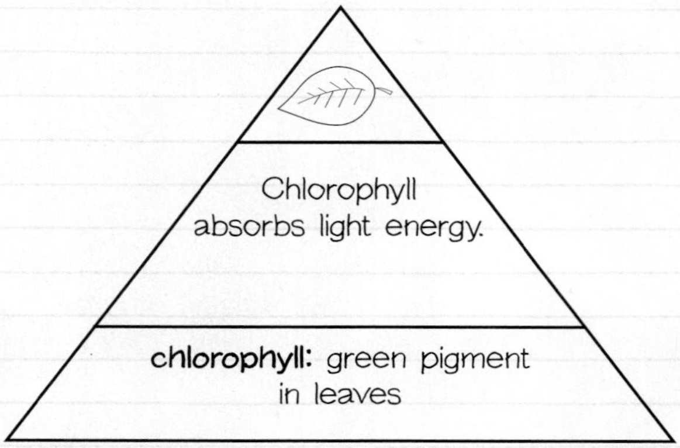

Chlorophyll absorbs light energy.

chlorophyll: green pigment in leaves

2.1 Chemical reactions take place inside cells.

CALIFORNIA
Content Standard

7.1.a Students know cells function similarly in all living organisms.

BEFORE, you learned

- All living things are made of cells
- Cells need energy to sustain life
- Plant and animal cells have similarities and differences

NOW, you will learn

- About the types of elements found in all cells
- About the functions of large molecules in the cell
- Why water is important to the activities of the cell

VOCABULARY

chemical reaction p. 42
carbohydrate p. 42
lipid p. 43
protein p. 43
nucleic acid p. 43

THINK ABOUT

What are cells made of?

Food provides you with important substances for your body. Have you ever heard the words *protein, carbohydrate,* and *lipid*? Each of the foods shown in the photograph provides some of these substances. Your cells break down these substances for energy and to make other substances. Cells of other organisms also use, break down, and make substances. Can you guess what types of organisms are the sources of the substances in the photograph?

All cells are made of the same elements.

People use microscopes to observe the tiny cells that make up all living things. A light microscope can even show the parts of a cell. But it cannot show the basic building blocks of matter. All matter in the universe—living and nonliving—is made of particles called atoms. Different substances are made of different types of atoms. Each element has its own type of atom. More than a hundred different elements exist. Each element has its own properties. For example, part of the air around you is oxygen—a colorless, odorless gas. Atoms of oxygen, joined with other atoms, make up most of your body.

OUTLINE
Take notes on this main idea. You can use the beginning of an outline shown on page 40 to get you started.

I. Main idea
  A. Supporting idea
    1. Detail
    2. Detail
  B. Supporting idea

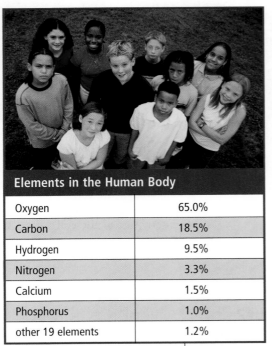

Elements in the Human Body

Oxygen	65.0%
Carbon	18.5%
Hydrogen	9.5%
Nitrogen	3.3%
Calcium	1.5%
Phosphorus	1.0%
other 19 elements	1.2%

Source: CRC Handbook of Chemistry and Physics

Of all the elements found on Earth, about 25 are essential for life. As you can see from the table at left, just 6 elements account for about 99 percent of the mass of the human body. Atoms of oxygen and atoms of carbon together make up more than 80 percent of your body. But very little of this matter exists as single atoms. Instead, most of the matter in and around you is in the form of molecules.

A molecule consists of two or more atoms joined together. The atoms can be of the same element. For example, a molecule of oxygen gas (O_2) is made of two atoms of oxygen. Molecules can also be made of atoms of different elements. For example, a molecule of water (H_2O) is made of two atoms of hydrogen (H) joined with one atom of oxygen (O).

Most activities that take place within cells involve the interaction of atoms and molecules. A **chemical reaction** is a process in which bonds between atoms are broken and new bonds are formed. Chemical reactions rearrange the atoms into different molecules. Energy is needed to break bonds between atoms. Energy is released when new bonds form.

Large molecules support cell function.

RESOURCE CENTER
CLASSZONE.COM

Explore molecules in living things.

There are four main types of large molecules that make up living things: carbohydrates, lipids, proteins, and nucleic acids. These molecules work together in a cell. The four types of molecules in all living things contain carbon atoms. These large molecules are made up of smaller parts called subunits.

Carbohydrates

sugars

Carbohydrates provide structure and store energy in cells. Complex carbohydrates, such as cellulose, are made of **sugars.**

A **carbohydrate** (KAHR-boh-HY-DRAYT) is a type of molecule made up of subunits of sugars. Carbohydrates are used for energy. They are also used for structure. Carbohydrates can be broken down to provide the cell with energy. Simple carbohydrates are sugars made from atoms of carbon, oxygen, and hydrogen. Inside cells, sugar molecules are broken down. This process provides usable energy for the cell.

Simple sugar molecules can be linked into long chains to form more complex carbohydrates, such as starch, cellulose, and glycogen. Starch and cellulose are complex carbohydrates made by plant cells. When a plant cell makes more sugar than it can use, extra sugar molecules are stored in long chains called starch. Plants also make cellulose, which is the material that makes up the cell wall.

Lipids

Lipids are the fats, oils, and waxes found in living things. Like carbohydrates, simple lipids are made of atoms of carbon, oxygen, and hydrogen. Lipids can be used by cells for energy and for making structures. However, atoms in lipids are arranged differently from atoms in carbohydrates. Many common lipids consist of a molecule called glycerol bonded to long chains called fatty acids. This structure gives lipids unique properties. One extremely important property of most lipids is that they do not dissolve in water.

How do cells use carbohydrates and lipids?

head

fatty acid tails

Lipids make up the membranes surrounding the cell and organelles. Fatty acids form long tails.

Proteins

Proteins are a type of molecule made of smaller molecules called amino acids. Amino acids contain the elements carbon, oxygen, hydrogen, nitrogen, and sometimes sulfur. In proteins, amino acids are linked into long chains that fold into three-dimensional shapes. The structure and function of a protein are determined by the type, number, and order of the amino acids in it.

Your body gets amino acids from breaking down protein in foods such as meat, eggs, cheese, and some beans. After taking in amino acids, your cells use them to build proteins needed for the cells to function. Some amino acids can be made by the body. Others must be taken in from an outside food source.

There are many types of proteins. Enzymes are proteins that control chemical reactions in the cells. Other proteins support the growth and repair of cells. The action of proteins in your muscles allows you to move. Some of the proteins in your blood fight infections. Another protein in your blood delivers oxygen to all the cells in your body. Proteins are also important parts of cell membranes. Some proteins in the cell membrane transport materials into and out of the cell.

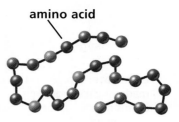
amino acid

Proteins are made up of **amino acids**. Proteins carry out most of the chemical activity in cells.

Nucleic Acids

Nucleic acids (noo-KLEE-ihk) are the molecules that hold the instructions for cells to develop, grow, and reproduce themselves. There are two types of nucleic acids: DNA and RNA. Both DNA and RNA are made from carbon, oxygen, hydrogen, nitrogen, and phosphorus. The subunits of nucleic acids are called nucleotides.

DNA provides the information used by a cell for making proteins the cell needs. This information is in the form of a code based on the specific order of different nucleotides in the DNA.

nucleotide

Nucleic acids store and translate the genetic information a cell needs to function. Nucleic acids, such as DNA, are made up of **nucleotides**.

The pattern of nucleotides in DNA is then coded into RNA. RNA delivers the information into the cytoplasm. Other types of RNA molecules in the cytoplasm produce the proteins.

 CHECK YOUR READING What is the function of DNA and RNA?

About two-thirds of every cell is water.

hydrogen

oxygen

Each **water** molecule is made of two **hydrogen** atoms bonded to one **oxygen** atom.

All of the chemical reactions inside the cell take place in water. In fact, water makes up about 70 percent of most cells. Chemical reactions also take place in water outside the cell membrane.

Water has an important property—its molecules are polar. Polar molecules have a region of positive charge and a region of negative charge. The hydrogen atoms have a slight positive charge. They attract negative regions of other polar molecules and repel positive regions. The oxygen atom in a water molecule has a slight negative charge and so it attracts positive regions. Many other materials are either made of polar molecules or break easily into pieces with positive and negative charges. These materials tend to dissolve in water because the interactions between charges tend to move the molecules around. Other molecules, such as those in fats and oils, tend to stay together and not dissolve in water.

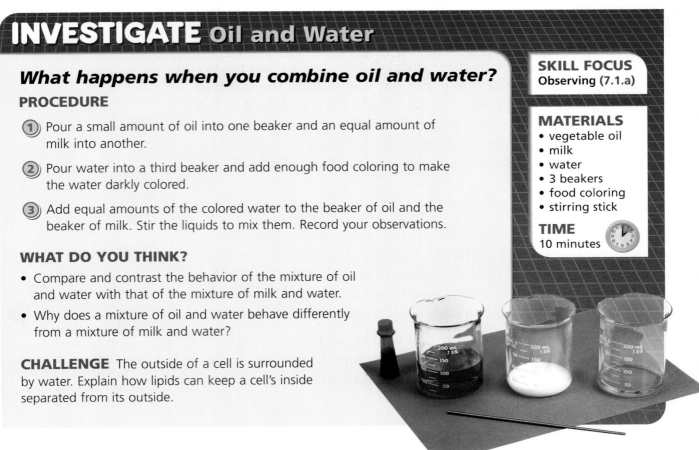

INVESTIGATE Oil and Water

What happens when you combine oil and water?

PROCEDURE

1. Pour a small amount of oil into one beaker and an equal amount of milk into another.

2. Pour water into a third beaker and add enough food coloring to make the water darkly colored.

3. Add equal amounts of the colored water to the beaker of oil and the beaker of milk. Stir the liquids to mix them. Record your observations.

WHAT DO YOU THINK?

- Compare and contrast the behavior of the mixture of oil and water with that of the mixture of milk and water.

- Why does a mixture of oil and water behave differently from a mixture of milk and water?

CHALLENGE The outside of a cell is surrounded by water. Explain how lipids can keep a cell's inside separated from its outside.

SKILL FOCUS
Observing (7.1.a)

MATERIALS
- vegetable oil
- milk
- water
- 3 beakers
- food coloring
- stirring stick

TIME
10 minutes

Cell Membrane

The cell membrane is made of a double layer of lipids.

Lipids have a polar head and two nonpolar tails.

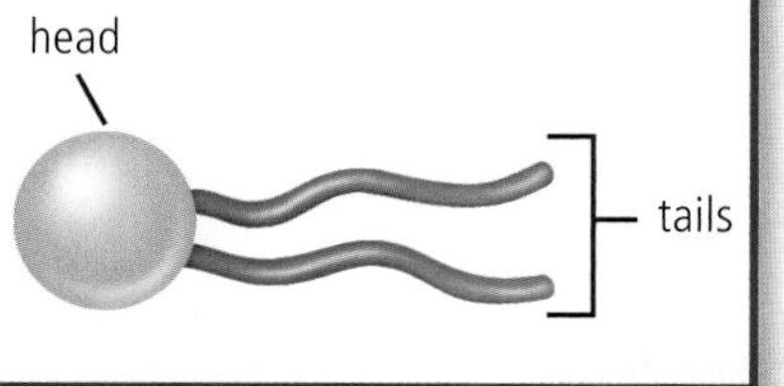

head

tails

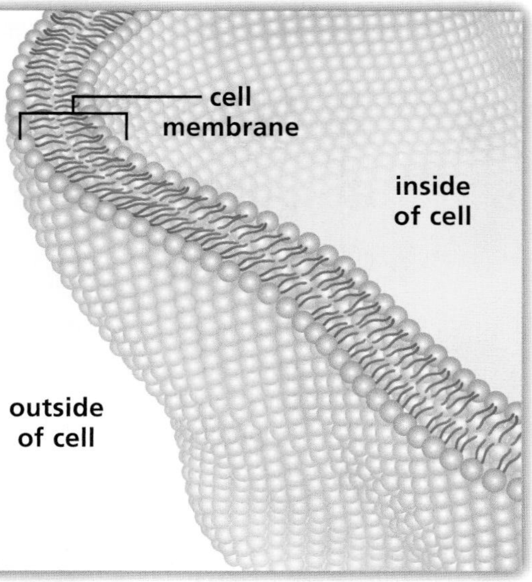

cell membrane

inside of cell

outside of cell

Most lipids do not dissolve in water. A special type of lipid makes up cell membranes. These special lipid molecules have two parts: a head and two tails. The head is polar and so tends to be pulled by water molecules. The tails are not polar. The tails tend to interact with other tails, rather than the water molecules.

As you can see in the diagram above, the heads of some lipids in cell membranes face outward, toward the water that surrounds the cell. The heads of other lipids face toward the watery inside of the cell. The tails of the two sets of lipids form the inside of the membrane and makes the barrier between the inside and outside of the cell.

READING **TiP**
As you read about the properties of cells, notice the arrangements of lipids in the diagram of the cell.

 CHECK YOUR READING How do the heads and tails of lipids help form a barrier in water?

2.1 Review

KEY CONCEPTS

1. Explain how just a few elements can make up all living things. (7.1.a)

2. What functions do proteins, carbohydrates, lipids, and nucleic acids perform? (7.1.a)

3. What does it mean to describe water molecules as being polar? (7.1.a)

CRITICAL THINKING

4. **Compare and Contrast** How are carbohydrates and lipids similar? How are they different?

5. **Draw Conclusions** What do the major types of molecules that make up living things have in common?

⬤ CHALLENGE

6. **Model** Some people have compared the nucleic acids DNA and RNA to a blueprint for life. How are DNA and RNA like a blueprint? How are they different from a blueprint?

SCIENCE on the JOB

Natural Dyes and Cells

7.1.b Students know the characteristics that distinguish plant cells from animal cells, including chloroplasts and cell walls.

Where does the blue in your blue jeans come from? How about the red, yellow, green, or pink in your favorite wool or cotton sweater? Most fabrics are colored with dyes made in labs, but some designers prefer to use natural dyes and natural cloth. All textile designers must understand the science of dyes and fibers to produce the colors they want.

Fibers

Natural fibers come either from plants or animals. Wool is an animal fiber. Silk is also made up of animal cells. Cotton, linen, and rayon are fibers made from plants. Plant fibers have thick cell walls, made mostly of cellulose. Animal fibers, on the other hand, contain mainly proteins.

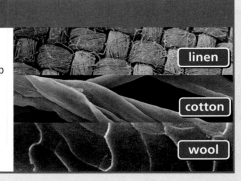

linen

cotton

wool

silk

Dyes

Most natural dyes come from plants, but sometimes insects are used. The indigo plant is used for most blue dyes, including dye for blue jeans. Insects are most often used to make reds. All dyes are made of molecules—carbon, oxygen, hydrogen, and other atoms. The molecules of the dye bind to the molecules of the fibers, adding the dye's color to the fiber.

Color Fixers

A mordant is a chemical compound that combines with dye as a color fixer, or color keeper. The mordant strengthens the bonds between natural dye molecules and fibers. A stronger bond means the color is less likely to fade or wash out of the fibers. Most mordants are liquid solutions containing metals, such as chromium.

EXPLORE

1. **EXPERIMENT** Design an experiment using onion skins, beets, or blackberries to color white wool or white cotton. The procedure should include chopping the plant and heating it with water to make the dye. Be sure that your procedure includes only one variable. Your experiment should start with a question, such as "How do the fabrics differ?" or "Which dye works best?"

2. **CHALLENGE** Using different mordants with the same dye can produce different colors. For example, dandelion leaf dye produces yellow-green, gray-green, tan, or gold with different mordants. Explain why this happens.

2.2

KEY CONCEPT

Cells capture and release energy.

CALIFORNIA
Content Standards

7.1.b Students know the characteristics that distinguish plant cells from animal cells, including chloroplasts and cell walls.

7.1.d Students know that mitochondria liberate energy for the work that cells do and that chloroplasts capture sunlight energy for photosynthesis.

VOCABULARY

chemical energy p. 47
glucose p. 47
photosynthesis p. 48
chlorophyll p. 48
cellular respiration p. 50
fermentation p. 52

OUTLINE
Remember to include this heading in your outline of this section.

I. Main idea
  A. Supporting idea
    1. Detail
    2. Detail
  B. Supporting idea

◀ **BEFORE, you learned**

• The cell is the basic unit of all living things
• Plant cells and animal cells have similarities and differences
• Plants and animals need energy and materials

▶ **NOW, you will learn**

• Why cells need energy
• How energy is captured and stored
• How plants and animals get energy

THINK ABOUT

What do these cells have in common?

Both muscle cells and plant cells need energy to live. Your muscle cells need energy to help you move and perform other functions. Even though plant cells don't move in the same way that muscles move, they still need energy. How do muscle cells and plant cells get energy?

leaf cells

muscle cells

All cells need energy.

To stay alive, cells need a constant supply of energy. All cells use chemical energy. **Chemical energy** is the energy stored in the bonds between atoms of every molecule. To stay alive, cells must be able to release the chemical energy in the bonds.

A major energy source for most cells is stored in a sugar molecule called **glucose.** When you need energy, cells release chemical energy from glucose. You need energy to run and walk—and even during sleep. Your cells use energy from food to carry out all of their activities.

Think about muscle cells. When you run, muscle cells release chemical energy from glucose to move your legs. The more you run, the more glucose your muscle cells need. You eat food to restore the glucose supply in your muscles. But how do plant cells get more glucose? Plants transform the energy in sunlight into the chemical energy in glucose and other sugars.

CHECK YOUR READING What are two ways that cells get glucose?

Some cells capture light energy.

The original source of energy for almost all organisms is sunlight. Plants change the energy in sunlight into a form of energy their cells can use—the chemical energy in glucose. All animals benefit from the ability of plants to convert sunlight to food energy. Animals either eat plants, or they eat other animals that have eaten plants.

Photosynthesis (FOH-toh-SIHN-thih-sihs) is the process that plant cells use to change the energy from sunlight into chemical energy. Photosynthesis takes place in plant cells that have chloroplasts. Chloroplasts contain **chlorophyll** (KLAWR-uh-fihl), a light-absorbing pigment, or colored substance, that traps the energy in sunlight.

The process of photosynthesis involves a series of chemical steps, or reactions. The illustration on the next page shows an overview of how photosynthesis changes starting materials into new products.

READING TiP

As you read each numbered item here, find the number on the diagram on page 49.

1 **The starting materials** of photosynthesis are carbon dioxide and water. The plant takes in carbon dioxide from the air and water from the soil.

2 **The process** takes place when carbon dioxide and water enter the plant's chloroplasts. Chlorophyll captures energy from sunlight, which is used to change carbon dioxide and water into new products.

3 **The products** of photosynthesis are oxygen and sugars such as glucose. The plant releases most of the oxygen to the air as a waste product and keeps the glucose for its energy needs.

 Summarize photosynthesis. Remember that a summary includes only the most important information.

Plants do not immediately use all of the glucose they make. Some of the glucose molecules are linked together to build large carbohydrates called starch. Plants can store starch and later break it down into glucose or other sugars when they need energy. Sugars and starches supply food for animals that eat plants.

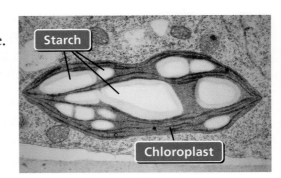

The starch in this plant cell stores energy.

CHECK YOUR READING How do plants store glucose?

Photosynthesis

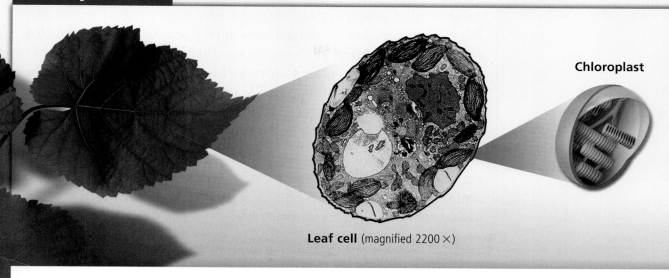

Chloroplast

Leaf cell (magnified 2200 ×)

1 **The starting materials** Carbon dioxide from the air and water from the soil enter the chloroplasts.

2 **The process** Inside the chloroplasts, chlorophyll captures energy from sunlight. This energy is used to change starting materials into new products.

3 **The products** Glucose supplies energy and is a source of materials for the plant; most oxygen is released into the air.

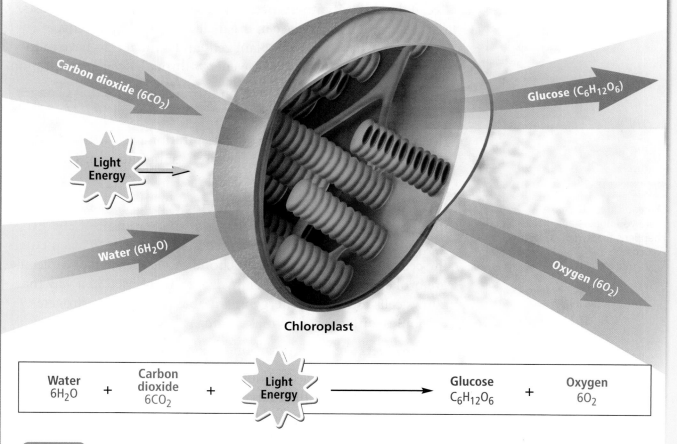

Carbon dioxide ($6CO_2$)

Glucose ($C_6H_{12}O_6$)

Light Energy

Water ($6H_2O$)

Oxygen ($6O_2$)

Chloroplast

Water $6H_2O$	+	Carbon dioxide $6CO_2$	+	Light Energy	$\longrightarrow$	Glucose $C_6H_{12}O_6$	+	Oxygen $6O_2$

READING VISUALS In what part of the diagram are starting materials changed?

All cells release energy.

All cells must have energy to function. Glucose and other sugars are cell food. When they are broken down, they are the power source for cell activities in almost all living things. When glucose is stored as glycogen or taken in as starch, it must be broken down into individual sugar molecules before cells are able to use it. Chemical energy is stored in the bonds of sugars. When a sugar molecule is broken down, a usable form of energy is released for the cell's life functions.

Cells can release energy in two basic processes: cellular respiration and fermentation. Cellular respiration requires oxygen, but fermentation does not. In addition, cellular respiration releases much more usable energy than does fermentation.

 What is released when a sugar molecule is broken down?

Cellular Respiration

Cellular respiration is a process in which cells use oxygen to release energy stored in sugars such as glucose. In fact, most of the energy used by the cells in your body is provided by cellular respiration.

Recall that photosynthesis occurs in organelles called chloroplasts. Cellular respiration takes place in organelles called mitochondria. As you read in Chapter 1, both plant cells and animal cells have mitochondria. Both types of cells release energy through cellular respiration.

Like photosynthesis, cellular respiration is a process that changes starting materials into new products.

READING TiP

Reread step 2 to make sure you understand what happens to oxygen and glucose.

1 **The starting materials** of cellular respiration are sugars—such as glucose—and oxygen. First glucose is split into two. This releases a small amount of energy.

2 **The process** begins when glucose in the cytoplasm is broken down into smaller molecules. This releases a small amount of energy. These molecules then move into the mitochondria. Oxygen enters the cell and travels into the mitochondria. As the smaller molecules are broken down even further, hydrogen is released in a way that allows cells to capture energy in a usable form. The hydrogen combines with oxygen to make water.

3 **The products** are energy, carbon dioxide, and water.

Some of the energy released during cellular respiration is transferred to other molecules. They then carry the energy where it is needed for the activities of the cell. The rest of the energy is released as heat. Carbon dioxide formed during cellular respiration is released by the cell.

 What are the three products of cellular respiration?

Cellular Respiration

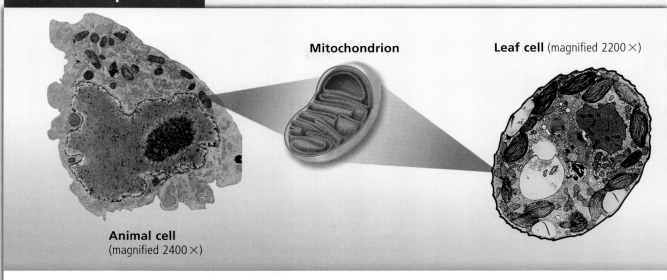

Mitochondrion

Leaf cell (magnified 2200×)

Animal cell
(magnified 2400×)

1 **The starting materials** Glucose and oxygen enter the cell.

2 **The process** Glucose is split into smaller molecules. Inside the mitochondria more chemical bonds are broken. Oxygen is needed for this process.

3 **The products** Energy is released, and water and carbon dioxide are produced.

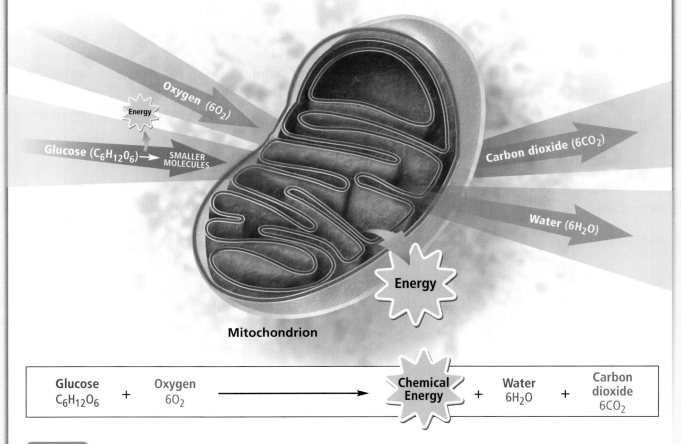

Energy

Oxygen (6O$_2$)

Glucose (C$_6$H$_{12}$O$_6$) → SMALLER MOLECULES

Carbon dioxide (6CO$_2$)

Water (6H$_2$O)

Energy

Mitochondrion

| Glucose $C_6H_{12}O_6$ | + | Oxygen $6O_2$ | → | Chemical Energy | + | Water $6H_2O$ | + | Carbon dioxide $6CO_2$ |

READING VISUALS   Where in the process is energy released?

Photosynthesis and Respiration Cycle

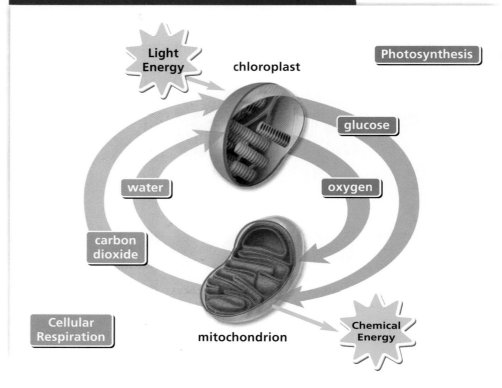

You may find it interesting to compare cellular respiration with photosynthesis. The diagram above highlights the cycle that occurs between photosynthesis and cellular respiration. Notice that the starting materials of one process are also the products of the other process. This cycle does not necessarily occur in the same cell, or even in the same organism.

Fermentation

VOCABULARY
Add a word triangle diagram for *fermentation* to your notebook. Your triangle could include a sketch of a loaf of bread.

Fermentation is the process by which cells release energy without oxygen. Recall that in cellular respiration the cell first breaks glucose into smaller molecules. This releases a small amount of energy. Without oxygen, cellular respiration cannot continue. When no oxygen is present in eukaryotic cells, these smaller molecules stay in the cytoplasm. Fermentation occurs in the cytoplasm, not in the mitochondria.

There are two types of fermentation. Both types of fermentation help the cell break down sugars and release energy. Alcoholic fermentation produces alcohol and carbon dioxide. Lactic acid fermentation produces lactic acid.

CHECK YOUR READING Use a Venn diagram to compare and contrast fermentation and cellular respiration.

The production of many foods that people eat every day involve either alcoholic fermentation or lactic acid fermentation. Three of these foods are bread, yogurt, and cheese.

Bread is often made by mixing flour, milk, and sugar with a microorganism you know as yeast. Yeast runs out of oxygen and uses fermentation to convert the sugar into alcohol and carbon dioxide. Bubbles of carbon dioxide gas forming inside the dough cause it to rise. When the dough is baked, the small amount of alcohol evaporates. The yeast is killed, and the carbon dioxide bubbles give the bread a light, spongy structure.

Some bacteria release energy through lactic acid fermentation. These bacteria convert the sugar found in milk into lactic acid. The bacteria are used to make yogurt, cheese, and sourdough bread. Lactic acid changes the acidity of a bread mixture to give it a slightly sour flavor. In yogurt, the buildup of lactic acid causes the milk to thicken, producing the creamy texture of yogurt. If fermentation continues for a long time, the milk eventually turns into cheese.

CALIFORNIA Focus

Since the days of the gold rush, San Francisco has been famous for its sourdough bread. Fermentation products from local strains of yeast (*Candida milleri*) and bacteria (*Lactobacillus sanfrancisco*) give the bread its special, sour flavor.

INVESTIGATE Fermentation

How can you tell if fermentation releases material?

PROCEDURE

1. Add 1/2 teaspoon of yeast to the empty water bottle.
2. Fill the bottle about three-quarters full with the sugar solution.
3. Place the balloon tightly around the mouth of the bottle.
4. Gently swirl the bottle to mix the yeast and sugar solution.
5. After 20 minutes, observe the balloon and record your observations.

WHAT DO YOU THINK?

- What changes did you observe? What do you think is the source of energy that caused these changes?
- What accounts for the change in the amount of gas inside the balloon?

CHALLENGE Design an experiment to answer the following question. How might the temperature of the sugar solution affect the process?

SKILL FOCUS
Observing (7.1.a)

MATERIALS
- dry yeast
- measuring spoons
- small water bottle
- warm sugar solution
- balloon

TIME
30 minutes

Energy and Exercise

Your muscle cells, like some organisms, are able to release energy through both cellular respiration and fermentation. While you are at rest, your muscle cells use specialized molecules to store both energy and oxygen.

During hard exercise, your muscle cells may use up all their stores of energy and oxygen. Then your muscle cells rely on fermentation to break down sugars. There is much less energy available to cells that use fermentation. That is why you cannot continue to run rapidly for long distances. When your cells use fermentation to release energy, one of the waste products is lactic acid. The lactic acid can cause a burning sensation in your muscles.

APPLY Why might these students feel a burning sensation in their arm muscles while doing pull-ups?

When you stop after this type of exercise, your muscles continue to hurt and you continue to breathe hard for many minutes. During this time, your muscles are playing catch-up. They use the oxygen brought into your blood by your heavy breathing to finish breaking down the byproducts of fermentation. As the lactic acid is converted into carbon dioxide and water, the burning sensation in your muscles goes away. Your muscles build back up their stores of energy and oxygen until the next time they are needed.

 CHECK YOUR READING How do your muscles release energy during hard exercise?

2.2 Review

KEY CONCEPTS

1. Which form of energy is especially important for living things? Why? (7.1.d)
2. How is photosynthesis important to life on Earth? (7.1.d)
3. What starting materials do cells need for cellular respiration? (7.1.d)

CRITICAL THINKING

4. **Compare and Contrast** How are photosynthesis and cellular respiration similar? How are they different?
5. **Predict** Suppose that in a lab you could remove all the oxygen from a terrarium. What would happen to the plants? Why?

⬤ CHALLENGE

6. **Synthesize** In everyday language, the word *respiration* refers to breathing. How is breathing related to cellular respiration? **Hint:** The air we breathe out contains more carbon dioxide than the air we breathe in.

MATH in SCIENCE

MATH TUTORIAL
CLASSZONE.COM
Click on Math Tutorial for more help with interpreting line graphs.

Math 7.AF.1.5

SKILL: INTERPRETING GRAPHS

Carbon Dioxide Levels in Biosphere 2

Biosphere 2 is a research and education center in Arizona that can house people, plants, and animals. It was built to find out whether people could get the food and breathable air needed to survive in a small sealed environment over a two-year period.

Example

Data on carbon dioxide levels in the air of Biosphere 2 were collected at 15-minute intervals for several weeks. The graph below shows the amounts of carbon dioxide (CO_2) in the air on January 20, 1996.

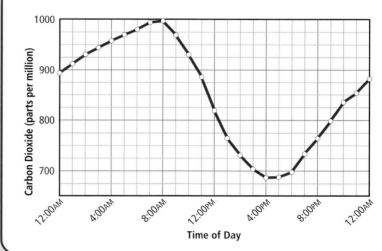

Answer the following questions.

1. What intervals are shown on the x-axis? What is shown on the y-axis?

2. At what time of day does the carbon dioxide concentration reach its highest point? About how many parts per million of CO_2 are in the air at that time?

3. Between what hours is the CO_2 level decreasing?

CHALLENGE The data in the graph were collected on a sunny day. How might the graph look different if the day had been overcast?

KEY CONCEPT

2.3 Materials move across the cell's membranes.

CALIFORNIA Content Standard

7.1.a Students know cells function similarly in all living organisms.

BEFORE, you learned

- All cells have an outer covering called the cell membrane
- Cells need starting materials for life-sustaining processes
- Cells need to get rid of waste products

NOW, you will learn

- How materials move into and out of the cell through the cell membrane
- How energy is involved in transporting some materials into and out of cells
- How surface area affects transport in cells

VOCABULARY

diffusion p. 56
passive transport p. 58
osmosis p. 59
active transport p. 60

EXPLORE Diffusion (7.1.a)

How do particles move?

PROCEDURE

1. Fill the beaker with tap water.
2. Add 3 drops of food coloring to the water.
3. For 10 minutes, observe what happens. Write down your observations.

WHAT DO YOU THINK?
- What changes did you observe?
- What might have caused the changes?

MATERIALS
- beaker
- water
- food coloring

VOCABULARY
Add a word triangle diagram for *diffusion* to your notebook.

Some materials move by diffusion.

When you walk toward the shampoo section in a store, you can probably smell a fragrance even before you get close. The process by which the scent spreads through the air is an example of diffusion. **Diffusion** (dih-FYOO-zhuhn) is the process by which molecules spread out, or move from areas where there are many of them to areas where there are fewer of them.

Diffusion occurs because the molecules in gases, liquids, and even solids are in constant motion in all directions. This random movement of molecules tends to spread molecules out until they are evenly distributed. But diffusion does more than just spread a scent around a room. Diffusion helps cells maintain conditions necessary for life. For example, the oxygen needed for cellular respiration enters cells by diffusion. Similarly, the carbon dioxide produced by cellular respiration leaves cells by diffusion.

Concentration

Diffusion occurs naturally as particles move from an area of higher concentration to an area of lower concentration. The concentration of a substance is the number of particles of that substance in a specific volume. For example, if you dissolved 9 grams of sugar in 1 liter of water, the concentration of the sugar solution would be 9 grams per liter, or 9 g/L. When there is a difference in the concentration of a substance between two areas, diffusion occurs.

Generally, the greater the difference in concentration between two areas, the more rapidly diffusion occurs. As the difference in concentration decreases, diffusion slows down. The number of particles moving to one area is balanced by the number moving in the other direction. Particles are still moving in all directions, but these movements do not change the concentrations.

 CHECK YOUR READING Summarize what happens during diffusion. (Remember, a summary includes only the most important information.)

Concentration and Diffusion

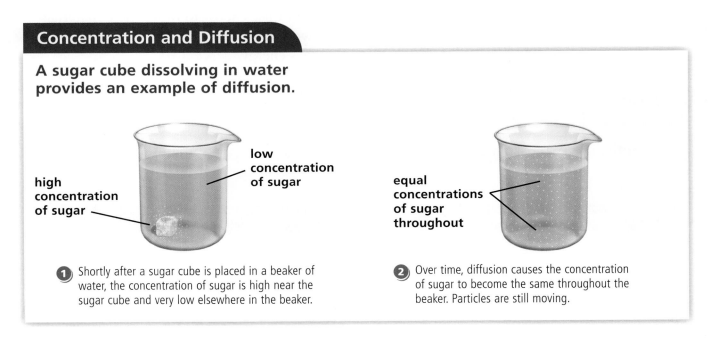

A sugar cube dissolving in water provides an example of diffusion.

high concentration of sugar

low concentration of sugar

equal concentrations of sugar throughout

① Shortly after a sugar cube is placed in a beaker of water, the concentration of sugar is high near the sugar cube and very low elsewhere in the beaker.

② Over time, diffusion causes the concentration of sugar to become the same throughout the beaker. Particles are still moving.

Diffusion in Cells

Diffusion is one way by which materials move in and out of cells. Small molecules such as oxygen can pass through tiny gaps in the cell membrane by diffusion. For example, consider the conditions that result from photosynthesis in a leaf cell.

RESOURCE CENTER
CLASSZONE.COM

Learn more about diffusion.

- Photosynthesis produces oxygen inside the cell.
- The concentration of oxygen molecules becomes higher inside the cell than outside.
- Oxygen molecules move out of the cell by diffusion.

VOCABULARY
Add a word triangle diagram for *passive transport* to your notebook. You may want to use words instead of a sketch in the top part of your triangle.

In a plant cell, some of the oxygen produced by photosynthesis is used in cellular respiration. The remaining oxygen diffuses out of the cell. Much of it escapes to the air. Some of it diffuses to other cells where there is a lower concentration of oxygen. This process of diffusion continues from one cell to the next.

Remember that cell membranes are made of lipids. The lipids prevent large molecules, such as glucose, from passing through the membrane. Some molecules, such as oxygen, pass right through the membranes. Oxygen molecules pass back and forth until the concentration of oxygen is the same on both sides of the membrane. Diffusion occurs right through the cell membrane.

Some molecules can move through special passages in the cell membrane. Each passage is formed by proteins that allow just one type of molecule, such as glucose, to pass.

When molecules move through the cell membrane in either of these ways, they tend to balance the concentration on the two sides of the membrane. The cell does not use energy to move these materials. Scientists use the term **passive transport** for the movement of materials that does not use the cell's energy.

CHECK YOUR READING What is passive transport? Your answer should mention energy.

Passive Transport

Materials move across a cell membrane continuously.

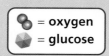

= oxygen
= glucose

Different concentrations

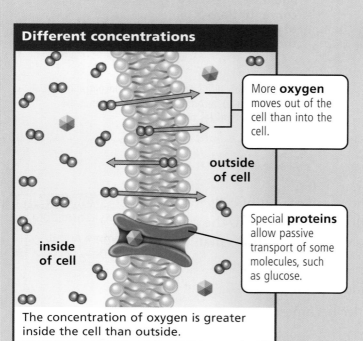

More **oxygen** moves out of the cell than into the cell.

outside of cell

inside of cell

Special **proteins** allow passive transport of some molecules, such as glucose.

The concentration of oxygen is greater inside the cell than outside.

Equal concentrations

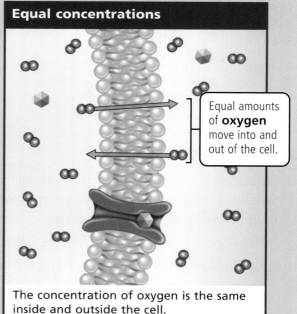

Equal amounts of **oxygen** move into and out of the cell.

The concentration of oxygen is the same inside and outside the cell.

Osmosis

You have read about the importance of water to cells. Water molecules move through cell membranes by diffusion. The diffusion of water through a membrane is given a special name, **osmosis** (ahz-MOH-sihs). If the concentration of water is higher outside a cell than inside, water moves into the cell. If the concentration of water is lower outside a cell, water moves out of the cell.

You can easily observe the effect of osmosis on plants. If you forget to water a plant, it wilts. Why? The soil dries out, and the plant's roots have no water to absorb. As a result, water leaves the plant cells by osmosis and they shrink. If you water the plant, water becomes available to enter the shrunken cells by osmosis. The leaves will return to normal as water moves into the cells.

Without water, a plant droops. The cells have little water in their vacuoles, shown in blue. (magnified 1200×)

Water moves into leaf cells by osmosis and fills the vacuoles, shown in blue. (magnified 1200×)

Some transport requires energy.

Not all materials that move into and out of a cell can do so by diffusion. For cells to carry out life functions, materials must often move from areas of low concentration into areas of high concentration. This process of moving materials requires energy.

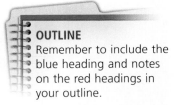

OUTLINE
Remember to include the blue heading and notes on the red headings in your outline.

Active Transport

Active transport is the process of using energy to move materials through a membrane. This process is different from diffusion and other types of passive transport, which do not require energy.

CHECK YOUR READING How is active transport different from passive transport?

VISUALIZATION
CLASSZONE.COM

Observe active transport at work.

Cells use active transport to perform important life functions, including the removal of excess salt from the body. Consider the example of active transport in marine iguanas, shown below. These lizards swim and feed in the salty ocean. As a result, they soak up a lot of salt. Too much salt can seriously damage the iguanas' cells, so the cells must get rid of the excess.

The solution to the marine iguana's salt problem is found in two small glands between its eyes and nostrils. Cells in these glands remove excess salt from the blood by active transport. Even when cells in these glands have a higher concentration of salt than is in the iguana's blood, the cells use chemical energy to continue taking salt out of the blood. The gland forms a droplet of salt, which the iguana easily blows out through its nostrils.

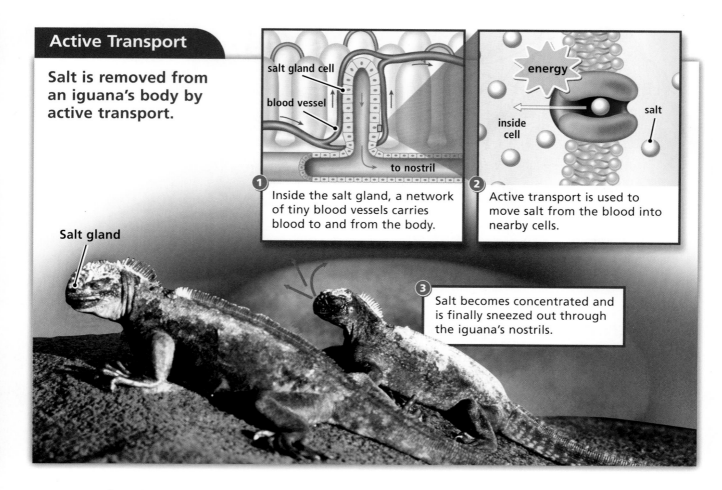

Active Transport

Salt is removed from an iguana's body by active transport.

salt gland cell

blood vessel

to nostril

1. Inside the salt gland, a network of tiny blood vessels carries blood to and from the body.

energy

inside cell

salt

2. Active transport is used to move salt from the blood into nearby cells.

Salt gland

3. Salt becomes concentrated and is finally sneezed out through the iguana's nostrils.

You may not be able to blow salt out of your nostrils, but your kidneys help maintain healthful salt levels in your body. Your kidneys filter wastes from your blood by active transport. Cells in the kidneys remove excess salt from the blood.

Endocytosis

Cells also need to move materials that are too large to go through the cell membrane or a protein channel. As the diagram below illustrates, endocytosis (EHN-doh-sy-TOH-sihs) occurs when a large bit of material is captured within a pocket of the membrane. This pocket breaks off and forms a package that moves into the cell. Cells in your body can use endocytosis to absorb essential nutrients, like iron.

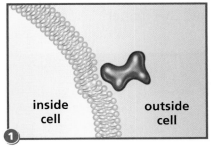
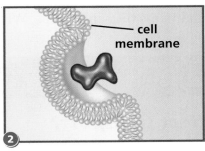
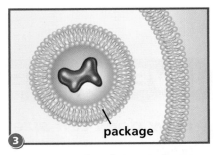

1. As a particle approaches, the cell membrane folds inward, creating a pocket.

2. The particle moves into the pocket, and the membrane closes around it, forming a package.

3. The package breaks away from the cell membrane, bringing the particle into the cell.

Exocytosis

When a cell needs to get rid of large materials, the process of endocytosis is reversed. In exocytosis (EHK-soh-sy-TOH-sihs), a membrane within the cell encloses the material that needs to be removed. This package moves to the cell membrane, joins with it, and the material is expelled. Cells often use exocytosis to flush out waste materials or to expel proteins or hormones made by the cell.

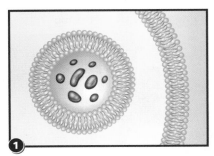
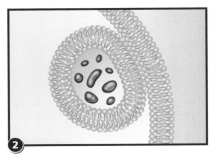
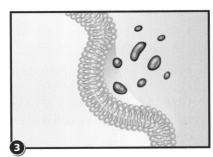

1. A membrane-enclosed package carries materials from inside the cell to the cell membrane.

2. The membrane of the package attaches to the cell membrane, and the two membranes merge.

3. The materials are pushed out of the cell as the membrane of the package becomes part of the cell membrane.

Cell size affects transport.

Most cells are very small. In fact, most cells are too small to be seen without a microscope. The average cell in your body is about 20 micrometers (0.02 millimeters) in diameter. Most of the cells on this planet are bacteria, which are only 3 to 5 micrometers in diameter. How can something as important as a cell be so tiny? Actually, if cells were not so small, they could never do their jobs.

Everything the cell must take in or get rid of has to go through the cell membrane. The amount of cell membrane limits the ability of cells to get substances from the outside or transport waste and other materials to the outside. This ability is related to surface area. The relationship between surface area and volume controls cell size. As a cell gets larger, its volume increases faster than its surface area if the cell maintains the same shape. Why does this matter?

INVESTIGATE Cells

How does cell size affect transport?

Demonstrate how small size helps make it possible for cells to get resources.

PROCEDURE

1. Use the knife to cut a large piece of egg white from the egg.

2. Trim the egg white into a small cube, about 1 cm square, and a large cube, about 2 cm square.

3. Pour 100 mL of water into the beaker. Add 10 drops of blue food coloring and stir. Place both cubes into the solution. Leave them in the colored water overnight.

4. Remove each cube gently from the water with a spoon. Place both on a paper towel. With the knife, cut each cube in half. Use the ruler to measure how far the blue water penetrated into the surface of each one.

WHAT DO YOU THINK?

- Record your observations. Which piece of egg was penetrated more, compared with its total diameter, by the blue water?

- Why was there a difference in water penetration?

CHALLENGE Predict what would happen to an egg left in its shell and placed in the blue water overnight.

SKILL FOCUS
Modeling (7.1.a)

MATERIALS
- 2 hard-boiled, peeled eggs
- knife
- ruler
- 100 mL water
- glass beaker
- dark blue food coloring
- spoon
- paper towel

TIME
30 minutes for setup

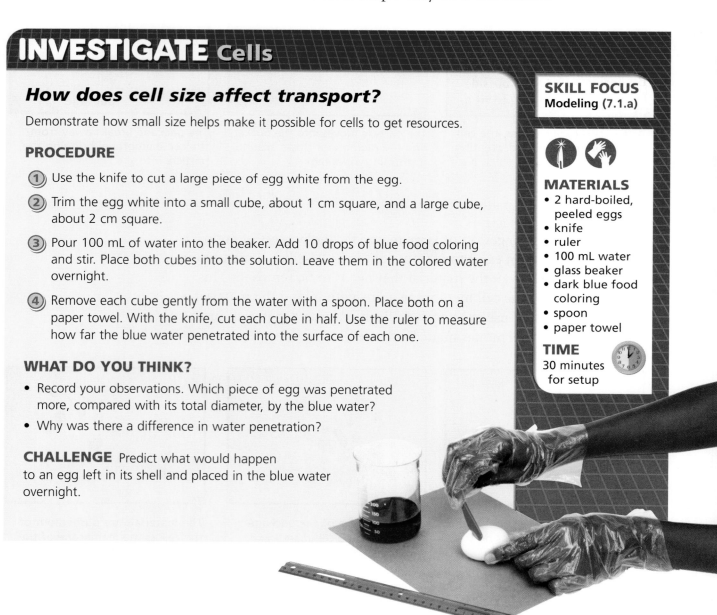

Surface Area and Volumes of Cubes				
	Number of Cubes	Side Length	Surface Area	Volume
4 cm	1	4 cm	96 cm^2	64 cm^3
2 cm	8	2 cm	192 cm^2	64 cm^3
1 cm	64	1 cm	384 cm^2	64 cm^3

As the cell gets bigger, there comes a time when its surface area is not large enough to allow resources to travel to all parts of the cell. Bird eggs and frog eggs are much larger than typical cells, but they have a storehouse of food and also rapidly divide to produce multicellular embryos. In fact, a multicellular embryo is a good illustration of another way cells get around the surface-area-to-volume problem: they divide. The ratio of surface area to volume in newly divided cells is much higher, providing more surface area for exchanging materials.

A cell's shape also affects its surface area. For example, some single-celled organisms are thin and flat, providing increased surface area. Other cells, such as nerve cells and muscle cells, are long and thin, which also gives them a higher ratio of surface area to volume.

READING TiP

Look at the chart above. Notice that the volumes are all the same, but the surface area changes.

 CHECK YOUR READING How is diffusion different in a small, flat cell and a large, round cell?

2.3 Review

KEY CONCEPTS

1. How are the processes of diffusion and osmosis alike? (7.1.a)

2. What is the difference between active and passive transport? Use the term *energy* in your answer. (7.1.a)

3. How does the surface area of a cell limit the growth of the cell? (7.1.a)

CRITICAL THINKING

4. **Apply** If you put a carnation in water, through what process does the water enter the stem?

5. **Predict** If a marine iguana were to spend a few days in a freshwater tank, would it continue to blow salt droplets from its nostrils? Why or why not?

⬤ CHALLENGE

6. **Predict** Freshwater protozoa, which are unicellular organisms, have a greater concentration of salt inside them than does the surrounding water. Does water move into or out of the protozoa?

CHAPTER INVESTIGATION

Diffusion

OVERVIEW AND PURPOSE The cell membrane controls what diffuses into and out of a cell. What factors affect the diffusion of substances across the cell membrane? In this investigation, you will

- observe the diffusion of a solution through plastic wrap
- determine how the concentration of iodine affects the amount of diffusion in a given time

▶ Problem

How does the concentration of a substance affect its diffusion through a membrane?

▶ Hypothesize

After step 4, write a hypothesis to explain how the concentration of iodine will affect the amount of diffusion in 20 minutes. Your hypothesis should be in the form of an "if . . . , then . . . , because . . . " statement.

▶ Procedure

1. Make a data table like the one shown on the sample notebook page.

2. Use one eyedropper to put several drops of cornstarch solution on the lid of the jar. With another eyedropper, add a few drops of Lugol's iodine to the solution on the lid. Observe and record what happens when iodine mixes into water and starch.

   step 2

3. Fill the jar about three-fourths full with the cornstarch solution. Place the plastic wrap loosely over the jar. Adjust it so that the center of the plastic dips a little into the cornstarch solution.

   step 4

4. Pour 10 mL of the iodine solution that you are given (A, B, or C) on the plastic wrap membrane. Solution A is the most concentrated and C is the least. Record your observations. Now write your hypothesis.

MATERIALS

- eyedroppers
- cornstarch solution
- baby food jar with lid
- plastic wrap
- Lugol's iodine solution
- iodine solution A, B, or C
- graduated cylinder (if available)

  7.1.a, 7.7.c

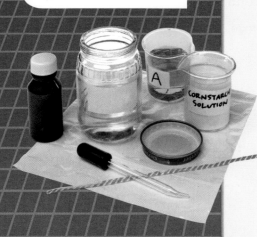

Content Standard
7.1.a Students know cells function similarly in all living organisms.

Investigation Standard
7.7.c Communicate the logical connection among hypotheses, science concepts, tests conducted, data collected, and conclusions drawn from the scientific evidence.

5 Examine the solutions above and below the membrane after 20 minutes. Record any color changes, as well as the intensity of any changes, that you observe. Also look at your classmates' solutions, noting which solution (A, B, or C) each used.

▶ Observe and Analyze

Write It Up

1. **IDENTIFY VARIABLES** Identify the constants. What is the same in the experiment for all groups?

   Identify the independent variable. What is being changed between groups?

   Identify the dependent variable. What is being observed?

2. **RECORD OBSERVATIONS** Draw before-and-after pictures of your setup and label each drawing. Be sure to show the colors of the solutions on both sides of the membrane in each drawing.

3. **INFER** Make a drawing to show the direction in which molecules diffused through the membrane in your experiment.

4. **COMPARE AND CONTRAST** Compare the observations you made about your iodine solution with the observations made by your classmates. Be sure to record which iodine solution (A, B, or C) produced which changes.

▶ Conclude

Write It Up

1. **ANALYZE** Which iodine solution (A, B, or C) produced the greatest color change?

2. **INTERPRET** Do the class's results support your hypothesis? Explain.

3. **IDENTIFY LIMITS** Describe anything that might have varied from group to group. How might these variations affect your results?

4. **INTERPRET** Did starch diffuse through the membrane into the iodine solution? How do you know? Did iodine diffuse through the membrane into the cornstarch solution? How do you know?

5. **INFER** Which solution do you think contains larger molecules, cornstarch or iodine? Why weren't the larger molecules able to diffuse through the membrane?

6. **APPLY** Identify two real-life situations in which diffusion occurs.

▶ INVESTIGATE Further

CHALLENGE Investigate the role of temperature in diffusion. Predict how changes in the temperature of the iodine solution will affect the diffusion process. Explain.

Diffusion

Table 1. Color Changes

Solution	Color at 0 min		Color at 20 min	
	cornstarch solution	iodine solution	cornstarch solution	iodine solution
A				
B				
C				

Chapter Review

the **BIG** idea

All cells need energy and materials for life processes.

CONTENT REVIEW
CLASSZONE.COM

KEY CONCEPTS SUMMARY

1 Chemical reactions take place inside cells.

All cells are made of the same elements. Cells contain four types of large molecules—**carbohydrates, lipids, proteins,** and **nucleic acids**—that support cell function.

About two-thirds of every cell is water. The properties of water are important to cell function.

carbohydrates

lipids

proteins

nucleotide

VOCABULARY
chemical reaction p. 42
carbohydrate p. 42
lipid p. 43
protein p. 43
nucleic acid p. 43

---

2 Cells capture and release energy.

All cells need energy. Some cells capture light energy through **photosynthesis.** All cells release chemical energy.

Cellular respiration and **fermentation** are two ways that cells release energy from glucose.

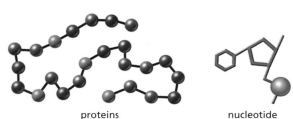

Light Energy

Cellular Respiration

glucose

water

oxygen

Photosynthesis

carbon dioxide

Chemical Energy

VOCABULARY
chemical energy p. 47
glucose p. 47
photosynthesis p. 48
chlorophyll p. 48
cellular respiration
 p. 50
fermentation p. 52

---

3 Materials move across the cell's membranes.

Passive transport does not use a cell's energy. It is the movement of materials to an area of lower concentration. **Diffusion** and **osmosis** are examples of passive transport.

Active transport uses a cell's energy. It is both the movement of materials to an area of higher concentration and the movement of large materials.

passive transport

active transport

VOCABULARY
diffusion p. 56
passive transport p. 58
osmosis p. 59
active transport p. 60

Reviewing Vocabulary

Use terms from the vocabulary lists on page 66 to answer these questions.

1. Which molecule stores information?

2. Which term describes the process when two or more atoms bond together?

3. What kind of energy do cells use?

4. Which term describes the process in which cells release energy without using oxygen?

5. Which process occurs in chloroplasts?

6. From what sugar molecule do many living things release energy?

7. Which chemical that aids in photosynthesis do you find in a chloroplast?

8. Which term means "diffusion of water across cell membranes"?

9. What two processes have opposite effects?

10. Use a Venn diagram to compare and contrast passive transport and active transport.

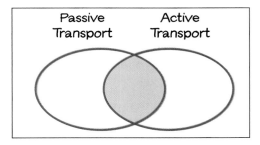

Passive Transport   Active Transport

Reviewing Key Concepts

Multiple Choice *Choose the letter of the best answer.*

11. The fats, oils, and waxes found in living things are known as (7.1.a)
    - **a.** lipids
    - **b.** proteins
    - **c.** carbohydrates
    - **d.** glucose

12. What do cells use as a source of energy and for energy storage? (7.1.a)
    - **a.** proteins
    - **b.** water
    - **c.** cytoplasm
    - **d.** carbohydrates

13. Leaf cells use chlorophyll to absorb (7.1.b)
    - **a.** oxygen
    - **b.** light energy
    - **c.** carbon dioxide
    - **d.** glucose

14. The cells of a redwood tree require oxygen for the process of (7.1.d)
    - **a.** photosynthesis
    - **b.** cellular respiration
    - **c.** fermentation
    - **d.** endocytosis

15. In fermentation, cells release energy without (7.1.a)
    - **a.** alcohol
    - **b.** water
    - **c.** glucose
    - **d.** oxygen

16. Both a whale and a seaweed use which of the following to change glucose into energy? (7.1.a)
    - **a.** water
    - **b.** photosynthesis
    - **c.** cellular respiration
    - **d.** bonding

17. The movement of materials across a cell membrane, requiring energy, is called (7.1.a)
    - **a.** diffusion
    - **b.** osmosis
    - **c.** passive transport
    - **d.** active transport

Short Answer *Write a short answer to each question.*

18. Why is water needed by cells? (7.1.a)

19. Describe the main function of nucleic acids. (7.1.a)

20. What is the role of chlorophyll in a plant's leaves? (7.1.d)

21. Explain why a carrot feels spongy after being soaked in salt water. (7.1.a)

22. Explain how the ways in which plants and animals get their energy differ. (7.1.b)

Thinking Critically

The illustration below summarizes the relationship between photosynthesis and cellular respiration. Use it to answer the next three questions.

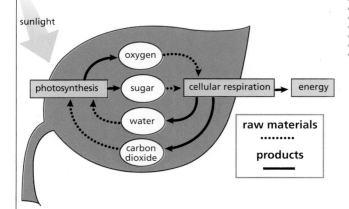

23. **OBSERVE** What are the starting materials of photosynthesis? What are the starting materials of cellular respiration? (7.1.d)

24. **OBSERVE** What are the products of photosynthesis? What are the products of cellular respiration? (7.1.d)

25. **DRAW CONCLUSIONS** What does the diagram above reveal about the connections between photosynthesis and cellular respiration? (7.1.d)

26. **RECOGNIZE CAUSE AND EFFECT** Explain why chemical reactions are essential to living creatures. (7.1.a)

27. **MODEL** How does a glass filled with oil and water illustrate the properties of a cell membrane? What properties does it not illustrate? (7.1.a)

28. **INFER** The French scientist Louis Pasteur mixed yeast and grape juice in a sealed container. When he opened the container, the grape juice contained alcohol. Explain what happened. (7.1.a)

29. **DRAW CONCLUSIONS** Why would it be harmful to your health to drink seawater? (7.1.a)

Process	Requires Energy?	Moves from Higher to Lower Concentration?
Diffusion	no	yes
Osmosis		
Active transport		
Passive transport		

30. **CHART INFORMATION** Copy and complete the chart shown above. The first line is done for you. (7.1.a)

31. **PREDICT** Look at the diagram at the right. The bag has pores that are bigger than the sugar molecules. What will be true of the concentration of the sugar water after a few hours? (7.1.a)

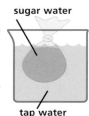

the BIG idea

32. **COMPARE AND CONTRAST** Look again at the picture on pages 38–39. Now that you have read the chapter, how would you add to or change your answer to the question? (7.1.d)

33. **INFER** Does your body get all its energy from the Sun? Explain. (7.1.d)

34. **WRITE** Imagine that your community has a high level of carbon dioxide emission from cars and factories. A developer wants to build a shopping center on the remaining forest land. Would this action increase or decrease carbon dioxide levels? Why? Write a paragraph explaining your answer. (7.1.d)

UNIT PROJECTS

Check your schedule for your unit project. How are you doing? Be sure that you have placed data or notes from your research in your project folder.

Analyzing Data

 7.1.b, 7.1.d

Elodea *plants in beakers of water were placed at different distances from a light source. The number of bubbles that formed on the plants was counted and recorded. The data table shows the results.*

Beaker	Distance from light	Bubbles per minute
1	200 cm	2
2	100 cm	10
3	50 cm	45
4	20 cm	83

Study the data and answer the questions below.

1. What gas do the bubbles consist of?

  a. carbon dioxide   **c.** water vapor

  b. hydrogen   **d.** oxygen

2. What is the relationship between the distance from the light source and the rate of bubble formation?

  a. The rate increases as the distance increases.

  b. The rate decreases as the distance increases.

  c. The rate stays the same as the distance increases.

  d. The rate changes in a way unrelated to distance.

3. If another beaker with *elodea* were placed 150 cm from the light, about how many bubbles would form each minute?

  a. 1   **c.** 11

  b. 7   **d.** 24

4. What is the independent variable in this experiment?

  a. type of plant   **c.** distance from light

  b. number of bubbles   **d.** amount of time

5. Which graph best represents the data shown in the table?

a.
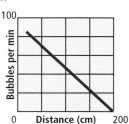

c.
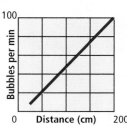

b.
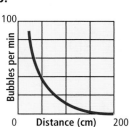

d.
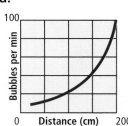

Extended Response

Answer each question. Include some of the terms shown in the word box. In your answers underline each term you use.

chemical energy	cellular respiration
osmosis	chloroplasts
fermentation	glucose
photosynthesis	diffusion

6. A person rides his bicycle several miles. What process is used by the cells in his legs to release energy at the beginning of the ride? at the end of the ride? Explain.

7. A student places a plant in a sealed container and puts the container on a windowsill. She leaves the plant there for a week. Will the plant have the starting materials it needs to carry out photosynthesis during the entire week? Explain.

Cell Division

the **BIG** idea

Organisms grow, reproduce, and maintain themselves through cell division.

Key Concepts

SECTION

1 Cell division occurs in all organisms.
Learn about the functions of cell division.

SECTION

2 Cell division is part of the cell cycle.
Learn about the cell cycle and the process of mitosis.

SECTION

3 Both sexual and asexual reproduction involve cell division.
Learn how sexual reproduction compares with asexual reproduction.

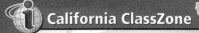

California ClassZone

CLASSZONE.COM

Chapter 3 online resources: Content Review, Simulation, Visualization, three Resource Centers, Math Tutorial, Test Practice

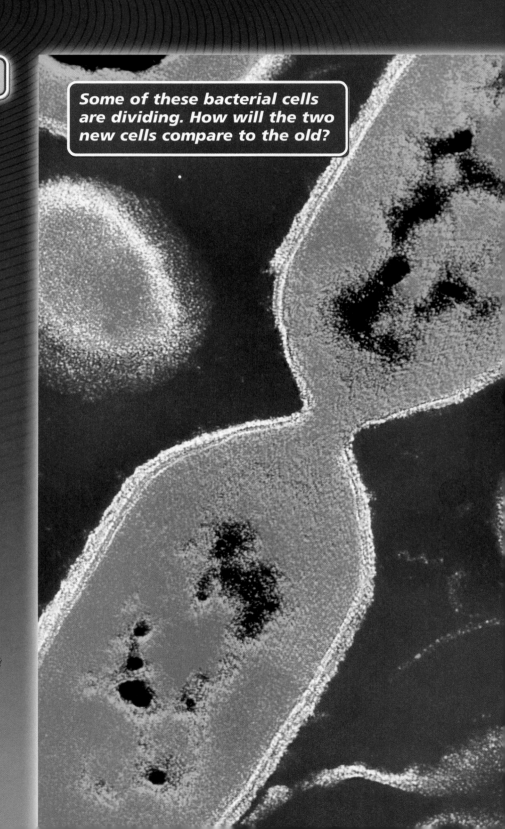

Some of these bacterial cells are dividing. How will the two new cells compare to the old?

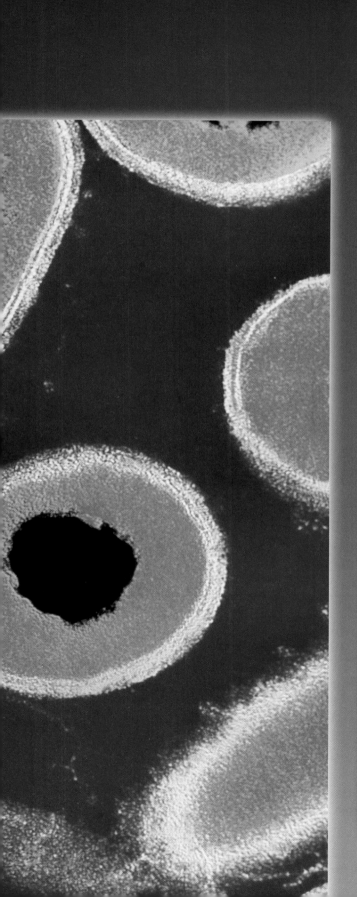

EXPLORE (the **BIG** idea)

Division and Volume

> **7.1.e** Students know cells divide to increase their numbers through a process of mitosis, which results in two daughter cells with identical sets of chromosomes.

Take a piece of clay and divide it in half. Now you have two pieces of clay, each half the size of the original piece. Divide each of the two new pieces in half, producing four pieces, each a quarter of the original piece in size.

Observe and Think What will happen if you keep dividing the pieces in half? How might the division of the cells in living things be different?

Internet Activity: Cell Division

> **7.1.e** Students know cells divide to increase their numbers through a process of mitosis, which results in two daughter cells with identical sets of chromosomes.

Go to **ClassZone.com** to match images of cells dividing with the different stages of cell division.

Observe and Think At which stage do the two daughter cells first appear? Are the stages the same for plant and animal cells?

NSTA
scilinks.org
SciLINKS

Cellular Mitosis **Code: MDL033**

Getting Ready to Learn

◀ CONCEPT REVIEW

- The cell is the basic unit of structure and function in living things.
- All cells come from other cells.
- DNA provides the instructions a cell needs to function and reproduce.

◀ VOCABULARY REVIEW

cell membrane p. 20

nucleus p. 20

cycle *See Glossary.*

CONTENT REVIEW
CLASSZONE.COM

Review concepts and vocabulary.

▶ TAKING NOTES

COMBINATION NOTES

To take notes about a new concept, first make an informal outline of the information. Then make a sketch of the concept and label it so you can study it later.

VOCABULARY STRATEGY

Write each new vocabulary term in the center of a **frame game** diagram. Decide what information to frame it with. Use examples, descriptions, sentences that use the term in context, or pictures. You can change the frame to fit each term.

See the Note-Taking Handbook on pages R45–R51.

SCIENCE NOTEBOOK

NOTES

Mitosis has four phases.

- prophase: chromosomes become visible

- metaphase: chromosomes line up in middle

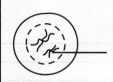

prophase

chromosome

metaphase

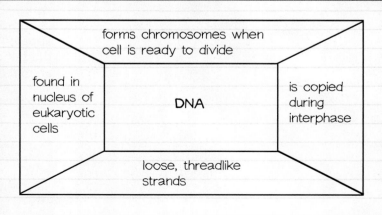

	forms chromosomes when cell is ready to divide	
found in nucleus of eukaryotic cells	DNA	is copied during interphase
	loose, threadlike strands	

Cell division occurs in all organisms.

7.1.c Students know the nucleus is the repository for genetic information in plant and animal cells.

7.2.e Students know DNA (deoxyribonucleic acid) is the genetic material of living organisms and is located in the chromosomes of each cell.

VOCABULARY

DNA p. 74
chromosome p. 75

◄ BEFORE, you learned

- Cells come from other cells
- Cells take in and release energy and materials
- In a multicellular organism, cells specialize

► NOW, you will learn

- How genetic material is organized in cells
- About the functions of cell division in multicellular organisms

---

EXPLORE Cell Division (7.1.e)

How is organization helpful?

PROCEDURE

(1) Work with two other students. Ask your teammates to put on blindfolds.

(2) Give the unpaired socks to one teammate and the paired socks to the other teammate.

(3) Tell your teammates to separate the socks into two identical piles of single socks. Each pile should have one sock from each pair. Allow your teammates two minutes to work on this task.

WHAT DO YOU THINK?
Which group of socks was more accurately separated into two identical sets? Why?

MATERIALS
- 2 blindfolds
- groups of paired and unpaired socks
- stopwatch

Cell division is involved in many functions.

Cell division occurs in all organisms, but performs different functions. Unicellular organisms reproduce through cell division. Cell division helps multicellular organisms grow, develop, repair themselves, and reproduce.

You are probably bigger this year than you were last year. One characteristic of all living things is that they grow. Your body is made up of cells. Although cells themselves grow, most growth in multicellular organisms occurs when cells produce new cells. In this chapter you will read about cell division in eukaryotic cells.

▼ REMINDER

Most multicellular organisms are made up of eukaryotic cells. A eukaryotic cell has a nucleus that contains genetic material.

The genetic material of eukaryotic cells is organized in chromosomes.

The genetic material of a cell contains information needed for the cell's growth and other activities. When a cell divides into two new cells, each new cell receives a full set of genetic material. The genetic material in cells is contained in DNA molecules.

DNA

The genetic material in cells is called DNA—deoxyribonucleic acid (dee-AHK-see-RY-boh-noo-KLEE-ihk). **DNA** is a molecule that contains information for an organism's growth and functions. You read in Chapter 1 that James Watson and Francis Crick worked with other scientists to build a model of DNA in 1953. They showed that DNA is made of two strands joined like a twisted ladder, or a double helix. You will learn more about DNA in Chapter 4.

 What is DNA?

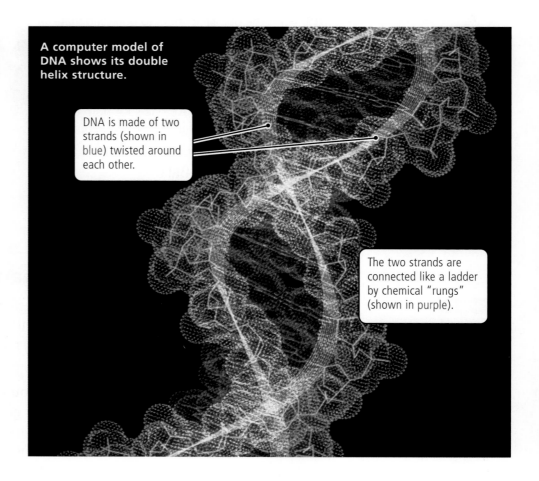

A computer model of DNA shows its double helix structure.

DNA is made of two strands (shown in blue) twisted around each other.

The two strands are connected like a ladder by chemical "rungs" (shown in purple).

Chromosomes

In a eukaryotic cell, most of the cell's DNA is in the nucleus. During most of a cell's life cycle, DNA exists as a mass of loose strands. While the DNA is spread throughout the nucleus, the cell performs the functions needed for survival. During this time, the DNA is replicated, or copied.

DNA is wrapped around proteins like thread around a spool and compacted into structures called **chromosomes** (KROH-muh-SOHMZ). Before a cell divides, the chromosomes compact more. They become visible under a light microscope. During cell division, a replicated chromosome can be seen as two identical structures called chromatids that are held together by a centromere.

Within each species of organism, the number of chromosomes is constant. For example, humans have 46 chromosomes. Fruit flies, however, have 8 chromosomes, and ferns may have more than 100.

CHECK YOUR READING Describe the relationship between DNA and chromosomes.

VOCABULARY
Make a frame game diagram in your notebook for the term *chromosome*.

READING TiP
Compare the diagram of DNA below with the computer model on page 74.

Organization of Genetic Material

The DNA in chromosomes is wrapped around a protein core until it is very condensed.

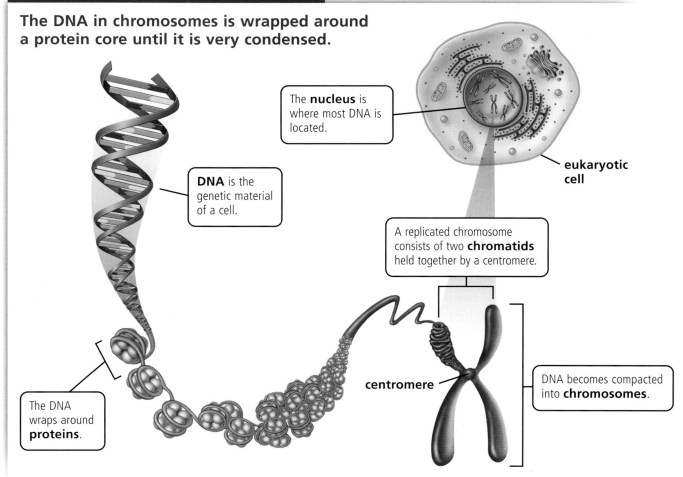

The **nucleus** is where most DNA is located.

DNA is the genetic material of a cell.

eukaryotic cell

A replicated chromosome consists of two **chromatids** held together by a centromere.

The DNA wraps around **proteins**.

centromere

DNA becomes compacted into **chromosomes**.

How does DNA fit inside the nucleus?

PROCEDURE

① Select four pieces of yarn of different colors and four craft sticks. Push the yarn together into a loose ball. Observe how much space it takes up and how the individual pieces are organized.

② Wrap each piece of yarn around a craft stick. Wrap the yarn so that the coils are tightly packed but do not overlap.

WHAT DO YOU THINK?

• What did you observe about the loosely balled yarn?

• What does the loosely balled yarn represent?

• What does the yarn on the craft sticks represent?

• Why does the yarn on the craft sticks take up less space than the ball of yarn?

CHALLENGE How does the yarn's being wrapped on the craft sticks make it easier to separate the different colors?

SKILL FOCUS
Modeling (7.1.c)

MATERIALS
• yarn
• craft sticks

TIME
20 minutes

Cell division is involved in growth, development, and repair.

COMBINATION NOTES
Remember to take notes and draw sketches to help you understand the main idea: *Cell division is involved in growth, development, and repair.* Be sure to include the red heads in your notes.

Multicellular organisms vary greatly in size and complexity. You may not think that you have much in common with an ant or an oak tree. Actually, you share many characteristics with these organisms. For example, both you and they are made of trillions of cells. But, like most organisms, you and they started out as single cells. In multicellular organisms, cell division is essential for reproduction and three other major functions: growth, development, and repair.

Through cell division, a single cell becomes two cells. Those two cells divide into four, the four cells divide into eight, and so on. A multicellular organism grows because cell division increases the number of cells in it. As the organism develops and its cells divide, many of the cells become specialized. Most of them continue to divide.

Even when growth and development appear to stop, cell division is still occurring. When an organism ages or is injured, the worn-out or damaged cells need to be replaced by new cells. For example, the cells that make up the lining of your throat have a short life span—only a few days. These cells are constantly dividing and replacing the cells that have died.

Growth

In general, a large organism does not have larger cells than a small organism; it simply has many more cells than the small organism. When you were small, your body contained fewer cells than it has now. By the time you reach adulthood, your body will be made up of about 100 trillion cells.

Individual cells grow in size, but there are limits to the size that cells can reach. As you learned in Chapter 2, cells need a high ratio of surface area to volume in order to function. As a cell grows, that ratio decreases. When the cell divides into two smaller cells, the ratio of surface area to volume for each cell increases.

Scientists are still searching for answers about how cell size is related to the control of cell division. Some scientists think that there is no single factor that controls cell division. Instead, they think that many cell processes added together control when a cell divides.

 CHECK YOUR READING Describe how the number of cells in a multicellular organism changes as the organism grows.

Growth and Development

Multicellular organisms, such as this sea turtle, grow and develop through cell division.

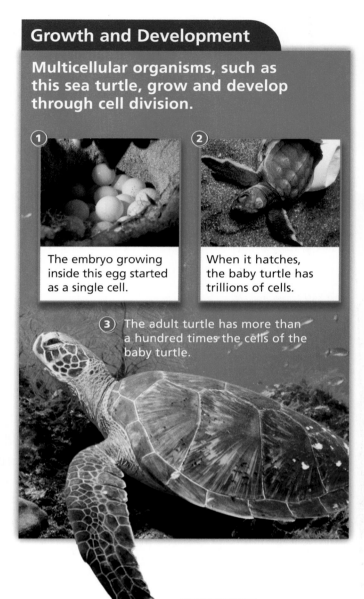

① The embryo growing inside this egg started as a single cell.

② When it hatches, the baby turtle has trillions of cells.

③ The adult turtle has more than a hundred times the cells of the baby turtle.

Development

A multicellular organism begins as a single cell and grows into a larger organism through cell division. However, cell division alone does not allow an organism to develop. If cell division were the only process occurring, the organism would end up as a group of identical cells. But during development, cells become specialized to perform particular functions.

These cells may take on shapes or structures that help them perform their functions. Some cells might become skin cells, while others might become nerve cells. These cells still have the same set of genetic material as all the other cells in an organism's body, but as the organism develops, they specialize.

 CHECK YOUR READING Give two examples of specialized cells from the paragraph above.

READING TIP

Connect what you have read about growth and development with the photographs above.

Repair

You may have cut yourself at one time or another. Perhaps you have even broken a bone in your arm or leg. The body repairs injuries such as these by means of cell division. For example, when your skin is cut, skin cells on either side of the cut make new cells to heal the wound. You can see the process of healing in the diagram below.

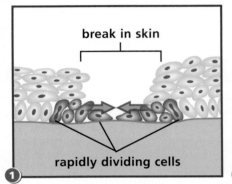

break in skin

rapidly dividing cells

1 Cells in the lower layer begin to divide quickly and move into the break in the skin.

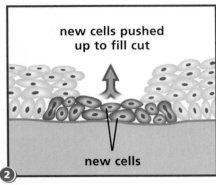

new cells pushed up to fill cut

new cells

2 The area is filled as new cells continue to divide.

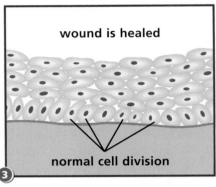

wound is healed

normal cell division

3 Once the break in the skin is filled, the cells stop dividing rapidly.

As cells age and die, they need to be replaced. In the human body—which is made up of about 200 different types of cells—cells are replaced at different rates. Your skin cells wear out quickly, so they need to be replaced often. Every minute or so, your skin loses thousands of cells, which are replaced with new ones. In contrast, most of the cells in your brain live a long time and do not divide very often.

 CHECK YOUR READING What role does cell division play in healing the body?

3.1 Review

KEY CONCEPTS

1. Why is cell division important? (7.2.e)
2. How is genetic material organized in eukaryotic cells? (7.2.e)
3. Explain how cell division is involved in the growth, development, and repair of an organism. (7.2.e)

CRITICAL THINKING

4. **Summarize** Explain how DNA compacts before a eukaryotic cell divides.
5. **Infer** Why do you think that injuries to the skin generally heal faster than injuries to the brain?

⬤ CHALLENGE

6. **Apply** Large cuts often form scars, which are made of a different type of skin cell. What characteristic might scar cells have to help them heal large cuts?

Dyes Show Nerve Growth

7.1.f Students know that as multicellular organisms develop, their cells differentiate.

Scientists used to think that, by the end of childhood, a person had all the brain cells he or she would ever have. They thought that the brain could not replace damaged nerve cells.

However, a surprising discovery has shown that new nerve cells do grow in the brains of both adult monkeys and adult humans!

Dr. Elizabeth Gould noticed that new nerve cells can grow in adult monkey brains.

The Discovery

The discovery involves a chemical known as bromodeoxyuridine (BrdU), which can be used to detect new cancer cells.

- BrdU highlights the DNA of cells that are reproducing, such as cancer cells.

- BrdU also makes it possible to count the new cells that are being created, because they stand out as well.

- The cells that have been highlighted with BrdU can be seen under a microscope when they are illuminated with a special light.

When scientists used this technique to examine certain areas in the brains of monkeys and of adult humans who had died of cancer, they found that new nerve cells had grown in the brains of each. Thus, the chemical properties of BrdU allowed scientists to discover new nerve cells growing in places where scientists had previously never expected to see them.

Hope for the Future

If new nerve cells grow in these tissues, it may be possible to stimulate growth in damaged nerve tissue such as that in the spinal cord. If researchers discover how growth in nerve cells is triggered, there may be new hope for people who have nervous systems damaged by accidents or by diseases such as Parkinson's disease.

EXPLORE

1. **SYNTHESIZE** How could you use chemicals, such as small dots of ink, in an experiment to show how your fingernails grow?

2. **CHALLENGE** What are some possible effects of the growth of new nerve cells?

RESOURCE CENTER
CLASSZONE.COM

Find out more about new nerve cell growth.

KEY CONCEPT

3.2 Cell division is part of the cell cycle.

CALIFORNIA Content Standards

7.1.c Students know the nucleus is the repository for genetic information in plant and animal cells.

7.1.e Students know cells divide to increase their numbers through a process of mitosis, which results in two daughter cells with identical sets of chromosomes.

VOCABULARY

cell cycle p. 80
interphase p. 81
mitosis p. 81
cytokinesis p. 81

◀ **BEFORE, you learned**

- Cells come from other cells through cell division
- A cell must have a full set of genetic material to function
- Cell division enables multi-cellular organisms to develop, grow, and repair themselves

▶ **NOW, you will learn**

- About two main stages in the cell cycle
- About the changes that occur in cells before mitosis
- About the events that take place during mitosis

THINK ABOUT

What is a cycle?

Many things in your everyday life are cycles. A cycle is any activity or set of events that regularly repeats. Cycles can be short, like the sequence of events that make your heart beat, or they can be very long, like the turning of our galaxy. One example of a cycle is shown at the right. The photographs show a tree during four seasons in a northern climate. How are these seasons a cycle?

RESOURCE CENTER
CLASSZONE.COM

Learn about the cell cycle.

The cell cycle includes interphase and cell division.

Living things grow, reproduce, and die in a process called a life cycle. The life cycle of a tree, for example, begins with a seed. Under the right conditions, the seed begins to grow. It produces a very small plant, which may grow over many years into a towering tree. When it is mature, the tree makes its own seeds, and the cycle begins again.

Cells have a life cycle too, called the cell cycle. The **cell cycle** is the normal sequence of development and division of a cell. The cell cycle consists of two main phases. The cell carries out its normal functions during a phase called interphase. The second general phase involves cell division. When a eukaryotic cell divides, its nucleus must also divide. This process is called mitosis. Each phase in the cell cycle requires a certain period of time—from hours to days or years, depending on the type of cell.

80 Unit 1: **Cells and Heredity**

Interphase

Interphase is the part of the cell cycle during which a cell is not dividing. Much activity takes place in this phase of the cell's life. During interphase, the cell grows to about twice the size it was when it was first produced. The cell also engages in normal life activities, such as transporting materials in and transporting wastes out. Also, cellular respiration occurs, which provides the energy the cell needs.

Changes that occur during interphase prepare a cell for division. Before a cell can divide, it replicates its DNA exactly. Correct copying of the DNA is very important. It ensures that, after cell division, each new cell gets a complete set of DNA. Organelles also duplicate.

 CHECK YOUR READING What cell processes occur during interphase?

VOCABULARY
Make a frame game diagram for *interphase*.

Cell Division Phase

Mitosis is the part of the cell cycle during which the nucleus divides. Prokaryotes do not go through mitosis because they have no nucleus. In most cells, mitosis is the shortest period in the life cycle. The function of mitosis is to move the DNA and other material in the parent cell into position for cell division. When the cell divides, each new cell gets a full set of DNA and other cell structures. **Cytokinesis** (sy-toh-kuh-NEE-sihs) is the division of the parent cell's cytoplasm, including mitochondria and other structures. Cytokinesis occurs immediately after mitosis.

Cell Cycle

The events that happen during the life of a cell are called the cell cycle.

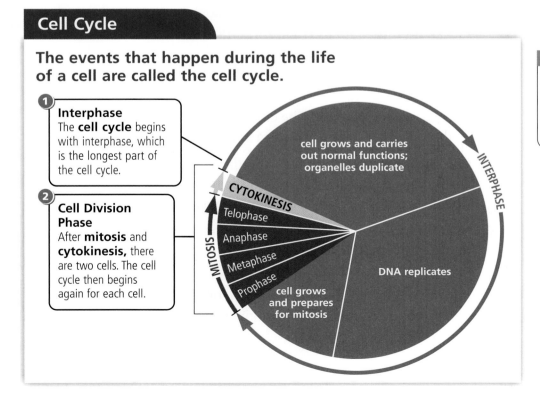

1 Interphase
The **cell cycle** begins with interphase, which is the longest part of the cell cycle.

2 Cell Division Phase
After **mitosis** and **cytokinesis,** there are two cells. The cell cycle then begins again for each cell.

cell grows and carries out normal functions; organelles duplicate

CYTOKINESIS
Telophase
Anaphase
Metaphase
Prophase
cell grows and prepares for mitosis

INTERPHASE

MITOSIS

DNA replicates

READING TiP
The arrows in the diagram represent the passage of time. Interphase is shown in red, mitosis in purple, and cytokinesis in yellow.

As a result of mitosis and cytokinesis, the original—or parent—cell splits into two genetically identical daughter cells. In this case, the term *daughter cell* does not mean that it's female. It is a term scientists use to refer to these new cells. Each daughter cell receives a complete set of DNA from the parent cell.

Cell division produces two genetically identical cells.

Recall that many cells in your body are continually dividing into new cells. The new cells help your body grow, develop, and replace worn-out parts. Though your body cells divide at different rates, the same process—mitosis—divides their genetic material.

Cell division produces daughter cells that are genetically identical to each other. They are genetically identical to their parent cell, which no longer exists. A skin cell, for example, divides and produces two new skin cells genetically identical to the original skin cell.

 How are daughter cells like the parent cell?

Steps of Mitosis

The process of mitosis divides the genetic material evenly between the daughter cells. Mitosis is a continuous process, but scientists divide the events of mitosis into four smaller phases.

VISUALIZATION
CLASSZONE.COM
Watch the process of mitosis in action.

READING TiP

For each numbered step, find the matching number in the diagram on page 83. For example, find the chromatids in step 1.

① **Chromosomes appear.** During prophase, the DNA in the nucleus of a cell condenses. The resulting chromosomes become visible. Each chromosome consists of two identical chromatids held together by a centromere. The membrane around the nucleus breaks down.

② **Chromosomes line up.** The chromosomes line up in the middle of the cell. This stage is called metaphase.

③ **Chromosomes separate.** During the stage called anaphase, the chromatids split, resulting in two separate, identical chromosomes. These chromosomes are pulled to opposite sides of the cell.

④ **Nuclei form.** A new nuclear membrane forms around each group of chromosomes during telophase. The chromosomes return to their threadlike form.

Mitosis is finished, and the cell's genetic material has been divided. The next step in cell division is cytokinesis.

Cell Division

Before mitosis, the cell's DNA is copied during interphase.

Interphase

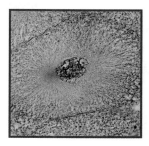

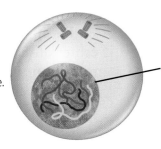

The cell has grown and is ready to divide.

The nucleus contains two complete copies of DNA.

Mitosis produces two new cells with identical copies of DNA.

Chromosome

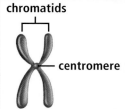

chromatids

centromere

① Chromosomes appear.
Prophase

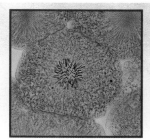

The nuclear membrane breaks down.

Long strands of DNA condense to distinct chromosomes, each with two chromatids that are exact copies of each other.

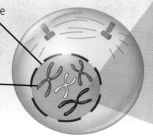

② Chromosomes line up.
Metaphase

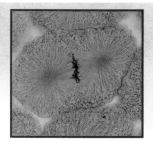

Chromosomes line up in the middle of the cell.

③ Chromosomes separate.
Anaphase

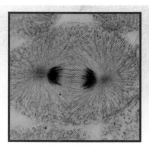

Chromatids of each chromosome split into two separate chromosomes.

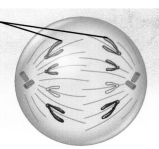

Separated chromosomes are pulled to opposite sides of the cell.

④ Nuclei form.
Telophase, Cytokinesis

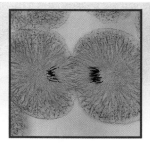

New nuclear membranes form.

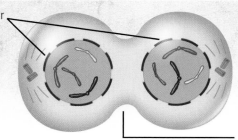

Cell pinches and divides.

Division of the Cytoplasm

READING TIP

As you read about cytokinesis, refer to the images of plant and animal cells on page 85.

Cytokinesis, or the division of the parent cell's cytoplasm, immediately follows mitosis in most eukaryotic cells. Cytokinesis differs slightly in animal cells and plant cells.

During cytokinesis in an animal cell, a fiber ring forms in the center of the dividing cell. The fiber ring contracts, pulling the cell membrane inward. Eventually, the cell is pinched into two daughter cells.

In a plant cell, the cell wall prevents the cell membrane from being pulled inward. A structure called a cell plate grows between the two new nuclei. The cell plate develops into a membrane and eventually becomes part of the cell wall of each of the new cells.

 CHECK YOUR READING How does cytokinesis differ in plant cells and animal cells?

INVESTIGATE Cell Division

How can you model the cell cycle?

PROCEDURE

① Divide the poster board into six spaces, and draw arrows from one space to the next to indicate a cycle. Label the spaces, in order, "Interphase," "Prophase," "Metaphase," "Anaphase," "Telophase," and "Cytokinesis."

② In each space, make a model of a cell and its DNA in the indicated phase. Make sure you represent the cell membrane, the nuclear membrane—when it is present—and the DNA.

WHAT DO YOU THINK?

- In which phase is the nuclear membrane present?
- In which phases are the chromosomes condensed?
- What do the arrows in your model show?

CHALLENGE How do you think cell division would differ in prokaryotic cells? Do you think cell division in prokaryotic cells would be more or less complex than in eukaryotic cells? Make drawings to show how you think a prokaryotic cell might divide.

SKILL FOCUS
Making models
(7.1.e)

MATERIALS
- poster board
- markers
- pipe cleaners
- packing peanuts
- glue
- scissors
- yarn

TIME
30 minutes

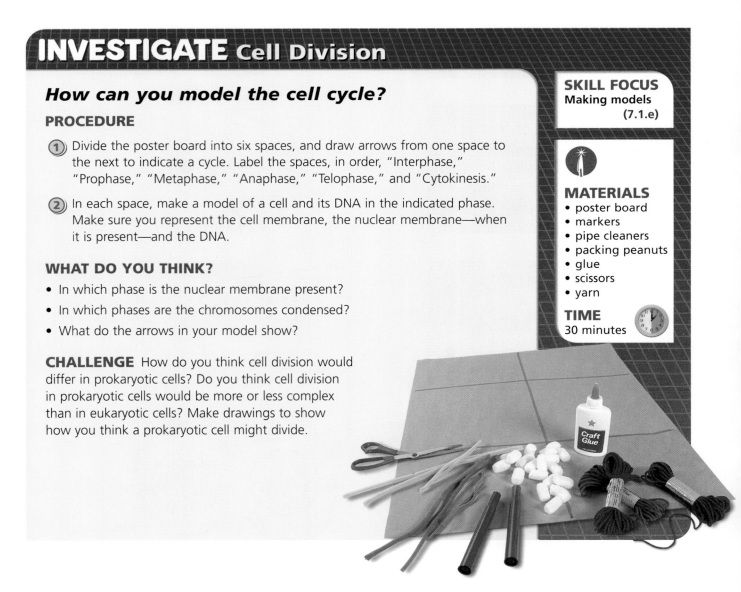

Cytokinesis

Cytokinesis happens in both plant and animal cells.

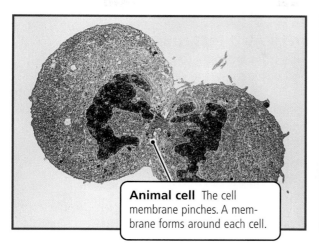

Animal cell The cell membrane pinches. A membrane forms around each cell.

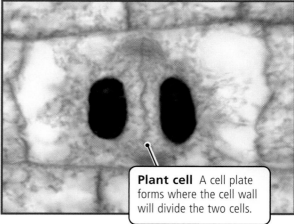

Plant cell A cell plate forms where the cell wall will divide the two cells.

READING VISUALS COMPARE AND CONTRAST How does the process of cytokinesis in the animal cell on the left compare with that of the plant cell on the right?

At the end of cytokinesis, the two daughter cells are completely separated. Each is surrounded by a cell membrane. Each daughter cell has some of its parent cell's cytoplasm, including organelles. Although daughter cells are genetically identical to their parent cell, they are smaller. The daughter cells are now in interphase. DNA is threadlike in the nucleus and replicates. The cells may enter a period of growth. At that time they take in resources they need to increase the amount of their cytoplasm and to grow to full size. When cells are fully grown, they are about the same size as the parent cell was before division.

 What happens to cells after cytokinesis?

3.2 Review

KEY CONCEPTS

1. What are the two main parts of the cell cycle? (7.1.e)

2. Describe the state of a cell about to start mitosis. (7.1.e)

3. How is the genetic material in two daughter cells similar to the genetic material in the original parent cell? (7.1.e)

CRITICAL THINKING

4. **Sequence** Describe in order the steps that occur during mitosis.

5. **Compare and Contrast** How is the cell cycle like the cycle of the seasons? How does it differ?

⬤ CHALLENGE

6. **Infer** You know that mitosis does not happen in prokaryotes. Do you think cytokinesis happens in prokaryotes? Explain your answer.

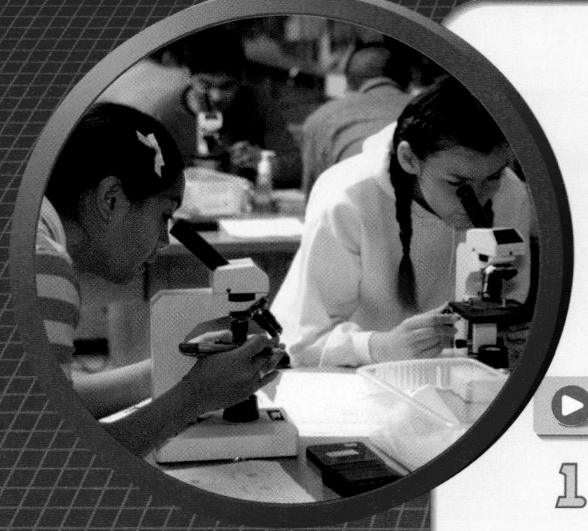

CHAPTER INVESTIGATION

Stages of the Cell Cycle

OVERVIEW AND PURPOSE In this activity you will observe cells from an onion root tip that are undergoing mitosis. You will identify and draw cells in different stages of mitosis and the cell cycle. Then you will count the number of cells in each stage. Remember to record this information in your **Science Notebook.**

▶ Procedure

1. Make a data table like the one shown on the sample notebook page.

2. Obtain a prepared slide of an onion root tip. Place the slide on the microscope stage. Using the low-power objective, adjust the focus until the root tip is clear.

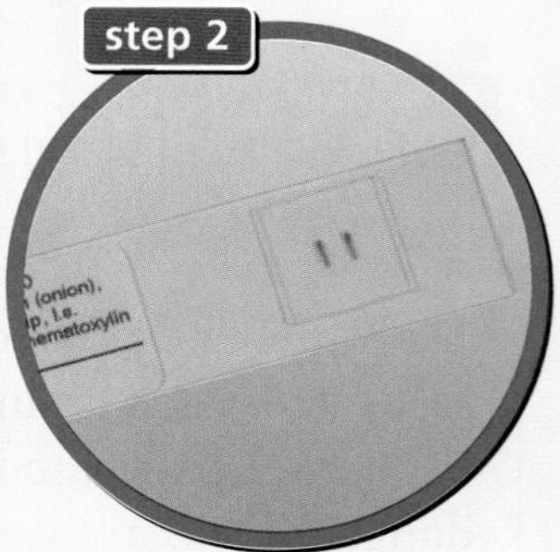

   step 2

3. Move the slide until you are looking at the region just above the root tip. The cells in this area were in the process of mitosis when the slide was made.

4. Look at the boxlike cells arranged in rows. The DNA in these cells has been stained to make it more visible. Select a cell in interphase. Switch to high power and sketch this cell in your notebook.

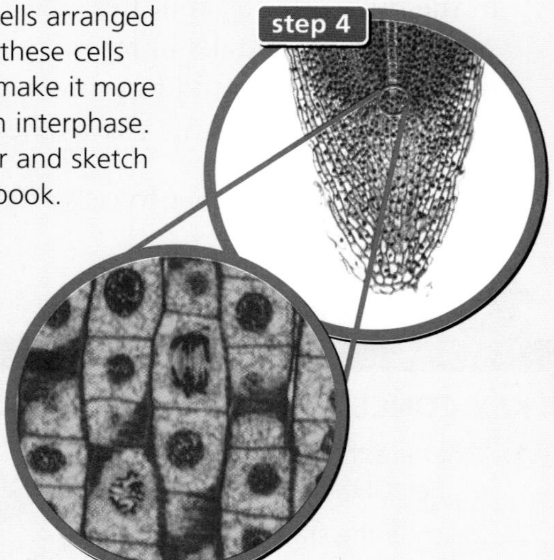

   step 4

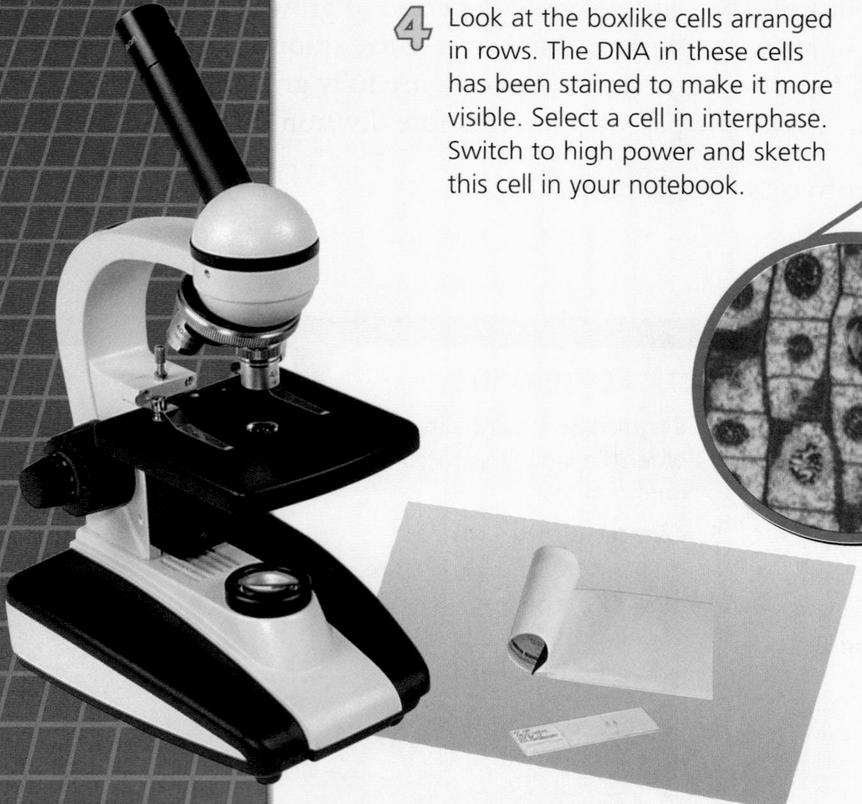

MATERIALS
- prepared slides of onion root tip cells
- light microscope

  7.1.c, 7.1.e, 7.7.a

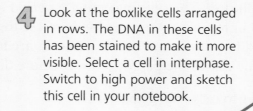

Content Standard
7.1.e Students know cells divide to increase their numbers through a process of mitosis, which results in two daughter cells with identical sets of chromosomes.

Investigation Standard
7.7.a Select and use appropriate tools and technology (including calculators, computers, balances, spring scales, microscopes, and binoculars) to perform tests, collect data, and display data.

5 Repeat step 3 for cells in the various stages of mitosis: prophase, metaphase, anaphase, and telophase. Refer to the diagram on page 83 to identify cells in each stage.

6 Under low-power magnification, choose 25 cells at random. Decide which stage of the cell cycle each cell is in. Record the number of cells in each stage in your data table.

▶ Observe and Analyze

Write It Up

1. **OBSERVE** Look at your sketches of the stages of mitosis. Describe the events in each stage.

2. **ANALYZING DATA** Was there any one stage of the cell cycle that was occurring in the majority of cells you observed? If so, which was it?

▶ Conclude

1. **INFER** What might the differences in the number of cells in each stage of the cell cycle mean?

2. **IDENTIFY LIMITS** Were there any cells that were difficult to classify as being in one particular phase of the cell cycle? What do these cells suggest to you about the process of mitosis?

3. **APPLY** Where does new root growth take place? Explain your answer.

▶ INVESTIGATE Further

CHALLENGE From your data table, calculate the percent of cells in each stage of the cell cycle. Use those numbers to predict how much time a cell spends in each stage. You can base your calculation on a total cell cycle of 24 hours.

Stages of the Cell Cycle

Table 1. Number of Cells in Each Stage of the Cell Cycle

Stage	Sketch	Number of Cells Observed
Interphase		
Prophase		
Metaphase		
Anaphase		
Telophase		

3.3 Both sexual and asexual reproduction involve cell division.

CALIFORNIA
Content Standard

7.2.a Students know the differences between the life cycles and reproduction methods of sexual and asexual organisms.

BEFORE, you learned

- Cells go through a cycle of growth and division
- Mitosis produces two genetically identical cells

NOW, you will learn

- About cell division and asexual reproduction
- How sexual reproduction and asexual reproduction compare

VOCABULARY

asexual reproduction p. 88
binary fission p. 89
regeneration p. 90

THINK ABOUT

How does cell division affect single-celled organisms?

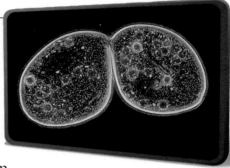

In multicellular organisms, cell division functions in growth, repair, and development. But in unicellular organisms, each cell is itself an organism. Unicellular organisms, like this paramecium, also undergo cell division. What are some possible results of cell division in unicellular organisms? How might they compare with the results of cell division in multicellular organisms?

Asexual reproduction involves one parent.

COMBINATION NOTES
Begin taking notes on the main idea: *Asexual reproduction involves one parent.* Be sure to include sketches of each method of reproducing.

You have learned how cells divide to produce two daughter cells. If each cell is a whole organism—a unicellular organism—then cell division produces two new organisms. In other words, the organism reproduces. Each new organism can live independently and is called an offspring. This form of reproduction is called asexual reproduction. In **asexual reproduction** a parent organism produces offspring that are genetically identical to the parent—the offspring's genes are an identical copy of the parent's genes.

In multicellular organisms, cell division produces two daughter cells. It does not usually produce offspring. For example, a skin cell divides to produce two new skin cells. The new cells are part of the skin—part of the organism—and do not live apart from the body. You will read later how multicellular organisms reproduce.

Cell Division in Unicellular Organisms

Cell division is one form of asexual reproduction. It occurs in two main ways that depend on whether the cell has a nucleus or not. In both processes, the parent divides into two offspring. The offspring are genetically identical to the parent.

Remember that a unicellular organism without a nucleus is called a prokaryote. A prokaryote can reproduce by a simple form of cell division. **Binary fission** occurs when the parent organism replicates its DNA and then splits in two, producing two offspring. Prokaryotes that reproduce by binary fission include unicellular organisms such as bacteria and archaea.

Eukaryotes—organisms whose cells have a nucleus—can be unicellular or multicellular. In unicellular eukaryotes, reproduction can occur by mitosis and cytokinesis—the other form of cell division. The organism undergoes mitosis, replicating and separating its chromosomes. Then its cytoplasm is divided through cytokinesis. Examples of single-celled eukaryotic organisms that reproduce by cell division include algae, some yeasts, and protozoans such as paramecia.

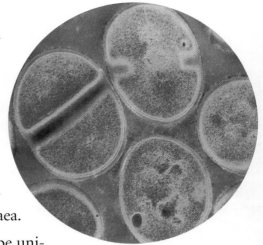

Binary fission results in two nearly equal, independent cells, as shown in these bacteria.

Budding

Another form of asexual reproduction is called budding. Budding is a process in which an organism develops tiny outgrowths, called buds. The organism may have more than one bud at once. Each bud forms from a parent's cell, so the buds are genetically identical to the parent. The bud grows until it forms a complete or nearly complete new organism. The organism may remain attached to its parent. Most often, when a bud reaches a certain size, it breaks free of the parent and becomes a separate organism.

Some unicellular and some multicellular organisms reproduce by budding. In some of these multicellular organisms, buds can form from any cell of the body. For example, hydras are multicellular eukaryotes that live in fresh water and reproduce by budding. In other multicellular organisms, only specialized cells in the body develop buds. For example, plants called kalanchoe (KAL-uhn-KOH-ee) produce tiny buds only from the tips of the leaves. Each kalanchoe bud has genes identical to its parent and can develop into an independent kalanchoe plant.

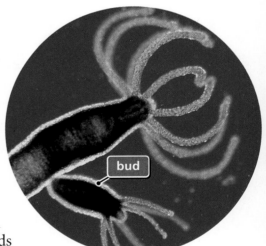

Budding Hydras reproduce by pinching off small buds.

 How is budding similar to binary fission?

Regeneration

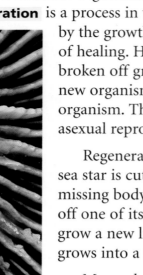

Regeneration
This sea star is regenerating its legs that were lost.

Some multicellular organisms can reproduce by regeneration. **Regeneration** is a process in which missing body parts are replaced by the growth of new tissue. Regeneration is a form of healing. However, sometimes a body part that has broken off grows into a whole new organism. The new organism is genetically identical to the original organism. Thus, regeneration can be a form of asexual reproduction.

Regeneration can be observed in sea stars. If a sea star is cut in half, each half can regenerate its missing body parts. Sometimes a sea star will drop off one of its limbs. The animal will eventually grow a new limb. In a few species of sea stars the limb grows into a new animal.

Many plants can reproduce by regeneration. Even though the tissues in a leaf, root, or stem are specialized, many can produce tissues of other types. People use this ability of plants when they take cuttings, such as a stem, from a plant. Cells near the cut produce different types of tissues that grow into roots and other missing parts.

 CHECK YOUR READING Describe the process of regeneration in sea stars.

Asexual Reproduction and Health

RESOURCE CENTER
CLASSZONE.COM

Learn more about asexual reproduction.

You have probably had the following experience. In the morning you feel fine. By afternoon, you have a strange feeling that something is not quite right, but you are well enough to function normally. You may even continue to feel well at dinner, and you eat heartily. Then, later that evening, it hits you. You're sick. That tickle in your throat has become a sore throat. How did you get so sick so fast?

A harmful type of bacteria may have caused your illness. Remember that bacteria are unicellular prokaryotes. They reproduce by binary fission, which can occur very fast. After a cell divides, it takes a while before the new cells can divide. Each time the cells divide, they produce a new generation of cells. The time it takes for offspring to grow and produce new offspring is called the generation time. Some types of bacteria can produce a new generation in less than 30 minutes.

With each generation, the number of bacteria can double. Two bacteria become four, then eight, then sixteen. After twenty-four generations, there can be millions of bacteria. The type of bacteria that causes strep throat can multiply so fast that you might become sick within a day or so. A sample of the bacteria from your throat can be placed in a Petri dish, where it quickly produces enough bacteria to analyze.

The fast growth of other bacteria can be good for your health. If you have to take an antibiotic medicine to kill the harmful bacteria, the medicine will also kill the bacteria that are normally in your body to help you digest food. However, when you finish the medicine, the helpful bacteria can grow back quickly.

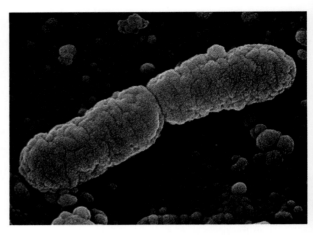

Asexual reproduction
A single bacterium divides into two bacteria during asexual reproduction.

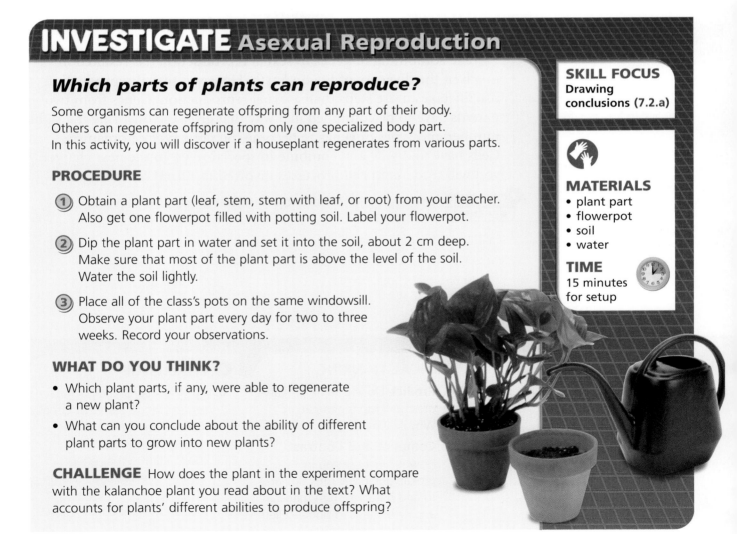

INVESTIGATE Asexual Reproduction

Which parts of plants can reproduce?

Some organisms can regenerate offspring from any part of their body. Others can regenerate offspring from only one specialized body part. In this activity, you will discover if a houseplant regenerates from various parts.

PROCEDURE

1. Obtain a plant part (leaf, stem, stem with leaf, or root) from your teacher. Also get one flowerpot filled with potting soil. Label your flowerpot.

2. Dip the plant part in water and set it into the soil, about 2 cm deep. Make sure that most of the plant part is above the level of the soil. Water the soil lightly.

3. Place all of the class's pots on the same windowsill. Observe your plant part every day for two to three weeks. Record your observations.

WHAT DO YOU THINK?

- Which plant parts, if any, were able to regenerate a new plant?
- What can you conclude about the ability of different plant parts to grow into new plants?

CHALLENGE How does the plant in the experiment compare with the kalanchoe plant you read about in the text? What accounts for plants' different abilities to produce offspring?

SKILL FOCUS
Drawing conclusions (7.2.a)

MATERIALS
- plant part
- flowerpot
- soil
- water

TIME
15 minutes for setup

Sexual reproduction involves two parent organisms.

CALIFORNIA Focus

The Mather Field Vernal Pools of Sacramento County appear with the winter rains, become green for a few short months, and then dry out for the rest of the year. Many organisms in the pools reproduce sexually as the water vanishes. Eggs, seeds, and other forms start growing when the water becomes available again.

You have read how one organism can produce offspring through asexual reproduction. The offspring are genetically identical to the parent. In contrast, many multicellular organisms reproduce by sexual reproduction. In sexual reproduction, the genes of two parent organisms are combined to produce offspring that are not exactly the same as either parent. A plant that grows from a seed and an animal that grows from an egg each have genetic material from two parents. The table below compares and contrasts the two types of reproduction.

Asexual and Sexual Reproduction	
Asexual Reproduction	**Sexual Reproduction**
One parent organism	Two parent organisms
Offspring's genes are identical to parent's genes.	Offspring's genes are combined from two parents.
Can reproduce quickly	Usually reproduce more slowly

The combining of genes in sexual reproduction has resulted in much of the diversity of life on Earth. However, sexual reproduction usually takes more steps than asexual reproduction. Genes from two parents have to be combined in a way that gives the offspring the right number and types of genes to become the same type of organism. Cells have to divide and combine in special ways. In the next chapter, you will read about cell processes involved in sexual reproduction.

CHECK YOUR READING List two major differences between asexual and sexual reproduction.

Review

KEY CONCEPTS

1. How does binary fission relate to cell division? (7.2.a)

2. What is a bud, and where does it form on an organism that reproduces asexually? (7.2.a)

3. Compare sexual and asexual reproduction. (7.2.a)

CRITICAL THINKING

4. **Predict** Do you think prokaryotes undergo regeneration? Why or why not?

5. **Compare and Contrast** How is binary fission in prokaryotic organisms similar to and different from mitosis and cytokinesis in single-celled eukaryotic organisms?

CHALLENGE

6. **Synthesize** Some bacteria can exchange pieces of genetic material with one another through a process called conjugation. What effect might this exchange have on the offspring of the bacteria that underwent conjugation?

MATH in SCIENCE

MATH TUTORIAL
CLASSZONE.COM

Click on Math Tutorial
for more help with
exponents.

 Math 7.MR.2.5
Science 7.1.e

SKILL: USING EXPONENTS

Divide and Multiply

Each time a parent cell divides, the result is two new cells. The new cells are a new generation that in turn divides again. The increase in the number of cells can be shown using exponents. Each cell of each new generation produces two cells. This type of increase in the number of objects is often called exponential growth.

Example

What is the numerical sequence when cells divide to form new cells? You can model this type of progression by using a plain piece of paper.

(1) To represent the first division, fold the piece of paper in half.

(2) Fold it in half again, and it will show the second division. Fold it again and again to represent succeeding divisions.

(3) Write the sequence that shows the number of boxes on the paper after each fold.

2, 4, 8, 16, . . .

(4) Notice that after one division (fold), there are 2 cells (boxes), or 2^1 cells. Two divisions yield 2 • 2 cells, or 2^2 cells. And after three divisions, there are 2 • 2 • 2 cells, or 2^3 cells.

ANSWER The sequence can be written with exponents:
$2^1, 2^2, 2^3, 2^4, . . .$

Answer the following questions.

1. Suppose the cells divide for one more generation after the 4 described above. How can this be written as an exponent of 2? How many cells will there be?

2. How many cells would exist in the tenth generation? Write the number using an exponent.

3. Suppose you took the paper in the example and folded it in thirds each time, rather than in half. Make a table showing the number of boxes after each folding. Use numbers with exponents to write the sequence.

4. Write the following number sequence as a sequence of numbers with exponents: 5, 25, 125, 625, . . .

5. Write the following number sequence as a sequence of numbers without exponents: $10^1, 10^2, 10^3, 10^4, . . .$

CHALLENGE Before you begin folding, you have a single sheet of paper, or 1 unit. The parent cell is also a single unit. Use this information to explain why $2^0 = 3^0$.

3 Chapter Review

the BIG idea

Organisms grow, reproduce, and maintain themselves through cell division.

CONTENT REVIEW
CLASSZONE.COM

◀ **KEY CONCEPTS SUMMARY**

(1) Cell division occurs in all organisms.

- In unicellular organisms the function of cell division is reproduction.
- In multicellular organisms the functions of cell division include growth, development, and repair.

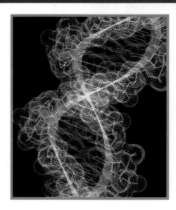

VOCABULARY
DNA p. 74
chromosome p. 75

(2) Cell division is part of the cell cycle.

The **cell cycle** has two main phases, **interphase** and **mitosis.** Most of the life cycle of a cell is spent in interphase. During mitosis, the nucleus divides.

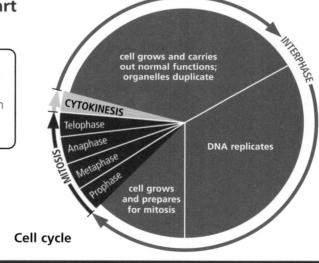

cell grows and carries out normal functions; organelles duplicate

INTERPHASE

CYTOKINESIS

Telophase

Anaphase

Metaphase

Prophase

MITOSIS

DNA replicates

cell grows and prepares for mitosis

Cell cycle

VOCABULARY
cell cycle p. 80
interphase p. 81
mitosis p. 81
cytokinesis p. 81

(3) Both sexual and asexual reproduction involve cell division.

Some organisms reproduce asexually. Both asexual and sexual reproduction involve cell division.

Asexual and Sexual Reproduction	
Asexual Reproduction	**Sexual Reproduction**
One parent organism	Two parent organisms
Offspring's genes are identical to parent's genes.	Offspring's genes are combined from two parents.
Can reproduce quickly	Usually reproduce more slowly

VOCABULARY
asexual reproduction p. 88
binary fission p. 89
regeneration p. 90

Reviewing Vocabulary

On a separate sheet of paper, write a sentence describing the relationship between the terms in each pair.

1. cell cycle, interphase

2. mitosis, cytokinesis

3. chromosome, DNA

4. parent, offspring

Reviewing Key Concepts

Multiple Choice *Choose the letter of the best answer.*

5. Most of the growth in your body occurs because your cells (7.1.e)
   - **a.** join together
   - **b.** take in oxygen
   - **c.** make proteins
   - **d.** divide

6. The stage in a cell's life when it is not in the process of dividing is called (7.1.e)
   - **a.** interphase
   - **b.** the cell cycle
   - **c.** mitosis
   - **d.** cell division

7. What wraps around proteins and then compacts to form visible chromosomes? (7.2.e)
   - **a.** carbohydrates
   - **b.** prokaryotes
   - **c.** the nucleus
   - **d.** DNA

8. What ratio increases when a cell divides into two smaller cells? (7.1.e)
   - **a.** volume to length
   - **b.** length to width
   - **c.** surface area to volume
   - **d.** width to surface area

9. The cytoplasm contains mitochondria and other organelles. During which process is the cytoplasm divided into daughter cells? (7.1.e)
   - **a.** mitosis
   - **b.** photosynthesis
   - **c.** cytokinesis
   - **d.** replication

10. During what part of the cell cycle are organelles copied? (7.1.e)
    - **a.** prophase
    - **b.** synthesis
    - **c.** anaphase
    - **d.** interphase

11. Pairs of connected chromatids become visible just before cell division. A pair of chromatids is (7.2.e)
    - **a.** two copies of DNA that will separate
    - **b.** one copy of DNA that will be replicated
    - **c.** two different strands of DNA that were stuck together
    - **d.** two wrinkles in the cell membrane

12. Binary fission is similar to mitosis and cytokinesis because (7.2.a)
    - **a.** the new cell stays attached to the parent
    - **b.** the nucleus divides into two copies
    - **c.** a cell wall forms between the daughter cells
    - **d.** the parent cell divides into two daughter cells

13. If a sea star is cut in half, it can regrow the missing part of its body through (7.2.a)
    - **a.** binary fission
    - **b.** budding
    - **c.** sexual reproduction
    - **d.** regeneration

14. Which of these is always a form of reproduction? (7.2.a)
    - **a.** binary fission
    - **b.** mitosis
    - **c.** cytokinesis
    - **d.** cell division

15. Which sequence is correct for mitosis? (7.1.e)
    - **a.** chromosomes appear, chromosomes separate, chromosomes line up, nuclei form
    - **b.** chromosomes appear, chromosomes line up, chromosomes separate, nuclei form
    - **c.** chromosomes line up, nuclei form, chromosomes separate, chromosomes appear
    - **d.** chromosomes separate, chromosomes appear, nuclei form, chromosomes line up

Short Answer *Write a short answer to each question.*

16. What is the difference between cytokinesis in plant and animal cells? (7.1.c)

17. Describe what happens in a cell during interphase. Your answer should mention DNA. (7.2.e)

18. Describe the functions of cell division in both unicellular and multicellular organisms. (7.1.e)

19. IDENTIFY CAUSE Describe some of the reasons that cells divide. (7.1.e)

This illustration shows a plant and the cutting that was taken from it, which is growing in a container of water. Use the illustration to answer the next six questions.

20. OBSERVE From which part of the plant was the cutting taken? (7.2.a)

21. INFER Where did the cutting get the genetic information that controls its development? (7.1.c)

22. INFER What is the genetic relationship between the original plant and the cutting? (7.2.a)

23. SYNTHESIZE What process causes both the cutting and the original plant to grow? (7.2.a)

24. SUMMARIZE Write a brief summary of the process that causes growth in both plants. (7.2.a)

25. PREDICT These plants can also reproduce using seeds. How is the cutting the same as the plant that would grow from a seed? How is the cutting different? (7.2.a)

26. CALCULATE A single bacterium enters your body at 10:00 A.M. This type of bacteria reproduces at a rate of one generation every 30 minutes. How many bacteria of this type will be in your body by 8:00 P.M. that evening? Hint: Every 30 minutes the number of bacteria doubles.

The diagrams below show 4 parts of a process. Use them to answer the following three questions.

a.   c.

b.   d.

27. SEQUENCE What is the correct order of the four diagrams above? (7.1.e)

28. SYNTHESIZE Draw two diagrams, one showing what you would see before the process shown above begins, and one showing what you would see after the conclusion of the process. (7.7.d)

29. MODEL On a separate sheet of paper, draw your own simple model of the process of mitosis. (7.1.e)

the BIG idea

30. SUMMARIZE Look again at the question on the photograph on pages 70–71. Now that you have studied this chapter, how would you change your answer to the question? (7.1.e)

31. SYNTHESIZE How do the concepts in this chapter relate to the concepts in the cell theory? (7.1.e)

UNIT PROJECTS

If you need to do an experiment for your unit project, gather the materials. Be sure to allow enough time to observe results before the project is due.

Analyzing Data

7.1.e, 7.2.e

This diagram shows the approximate length of the cell cycle for a typical skin cell in the human body.

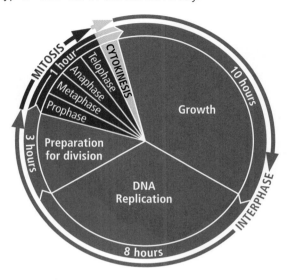

Use the diagram to answer the questions below.

1. How long does the growth phase of the cell cycle take?
  a. 1 hour   **c.** 8 hours
  b. 3 hours   **d.** 10 hours

2. How much time does the cell cycle spend in interphase?
  a. 1 hour   **c.** 21 hours
  b. 10 hours   **d.** 22 hours

3. What is the total length of time it takes for the skin cell to complete one full cell cycle?
  a. 10 hours   **c.** 21 hours
  b. 18 hours   **d.** 22 hours

4. What phase of the cell cycle takes about 8 hours?
  a. DNA replication
  b. mitosis
  c. growth
  d. preparation for cell division

5. Suppose another type of skin cell takes 44 hours to complete one cell cycle. If all of the phases are proportional to the length of time shown in the diagram, how long will the preparation for cell division phase last?
  a. 3 hours   **c.** 10 hours
  b. 6 hours   **d.** 20 hours

6. According to the diagram, what is the second stage in mitosis?
  a. prophase   **c.** telophase
  b. metaphase   **d.** cytokinesis

Extended Response

Answer the two questions. Include some of the terms shown in the word box. Underline each term you use in your answers.

cell cycle	metaphase	mitosis
anaphase	prophase	telophase

7. A scientist is studying the stages of cell division in the cells of an onion root. The scientist counts 100 cells and identifies which stage of cell division each cell is in at a given moment. He counts a total of 85 cells in interphase, 8 cells in prophase, 3 cells in metaphase, and 2 cells each in anaphase and telophase. A typical onion cell takes about 12 hours to complete the cell cycle. Using the information in the diagram and the data given here, how can you account for these numbers?

8. Your science class is investigating the effect of temperature on the rate of mitosis in onion plants. You hypothesize that the higher the temperature, the faster cells undergo mitosis. How could you set up an experiment to support your hypothesis? Describe the materials you would use and the steps you would take in your procedure.

CHAPTER

4 Patterns of Heredity

the **BIG** idea

In sexual reproduction, genes are passed from parents to offspring in predictable patterns.

Key Concepts

SECTION

1 Living things inherit traits in patterns.
Learn about traits and how living things inherit traits from their parents.

SECTION

2 Patterns of heredity can be predicted.
Learn how math can be used to predict patterns of heredity.

SECTION

3 DNA is divided during meiosis.
Learn about the process of meiosis.

SECTION

4 Cells use DNA and RNA to make proteins.
Learn about DNA, RNA, and how cells make proteins.

California ClassZone

CLASSZONE.COM

Chapter 4 online resources: Content Review, two Simulations, Visualization, three Resource Centers, Math Tutorial, Test Practice

EXPLORE (the BIG idea)

What similarities can you see between this mother wolf and her two offspring?

Combinations

7.2.b Students know sexual reproduction produces offspring that inherit half their genes from each parent.

Take one bag that has 4 blue slips of paper and one bag that has 4 red slips of paper. Mix or combine the slips of paper in the bags. Try to make as many different combinations of the slips of paper as you can. Be sure that each bag has 4 slips of paper after each time you make a new combination.

Observe and Think
How many ways could you mix the materials? How were the combinations alike and different?

Internet Activity: Mendel's Experiment

7.2.d Students know plant and animal cells contain many thousands of different genes and typically have two copies of every gene. The two copies (or alleles) of the gene may or may not be identical, and one may be dominant in determining the phenotype while the other is recessive.

Go to **ClassZone.com** to try a virtual version of Mendel's experiments with pea plants. Breed virtual plants and observe the traits of the offspring. Learn about the patterns of inherited traits that Mendel found during his experiments.

Observe and Think
What do Mendel's experiments teach us about heredity?

NSTA
scilinks.org
SCiLINKS

Heredity Code: MDL034

Getting Ready to Learn

◀ CONCEPT REVIEW

- Life comes from life.
- Mitosis produces cells with identical genetic information.
- Some organisms reproduce through asexual reproduction.

◀ VOCABULARY REVIEW

DNA p. 74

chromosome p. 75

mitosis p. 81

asexual reproduction p. 88

CONTENT REVIEW
CLASSZONE.COM

Review concepts and vocabulary.

▶ TAKING NOTES

CHOOSE YOUR OWN STRATEGY

Take notes using one or more of the strategies from earlier chapters—**main idea web, combination notes,** or **mind map.** Feel free to mix and match the strategies, or use an entirely different note-taking strategy.

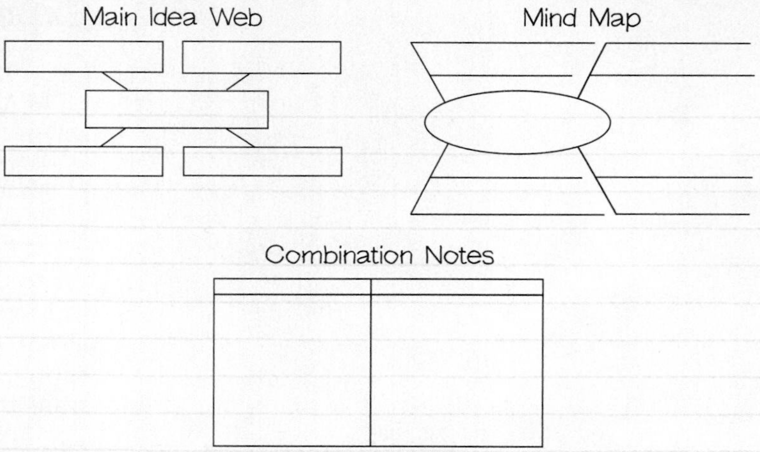

VOCABULARY STRATEGY

Think about a vocabulary term as a **magnet word** diagram. Write the other terms or ideas related to that term around it.

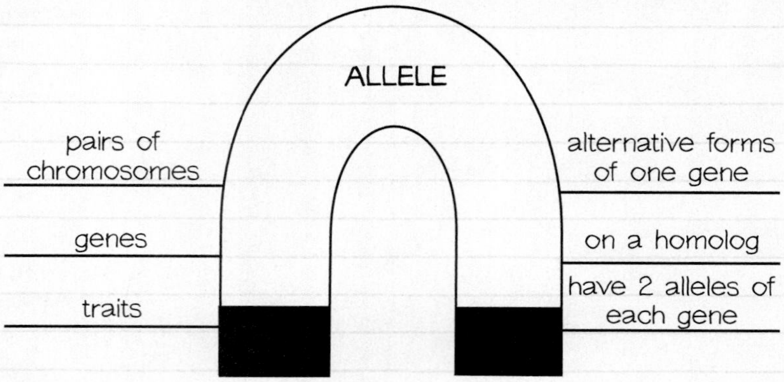

See the Note-Taking Handbook on pages R45–R51.

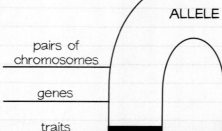

SCIENCE NOTEBOOK

Main Idea Web

Mind Map

Combination Notes

ALLELE

pairs of chromosomes — alternative forms of one gene

genes — on a homolog

traits — have 2 alleles of each gene

KEY CONCEPT

Living things inherit traits in patterns.

CALIFORNIA
Content Standards

7.2.c Students know an inherited trait can be determined by one or more genes.

7.2.d Students know plant and animal cells contain many thousands of different genes and typically have two copies of every gene. The two copies (or alleles) of the gene may or may not be identical, and one may be dominant in determining the phenotype while the other is recessive.

VOCABULARY

sexual reproduction p. 102
gene p. 102
heredity p. 102
allele p. 103
phenotype p. 106
genotype p. 106
dominant p. 107
recessive p. 107

BEFORE, you learned

• Cells come from other cells
• Cells contain DNA in chromosomes
• Some organisms produce offspring through asexual reproduction

NOW, you will learn

• How genes for traits are passed from parent to offspring
• About discoveries made by Gregor Mendel
• About dominant and recessive alleles

THINK ABOUT

What characteristics might be inherited?

How would you describe the girl in the photograph? Make a list of some characteristics you can observe and some characteristics you can infer. You might list her hair color and her ability to read. Some of her characteristics are learned or acquired from the environment around her. Some of her characteristics are inherited from her parents. Which of the characteristics on your list do you think were inherited? Which of the characteristics do you think were acquired?

Parents and offspring are similar.

You are an individual organism with a unique combination of characteristics. These characteristics are also known as traits. Many of your traits may resemble those your parents have, including your hair color, eye color, and blood type. These characteristics are called inherited traits.

Some traits are acquired, not inherited. An acquired trait is developed during your life. Learned behaviors are one type of acquired trait. For example, your ability to read and write is an acquired trait—a skill you learned. You were not born knowing how to read. If you have children, they will not be born knowing how to read either. They will have to learn the skill just as you did.

NOTE-TAKING STRATEGY
Take notes on the idea that parents and offspring are similar by using a strategy from an earlier chapter or one of your own.

Some traits are acquired, some traits are inherited, and some traits are a combination of both. For example, your hair color is a trait that you inherited from your parents. However, your hair color also can be affected by sunlight and chemicals in your environment.

 **CHECK YOUR READING** How are inherited traits and acquired traits different? Give one example of each.

RESOURCE CENTER
CLASSZONE.COM
Find out more about sexual reproduction.

In this chapter, you will learn why the offspring produced through sexual reproduction are not identical to either of their parents. During **sexual reproduction** each parent contributes a cell that contains genetic information. The two cells combine to form the offspring. First, you will learn how traits of offspring are related to traits of their two parents. Then you will learn more about how cells divide and combine and about how DNA affects traits.

Genes are on chromosome pairs.

Remember that long strands of DNA wrap around proteins to make up a cell's chromosomes. A **gene** is a segment of DNA at a specific location on a chromosome that influences hereditary characteristics. Each gene has a code for information that influences a trait. Scientists say that genes "code for" traits.

READING TIP

A code is a set of symbols and rules used to carry information—like words in a book.

Heredity is the passing of genes from parents to offspring. An organism does not inherit the traits themselves from its parents. It inherits the genes that code for the traits. Most traits are not coded for by just one gene. Some characteristics are affected by many genes in complicated ways. Scientists still have much to learn about which genes affect which characteristics.

In most eukaryotes, cells contain pairs of chromosomes of the same type. One chromosome of the pair comes from one parent, and the other comes from the other parent. The chromosomes in a pair are called homologs. The homologs are the same size and shape and carry the same genes.

Look at the diagram of chromosomes on the left. The genes are located at specific sites on each homolog.

Chromosomes and Genes

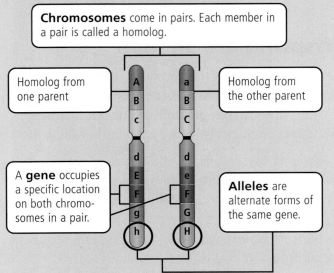

The letters on the pair of chromosomes below represent alleles.

Chromosomes come in pairs. Each member in a pair is called a homolog.

Homolog from one parent

Homolog from the other parent

A **gene** occupies a specific location on both chromosomes in a pair.

Alleles are alternate forms of the same gene.

For example, the gene that codes for a plant's height may be located at site H. Although both homologs have the gene for height at site H, the genes may not be identical. They may be variations instead. Different forms of the same gene are called **alleles** (uh-LEELZ).

Thus, the homolog—chromosome—from one parent might have an allele at site H for tall height, while the allele at site H on the other homolog may be for short height. Another plant might have two alleles for short height, while a third plant has two alleles for medium height. There can be many alleles of a particular gene within a species.

READING TIP

The word *homolog* comes from the Greek words *homos*, which means "same," and *logos*, which means "proportion."

⬧ CHECK YOUR READING   What are alleles?

Each species has a specific number of chromosomes. Chimpanzees have 48 chromosomes—24 pairs. Fruit flies have 8 chromosomes—4 pairs. Humans have 46 chromosomes—23 pairs. Scientists number the pairs of chromosomes for reference. Human chromosomes are numbered in pairs of homologs from 1 through 22; pair 23 contains the two sex chromosomes.

In humans, the sex chromosomes are called the X-chromosome and the Y-chromosome. A human female has two X-chromosomes. A human male has one X-chromosome and one Y-chromosome. The presence of the Y-chromosome determines the sex of an offspring. The X- and Y-chromosomes also contain important genes, just as other chromosomes do.

Human Chromosomes

Humans have 23 pairs of chromosomes, for a total of 46. One of these pairs, shown below, determines the sex of the offspring.

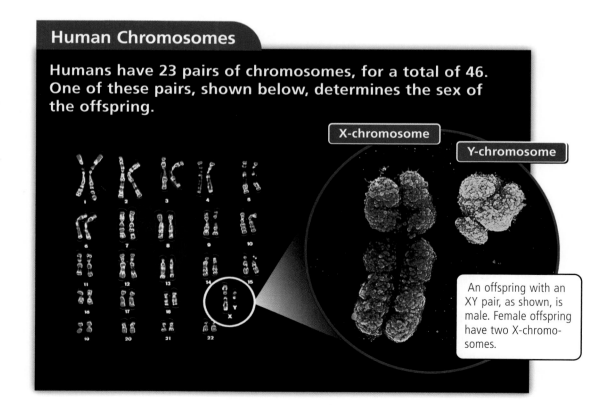

X-chromosome

Y-chromosome

An offspring with an XY pair, as shown, is male. Female offspring have two X-chromosomes.

Gregor Mendel made some important discoveries about heredity.

The first major experiments in heredity were performed by a monk named Gregor Mendel, who lived in Austria during the mid-1800s. Before Mendel became a monk, he attended a university and studied science and mathematics. He used this knowledge when he investigated the inheritance of traits among the pea plants in the monastery's garden.

Mendel took very detailed notes, carefully recording all the data from his many experiments. He studied seven different traits: plant height, flower and pod position, seed shape, seed color, pod shape, pod color, and flower color. He studied each trait separately. He started with plants that were true-breeding for that one particular trait. A true-breeding plant is one that always produces offspring with a particular trait when it self-pollinates, or pollinates its own flowers. Pea plants usually self-pollinate in nature.

READING TIP

The root of the word *trait* means to "draw out." It was originally used in the sense of drawing out a line. This same idea works in heredity if you think of drawing a connection between parents and offspring.

CALIFORNIA Focus

Thomas Hunt Morgan was an American zoologist and geneticist. His research with the fruit fly led to the discovery that a series of linked genes on chromosomes is a source of identifiable hereditary traits. Morgan organized the biology division at the California Institute of Technology in 1928. His work and experiments were instrumental in creating the field of genetics.

One Example

In his experiments with plant height, Mendel used two sets of plants. One set was true-breeding for plants of regular height, and the other was true-breeding for plants of short, or dwarf, height.

1 Mendel paired as parents one plant from each set. Mendel called the plants that resulted from this cross the first generation. All of the plants from this first generation were of regular height. The dwarf-height trait seemed to have disappeared.

2 Mendel then let the first-generation plants self-pollinate. He called the offspring that resulted from this self-pollination the second generation. About three-fourths of the second-generation plants were of regular height. About one-fourth were of dwarf height. So the trait that seemed to disappear in the first generation appeared again in the second generation.

Mendel's experiments with other traits showed similar patterns.

 CHECK YOUR READING Summarize the pattern shown in Mendel's experiments with plant height.

Mendel's Conclusions

Mendel developed a hypothesis to explain the patterns he observed. He realized that each plant must have two "factors" for each possible trait, such as height. One factor comes from each parent. A plant shows a trait, such as regular height, from one of its factors. The second factor could be masked, or hidden, by the first.

Mendel's Pea Plants

Mendel observed variation in the height of pea plants (regular or dwarf height). By crossing plants with specific traits, he concluded that offspring get factors for each trait from both parents.

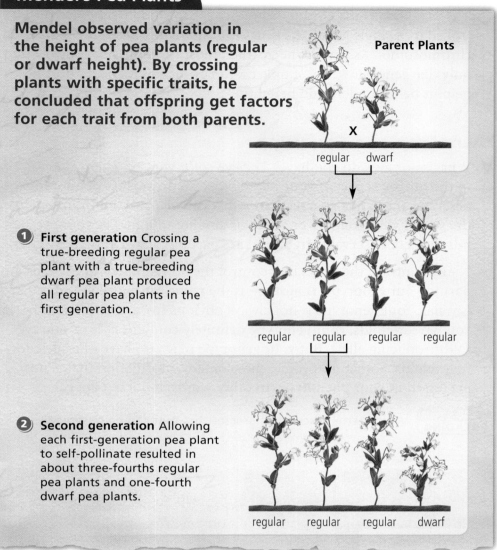

Parent Plants

regular   dwarf

1. **First generation** Crossing a true-breeding regular pea plant with a true-breeding dwarf pea plant produced all regular pea plants in the first generation.

regular   regular   regular   regular

2. **Second generation** Allowing each first-generation pea plant to self-pollinate resulted in about three-fourths regular pea plants and one-fourth dwarf pea plants.

regular   regular   regular   dwarf

A plant with one regular-height factor and one dwarf-height factor grows to regular height. The factor for dwarf height is masked. Dwarf height occurs only if both of the plant's factors are for dwarf height. All of the plants in the first generation shown above have one dwarf-height factor and one regular-height factor. They are regular height because the regular-height factor masks the dwarf-height factor.

Later experiments allowed Mendel to draw more conclusions about how these factors are distributed. Since the mid-1800s, Mendel's experiments and conclusions have been the basis for most of the scientific thought about heredity. The things he called factors are what we now call genes and alleles.

CHECK YOUR READING How many factors, or genes, does each plant have for each possible trait?

Alleles interact to produce traits.

The pea-plant traits Gregor Mendel chose to study were each controlled by a single gene. The genes for different traits were on different chromosomes. As you learned earlier, most traits are not controlled by only one gene. However, simple examples such as Mendel's peas do help us better understand heredity.

Phenotype and Genotype

READING TiP

The words *phenotype* and *phenomenon* have a similar root word meaning "to appear."

VOCABULARY
Make word magnet diagrams for the terms *phenotype* and *genotype*.

What color eyes do you have? The eye color you see when you look in the mirror is part of your phenotype. An organism's **phenotype** describes the actual characteristics that can be observed. Your height, the size of your feet, the presence or absence of a fold in your eyelids—all are observable traits and are part of your phenotype.

By contrast, the genes that control the development of eyefolds are part of your genotype. **Genotype** is the name for the alleles an organism has. Your genotype is not always obvious from your phenotype. If you have eyefolds, your genotype definitely contains at least one eyefold-producing allele. But your genotype may also have one allele for no eyefolds. Sometimes your genes contain information that is not expressed in your phenotype. In other words, it doesn't appear.

CHECK YOUR READING Which term describes characteristics that can be observed?

eye with folds at the corner of the eyelids

eye without folds at the corner of the eyelids

The photograph shows **phenotypes** of the eyefold gene. A person with eyefolds is shown to the left, a person without eyefolds to the right.

Dominant and Recessive Alleles

The eyefold gene, which controls the development of folds in the eyelids, has two alleles: eyefolds and no-eyefolds. If you have even one copy of the allele that codes for eyefolds, you will have eyefolds. This happens because the allele that codes for eyefolds is dominant. A **dominant** allele is one that is expressed in the phenotype even if only one copy is present in the genotype. If the other allele is an alternative form, that allele's trait will not be expressed.

Suppose your genotype contains a no-eyefolds allele. The no-eyefolds allele is recessive. A **recessive** allele is one that is expressed in the phenotype only when two copies of it are present on the homologs. If one chromosome in the pair has a dominant allele and the other has a recessive allele, the dominant allele will be expressed in your phenotype. If you do not have eyefolds, it is because you have two no-eyefolds alleles—one from each parent.

 CHECK YOUR READING Under what conditions is a recessive allele expressed in an offspring's phenotype?

The interaction of dominant and recessive alleles means that it is possible for two brown-haired parents to have a blond child.

Hair color is determined by multiple genes, can be affected by the environment, and sometimes changes over time. However, in some cases it has a dominant-recessive pattern similar to that of the eyefold gene. As in the family shown at right, parents who both have brown hair can have a blond child. The allele for brown hair is dominant, so if both parents have alleles for both brown hair and blond hair, the brown-hair allele is more likely to be expressed. Their child, however, could have two blond-hair alleles—one from each parent—and therefore have blond hair instead of brown.

4.1 Review

KEY CONCEPTS

1. Explain the difference between acquired and inherited traits. (7.2.c)

2. Describe the conclusions that Mendel drew from his experiments with pea plants. (7.2.c)

3. What type of alleles are expressed only if two identical copies exist on the homologs of the offspring? (7.2.d)

CRITICAL THINKING

4. **Compare and Contrast** What is the difference between a genotype and a phenotype?

5. **Analyze** Explain why a person with an allele for a particular trait may not have a phenotype that shows the trait.

⬤ CHALLENGE

6. **Apply** In guinea pigs, the allele for black fur is dominant over the allele for brown fur. If you had two parent guinea pigs, each with brown fur, what color fur might the offspring have, and why?

CHAPTER INVESTIGATION

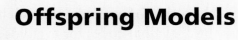

Offspring Models

OVERVIEW AND PURPOSE Sexual reproduction combines genes from two parent organisms and results in diversity among offspring. In this activity, you will
- design a model of an offspring
- determine how the offspring exhibits portions of both genotype and phenotype from its parents

▶ **Problem**

Write It Up

How are traits passed from parent to offspring?

▶ **Procedure**

MATERIALS
- sets of bags (parents' genotypes)
- foam balls (body segments)
- colored toothpicks (antennae)
- small paper clips (wings)
- colored pipe cleaners (legs)
- colored pushpins (eyes)

7.2.b, 7.2.c, 7.2.d, 7.7.d

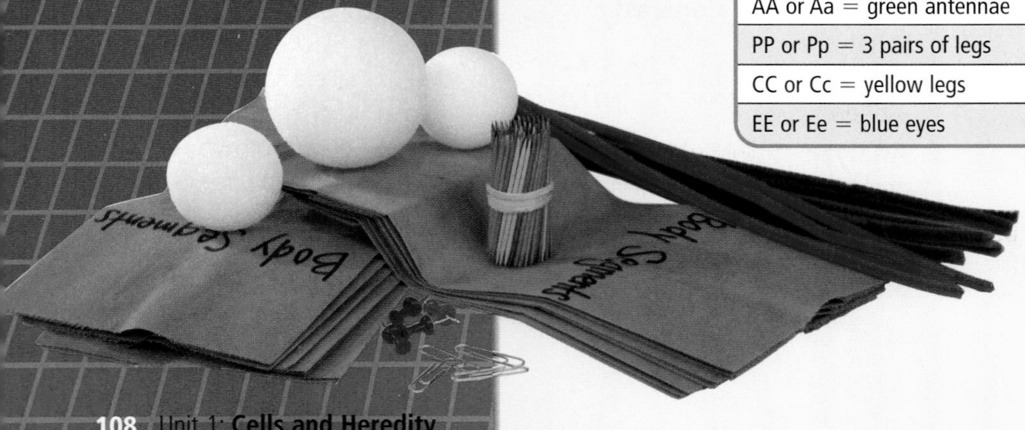

1. Make data tables like those shown on the sample notebook page.

2. You should have two sets of six bags each. Choose one set to represent the female parent and one set to represent the male parent. Each bag contains letters written on slips of paper. These letters represent the parent's alleles for one trait. Capital letters represent dominant alleles, and lowercase letters represent recessive alleles.

3. Take a slip from one bag, and record the allele in Table 1. Return the slip to the bag. Repeat this procedure for each remaining bag. Record the offspring's genotype as pairs of letters in Table 1.

4. Use the table below to determine the phenotype of the offspring. For example, if the offspring genotype includes Aa, record the phenotype "green antennae" in Table 1.

Genotypes and Phenotypes	
BB or Bb = 3 body segments	bb = 2 body segments
WW or Ww = 2 pairs of wings	ww = 1 pair of wings
AA or Aa = green antennae	aa = red antennae
PP or Pp = 3 pairs of legs	pp = 2 pairs of legs
CC or Cc = yellow legs	cc = orange legs
EE or Ee = blue eyes	ee = green eyes

Content Standard
7.2.b Students know sexual reproduction produces offspring that inherit half their genes from each parent.

Investigation Standard
7.7.d Construct scale models, maps, and appropriately labeled diagrams to communicate scientific knowledge (e.g., motion of Earth's plates and cell structure).

5 Choose the materials you need to assemble the offspring. You can use toothpicks to attach the body segments. Push the pipe cleaners, toothpicks, and wings into the foam balls. **CAUTION: Take care when handling the pushpins and the toothpicks.**

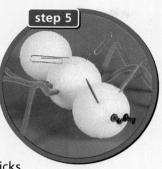

step 5

Observe and Analyze

Write It Up

1. **OBSERVE** Does the offspring look the way you would expect either parent to look? Explain.

2. **ANALYZE** How many different genotypes are possible for each trait? Explain.

Conclude

Write It Up

1. **INFER** What are the possible genotypes of the parents? Fill in Table 2.

2. **INTERPRET** Can you tell how the genotypes of the parents differ from that of the offspring? Explain.

3. **INTERPRET** How does the offspring model illustrate what you have learned about heredity?

4. **APPLY** In humans, blue eyes are the phenotype for two recessive alleles. Might two parents with blue eyes have a brown-eyed offspring? Explain.

INVESTIGATE Further

CHALLENGE Repeat the procedure, but this time use alleles taken from your model offspring and those of a model offspring made by one of your classmates. Record the genotype and determine the phenotype of this second-generation offspring.

Offspring Models

Table 1. Parent and Offspring Family Traits

Trait	Female Allele	Male Allele	Offspring Genotype	Offspring Phenotype
Body segments				
Pairs of wings				
Antennae color				
Pairs of legs				
Color of legs				
Color of eyes				

Table 2. Possible Parent Genotypes

Trait	Female Parent	Male Parent
Body segments		
Pairs of wings		
Antennae color		
Pairs of legs		
Color of legs		
Color of eyes		

4.2 Patterns of heredity can be predicted.

CALIFORNIA
Content Standards

7.2.b Students know sexual reproduction produces offspring that inherit half their genes from each parent.

7.2.c Students know an inherited trait can be determined by one or more genes.

7.2.d Students know plant and animal cells contain many thousands of different genes and typically have two copies of every gene. The two copies (or alleles) of the gene may or may not be identical, and one may be dominant in determining the phenotype while the other is recessive.

VOCABULARY

Punnett square p. 110
probability p. 112

> **NOTE-TAKING STRATEGY**
> Use a strategy from an earlier chapter or choose one of your own to take notes on how Punnett squares show possible patterns of heredity.

BEFORE, you learned

- Genes are passed from parents to offspring
- Offspring inherit genes in predictable patterns

NOW, you will learn

- How Punnett squares can be used to predict patterns of heredity
- How probability can be used to predict patterns of heredity

---

EXPLORE Probability (7.2.c)

How can probability help predict results?

PROCEDURE

1. Toss both coins 10 times. For each toss, record the combination of heads and/or tails.

2. For each combination (two heads, two tails, or a head and a tail), add up the number of tosses.

WHAT DO YOU THINK?

- Which combination happened most often?
- If you tossed both coins one more time, which combination would be the most likely result? Can you know for sure? Why or why not?

MATERIALS

- two coins
- pencil and paper

Punnett squares show possible outcomes for inheritance.

Mendel noticed that traits are inherited in patterns. You know that each parent has two alleles for a particular gene. Only one of these alleles is passed on to an offspring. Each offspring may get either one of the two alleles from that parent. Each offspring also gets just one allele from the other parent. The offspring's two alleles produce a trait. To understand the patterns of traits in parents and offspring, you have to look at the patterns of alleles.

One tool for understanding the patterns of how traits are expressed is called a Punnett square. A **Punnett square** illustrates how two parents' alleles might combine in offspring. The Punnett square on page 111 shows how alleles for pea-plant height would be distributed among offspring in Mendel's first-generation cross. The dominant allele (D) is regular height, and the recessive allele (d) is dwarf height.

The top of the Punnett square shows one parent's alleles for this trait—two dominant regular-height alleles (DD). The side of the Punnett square shows the other parent's alleles for this trait—two recessive dwarf-height alleles (dd).

A Punnett square for one trait is made up of four boxes. Each box shows one way the alleles from each parent could combine in an offspring. You can see below that any offspring would have the genotype of one dominant allele and one recessive allele (Dd). Each offspring would express the phenotype of the dominant allele, in this case regular height.

READING TiP

As you read about Punnett squares, connect each sentence with the diagram below.

 CHECK YOUR READING What is a Punnett square?

Using Punnett Squares

The Punnett square below shows the possible allele combinations for an offspring of one parent with two dominant (D) regular-height alleles and one parent with two recessive (d) dwarf-height alleles.

 SIMULATION
CLASSZONE.COM

Predict offspring traits with virtual Punnett squares.

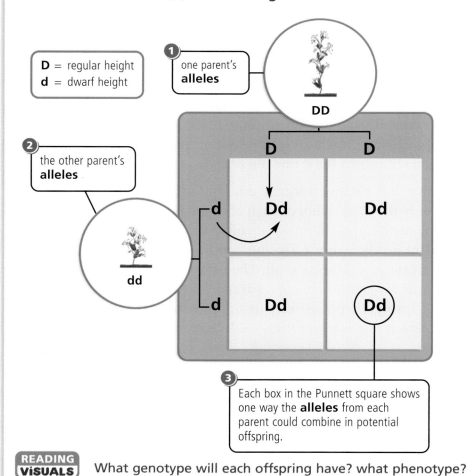

D = regular height
d = dwarf height

1 one parent's **alleles**

DD

2 the other parent's **alleles**

dd

	D	D
d	Dd	Dd
d	Dd	Dd

3 Each box in the Punnett square shows one way the **alleles** from each parent could combine in potential offspring.

READING VISUALS What genotype will each offspring have? what phenotype?

Percentages can express the probability of outcomes.

VOCABULARY
Remember to create a word magnet diagram for the term *probability*.

Punnett squares help scientists determine probabilities. A **probability** is the likelihood, or chance, of a specific outcome in relation to the total number of possible outcomes. Each box of a Punnett square represents a possible outcome—one possible combination of alleles from two specific parents.

The Punnett square on page 113 shows that there are exactly four possible outcomes for the offspring's genotype. For example, one box represents an offspring genotype of bb, or two alleles for brown fur. The probability that any one offspring of these two parent guinea pigs will have genotype bb is one in four. You can also express the probability as a percent. One (bb) divided by four (total) is the same as 25 divided by 100, or 25 percent. Each box in a simple Punnett square represents a probability of 25 percent.

 CHECK YOUR READING What are two ways that you can express a probability?

Now look at the phenotypes—the fur colors. The parent guinea pigs shown on page 113 both have black fur. Each has genotype Bb for the trait of fur color—one dominant allele and one recessive allele. The allele for black fur (B) is dominant, so a guinea pig with one or two copies of this allele will have black fur. Genotypes BB and Bb both result in a phenotype of black fur. Only a pair of recessive alleles, genotype bb, results in a phenotype of brown fur. Three of the possible combinations of alleles, one BB and two Bb, result in black fur. The probability that an offspring will have black fur is three out of four, or 75 percent. The probability of brown fur is one out of four, or 25 percent.

Notice that a Punnett square does not show the actual offspring. It shows only the probability of each combination of alleles—and the resulting phenotype—for any one offspring. The two parent guinea pigs might produce four offspring, but they might produce one offspring, or twenty, or none at all. The probability of brown fur is one out of four for each offspring separately. If these two parents produce many offspring, then it is likely that approximately one-fourth of them—about one in every four—will have brown fur.

CHECK YOUR READING What is the purpose of a Punnett square?

The pattern shown by the box at left is a clue that a trait is determined by dominant and recessive alleles. When each parent has one dominant allele and one recessive allele, about one-quarter of their offspring will show the recessive trait.

The red square represents a one-in-four chance, or a probability of 25 percent. The blue squares together represent a three-in-four chance, or a probability of 75 percent.

Punnett Squares and Probabilities

The Punnett square below shows the possible ways alleles could combine in the offspring of two parent guinea pigs. Each parent has one dominant allele for black fur (B) and one recessive allele for brown fur (b).

B = black fur
b = brown fur

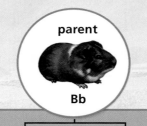

parent
Bb

parent
Bb

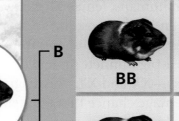

B   b

	B	b
B	BB	Bb
b	Bb	bb

possible offspring

The table below shows the probability of the various genotypes and phenotypes from the Punnett square above. Each probability is also shown as a percentage.

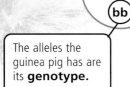

bb

The alleles the guinea pig has are its **genotype.**

Phenotype refers to the guinea pig's actual characteristics.

Genotype	Probability	Percentage	Phenotype	Probability	Percentage
BB	1 in 4	25%	Black fur	3 in 4	75%
Bb	2 in 4	50%			
bb	1 in 4	25%	Brown fur	1 in 4	25%

READING VISUALS Match the four sections of the Punnett square with the genotypes in the table.

Guinea pigs usually produce just a few offspring at a time, but pea plants can produce many peas in each generation. When Mendel experimented with pea plants, he was able to observe enough off-spring to estimate the probability of each possible outcome. When he observed many offspring from different combinations and genera-tions, he was able to make inferences. He inferred that each plant had exactly two factors for a trait—two alleles—and that one could be masked—a recessive allele does not appear in the phenotype.

CHECK YOUR READING How did the large number of offspring of pea plants help Mendel figure out heredity?

In humans, females have two X-chromosomes (XX). Males have an X-chromosome and a Y-chromosome (XY). The Punnett square on page 115 shows the sexes of possible offspring. Unlike the guinea-pig Punnett square, this one shows only two possible out-comes—XX and XY. The diagram also shows how to find the percentage chance that a potential offspring will be female.

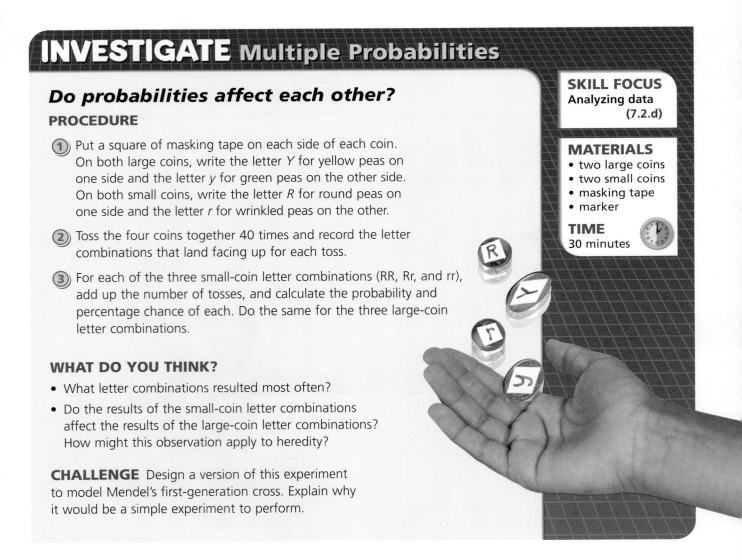

INVESTIGATE Multiple Probabilities

Do probabilities affect each other?

PROCEDURE

1. Put a square of masking tape on each side of each coin. On both large coins, write the letter Y for yellow peas on one side and the letter y for green peas on the other side. On both small coins, write the letter R for round peas on one side and the letter r for wrinkled peas on the other.

2. Toss the four coins together 40 times and record the letter combinations that land facing up for each toss.

3. For each of the three small-coin letter combinations (RR, Rr, and rr), add up the number of tosses, and calculate the probability and percentage chance of each. Do the same for the three large-coin letter combinations.

WHAT DO YOU THINK?

- What letter combinations resulted most often?
- Do the results of the small-coin letter combinations affect the results of the large-coin letter combinations? How might this observation apply to heredity?

CHALLENGE Design a version of this experiment to model Mendel's first-generation cross. Explain why it would be a simple experiment to perform.

SKILL FOCUS
Analyzing data
(7.2.d)

MATERIALS
- two large coins
- two small coins
- masking tape
- marker

TIME
30 minutes

Calculating Probability

Two humans, a female (XX) and a male (XY), have an offspring. The Punnett square below can be used to calculate the probability that an offspring will be female or male.

① To find the percentage chance of a female offspring, first count the possible XX combinations and the total possible outcomes. Express the result as a fraction.

② Two out of four ($\frac{2}{4}$) offspring will be female.

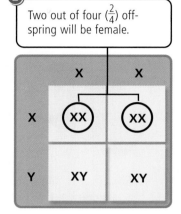

③ Rewrite this fraction with a denominator of 100:
$$\frac{2}{4} \times \frac{25}{25} = \frac{50}{100}$$

④ $\frac{50}{100}$ = 50%, so there is a 50% chance that an offspring will be female.

 READING VISUALS Compare this Punnett square with the pea-plant one on page 111 and the guinea pig one on page 113. How are they alike? How are they different?

Punnett squares and probability do not guarantee the outcome of a genetic cross. They simply show the probability of each possible outcome. While there is a 75 percent chance that an offspring will have black fur according to the Punnett square on page 113, you cannot be certain what color fur a particular offspring will actually have. Actual experimental results may not match predicted outcomes.

 CHECK YOUR READING Can a Punnett square tell you the specific outcome of a genetic cross? Why or why not?

4.2 Review

KEY CONCEPTS

1. Explain how Punnett squares show the possible outcomes of a genetic cross. (7.2.b)

2. How are fractions and percentages related? (7.2.b)

3. How can you find a probability, expressed as a percentage, from a Punnett square? (7.2.b)

CRITICAL THINKING

4. **Apply** If one pea plant had an allele for purple flowers and an allele for white flowers, would all its offspring have the same alleles? Explain.

5. **Predict** Would a cross of two dwarf-height pea plants produce regular-height offspring? *Hint:* Use a Punnett square to determine the answer.

▲ CHALLENGE

6. **Apply** In pea plants, the allele for smooth peas is dominant over the allele for wrinkled peas. Make a Punnett square and calculate the probability that two smooth-pea plants will have an offspring with wrinkled peas if each parent has one allele for smooth and one for wrinkled.

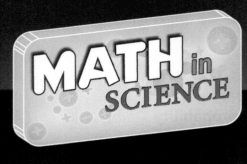

MATH TUTORIAL
CLASSZONE.COM
Click on Math Tutorial
for more help with
probability.

Math 7.MR.3.2
Science 7.2.d

Coat Coloring

The Shetland sheepdog, or Sheltie, has patches of color on its silky coat. A gene controls marbling of the colors, or merling. The merle gene comes in two forms: M for merling, or m for no merling.

A Sheltie with Mm has a merle coat.

A Sheltie with MM is mostly white with no merling.

A Sheltie with mm has solid patches with no merling.

Example

One Sheltie parent has a merle coat (Mm), and one has no merling (mm). With these two parents, what is the probability of a puppy with a merle coat?

(1) Make a Punnett square. Put the alleles from one parent on top. Put those of the other on the side.

(2) Fill in the blocks by combining the alleles.

(3) To find the probability of an outcome, count the blocks of that outcome and the total number of blocks.

(4) Express the probability as ___ out of 4.

ANSWER: There is a 2 out of 4 probability.

	M	m
m	Mm	mm
m	Mm	mm

Now, make your own Punnett square for Shelties.

1. Make a Punnett square to show two Sheltie parents, both with merle coats (Mm).

2. What is the probability of a merle puppy?

3. What are the chances of a puppy with no merling?

CHALLENGE Write each of the probabilities in questions 2 and 3 and the example as a percentage.

4.3 DNA is divided during meiosis.

CALIFORNIA Content Standards

7.2.a Students know the differences between the life cycles and reproduction methods of sexual and asexual organisms.

7.2.b Students know sexual reproduction produces offspring that inherit half their genes from each parent.

BEFORE, you learned

- Mitosis produces two genetically identical cells
- In sexual reproduction, offspring inherit genes from both parents
- Genetic traits are inherited in predictable patterns

NOW, you will learn

- Why meiosis is necessary for sexual reproduction
- How cells and chromosomes divide during meiosis
- How meiosis differs from mitosis

VOCABULARY

gamete p. 118
egg p. 118
sperm p. 118
fertilization p. 118
meiosis p. 119

EXPLORE Meiosis (7.2.a)

Why does sexual reproduction need a special form of cell division?

PROCEDURE

1. Suppose a cell with one pair of chromosomes divides by mitosis. In sexual reproduction, two cells combine to form a new cell. Model this division and combination with the pipe cleaners.

2. Now model a way for the new cell to end up with just one pair of chromosomes.

WHAT DO YOU THINK?

- What was wrong with the new cell produced at the end of step 1?
- Describe your model of the way a new cell could end up with the correct number of chromosomes.

MATERIALS

- 2 blue pipe cleaners
- 2 red pipe cleaners

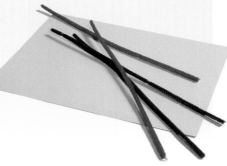

Meiosis is necessary for sexual reproduction.

In Section 4.1 you learned that two cells combine during the process of sexual reproduction. One of the cells contains genetic information from one parent. The other contains genetic information from the other parent. The two cells combine into a completely new cell, which becomes the offspring.

How does the genetic material of offspring produced by sexual reproduction compare with the genetic material of the parents?

Most cells in the human body contain 23 pairs of chromosomes—the 46 chromosomes that are normal for a human being. A cell that contains two sets of chromosomes (the full number for a species) is a $2n$ cell, also called a diploid cell. The n tells you the number of chromosomes in one set. The diploid ($2n$) number for human cells is 46. Because there are 23 pairs of chromosomes in human cells, n is 23. In fruit flies, the diploid number ($2n$) is 8. Therefore, n in fruit flies is 4. The $2n$ cells for a fruit fly contain 8 chromosomes.

Think about what would happen if two body cells were to combine. The resulting cell would have twice the normal number of chromosomes. Reproductive cells, called gametes, must differ from body cells.

Gametes are cells that contain half the usual number of chromosomes—one chromosome from each pair. Gametes are n cells, also called haploid cells. Human gametes contain 23 unpaired chromosomes. The gametes of a fruit fly contain 4 unpaired chromosomes. Gametes are found in the reproductive organs of plants and animals. An **egg** is a gamete that forms in the female reproductive organs. A gamete that forms in the male reproductive organs is a **sperm**.

 CHECK YOUR READING What is a gamete?

chromosome pair

single chromosome

diploid cell (**2n**)

haploid cell (**n**)

During sexual reproduction two gametes combine to become a $2n$ cell that can grow into a new offspring. **Fertilization** is the process that takes place when a sperm and an egg combine to form one new cell. The diagram on page 119 shows what happens to the chromosomes in gametes during fertilization. In humans, an n egg cell with 23 chromosomes joins an n sperm cell with 23 chromosomes to form a new $2n$ cell with 46 chromosomes.

When a sperm cell fertilizes an egg cell, the newly formed cell, which is called a zygote, gets all of its cytoplasm from the egg. The sperm cell adds only its set of chromosomes to the zygote. Why is this important? The cytoplasm contains all of the cell's organelles. Mitochondria—energy-releasing organelles—have their own DNA. Mitochondria come only from the mother. Thus, the DNA in the mitochondria is the same in the mother, the grandmother, the great-grandmother, and so on.

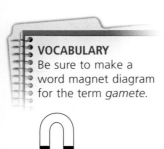

VOCABULARY
Be sure to make a
word magnet diagram
for the term *gamete*.

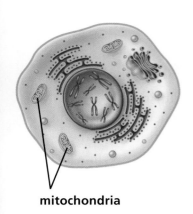

mitochondria

Fertilization

During fertilization, an *n* egg cell from a female combines with an *n* sperm cell from a male, producing a 2*n* fertilized egg cell, which develops into an offspring.

egg cell

egg cell
(female gamete)

n

fertilization →

fertilized
egg cell

2*n*

sperm cells

sperm cell
(male gamete)

n

You know that body cells divide through mitosis and cytokinesis. Mitosis produces two daughter cells, each containing exact copies of the chromosomes in the parent cell. Each daughter cell formed by mitosis is a standard diploid (2*n*) cell.

But to produce gametes, which are haploid, a different type of cell division is necessary. **Meiosis** is a special type of cell division that produces haploid (*n*) cells. During meiosis, a single cell goes through two cell divisions—meiosis I and meiosis II. Meiosis takes place only in the reproductive organs.

Cells divide twice during meiosis.

Before meiosis begins, the DNA in each chromosome of the parent cell is copied. A cell that is ready to divide has twice the usual amount of DNA. To end up with cells that have half the usual amount of DNA, there must be two divisions. The result is four haploid cells.

Recall that the chromosomes in a pair are called homologs. The two homologs have the same set of genes but different alleles. During the first part of meiosis, called meiosis I, the pairs of chromosomes separate. The cell divides into two cells. Each cell ends up with just one set of chromosomes (*n*). Each chromosome is made of two copies—chromatids, attached together. The chromatids separate during the second part of meiosis, called meiosis II. This second process does not change the number of unique chromosomes. It only separates the copies.

NOTE-TAKING STRATEGY
Use an earlier strategy or one that you think works well to take notes on the division of cells during meiosis.

Meiosis I

In the first step in producing gametes, the pairs of chromosomes are separated. The diagram on page 121 shows what would happen during meiosis in a species that has four chromosomes in its *2n* body cells.

1 **Chromosomes condense.** The threads of DNA coil up and become visible. As shown at left, each resulting chromosome is made up of two identical chromatids attached together. Each chromosome is also next to its partner chromosome.

2 **Chromosome pairs line up.** The pairs of chromosomes line up along the center of the cell.

3 **Chromosome pairs separate.** The pairs of chromosomes are pulled apart. The two sides of the cell end up with different chromosomes. This step divides the alleles of each gene.

4 **Two cells form.** The chromosomes are in two groups. Usually, the parent cell divides by cytokinesis into two daughter cells.

 CHECK YOUR READING What happens to the pairs of chromosomes during meiosis I?

Meiosis II

The second step in producing gametes begins with the two cells from meiosis I. Recall that each chromosome is made of two identical chromatids. In meiosis II, the chromatids are pulled apart. As you can see on page 121, the two cells divide to produce a total of four cells.

5 **Chromatids are still attached.** The cells prepare to divide again. Each cell has just one set of chromosomes (*n*). Each chromosome is still made of two copies—chromatids—attached together.

6 **Chromosomes line up.** The unpaired chromosomes line up along each cell's center.

7 **Chromatids separate.** The two attached copies of each chromosome separate and are pulled to opposite ends of each cell.

8 **Haploid cells form.** Each cell divides into two daughter cells, producing a total of four cells. Each haploid (*n*) daughter cell has one copy of one unpaired set of chromosomes.

During meiosis, one cell in an organism's reproductive system divides twice to form four *n* cells. In male reproductive systems, these cells become sperm. In female reproductive systems, at least one of these cells becomes an egg. In some species, including humans, only one of the four daughter cells produced by a female during meiosis becomes an egg. The rest usually dissolve back into the organism.

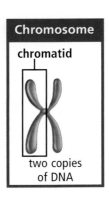

Chromosome

chromatid

two copies
of DNA

RESOURCE CENTER
CLASSZONE.COM

Learn more about
meiosis.

Meiosis

Meiosis reduces the number of chromosomes by half, producing four haploid (*n*) cells.

Meiosis I: Paired chromosomes separate

① Chromosomes condense.
Prophase I

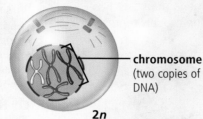

chromosome
(two copies of DNA)

2*n*

Chromosomes condense.
The nuclear membrane breaks down.

② Chromosome pairs line up.
Metaphase I

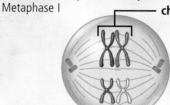

chromosome pair
(two homologs, each made of two chromatids)

Chromosomes arrange as pairs in the middle of the cell.

③ Chromosome pairs separate.
Anaphase I

The chromosomes of each pair separate and are pulled to opposite ends of the cell.

④ Two cells form.
Telophase I and Cytokinesis

The cell divides into two daughter cells. Each cell has half the usual number of chromosomes.

Meiosis II: Chromatids separate

⑤ Chromatids are still attached.
Prophase II

chromatids

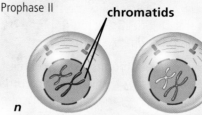

n   *n*

Each chromosome is made up of two chromatids.

⑥ Chromosomes line up.
Metaphase II

chromatids

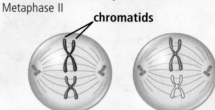

Chromosomes line up in the middle of the cell.

⑦ Chromatids separate.
Anaphase II

chromatids (single copy of DNA each)

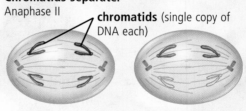

The chromatids separate and are pulled to opposite ends of the cell.

⑧ Haploid cells form.
Telophase II and Cytokinesis

n   *n*

n   *n*

Both cells divide, producing four haploid (*n*) cells.

INVESTIGATE Meiosis

How can you model meiosis?

PROCEDURE

(1) Use the markers to divide the poster board into two columns with four equal spaces in each column. Label the spaces as in the diagram on page 121.

(2) Tape a pair of pipe cleaners together in the middle to model a duplicated chromosome. Model a second duplicated chromosome. The models represent a pair of chromosomes—homologs.

(3) Place the models in the first space on the poster board. In your notebook, draw and label the chromatids as they appear during that phase. Describe what happens to the chromatids during that phase.

(4) Repeat step 3 for each phase in turn. Change the models as needed.

WHAT DO YOU THINK?

- When do the two chromatids of a chromosome separate?
- Why is each cell produced by meiosis called a haploid cell?

CHALLENGE When an egg cell forms, the cytoplasm from the original cell ends up in just one of the haploid cells. How could you model this?

SKILL FOCUS
Modeling (7.2.b)

MATERIALS
- markers
- poster board
- pipe cleaners
- transparent tape
- scissors

TIME
20 minutes

Combinations of Alleles

During meiosis, the pairs of chromosomes separate. Each gamete has a different combination of chromosomes. In other words, each gamete has just one set of alleles. During fertilization, the offspring receives one set of alleles from each parent. Thus, sexual reproduction produces offspring with different combinations of alleles.

Alleles are also shuffled into different combinations during the first step of meiosis I. A pair of chromosomes appears close together. Remember that a pair of chromosomes are homologs. Each has the same set of genes, but different alleles. When the two chromosomes are together, they can exchange segments of DNA. In other words, they can trade groups of alleles. This process is called crossing over. It provides an additional way for offspring to receive different combinations of alleles.

 What are two ways that offspring get different sets of alleles?

Meiosis and mitosis differ in some important ways.

You can see that the processes of meiosis and mitosis are similar in many ways. However, they also have several very important differences.

READING TiP

As you read about how meiosis and mitosis are different, refer to the diagrams on pages 83 and 121.

- Only cells that are to become gametes go through meiosis and cytokinesis. All other cells divide by mitosis and cytokinesis.

- A cell that divides by meiosis goes through two cell divisions, but the chromosomes are not copied before the second division. In mitosis, the chromosomes are always copied before division.

- Daughter cells produced by meiosis are haploid (*n*). They contain only half of the genetic material of the parent cell (one homolog from a chromosome pair).

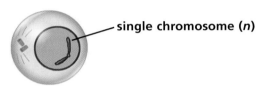

single chromosome (*n*)

cell produced by meiosis

- Daughter cells produced by mitosis contain exactly the same genetic material as the parent.

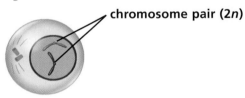

chromosome pair (2*n*)

cell produced by mitosis

CHECK YOUR READING What are four ways in which meiosis differs from mitosis?

4.3 Review

KEY CONCEPTS

1. What type of cell is needed for sexual reproduction? (7.2.a)

2. How many cell divisions occur during meiosis? Explain. (7.2.a)

3. In your own words, describe the differences between meiosis and mitosis. (7.2.a)

CRITICAL THINKING

4. **Compare and Contrast** What is divided during meiosis I? during meiosis II? Describe the difference.

5. **Communicate** Make a diagram to show how meiosis and fertilization are related.

⬥ CHALLENGE

6. **Synthesize** Why does meiosis II result in four *n* cells rather than four 2*n* cells?

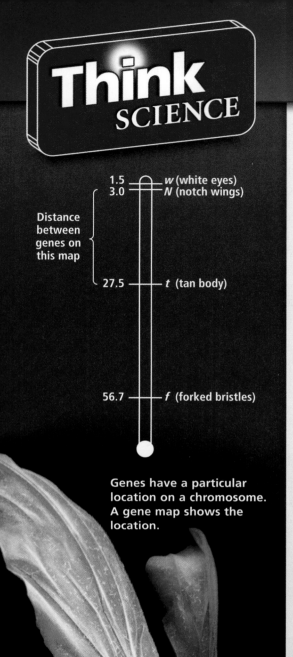

1.5 — w (white eyes)
3.0 — N (notch wings)

Distance between genes on this map

27.5 — t (tan body)

56.7 — f (forked bristles)

Genes have a particular location on a chromosome. A gene map shows the location.

Are Traits Linked?

Fruit flies are easy to breed in a laboratory and have many easily recognized genetic traits—different eye colors, body patterns, limb characteristics, and wing shapes. For these reasons, early geneticists studied fruit flies to learn how certain traits were inherited. Sometimes the experiments produced puzzling results. Here is an example from the laboratory of Thomas Hunt Morgan.

7.2.e Students know DNA (deoxyribonucleic acid) is the genetic material of living organisms and is located in the chromosomes of each cell.

▶ Observations

- In a generation of fruit flies, most red-eyed individuals were born with short wings.
- In the same generation, at least one fruit fly was born with red eyes and normal-sized wings.

▶ Hypotheses

Morgan and his coworkers made these hypotheses about genes and the patterns of inheritance:

- The gene for eye color and the gene for wing length are linked together on a fruit fly's chromosomes. These linked genes are usually inherited together.
- Sometimes during meiosis, one of the linked genes will "cross over" from one chromosome to its homolog. When this happens, a fruit fly will be born with one but not both of the linked alleles—red eyes, but not short wings.
- Genes that are farthest from each other on a chromosome are most likely to become separated. One may cross over during meiosis. Genes that are closest (linked) to each other are least likely to become separated.

▶ Further Discoveries

By studying the results of many breeding experiments, Morgan and his student, Alfred Sturtevant, could determine which genes were closest to and farthest from each other on the same chromosome. From this information, they drew a simple map showing the location of each of the fruit fly's linked genes.

▶ Determine Relevance

On Your Own Look at the map of a chromosome on this page. Which of the genes are most likely to be inherited together? Which genes might be most easily separated during meiosis?

As a Group Is it reasonable to think that information about a fruit fly's genes could apply to the genes of a human being? Discuss this topic in a small group and see if the group's members can agree.

Cells use DNA and RNA to make proteins.

CALIFORNIA Content Standard

7.2.e Students know DNA (deoxyribonucleic acid) is the genetic material of living organisms and is located in the chromosomes of each cell.

VOCABULARY

replication p. 127
RNA p. 128

BEFORE, you learned

- Traits pass from parents to offspring in predictable patterns
- Traits are passed on through genes
- In sexual reproduction, offspring get half their genes from each parent

NOW, you will learn

- How the structure of DNA stores information the cell needs
- How DNA is copied
- How RNA uses the information from DNA to make proteins

EXPLORE Templates (7.2.e)

How does a template work?

PROCEDURE

1. Write a set of rules to describe how the characters in line A relate to the characters in line B.

   A ☐ ◉ ◯ △ △ ☐

   B △ ◯ ◉ ☐ ☐ △

2. Place a piece of paper just under line C below. Use the rules from step 1 to produce a template—the corresponding pattern that goes with line C.

   C ◉ △ △ ☐ ◯ ◯

3. Give the rules and the template to a classmate to produce a copy of line C.

MATERIALS
- paper
- pencil

WHAT DO YOU THINK?
What is a template and how does it differ from a copy?

NOTE-TAKING STRATEGY
Take notes on the idea that DNA is the information molecule by using a strategy from an earlier chapter or one of your own.

DNA is the information molecule.

Recall that DNA is a molecule that stores information—the information needed to produce inherited traits. You could compare the information in DNA to the recipes in a cookbook. A recipe can tell you how to bake bread, prepare lasagna, or make a special soup. The cookbook, however, doesn't actually make any of these—you do. The "recipes" in the DNA "cookbook" carry all the information that a cell needs to function, to grow, and to divide. DNA doesn't do any of those things itself. DNA provides the recipes for a cell to make proteins. Proteins do most of the work of a cell and also make up much of the structure of a cell.

Proteins and Amino Acids

Proteins are large molecules that are made up of chains of amino acids. Twenty different amino acids combine in many different ways. Those combinations make up the thousands of different proteins found in the human body. Some proteins are small. For example, lysozyme is a protein that kills bacteria. It is made up of a sequence of 129 amino acids. Some proteins are large. For example, dystrophin is a huge protein in muscle cells. It is made up of 3685 amino acids.

CHECK YOUR READING What is the relationship between proteins and amino acids?

In order to produce a specific protein, a cell needs to put together the right sequence of amino acids. DNA stores the information that the cell needs to make each protein. Remember that the information is in the form of a code, or a set of rules and symbols. In this section, you will learn how the DNA code works. As you learn about the structure of the DNA molecule, think about the pieces as the symbols of a code. Think about the way the pieces fit together as the rules of a code.

DNA and the Genetic Code

The DNA molecule takes the shape of a double-stranded spiral. As you can see from the diagram at left, it is arranged like a twisted ladder. In Chapter 2, you read that the nucleic acids—DNA and RNA—are made of smaller pieces called nucleotides. These pieces make up the side rails and rungs of the ladder. One part of the nucleotide becomes part of one side rail. The other part, the nucleotide base, forms half of one rung. Two bases come together to form each rung, as one nucleotide base attaches to another from the opposite strand. You can see how the parts fit together in the diagram.

There are four different nucleotides in DNA, identified by their bases: adenine (A), thymine (T), cytosine (C), and guanine (G). Adenine always pairs with thymine (A-T) because they have sizes and shapes that match. Cytosine always pairs with guanine (C-G). The bases fit together like two pieces of a jigsaw puzzle. These bases are often referred to simply by their initials—A, T, C, and G. The phrase "all tigers can growl" may help you remember them.

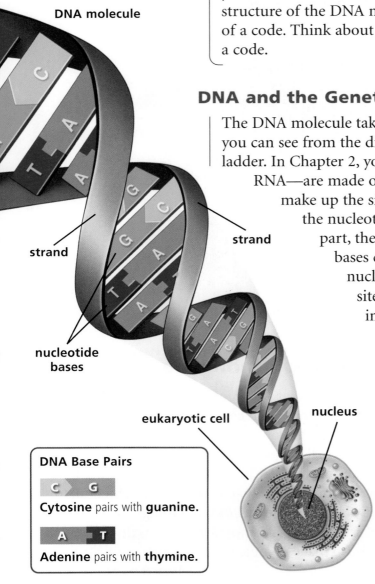

DNA molecule

strand

strand

nucleotide bases

eukaryotic cell

nucleus

DNA Base Pairs

C G

Cytosine pairs with **guanine.**

A T

Adenine pairs with **thymine.**

How does one molecule—DNA—contain information to produce a very different type of molecule—proteins? Recall that a gene is a segment of DNA. It provides the recipe for a cell to build a chain of amino acids. The sequence, or order, of bases in the gene forms a code. In a recipe for lasagna, the sequence of letters s-a-u-c-e or c-h-e-e-s-e tells you which ingredient to add next. In a similar way, a sequence of three bases tells a cell which amino acid to add next to the chain. The sequence of bases C-A-G is the code for the amino acid glutamine, while G-A-C is the code for aspartic acid.

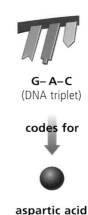

G– A–C
(DNA triplet)

codes for

aspartic acid
(an amino acid)

Replication produces two copies of DNA.

A cell usually has only one copy of each different molecule of DNA. During interphase, the DNA is loose in the nucleus. It is difficult to see with a light microscope. But before the cell divides, its DNA is copied, a process called **replication.** The chromosomes that condense at the start of mitosis have two copies of the DNA. Each daughter cell gets one copy.

The diagram below shows how one DNA molecule is replicated. First, the two strands of DNA separate. Then, each base on each strand is joined by the base of a nucleotide from the area around the DNA. C matches up with G, and A matches up with T. The result is two identical DNA molecules. Each molecule has one strand of old DNA and one strand of new DNA.

READING **TiP**

Replicate includes the root word meaning "to repeat."

Replication

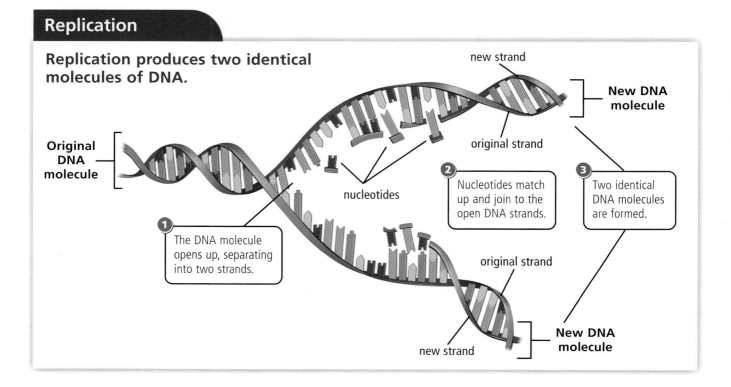

Replication produces two identical molecules of DNA.

new strand

New DNA molecule

original strand

Original DNA molecule

nucleotides

2 Nucleotides match up and join to the open DNA strands.

3 Two identical DNA molecules are formed.

1 The DNA molecule opens up, separating into two strands.

original strand

New DNA molecule

new strand

RESOURCE CENTER
CLASSZONE.COM
Learn more about DNA.

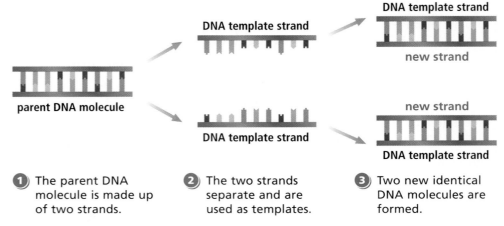

parent DNA molecule

DNA template strand

DNA template strand

DNA template strand
new strand

new strand
DNA template strand

1 The parent DNA molecule is made up of two strands.

2 The two strands separate and are used as templates.

3 Two new identical DNA molecules are formed.

READING TiP

Complementary has a root that means "to complete."

During replication, each strand of DNA is used as a template to produce a copy of the other strand. A template is a pattern or shape that produces a matching, or complementary, product. If you've ever made a plaster model of your hand, you've worked with a template. You press your hand into a soft material that leaves a mold of your hand. You then pour liquid plaster into the mold to produce a copy of your hand. The mold is a template. Its shape allows you to make a complementary shape that matches your hand.

 How is DNA copied?

RNA is needed to make proteins.

Remember that DNA contains information as a cookbook contains recipes. Cells need the DNA recipes to make chains of amino acids. DNA has just 4 bases—A, T, G, and C—to code for the 20 amino acids used by cells. It takes three bases to tell the cell which amino acid to add next to the chain. Therefore, the DNA code is called a triplet code.

To use a recipe, you must read it. You need to know how to connect the words in the recipe to the ingredients in your kitchen. To use the recipe in a gene, a cell must read the bases of DNA (deoxyribonucleic acid). It uses another nucleic acid called RNA to connect—physically—three bases to an amino acid. Ribonucleic acid, or **RNA,** uses the DNA's sequence of bases to link amino acids into chains that form proteins. RNA, like DNA, is made of nucleotides. Some RNA molecules have three bases on one end. The other end of the RNA molecule can attach to an amino acid. It can attach only to the amino acid that matches its sequence of three bases. So, RNA is the way the cell connects the code of DNA bases into the chains of amino acids needed to make proteins.

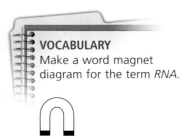
VOCABULARY
Make a word magnet diagram for the term *RNA*.

Types of RNA

Cooking means more than just reading a recipe. Three types of RNA are used to perform the tasks needed to make chains of amino acids. The three types are named after the tasks they perform.

You have just read about transfer RNA, or tRNA. It transfers an amino acid to the growing chain of amino acids. Transfer RNA has three bases on one end and can hold an amino acid on the other end.

But in your cells and other eukaryotic cells, the DNA is in the nucleus. The chains of amino acids are made in ribosomes in the cytoplasm. The DNA recipe is copied and then carried out of the nucleus into the cytoplasm. Messenger RNA, or mRNA, forms a copy of the recipe and carries this message to the ribosomes. Messenger RNA is like a short ribbon of a DNA strand.

Ribosomal DNA forms part of the ribosomes. It helps to match the tRNA molecules to the mRNA strip. It also helps to connect the amino acids into a chain and separate them from the tRNA.

In summary, the three types of RNA are:

- Messenger RNA (mRNA) forms a copy of the DNA recipe.
- Transfer RNA (tRNA) picks up amino acids and transfers them to where the chain is being made.
- Ribosomal RNA (rRNA) brings together the other two types of RNA to form the chain of amino acids.

The cell can use the three types of RNA again and again. Ribosomes are shorter than a strip of mRNA, so more than one ribosome can move along the mRNA at the same time. Thus, the cell can produce many identical chains of amino acids from a single strip of mRNA. The tRNA can carry one after another of its amino acids to the ribosomes. The ribosomes can act again and again on strips of mRNA.

CHECK YOUR READING What functions does RNA serve?

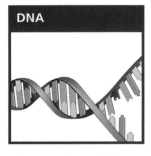

The genetic code is stored in DNA.

RNA matches an amino acid to a sequence of three bases.

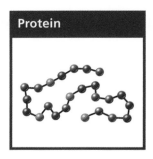

A chain of amino acids forms a protein.

Transcription

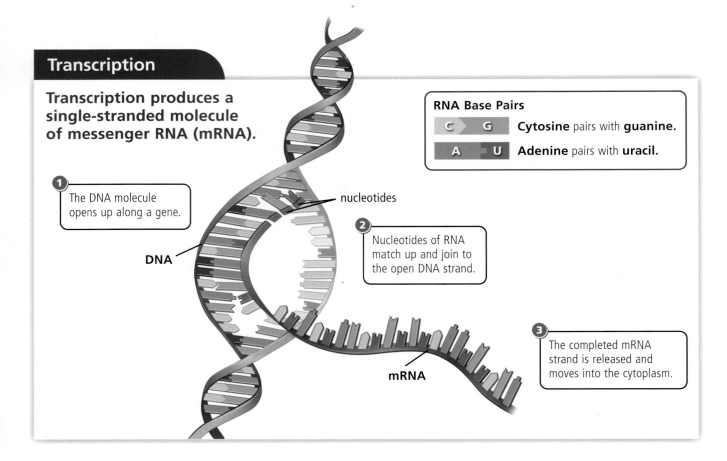

Transcription produces a single-stranded molecule of messenger RNA (mRNA).

RNA Base Pairs

C G   **Cytosine** pairs with **guanine.**

A U   **Adenine** pairs with **uracil.**

1 The DNA molecule opens up along a gene.

nucleotides

DNA

2 Nucleotides of RNA match up and join to the open DNA strand.

3 The completed mRNA strand is released and moves into the cytoplasm.

mRNA

▼ REMINDER

DNA base pairs:
  C-G, A-T
RNA base pairs:
  C-G, A-U

Transcription

The process of transferring information from DNA to mRNA is called transcription. The chemical structure of RNA is quite similar to the structure of DNA. Both are made up of four types of nucleotide bases. Three of the bases that make up RNA are the same as in DNA: guanine (G), cytosine (C), and adenine (A). However, the fourth base is uracil (U) rather than thymine.

During transcription, DNA is used as a template. Just one side of the DNA is used to make a complementary strand of mRNA. Only individual genes are transcribed, not a whole DNA molecule. The DNA opens up just where the gene is located. The two strands and their base pairs separate, as shown in the diagram above. Each base on the DNA template is then joined by a matching base of mRNA. Adenine pairs with uracil (A-U) and cytosine pairs with guanine (C-G).

Transcription is different from replication in some important ways. Only one strand of DNA is transcribed, which means that the mRNA molecule consists of a single strand. When transcription is complete, the mRNA is released. It does not stay attached to DNA. This means that many copies of mRNA can be made from the same gene in a short period of time. At the end of transcription, the DNA molecule closes.

△ **CHECK YOUR READING** How does DNA act as a template for messenger RNA?

How can you model transcription?

PROCEDURE

① Cut the ends of one color of sticky notes to represent DNA bases using the shapes on page 126. Label and arrange the DNA bases in the sequence ATCATTGAATGCA.

② Use the same color of sticky note to make the matching DNA sequence— TAGTAACTTACGT. Match the two sets of DNA bases.

③ Use the second color of sticky note to make the RNA bases A, U, C, and G (page 130). You will need 2–5 copies of each base.

④ Use the DNA sequence from Step 2 as a template. Line up the RNA bases that match the DNA to transcribe the DNA.

WHAT DO YOU THINK?

• What is your final RNA sequence?

• How does the RNA sequence compare with each DNA sequence?

CHALLENGE What might happen if all of the needed RNA bases are not available to make the correct sequence?

SKILL FOCUS
Modeling (7.2.e)

MATERIALS
• black marker
• sticky notes (2 colors)
• paper
• scissors

TIME
20 minutes

Translation

Replication and transcription pass along information that is coded in the language of nucleotide bases. To make a protein, a cell must translate this language of nucleotide bases into the language of amino acids. The assembly of amino acids in their proper sequence is called translation. Translation takes place in the cytoplasm of a cell. It involves all three types of RNA—mRNA, tRNA, and rRNA.

Proteins are made on ribosomes, structures that are made up of RNA and proteins. Recall that DNA is like a cookbook for making different proteins. The mRNA is a recipe for making one protein. The ribosome is the place where the cooking gets done. In this analogy, tRNA gathers the ingredients, which are amino acids.

A tRNA molecule is shaped in such a way that one end of it can attach to a specific amino acid. The other end of tRNA has a series of three bases that can match a series of three bases on a molecule of mRNA. Transfer RNA does the actual translation of bases to amino acid when it matches up with mRNA. The ribosomes connect the amino acids and remove them from the tRNA molecules. The diagram on page 132 shows the whole process.

DNA

Transcription

RNA

Translation

Protein

Translation

The assembling of amino acids to form a protein occurs in the cytoplasm.

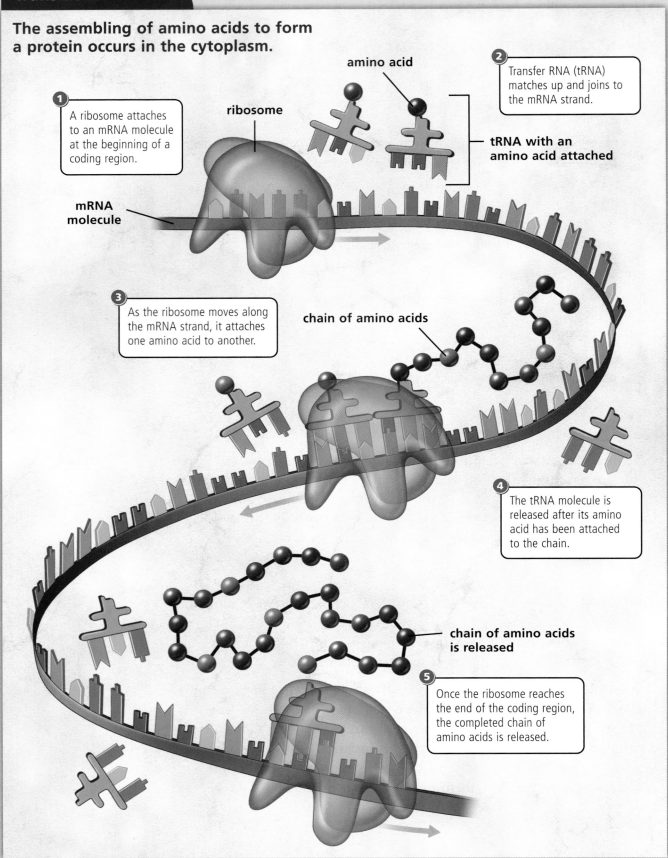

amino acid

ribosome

1 A ribosome attaches to an mRNA molecule at the beginning of a coding region.

mRNA molecule

2 Transfer RNA (tRNA) matches up and joins to the mRNA strand.

tRNA with an amino acid attached

3 As the ribosome moves along the mRNA strand, it attaches one amino acid to another.

chain of amino acids

4 The tRNA molecule is released after its amino acid has been attached to the chain.

chain of amino acids is released

5 Once the ribosome reaches the end of the coding region, the completed chain of amino acids is released.

Translation begins when a ribosome attaches to the beginning of an mRNA molecule.

 A tRNA molecule carrying an amino acid joins up to a matching triplet on mRNA on the ribosome.

 The ribosome attaches one amino acid to another as the ribosome moves along the mRNA molecule.

 Each tRNA molecule is released after the amino acid it carries is attached to the growing chain of amino acids.

 The ribosome completes translation when it reaches the end of the code for the protein. The new protein molecule, made of a chain of amino acids, is released.

 CHECK YOUR READING Describe how a cell makes a chain of amino acids.

READING TiP
Refer to the diagram on page 132 as you read the text. The numbers in the text match the numbers in the diagram.

The process of making proteins is basically the same in all cells. The flow of information in a cell goes from DNA to RNA to protein. But if DNA's function is to store the codes for proteins, how are DNA and heredity related? Proteins are responsible for an organism's traits. From height to eye color to the shape of your nose, you are a product of proteins.

VISUALIZATION
CLASSZONE.COM
Watch an animation of how proteins are made.

Not all proteins are made at all times or by all cells. The time at which a protein is made is very important. Some proteins are made only during early stages of an organism's development. These proteins have functions such as helping limbs grow in the right places and controlling the types of cells in organs. As cells become differentiated, they use different recipes in the DNA cookbook to carry out their different functions.

 CHECK YOUR READING How does DNA affect heredity?

4.4 Review

KEY CONCEPTS

1. Describe the shape of the DNA molecule and how nucleotide bases fit into that structure. (7.2.e)

2. What is a protein and what is it made of? (7.2.e)

3. Identify three types of RNA involved in protein synthesis and briefly describe what they do. (7.2.e)

CRITICAL THINKING

4. **Infer** What might happen if the wrong amino acid is attached to a tRNA molecule?

5. **Apply** Copy the following sequence of DNA bases: A-T-C-A-G-G. Write the complementary mRNA and tRNA sequences for this.

CHALLENGE

6. **Synthesize** Study the sequences you wrote for question 5. How does the tRNA sequence compare with the original DNA sequence?

4 Chapter Review

the **BIG** idea

In sexual reproduction, genes are passed from parents to offspring in predictable patterns.

KEY CONCEPTS SUMMARY

1 **Living things inherit traits in patterns.**

Offspring inherit **alleles**, which are forms of **genes**, from their parents. Alleles can be **dominant** or **recessive.** The alleles you have are your **genotype**; the observable characteristics that come from your genotype are your **phenotype.**

alleles

a gene

VOCABULARY
sexual reproduction
  p. 102
gene p. 102
heredity p. 102
allele p. 103
phenotype p. 106
genotype p. 106
dominant p. 107
recessive p. 107

---

2 **Patterns of heredity can be predicted.**

Punnett squares show possible outcomes of heredity. Percentages can be used with Punnett squares to express the **probability** of each possible outcome.

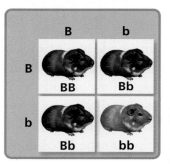

B = black fur
b = brown fur

VOCABULARY
Punnett square p. 110
probability p. 112

---

3 **DNA is divided during meiosis.**

Meiosis is a type of cell division needed for sexual reproduction. During meiosis, cells divide twice to produce **gametes.** Male and female gametes join when **fertilization** occurs.

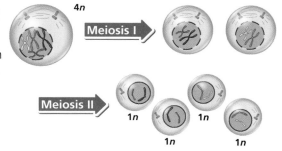

VOCABULARY
gamete p. 118
egg p. 118
sperm p. 118
fertilization p. 118
meiosis p. 119

---

4 **Cells use DNA and RNA to make proteins.**

DNA contains a code that enables a cell to make RNA and proteins. Replication copies the code before a cell divides.

- DNA's triplet code enables a cell to code for proteins.
- A cell's mRNA, tRNA, and ribosomes translate the code into a sequence of amino acids.
- The amino acids form a protein needed for cell function.

VOCABULARY
replication p. 127
RNA p. 128

Reviewing Vocabulary

Make a frame game diagram for each of the vocabulary terms listed below. Write the term in the center. Frame it with definitions, examples, descriptions, parts, or pictures.

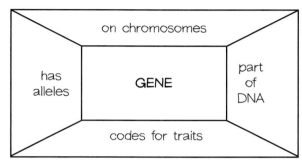

1. allele
2. heredity
3. sexual reproduction
4. probability

Describe how the following pairs of terms are related. Underline each vocabulary term in your answers.

5. phenotype, genotype

6. dominant, recessive

7. mitosis, meiosis

8. gene, allele

9. egg, gamete

Reviewing Key Concepts

Multiple Choice *Choose the letter of the best answer.*

10. Which is an example of an acquired trait? (7.2.c)
    a. eye color
    c. blood type
    b. hair color
    d. ability to read

11. The unit of heredity that determines a particular trait is known as a (7.2.c)
    a. chromosome
    c. gene
    b. gamete
    d. phenotype

12. A human female has which set of sex chromosomes? (7.2.b)
    a. XX
    c. XY
    b. YY
    d. XxYy

13. If one parent has two dominant alleles and the other parent has two recessive alleles, the offspring will have (7.2.d)
    a. the recessive phenotype
    b. the dominant phenotype
    c. two dominant alleles
    d. two recessive alleles

14. Cells for reproduction that contain half the usual number of chromosomes are (7.2.d)
    a. fertilized egg cells   c. alleles
    b. gametes   d. diploid cells

15. The process that produces haploid (*n*) cells is known as (7.2.a)
    a. mitosis   c. meiosis
    b. reproduction   d. fertilization

16. What happens when fertilization occurs? (7.2.a)
    a. Two 2*n* cells combine in a new cell.
    b. Two *n* cells combine into a new cell.
    c. Two 2*n* daughter cells are produced.
    d. Two *n* daughter cells are produced.

17. Which does **not** occur during meiosis? (7.2.a)
    a. Four haploid daughter cells are produced.
    b. Two diploid daughter cells are produced.
    c. Only cells that are gametes are produced.
    d. Daughter cells are produced that contain half the chromosomes of the parent cell.

18. What happens during replication? (7.2.a)
    a. DNA is copied.
    b. RNA is copied.
    c. Ribosomes are made.
    d. Proteins are made.

Short Answer *Write a short answer to each question.*

19. In what case would a recessive allele be expressed in the phenotype of an offspring? (7.2.d)

20. Describe the purpose of a Punnett square. (7.2.b)

21. How does the number of chromosomes in a person's gametes compare with the number of chromosomes in the body cells? (7.2.d)

Thinking Critically

22. ANALYZE How was Mendel able to infer that each offspring of two parent pea plants had a pair of factors for a particular trait? (7.2.b)

23. COMMUNICATE Briefly describe how heredity works. Use the terms *gene* and *chromosome* in your explanation. (7.2.c)

24. APPLY Can a dwarf pea plant ever have a dominant allele for height? Explain. (7.2.d)

25. ANALYZE How is a Punnett square used to show the genotype and phenotype of both parents and possible offspring? (7.2.d)

26. APPLY In rabbits, the allele for black fur is dominant over the allele for white fur. Two black rabbits have a litter of eight offspring. Six of the offspring have black fur and two have white fur. What are the genotypes of the parents? Explain. (7.2.d)

Use the Punnett square below to answer the next two questions.

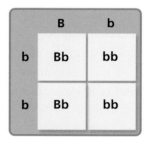

27. CALCULATE A parent has one dominant allele for black fur (B) and one recessive allele for white fur (b). The other parent has two recessive alleles for white fur. In this cross, what is the chance that an offspring will be born with black fur? with white fur? (7.2.d)

28. CALCULATE What is the percentage chance that an offspring will have the recessive phenotype? (7.2.d)

29. EVALUATE A person who carries a gene for a genetic disorder may not get the disorder. How can that be? (7.2.b)

30. EVALUATE How might selective breeding of a type of animal limit genetic diversity within the breed? (7.2.b)

31. ANALYZE This diagram shows the process of fertilization. Which of the cells shown are haploid? Explain. (7.2.a)

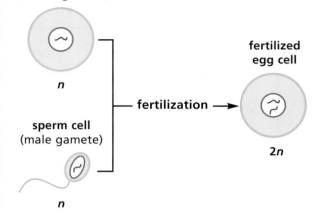

32. SUMMARIZE Briefly describe what happens during meiosis I and meiosis II. What is the function of meiosis? (7.2.a)

33. SEQUENCE List the steps in making a protein. Start with a gene on a DNA molecule. Include the chemicals involved in each step. (7.2.e)

the **BIG** idea

34. INFER Look again at the photograph on pages 98–99. Now that you have finished the chapter, how would you change or add details to your answer to the question on the photograph? (7.2.b)

35. SYNTHESIZE Write one or more paragraphs explaining how Mendel's observations of pea plants contributed to the study of modern genetics. Use these terms in your explanation. (7.2.d)

gene	genotype	dominant
allele	phenotype	recessive
trait		

UNIT PROJECTS

Evaluate all the data, results, and information from your project folder. Prepare to present your project. Be ready to answer questions posed by your classmates about your results.

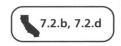
Analyzing Data

7.2.b, 7.2.d

The table below shows the phenotypes of pea-plant offspring.

Phenotypes of Pea Plants	
Phenotype	**Number of Offspring**
Regular (D)	12
Dwarf (d)	4

Use the table to answer the questions below.

1. What percentage of pea plants showed the dominant phenotype?
   a. 100 percent
   b. 75 percent
   c. 50 percent
   d. 25 percent

2. What percentage of pea plants showed the recessive phenotype?
   a. 100 percent
   b. 75 percent
   c. 50 percent
   d. 25 percent

3. What is the genotype of the dwarf pea plants?
   a. DD
   b. Dd
   c. dd
   d. cannot tell

4. What are the possible genotypes of the regular pea plants?
   a. DD and dd
   b. DD and Dd
   c. Dd and dd
   d. cannot tell

5. What are the genotypes of the parents?
   a. Dd and dd
   b. DD and Dd
   c. Dd and Dd
   d. dd and dd

6. Based on the data in the table, which statement is true?
   a. If both parents were Dd, then none of the offspring would be dwarf.
   b. If both parents were DD, then none of the offspring would be dwarf.
   c. If one parent were Dd and the other were dd, then none of the offspring would be regular.
   d. If one parent were DD and the other parent were dd, then none of the offspring would be regular.

Extended Response

Answer the two questions below in detail.

7. Traits for a widow's peak hairline (W) and curly hair (C) are controlled by dominant alleles. A family of eight has three children with widow's peaks. All six children have curly hair. Use your knowledge of heredity to write one or two paragraphs explaining the possible genotypes of the parents.

8. A student predicts that dominant traits are more common in the general population than traits with recessive alleles. Describe a procedure you might use to test this idea.

THE STORY OF Genetics

The human genome project, DNA evidence in criminal cases, cloning—news about genetics is everywhere. Some of the most exciting research in science today involves genes. The timeline shows that some important concepts that underlie the study of genetics were discovered hundreds of years ago. You will notice the influence of two major advances in technology—the development of the microscope during the 1600s, and the development of computer technology during the second half of the 1900s. The boxes below the timeline show how technology has led to new understandings and to applications of those understandings.

1674
Cells Are Everywhere
Anton van Leeuwenhoek uses a microscope to study pond water. He discovers the water is full of microscopic organisms, some made of single cells. These drawings show some of what he saw.

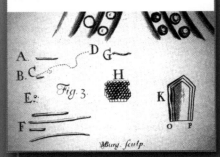

1665
Cells Discovered
Robert Hooke uses a microscope to study plant parts. What he sees and then records in this drawing are tiny repeating units, which he calls cells.

EVENTS

1650   1660   1670   1680

APPLICATIONS AND TECHNOLOGY

APPLICATION

Corn in Every Shape and Size

Early Native Americans grew 700 different kinds of popcorn. Their popcorn plants had big, hard seeds that exploded when they were heated. People who didn't want to have to explode their corn to eat it chose plants with softer seeds and grew them, and then chose the softest of those seeds to plant. Over hundreds of years, by choosing which plants to grow, people produced what we now eat as corn on the cob.

TECHNOLOGY

Seeing into the Cell

Single-glass lenses, such as the one Leeuwenhoek used, were available as long ago as 1267. The compound microscope was first made in 1595, but it was over 200 years before this technology provided clear images. These microscopes all used light to illuminate objects. Eventually, light microscopes could magnify objects up to 2000 $\times$.

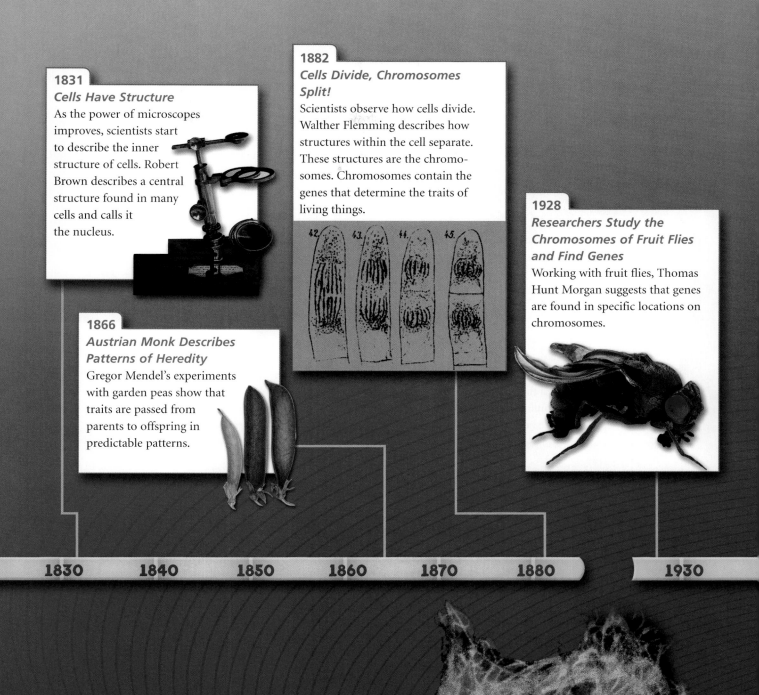

1831
Cells Have Structure
As the power of microscopes improves, scientists start to describe the inner structure of cells. Robert Brown describes a central structure found in many cells and calls it the nucleus.

1882
Cells Divide, Chromosomes Split!
Scientists observe how cells divide. Walther Flemming describes how structures within the cell separate. These structures are the chromosomes. Chromosomes contain the genes that determine the traits of living things.

1928
Researchers Study the Chromosomes of Fruit Flies and Find Genes
Working with fruit flies, Thomas Hunt Morgan suggests that genes are found in specific locations on chromosomes.

1866
Austrian Monk Describes Patterns of Heredity
Gregor Mendel's experiments with garden peas show that traits are passed from parents to offspring in predictable patterns.

1830 1840 1850 1860 1870 1880 1930

Cells have a highly organized structure. Color dyes are used to help us see the different parts of a cell.

1944
DNA—Genetic Material
Researchers studying *Streptococcus* transformation find that bacterial cells get their characteristics from DNA.

1973
DNA Recombined
In an amazing breakthrough, scientists have cut DNA from two different sources and recombined the DNA. The new DNA molecule replicates when placed inside a bacterium. Such bacteria can be used to make proteins that are useful to humans.

1951
Scientists Capture Image of DNA
Scientists searching for the secret of DNA structure get an enormous clue when Rosalind Franklin uses x-ray crystallography to create an image of DNA. Maurice Wilkins, James Watson, and Francis Crick are awarded the Nobel Prize in 1962 for building a model of the DNA double helix molecule.

1984
Chinese Scientists Alter Fish!
In an effort to produce fast-growing fish for food, a team working with Dr. Zuoyan Zhu makes the first genetically modified (GM) fish.

1950   1960   1970   1980

TECHNOLOGY

Seeing Molecules
In the 1930s, a microscope came into use that focuses a beam of electrons, instead of a beam of light, on an object. Now we can see things as small as the molecules inside cells.

The image of the chromosome at left was made using an electron microscope.

APPLICATION

DNA Frees Innocent Prisoner
Kevin Green was convicted of murder and spent 16 years in prison. While he was in jail, the California Department of Justice created a DNA database that contained the DNA fingerprints of many other convicted felons. When Green's defenders compared the DNA found at the murder scene with DNA fingerprints in the database, they found that it matched someone else's DNA fingerprint. The real murderer confessed, and Green is now a free man, thanks to genetics.

1984
Living Things Have Genetic Fingerprints

Human fingers have their own unique fingerprints. In a similar way, patterns in the DNA of each person are unique. These DNA fingerprints are compared here.

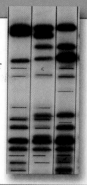

2000
Scientists Sequence Human Genome

Two groups of researchers, Celera and the Human Genome Project, publish the first draft of the sequence of DNA for all the chromosomes in a human cell.

 RESOURCE CENTER
CLASSZONE.COM
Find recent genetics updates.

1990   2000   Today

SPOTLIGHT on
DALE EMEAGWALI

Microbiologist Dale Emeagwali's goal is to answer fundamental questions about cellular processes. Her work has contributed to the fields of microbiology, molecular biology, and biochemistry. In 1996 she received the Scientist of the Year award from the National Technical Association, which honors researchers whose work has benefited many people.

Emeagwali's recent research has focused on cancer. Oncogenes are genes that transform normal cells into cancerous tumor cells. Emeagwali demonstrated a way to suppress the Ras oncogene, the most common gene in human cancers. The goal is to prevent cancerous tumors from forming. Emeagwali's work may lead to better treatments for cancer.

APPLICATION
Saved by a Gene Donor

In 1986 a baby girl named Ashanti DeSilva was born. One single mistake in her DNA meant that Ashanti's body could not make an important disease-fighting protein.

In 1981 researchers had figured out how to move a working gene from one mammal to another. Ashanti became the first person ever to receive a gene from someone else. Ashanti's doctors injected working copies of the affected gene into some of her white blood cells. Now her white blood cells work properly. Doctors and researchers are trying to apply the same techniques to other genetic disorders. There is still much work to be done.

ACTIVITIES

Reliving History

Use a hand lens or microscope to study a sample of water from a pond or puddle. Does your water sample contain structures similar to those drawn by Leeuwenhoek in 1674?

Writing About Science: Biography

Sharing information is important to scientific discovery. Learn more about individuals or groups involved in the discovery of DNA structure or sequencing the human genome. How important was cooperation in their work?

Earth and Life History

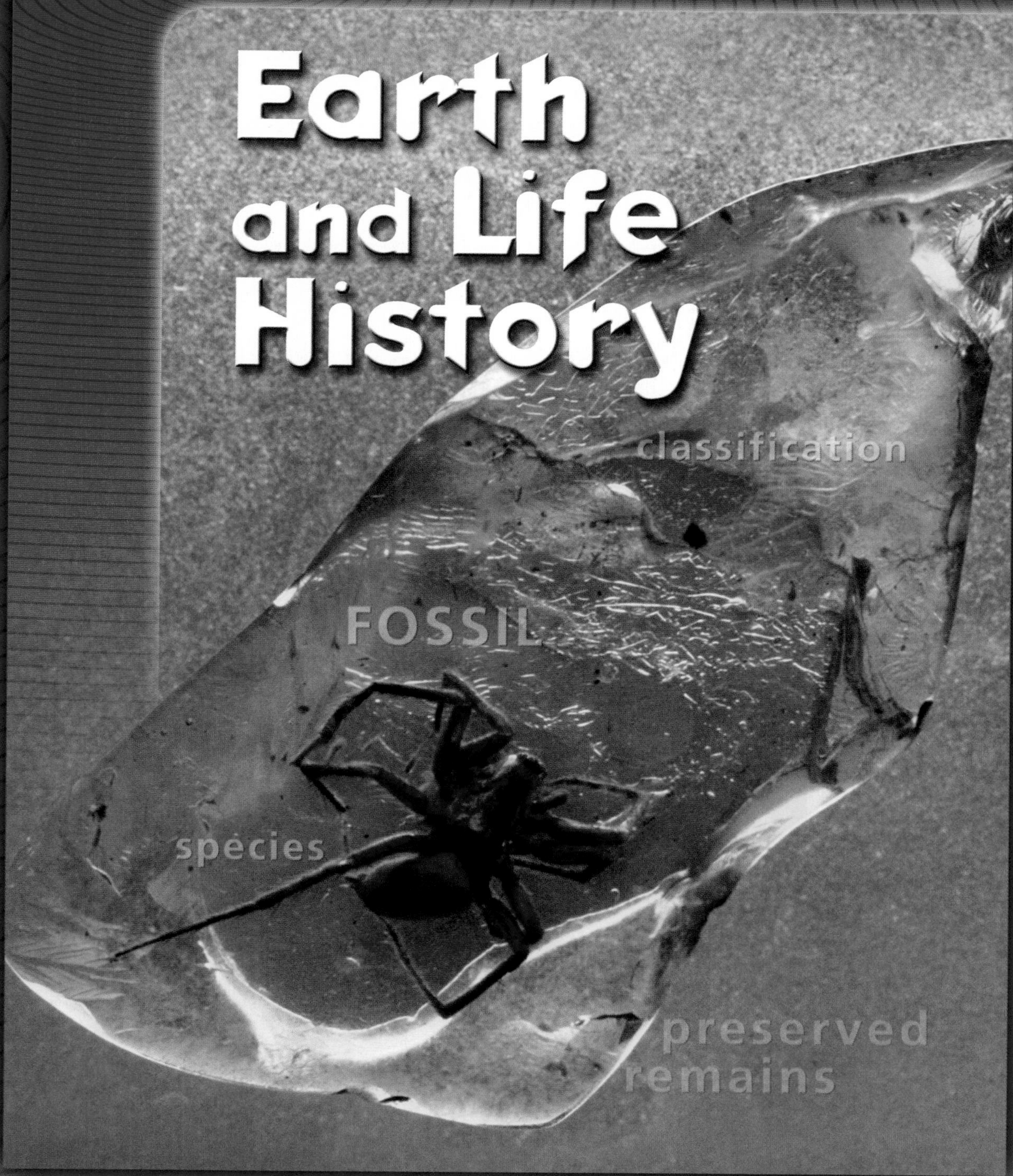

classification

FOSSIL

species

preserved remains

Contents Overview

Life By Degrees

California Content Standards

7.3.e Students know that extinction of a species occurs when the environment changes and the adaptive characteristics of a species are insufficient for its survival.

7.4.b Students know the history of life on Earth has been disrupted by major catastrophic events, such as major volcanic eruptions or the impacts of asteroids.

7.4.g Students know how to explain significant developments and extinctions of plant and animal life on the geologic time scale.

What happens when Earth's climate changes? Scientists are studying how climate change has influenced the evolution of life on Earth.

SCIENTIFIC AMERICAN FRONTIERS

Learn about how climate change affected life on Earth. See the video "Noah's Snowball."

Climate and Life

Throughout its history, Earth's climate has changed many times. Often the changes are gradual. They may seem small. However, an average global temperature change of just a few degrees can have a large impact on climate. Small changes in climate then cause big changes for plants and animals.

Changes of the Earth are recorded in layers of rocks and ice and the fossils within them. For example, scientists get a sense for Earth's climate at different times in the distant past by looking at fossils, the remains and traces of living things. If scientists find fossils of tropical plants in places near the arctic circle, then they may conclude that the climate in those places was different in the past.

Scientists have found that warmer climates have a greater diversity of organisms. One researcher examined fossils of tiny organisms called phytoplankton (FY-toh-PLANK-tuhn). During cooler climate periods, there were fewer types of phytoplankton than during warmer periods. The same is true for other organisms. Peter Wilf and Conrad Labandeira studied fossil plants. They were especially interested in the marks they found on the plants. The marks were left by plant-eating animals who bit the leaves. The warmer the climate was, the more types of plants there were—and the more kinds of animals were eating the plants.

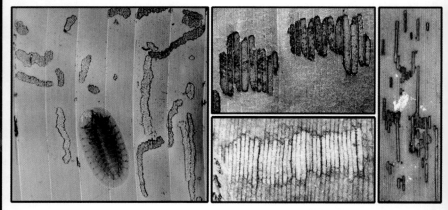

SOURCE: Images © 2000 AAAS

The chew marks of the hispine beetle larva on living ginger in Panama (left) look similar to fossilized chew marks found in Wyoming (three photos right).

Before-and-after photographs of the sky show that distinct bands appeared due to dust and ash from the 1991 volcanic eruption of Mt. Pinatubo in the Philippines.

Mass Extinction

Several times in Earth's past, many types of animals and plants have disappeared in a relatively short time. These events are called mass extinctions. While we don't know for sure what caused most of them, many scientists think climate change plays a role in mass extinctions.

The largest mass extinction in Earth's history happened at the end of the Permian (PER-mee-uhn) Period about 248 million years ago. Scientists estimate that 90–95 percent of animal species that lived in the water died out. About three-fourths of the vertebrates, or animals with backbones, living on land died out too.

Turn of Events

What caused this extinction? Using fossils, scientists have concluded that Earth's temperatures dropped. Material from erupting volcanoes may have blocked sunlight long enough to cool Earth. The low temperatures and lack of sunlight may have killed plants and animals.

Scientist Peter Ward has been studying the Permian extinction. He looked at ancient African rivers and found evidence that rivers had became clogged with soil. Plants normally holding soil in place may have been wiped out, causing the soil on the riverbanks to loosen. The plant extinction would also have led to animal extinction.

SCIENTIFIC AMERICAN FRONTIERS

View the "Noah's Snowball" segment of your Scientific American Frontiers video to learn about another hypothesis of how climate change affected life on Earth.

IN THIS SCENE FROM THE VIDEO ▶
Fossil hunters examine evidence of early life in China.

DEEP FREEZE Can you imagine what Earth would be like if it were completely covered in ice? Geologists Paul Hoffman and Dan Schrag suggest Earth was frozen over until about 600 million years ago. They think Earth's average temperature changed by just a few degrees, but it was enough to make the ice caps cover the planet. Only bacteria, kept warm by volcanoes, survived. And it was the volcanoes that changed the climate again, say Hoffman and Schrag. Volcanic eruptions caused the ice to melt. The scientists think this change might have taken only a hundred years. Not everyone agrees with the snowball hypothesis, but it could explain why new forms of life began to appear.

What Hit Them?

Not all scientists agree about what caused the Permian extinction. If an asteroid hit Earth, it would throw massive amounts of dust into the air. This could block sunlight and cool Earth's surface. An increase in volcanic eruptions is another possible cause.

The most famous extinction took place at the end of the Cretaceous Period. Winter temperatures may have followed an asteroid impact. This change would have caused many land animals—including dinosaurs—to become extinct.

Some species thrive in a new climate. They spread out and, over time, evolve to fill empty niches or unique roles in the environment. For example, before the Cretaceous extinction, the only mammals were small. After the dinosaurs became extinct, mammals filled the roles of large plant-eaters and meat-eaters.

Even today, climate changes continued. Earth's average temperature rose about half a degree Celsius in the twentieth century. Studying how past climate changes shaped life helps scientists predict how it may affect us in the future.

A large plant-eating mammal, *Chalicotherium grande*, roamed Asia millions of years ago.

? UNANSWERED Questions

Scientists have learned a lot about climate change and mass extinctions by studying fossils. There are many questions still to be answered.

- What caused changes in Earth's climates?
- What else might have caused mass extinctions?
- How might climate change affect life on Earth in the future?

UNIT PROJECTS

As you study this unit, work alone or with a group on one of the projects listed below. Use the bulleted steps to guide your project.

Museum Display (7.3.e)

What organisms survived the Permian extinction? What organisms went extinct?

- Create a museum display using art and text.
- Use visuals to show the organisms and the modern relatives that have close connections to them.

Design a Robot (7.3.e)

Often, scientists design robots to study dangerous or distant locations.

- Design an artificial robot that would be well-adapted to survive an event that causes a mass extinction.
- Explain why the design would help the robot remain in operation.

Species over Time (7.3.e)

Find out more about species that have gone extinct during recorded history.

- Choose one species that is now extinct.
- Present a timeline giving a history of that species.
- Describe what some of its ancestors and surviving related organisms are.
- Describe when it was last seen. Include some of the possible reasons for why it died out.

CAREER CENTER
CLASSZONE.COM

Learn more about careers in paleontology.

Views of Earth's Past

the BIG idea

Rocks, fossils, and other types of natural evidence tell Earth's story.

Key Concepts

SECTION
① Rocks provide a timeline for Earth.
Learn how information from rocks tells about Earth's past.

SECTION
② The geologic time scale shows Earth's past.
Learn about 4.6 billion years of Earth's history.

SECTION
③ Earth's past is revealed in rocks and fossils.
Learn about different kinds of fossils and what they tell about Earth's past.

🌐 **California ClassZone**

CLASSZONE.COM

Chapter 5 online resources: Content Review, Visualization, three Resource Centers, Math Tutorial, Test Practice

What does this footprint tell you about the animal that left it?

EXPLORE (the BIG idea)

How Long Has That Been There?

> **7.4.a** Students know Earth processes today are similar to those that occurred in the past and slow geologic processes have large cumulative effects over long periods of time.

Look inside a cabinet or refrigerator and choose one item to investigate. See if you can tell where the item was made, where it was purchased, how long it has been in the cabinet or refrigerator, and when it was last used.

Observe and Think How did you figure out the history of the item? What information did you use?

Internet Activity: Earth's History

> **7.3.c** Students know how independent lines of evidence from geology, fossils, and comparative anatomy provide the bases for the theory of evolution.

Go to **ClassZone.com** to learn about the story of the dinosaurs. Read about the evidence scientists used and how they used it to figure out what happened 65 million years ago.

Observe and Think What types of evidence did scientists use?

NSTA
scilinks.org
SCiLINKS

Earth's Story **Code: MDL055**

Getting Ready to Learn

◀ CONCEPT REVIEW

- Earth's surface is made up of large plates that interact.
- Unicellular organisms tend to be small while multicellular organisms can be larger and have specialized parts.

◀ VOCABULARY REVIEW

See Glossary for definitions.

fossil

igneous rock

metamorphic rock

sedimentary rock

CONTENT REVIEW
CLASSZONE.COM

Review concepts and vocabulary.

▶ TAKING NOTES

OUTLINE

As you read, copy the headings on your paper in the form of an outline. Then add notes in your own words that summarize what you read.

VOCABULARY STRATEGY

Write each new vocabulary term in the center of a **four square** diagram. Write notes in the squares around the term. Include a definition, some characteristics, and some examples. If possible, write some things that are not examples.

See the Note-Taking Handbook on pages R45–R51.

SCIENCE NOTEBOOK

I. Rocks provide a timeline for Earth.
- A. Changes in rocks provide a record of the past.
- B. There are three main types of rocks.
    1. igneous
    2. sedimentary
    3. metamorphic
- C. Layers of sedimentary rocks show relative age.
    1. igneous rock and sedimentary layers
    2. index fossils

Definition	Characteristics
fossils of organisms that were common, lived in many areas, existed during specific time spans	widespread, found in many parts of world

INDEX FOSSIL

Example	Nonexamples
Arnioceras semicostatum	footprints

KEY CONCEPT

Rocks provide a timeline for Earth.

⬤ CALIFORNIA
Content Standards

7.4.c Students know that the rock cycle includes the formation of new sediment and rocks and that rocks are often found in layers, with the oldest generally on the bottom.

7.4.d Students know that evidence from geologic layers and radioactive dating indicates Earth is approximately 4.6 billion years old and that life on this planet has existed for more than 3 billion years.

VOCABULARY

relative age p. 151
rock cycle p. 152
index fossil p. 155
absolute age p. 156
half-life p. 156

READING TiP

A geologist is a person who studies the origin, history, and structure of Earth.

◁ BEFORE, you learned

- Living things exchange materials with their environments
- Living things have different characteristics that they pass on to their offspring

▷ NOW, you will learn

- How one type of rock can change to another
- What the ages of rock layers reveal about Earth
- How the relative and absolute ages of rocks are determined

THINK ABOUT

How do you know what happened?

There are clues of past events all around you. Look at the tire tracks in the photograph to the right. How many different tires do you think made the tracks? Can you tell which tracks were made earlier and which tracks were made later?

Changes in rocks provide a record of the past.

Until the early 1900s, geologists didn't have a way to figure out the exact ages of objects that existed in Earth's past. Instead, they reconstructed Earth's story based on the relative ages of different clues, such as rocks, fossils, and other natural evidence. **Relative age** is the age of an event or object in relation to other events or objects. You probably know the relative ages for many things in your life. For example, if a friend tells you that she has an older brother and a younger brother, you know the relative ages of her brothers even if you don't know their exact ages.

Today, there are still many parts of Earth's history that cannot be given exact ages. Determining relative age continues to be an important way of piecing together the puzzle of Earth's past. Rocks provide much of the information needed to fit the pieces of the puzzle together.

The three main types of rocks form in different ways.

Remember that the three types of rocks are classified by how they form.

- Igneous rock forms when molten rock cools and becomes solid. This type of rock can form inside Earth or on the surface. Igneous rocks that originally formed deep inside Earth can reach Earth's surface over time. Deep rocks may be raised closer to the surface when mountains are pushed up. At the same time, other processes can wear away the rocks that cover the deeper rocks.

- Sedimentary rock usually forms when pieces of older rocks, plants, and other loose material get pressed or cemented together. This loose material, called sediment, is often carried by wind or water. Layers are formed from the buildup of the loose material. Sometimes, new minerals grow in the spaces within the material, cementing it together. Sedimentary rocks can also form in other ways.

- Metamorphic rock forms when heat or pressure causes existing rocks to change in structure, texture, or mineral composition. The new conditions can cause the structure of the original rock to change. New minerals grow in place of the original minerals. The rock becomes a metamorphic rock. Like igneous rocks, metamorphic rocks can be raised to Earth's surface over time.

 What are the three rock types? How do they form?

When you want to describe a person you can depend on, you may say that he or she is "like a rock." That's the way people think of rocks—as solid and unchanging. Nevertheless, rocks do change. But the changes usually occur over a huge span of time—millions to hundreds of millions of years. The **rock cycle** is the set of natural processes that form, change, break down, and re-form rocks.

A cycle is made up of repeating events that happen one after another. This does not mean that rocks move through the rock cycle in a particular order. As the illustration on page 153 shows, a rock at any point in the cycle can change in two or three different ways. Like all cycles, the rock cycle has no beginning or ending. It goes on continually.

 What questions do you have about how rocks change through the rock cycle?

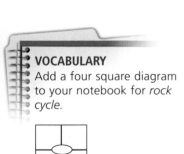

VOCABULARY
Add a four square diagram to your notebook for *rock cycle.*

The Rock Cycle

In the rock cycle, natural processes change each type of rock into other types. Rocks can take many paths through the rock cycle and change into other types in any order.

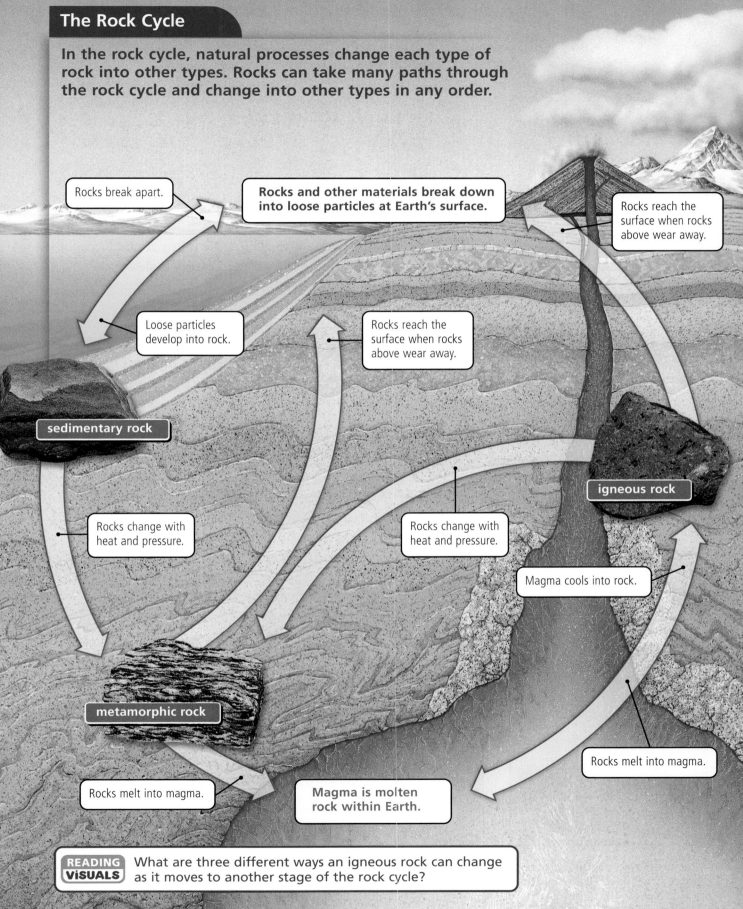

Rocks break apart.

Rocks and other materials break down into loose particles at Earth's surface.

Rocks reach the surface when rocks above wear away.

Loose particles develop into rock.

Rocks reach the surface when rocks above wear away.

sedimentary rock

igneous rock

Rocks change with heat and pressure.

Rocks change with heat and pressure.

Magma cools into rock.

metamorphic rock

Rocks melt into magma.

Rocks melt into magma.

Magma is molten rock within Earth.

READING VISUALS What are three different ways an igneous rock can change as it moves to another stage of the rock cycle?

younger

older

Because sedimentary rock forms in layers, the oldest layer of undisturbed sedimentary rock will be on the bottom and the youngest on top.

Layers of sedimentary rock show relative age.

Sedimentary rock layers contain information about the relative ages of events and objects in Earth's past. Sedimentary rocks can form from the sediments that settle to the bottom of lakes, rivers, and seas. Over time, the sediments change into horizontal layers of sedimentary rocks. The bottom layer of rock is oldest. Each layer above that is younger, and the top layer is youngest of all. This ordering is relative because you cannot be sure exactly when each layer formed, only that each layer is younger than the one below it. This idea is called superposition.

The principle of superposition states that when horizontal layers of sedimentary rock are undisturbed, the youngest layer is always on top. This is shown in the photograph on the left. But over millions of years, the movement of tectonic plates can disturb rock layers. A whole set of layers can be turned on its side. Rock layers can be bent, or even folded over, like taco shells that began as flat tortillas. If a set of rock layers has been disturbed, the youngest layer may no longer be on top. One way scientists determine the original order is to compare the disturbed rock layers with a similar but undisturbed stack of layers.

CHECK YOUR READING When might the youngest layer in a set of sedimentary rock layers not be on top?

Igneous Rock and Sedimentary Layers

Sedimentary rock layers can also be affected by igneous rock. Molten rock from within Earth can force its way up through the layers above it, cooling and forming igneous rock. Because the sedimentary rock layers have to be present before the molten rock cuts through them, the igneous rock must be younger than the layers it cuts through.

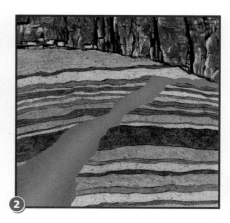

① Over time, sand and silt form horizontal layers of sedimentary rock.

② Molten rock cuts through the sedimentary rock layers.

③ A river wears away the rock, exposing younger igneous rock.

If the molten rock erupts and flows onto the surface, it forms a layer of igneous rock on top of the layers of sedimentary rock. Over time, more sedimentary rock layers may form on top of the igneous rock. The igneous rock layer is younger than the sedimentary layers under it. The sedimentary layers that form on top are even younger.

Index Fossils

Fossils contained within sedimentary rock can offer clues about the age of the rock. An organism that was fossilized in rock most likely lived during the same time span in which the rock formed. Using information from rocks and other natural evidence, scientists have determined when specific fossilized organisms lived. If people know how long ago a fossilized organism lived, then they can figure out the age of the rock in which the fossil was found.

Fossils of organisms that were common, that lived in many areas, and that lived only during specific spans of time are called **index fossils.** These characteristics of index fossils make them especially useful for figuring out when rock layers formed.

Index fossils are widespread—they are found in many different parts of the world. As a result, index fossils are used to compare the ages of rock layers in different parts of the world. You will learn more about different types of fossils in Section 3.

This rock contains the index fossil *Arnioceras semicostatum,* an organism that lived between 206 million and 144 million years ago.

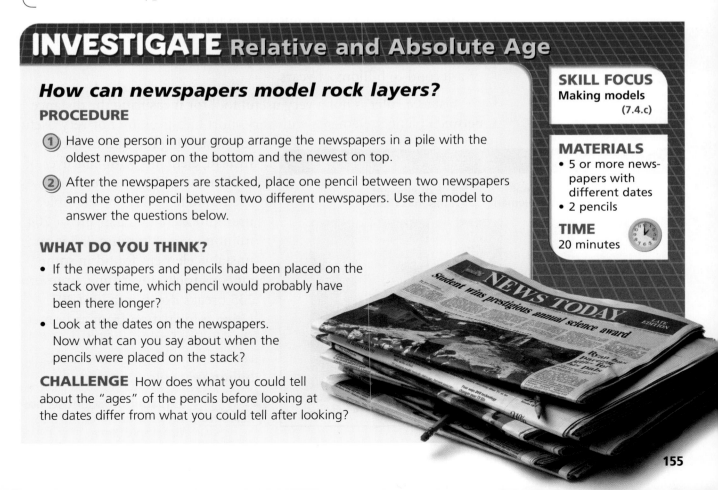

INVESTIGATE Relative and Absolute Age

How can newspapers model rock layers?

PROCEDURE

(1) Have one person in your group arrange the newspapers in a pile with the oldest newspaper on the bottom and the newest on top.

(2) After the newspapers are stacked, place one pencil between two newspapers and the other pencil between two different newspapers. Use the model to answer the questions below.

WHAT DO YOU THINK?

• If the newspapers and pencils had been placed on the stack over time, which pencil would probably have been there longer?

• Look at the dates on the newspapers. Now what can you say about when the pencils were placed on the stack?

CHALLENGE How does what you could tell about the "ages" of the pencils before looking at the dates differ from what you could tell after looking?

SKILL FOCUS
Making models
(7.4.c)

MATERIALS
• 5 or more newspapers with different dates
• 2 pencils

TIME
20 minutes

Radiometric dating can show absolute age.

READING TiP

Radiometric dating is a technique for estimating the age of an object by measuring the amounts of radioactive elements in it.

Think again about the friend who tells you that she has two brothers, one older than she is and one younger. You know the order in which they were born—that is, their relative ages. The older brother, however, might be 1 year older or 20 years older. The exact age of the younger brother is also still a mystery. To find out how much older or younger your friend's brothers are, you need to know their actual ages. The actual age of an event or object is called its **absolute age.**

CHECK YOUR READING What is the difference between relative age and absolute age? Use an example in your explanation.

Half-Life

To determine the absolute ages of rocks, scientists use a method called radiometric dating, also called radioactive dating. This method relies on the smallest unit of matter, the atom. Atoms make up everything on Earth, including you and rocks. The atoms of many chemical elements exist in various forms. Some of these forms are unstable and break down over time into another form. This breakdown—called radioactivity—is a very useful clock because a particular unstable form of an element always breaks down at the same rate into the same other form.

The rate of change of a radioactive element is measured in half-lives. A **half-life** is the length of time it takes for half of the atoms in a sample of a radioactive element to change from an unstable form into another form. Different elements have different half-lives, ranging from fractions of a second to billions of years.

Just as a ruler is not a very useful tool for measuring the distance between planets, elements with very short half-lives are not very useful for measuring the ages of rocks. Instead, elements with half-lives of millions to billions of years are used to date rocks. For example, uranium 235 has a half-life of 704 million years. Uranium 235 is an unstable element found in some igneous rocks. Over time, uranium 235 breaks down into lead 207. Using information from radiometric dating of rocks, scientists estimate that Earth is about 4.6 billion years old.

Over time, a radioactive element breaks down at a constant rate into another form.

Half-Life

■ % of original unstable element   ■ % of element that has changed

0 half-life	1 half-life	2 half-lives	3 half-lives	4 half-lives
100%	50% / 50%	75% / 25%	87.5% / 12.5%	93.75% / 6.25%

CHECK YOUR READING Explain how scientists use an element's half-life to date an object.

Radioactive Breakdown and Dating Rock Layers

Igneous rocks contain radioactive elements that break down over time. This breakdown can be used to tell the ages of the rocks.

① 1408 Million Years Ago

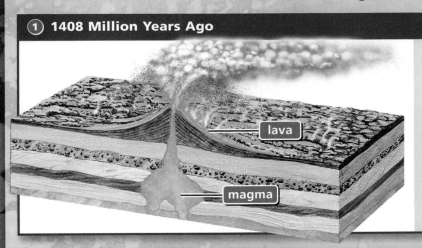

lava

magma

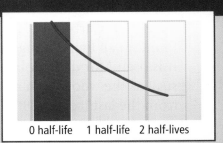

0 half-life   1 half-life   2 half-lives

When magma first hardens into rock, it contains some uranium 235 and no lead 207.

② 704 Million Years Ago

Over time, much of the volcano wore away and new sedimentary rock layers formed.

igneous rock

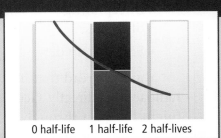

0 half-life   1 half-life   2 half-lives

After 704 million years, or one half-life, half of the uranium 235 in the igneous rock has broken down into lead 207.

③ Today

Radiometric dating shows that this igneous rock is about 1408 million years old.

These layers formed before the magma cut through, so they must be older than 1408 million years.

The layers that formed on top of the igneous rock must be younger than 1408 million years.

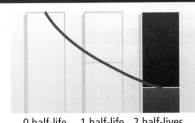

0 half-life   1 half-life   2 half-lives

After 1408 million years, or 2 half-lives, only one-fourth of the uranium 235 in the igneous rock remains.

READING ViSUALS How do the relative amounts of uranium 235 and lead 207 in the igneous rock change over time?

Radiometric dating works best with igneous rocks. Sedimentary rocks are formed from material that came from other rocks. For this reason, any measurements would show when the original rocks were formed, not when the sedimentary rock itself formed.

Just as uranium 235 can be used to date igneous rocks, carbon 14 can be used to find the ages of the remains of some things that were once alive. Carbon 14 is an unstable form of carbon, an element found in all living things. Carbon 14 has a half-life of 5730 years. It is useful for dating objects between about 100 and 70,000 years old, such as the wood from an ancient tool or the remains of an animal from the last ice age.

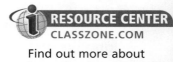

RESOURCE CENTER
CLASSZONE.COM
Find out more about how scientists date rocks.

Using Absolute and Relative Age

Scientists must piece together information from all methods of determining age to figure out the story of Earth's past.

- Radiometric dating of igneous rocks reveals their absolute age.
- Interpreting layers of sedimentary rock shows the relative order of events.
- Fossils help determine ages of sedimentary rock layers.

You have read that it is not possible to date sedimentary rocks with radioactivity directly. Geologists, however, can date any igneous rock that might have cut through or formed a layer between sedimentary layers. Then, using the absolute age of the igneous rock, geologists can estimate the ages of nearby sedimentary layers.

CHECK YOUR READING How might the absolute age of an igneous rock layer help scientists to determine the ages of nearby sedimentary rock layers?

 Review

KEY CONCEPTS

1. In what ways do new rocks form on Earth? (7.4.c)

2. What can you tell from undisturbed rock layers? Include the concept of relative age in your answer. (7.4.c)

3. How can index fossils help scientists determine the ages of rock layers? (7.4.d)

4. What property of radioactive elements makes them useful for determining absolute age? (7.4.d)

CRITICAL THINKING

5. **Provide Examples** What are some things in your life for which you know only their relative ages?

6. **Apply** In your daily life are there index events (like index fossils) that tell you approximate times even when you can't see a clock? What are they?

○ CHALLENGE

7. **Apply** A rock contains a radioactive element with a half-life of 100 million years. Tests show that the element in the rock has gone through three half-lives. How old is the rock?

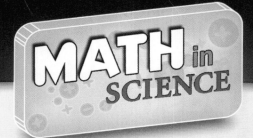

MATH TUTORIAL
CLASSZONE.COM

Click on Math Tutorial for more help with reading line graphs and multiplying whole numbers.

Math 7.MR.2.5
Science 7.4.d

Mammoths were close relatives of today's elephants. Mammoths lived during the last ice age and are now extinct.

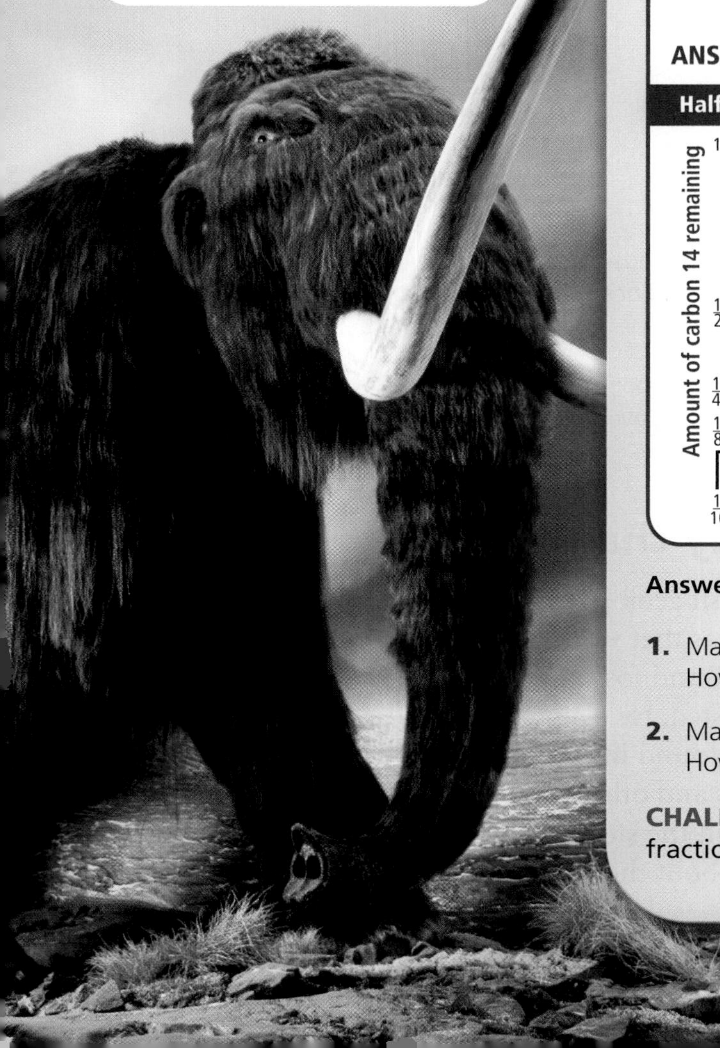

Dating Mammoth Bones

Imagine that scientists find an ancient lakebed with hundreds of well-preserved mammoth bones in it. They are able to measure the amount of carbon 14 that remains in the bones. Carbon 14 has a half-life of approximately 5700 years. How could you use the half-life of carbon 14 to determine how old the bones are?

Example

Mammoth bone A has $\frac{1}{4}$ of its original carbon 14. How old is mammoth bone A? Use the half-life of carbon 14 and the graph below.

(1) Find $\frac{1}{4}$ on the vertical axis and follow the line out to the red curved line.

(2) Then follow the line down to the horizontal axis to determine that the carbon 14 in the bone has been through 2 half-lives.

(3) $5700 \times 2 = 11,400$

    ↑   ↑

years per   number of
half-life   half-lives

ANSWER Bone A is 11,400 years old.

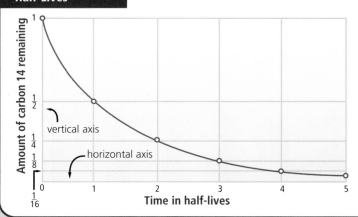

Answer the following questions.

1. Mammoth bone B has $\frac{1}{8}$ of its original carbon 14. How old is mammoth bone B?

2. Mammoth bone C has $\frac{1}{16}$ of its original carbon 14. How old is mammoth bone C?

CHALLENGE Mammoth bone D is 28,500 years old. What fraction of the original carbon 14 remains in bone D?

5.2 The geologic time scale shows Earth's past.

CALIFORNIA
Content Standards

7.4.a Students know Earth processes today are similar to those that occurred in the past and slow geologic processes have large cumulative effects over long periods of time.

7.4.b Students know the history of life on Earth has been disrupted by major catastrophic events, such as major volcanic eruptions or the impacts of asteroids.

BEFORE, you learned

- Rocks and fossils give clues about life on Earth
- Layers of sedimentary rocks show relative ages
- Radiometric dating of igneous rocks gives absolute ages

NOW, you will learn

- How Earth is always changing and has always changed in the past
- How the geologic time scale describes Earth's history

VOCABULARY

uniformitarianism p. 161
geologic time scale p. 163

EXPLORE Time Scales (7.4.g)

How do you make a time scale of your year?

PROCEDURE

1. Divide your paper into three columns.

2. In the last column, list six to ten events in the school year in the order they will happen. For example, you may include a particular soccer game or a play.

3. In the middle column, organize those events into larger time periods, such as soccer season or performance week.

4. In the first column, organize those time periods into even larger ones.

MATERIALS
- pen
- sheet of paper

WHAT DO YOU THINK?
How does putting events into categories help you to see the relationship among events?

OUTLINE
Remember to start an outline in your notebook for this section.

I. Main idea
  A. Supporting idea
    1. Detail
    2. Detail
  B. Supporting idea

Earth is constantly changing.

In the late 1700s a Scottish geologist named James Hutton began to question some of the ideas that were then common about Earth and how Earth changes. He found fossils and saw them as evidence of life forms that no longer existed. He also noticed that different types of fossilized creatures were found in different layers of rocks. Based on his observations of rocks and other natural evidence, Hutton came up with a new idea to explain the story told in the rocks. He was the first to present a hypothesis about the changing of Earth over time.

Hutton recognized that Earth is changing constantly. Think again about the rock cycle. Rocks are continually breaking down and forming. For example, wind, water, and ice all break down rocks. Other processes, such as volcanic eruptions and the building up of sediment, continue to form new rock. Earth's interior is constantly churning from powerful forces that move, fold, and raise the surface of Earth.

The same processes that changed Earth in the past continue to occur today. A billion years ago, a river would have carried particles of rock just as a river does today. Look at the photograph of sedimentary rock on the right. The surface of the sandstone preserves the ripples once made by wind or water. A geologist can examine the sandstone and determine the direction in which the water or wind was once moving. Similarly, volcanoes in the past would have erupted just as volcanoes do today. Hutton's theory of **uniformitarianism** (YOO-nuh-fawr-mih-TAIR-ee-uh-nihz-uhm) is the idea that

- Earth is an always-changing place
- the same forces of change at work today were at work in the past

Although this idea may seem simple, it is very important. The theory of uniformitarianism is the basis of modern geology.

 CHECK YOUR READING   What is the theory of uniformitarianism?

The surface of this sandstone preserves ancient sand ripples.

READING **TiP**

To remember what *uniformitarianism* means, think of the word *uniform,* which means "same."

WASHINGTON

Mount St. Helens
▲

Fast Change

READING **ViSUALS**   COMPARE AND CONTRAST These photographs show Mount St. Helens before and after it erupted in 1980. What changes can you observe?

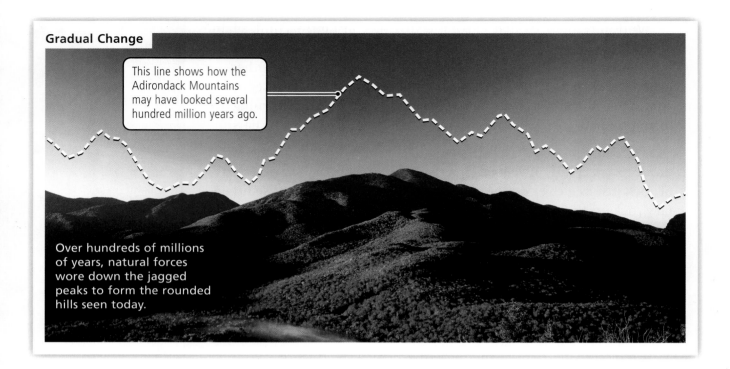

Gradual Change

This line shows how the Adirondack Mountains may have looked several hundred million years ago.

Over hundreds of millions of years, natural forces wore down the jagged peaks to form the rounded hills seen today.

Small, gradual changes become large changes over time.

Some changes on Earth are fast. A volcanic eruption, an earthquake, or a flood can cause huge changes over a period of minutes or days. Other changes on Earth are slow, or gradual. Mountains form and are worn down over many millions of years.

You might recall that a German scientist named Alfred Wegener proposed a hypothesis about continental drift in 1912. Wegener thought that the continents were once joined in a single landmass. He called this landmass Pangaea.

Wegener used evidence of fossils, rocks, and climate change to support his idea that the continents had moved apart over time. He learned that the fossils of a reptile *Mesosaurus* had been found in both South America and Africa, but nowhere else in the world. Clues in rocks also provided evidence to support his hypothesis. Wegener showed that the type of rock found in South America matched rocks found in Africa.

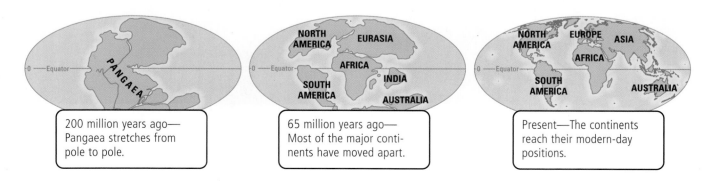

200 million years ago—Pangaea stretches from pole to pole.

65 million years ago—Most of the major continents have moved apart.

Present—The continents reach their modern-day positions.

Wegener's ideas eventually led to the theory of plate tectonics. This theory states that Earth's lithosphere is made up of huge plates that move over the surface of Earth. These plates move very slowly over time—only a few centimeters a year. The plates are always in motion, producing and destroying features on Earth as they move apart, scrape past each other, or push together. That constant plate motion even changed geography and climate. This, in turn, affected the distribution and evolution of living things as you will learn in Chapter 6.

Over the last 200 million years, the continents moved from a single landmass to the positions that we know today. Scientists determined that there were at least two other times in Earth's history, before Pangaea, where the continents formed one giant landmass. Scientists predict that the plates will move and form another giant landmass about 250 million years from now.

 CHECK YOUR READING Was Pangaea the only giant landmass? Explain your answer.

The geologic time scale divides Earth's history.

From a person's point of view, 4.6 billion years is a tremendous amount of time. To help make sense of it, scientists have organized Earth's history in a chart called the geologic time scale. The **geologic time scale** divides Earth's history into intervals of time defined by major events or changes on Earth.

Scientists use information from fossils and radiometric dating to figure out what happened over the 4.6 billion years of Earth's history. The oldest evidence of life is from about 3.8 billion years ago, but life may be even older. Organisms with more than one cell appeared around 1 billion years ago. Modern humans appeared only 100,000 years ago. You will learn more about these events in the next chapter.

Imagine Earth's history compressed into one year. If Earth forms on January 1, the first life we have evidence for appears in the beginning of March. Life with more than one cell appears months later, in the middle of October. Humans do not show up until 11 minutes before midnight on the last day of the year. They do not understand how old Earth is until about a second before midnight.

VOCABULARY
Add a four square diagram to your notebook for *geologic time scale.*

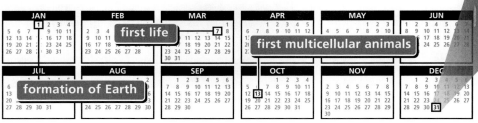

If Earth's history is compared to a calendar year, humans appear just before midnight on December 31.

READING TiP

As you read, find the eons, eras, and periods on the chart below.

Divisions of Geologic Time

The geologic time scale is divided into eons, eras, periods, and epochs (EHP-uhks). Unlike divisions of time such as days or minutes, the divisions of the geologic time scale have no fixed lengths. Instead, they are based on changes or events recorded in rocks and fossils.

Eon The largest unit of time is an eon. Earth's 4.6-billion-year history is divided into four eons.

Era Eons may be divided into eras. The most recent eon is divided into three eras: the Paleozoic, the Mesozoic, and the Cenozoic.

Period Each era is subdivided into a number of periods.

Epoch The periods of the Cenozoic, the most recent era, are further divided into epochs.

Geologic Time Scale

The geologic time scale divides Earth's history into eons, eras, periods, and epochs.

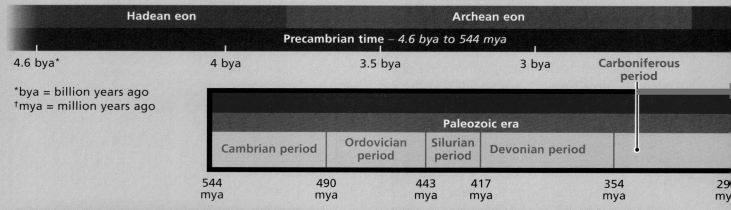

Hadean eon | Archean eon

Precambrian time – 4.6 bya to 544 mya

4.6 bya*   4 bya   3.5 bya   3 bya   Carboniferous period

*bya = billion years ago
†mya = million years ago

Paleozoic era

Cambrian period	Ordovician period	Silurian period	Devonian period	

544 mya   490 mya   443 mya   417 mya   354 mya   29 my

Precambrian Time at 3.6 Billion Years Ago

For nearly 4 billion years, during most of Precambrian time, no plants or animals existed.

Paleozoic Era at 544 Million Years Ago

At the beginning of the Paleozoic era, all life lived in the oceans.

The Hadean, Archean, and Proterozoic eons together are called Precambrian time and make up almost 90 percent of Earth's history. The fossil record for Precambrian time consists mostly of tiny organisms that cannot be seen without a microscope. Other early forms of life had soft bodies that rarely formed into fossils.

The Phanerozoic eon stretches from the end of Precambrian time to the present. Because so many more changes are recorded in the fossil record of this eon, it is further divided into smaller units of time. The smaller time divisions relate to how long certain conditions and life forms on Earth lasted and how quickly life forms changed or became extinct, or died out.

CALIFORNIA Focus

Fossil discoveries were made during construction on the Metro Red Line subway in Los Angeles in 2000. The fossils reveal that during the late Miocene epoch, part of the Tertiary period, Los Angeles was submerged under one-half to one mile of water!

 CHECK YOUR READING   What part of geologic time makes up most of Earth's history?

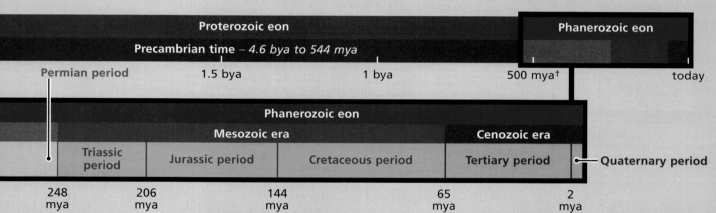

Proterozoic eon	Phanerozoic eon
Precambrian time – 4.6 bya to 544 mya	

| Permian period | 1.5 bya | 1 bya | 500 mya† | today |

Phanerozoic eon				
Mesozoic era			Cenozoic era	
Triassic period	Jurassic period	Cretaceous period	Tertiary period	Quaternary period

| 248 mya | 206 mya | 144 mya | 65 mya | 2 mya |

Mesozoic Era at 195 to 65 Million Years Ago

During the Mesozoic era, dinosaurs lived along with the first mammals, birds, and flowering plants.

Cenozoic Era at Present Day

The first humans appeared in the latter part of the Cenozoic era, which continues today.

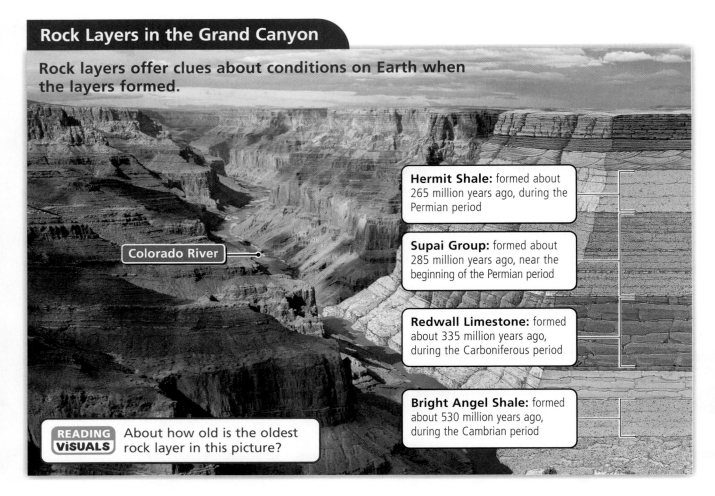

Rock Layers in the Grand Canyon

Rock layers offer clues about conditions on Earth when the layers formed.

Colorado River

Hermit Shale: formed about 265 million years ago, during the Permian period

Supai Group: formed about 285 million years ago, near the beginning of the Permian period

Redwall Limestone: formed about 335 million years ago, during the Carboniferous period

Bright Angel Shale: formed about 530 million years ago, during the Cambrian period

READING VISUALS About how old is the oldest rock layer in this picture?

Phanerozoic Eon

The most recent eon, the Phanerozoic, began around 544 million years ago. Its start marks the beginning of a fast increase in the diversity, or variety, of life. The Phanerozoic eon is divided into three eras:

- the Paleozoic, whose name means "ancient life"
- the Mesozoic, whose name means "middle life"
- the Cenozoic, whose name means "recent life"

READING TiP

As you read, find each era in the geologic time scale on pages 164–165.

The Paleozoic era is the first era of the Phanerozoic eon. At the start of the Paleozoic, all life lived in the ocean. Fish, the first animals with backbones, developed during this time. Toward the end of this era, life moved onto land. Reptiles, insects, and ferns were common. A mass extinction occurred at the end of the Paleozoic era, 248 million years ago. A mass extinction is when many different life forms all die out, or become extinct, at once. The cause of this extinction is not completely understood.

The Mesozoic era spans the next 183 million years and is best known for the dinosaurs that ruled Earth. Mammals, birds, and flowering plants also first appeared during the Mesozoic. For some of this time, parts of North America were covered by a vast sea.

Another mass extinction marks the end of the Mesozoic era. Dinosaurs and many other species became extinct. This extinction may have been caused by one or more giant asteroids that slammed into Earth, throwing huge amounts of dust into the air. The dust blocked the sunlight, causing plants to die and, along with them, many animals.

The Cenozoic era, the most recent era, began 65 million years ago and continues today. The Cenozoic is often called the Age of Mammals because it marks the time when mammals became a main form of life on Earth.

Around 22,000 years ago, early humans used mammoth bones as building materials. This reconstruction shows what a bone hut may have looked like.

The Cenozoic era is divided into two periods: the Tertiary and the Quaternary. The Quaternary period stretches from about 2 million years ago to the present. Most of the Quaternary has been a series of ice ages, with much of the planet covered in thick sheets of ice. Mammoths, saber-toothed cats, and other giant mammals were common during the first part of the Quaternary. Fossils of the first modern humans are also from this period; they are about 100,000 years old.

As the amount of ice on land shrank and grew, the ocean levels rose and fell. When the ocean levels fell, exposed land served as natural bridges that connected continents previously separated by water. The land bridges allowed humans and other animals to spread around the planet. Future scientists may use the rise of human civilization to define the end of the Quaternary and the beginning of a new period.

 CHECK YOUR READING How did falling ocean levels lead to the spread of humans and other animals on Earth?

5.2 Review

KEY CONCEPTS

1. Describe the concept of uniformitarianism. (7.4.a)
2. What does the geologic time scale measure? (7.4.a)
3. What was life like on Earth for most of its history? (7.4.b)

CRITICAL THINKING

4. **Apply** What period, era, and eon do you live in?
5. **Evaluate** Some cartoons have shown early humans keeping dinosaurs as pets. From what you know about Earth's history, is this possible? Why or why not?

⬥ CHALLENGE

6. **Infer** How might the geologic time scale be different if the event that caused the mass extinction 65 million years ago had never occurred?

CHAPTER INVESTIGATION

MATERIALS
• geologic time scale conversion chart
• adding-machine paper 5 meters long
• scissors
• colored markers, pens, or pencils
• metric tape measure or meter stick
• sticky notes

7.4.g, 7.7.d

Geologic Time

OVERVIEW AND PURPOSE Geologists use information from rocks, fossils, and other natural evidence to piece together the history of Earth. The geologic time scale organizes Earth's history into intervals of time called eons, eras, periods, and epochs. In this investigation you will
• construct a model of the geologic time scale
• place fossil organisms and geologic events in the correct sequence on the timeline

▶ Procedure

1. Complete the geologic time scale conversion chart. Use the conversion 1 mm = 1 million years to change the number of years for each eon, era, period, and epoch on the chart into metric measurements (millimeters, centimeters, and meters).

2. Lay the adding-machine paper out in front of you. At the far right end of the strip write "TODAY" lengthwise along the edge.

3. Starting from the TODAY mark, measure back 4.6 meters, or 4600 million years. Label this point "AGE OF EARTH." Cut off excess paper.

step 4

4. Fold the paper in half lengthwise and then fold it in half lengthwise again. Unfold the paper. The creases should divide your paper into four rows.

5. At the left end of the strip, label each row as shown: Eons, Eras, Periods, Epochs.

6. Using the numbers from your chart, measure each eon. Start each measurement from the TODAY line and measure back in time. For example, the Archean eon started 3800 million years ago, so measure back 3.8 meters from today. Mark that distance and write "ARCHEAN EON." Do the same for the other eons.

step 5

step 6

ARCHEAN EON
3800 million years ago (3.8 meters)

AGE OF EARTH   TODAY

Content Standard
7.4.g Students know how to explain significant developments and extinctions of plant and animal life on the geologic time scale.

Investigation Standard
7.7.d Construct scale models, maps, and appropriately labeled diagrams to communicate scientific knowledge (e.g., motion of Earth's plates and cell structure).

7 Repeat step 6 to measure and label the eras, periods, and epochs.

8 After all the eons, eras, periods, and epochs are measured and labeled, use the same measuring technique to add the fossils and events from the table below.

Table 1. Important Events in Earth's History

Fossils and Events	Time (millions of years ago)
First trilobite	554
First mammal	210
Greatest mass extinction	248
First green algae	1000
Early humans	2
Extinction of dinosaurs	65
First life forms	3800
Flowering plants	130

9 Draw pictures of the fossils and events or write the names of the fossils and events on the timeline. If you do not have space to write directly on the timeline, write on sticky notes and then place the sticky notes at the correct positions on the timeline.

Observe and Analyze

Write It Up

1. **COMPARE AND CONTRAST** The time from 4.6 billion years ago up until the beginning of the Phanerozoic eon is called Precambrian time. Find the part of your timeline that represents Precambrian time. How does Precambrian time compare in length with the rest of the geologic time scale?

2. **COMPARE AND CONTRAST** The Cenozoic era is the most recent era, and it includes the present. How does the Cenozoic era compare in length with the other eras?

3. **INTERPRET** Where on the timeline are the two major extinction events?

4. **INFER** What does the location of the two major extinction events suggest about how geologists divided the time scale into smaller units?

Conclude

Write It Up

1. **INTERPRET** Where are most of the life forms that you placed on your time line grouped?

2. **INFER** Judging by the locations of most of the life forms on your timeline, why do you think the shortest era on the timeline—the Cenozoic era—has been divided into so many smaller divisions?

3. **EVALUATE** What limitations or difficulties did you experience in constructing or interpreting this model of the geologic time scale?

4. **APPLY** Think about the relationships among fossils, rock layers, and the geologic time scale. Why do you think the geologists who first constructed the geologic time scale found it difficult to divide the first three eons into smaller time divisions?

INVESTIGATE Further

CHALLENGE Choose several more events or life forms mentioned in the chapter. For each, find either an absolute date or a relative date that will allow you to place it in the correct position in the geologic sequence. Draw or label these new items on your timeline. What new patterns or connections did adding these events or life forms to the timeline reveal?

Geologic Time Scale Conversion Chart

Division of Geologic Time	Millions of Years Ago It Began	Measurement
Eons		
Hadean	4600	4.6 meters
Archean	3800	
Proterozoic	2500	
Phanerozoic	544	
Eras		

5.3 Earth's past is revealed in rocks and fossils.

7.3.c Students know how independent lines of evidence from geology, fossils, and comparative anatomy provide the bases for the theory of evolution.

7.4.b Students know the history of life on Earth has been disrupted by major catastrophic events, such as major volcanic eruptions or the impacts of asteroids.

7.4.e Students know fossils provide evidence of how life and environmental conditions have changed.

VOCABULARY

original remains p. 174
ice core p. 175

BEFORE, you learned

- The movement of tectonic plates causes Earth's surface to change
- Small changes add up into large changes over time
- Sedimentary rocks can capture evidence of life forms

NOW, you will learn

- How most fossils form
- How different kinds of fossils show traces of life from Earth's past
- How ice cores and tree rings reveal conditions and changes in the environment

EXPLORE Rocks (7.4.d)

What can we learn from a rock?

PROCEDURE

1. Use a hand lens to examine the rock sample.
2. Make a sketch of any shapes you see in the rock.

WHAT DO YOU THINK?
- What do you think those shapes are?
- How did they get there?

MATERIALS
- rock sample
- hand lens
- paper and pencil

Fossils and original remains give clues about the past.

OUTLINE
Remember to take notes on this section in outline form.

I. Main idea
  A. Supporting idea
    1. Detail
    2. Detail
  B. Supporting idea

Fossils are important clues about past events. Fossils are traces or remains of living things from long ago. Remember that index fossils help scientists tell the ages of rocks. The same types of fossils are found in layers in different parts of the world. Scientists infer that these layers formed at about the same time. Using the information about rock formation, fossils, and other natural evidence, scientists are putting together the story of Earth's past.

For example, fossils also tell us about organisms, such as dinosaurs, that are now extinct. Even though no one has ever seen a dinosaur, people use fossil evidence to infer what dinosaurs looked like and how they behaved.

Types of Fossils

Fossils exist in many different forms. Most fossils are hardened animal remains such as shells, bones, and teeth. Perhaps you have seen displays of dinosaur skeletons in museums. These displays include fossil bones, such as the jawbone in the top photograph at right. Other fossils form when minerals replace the remains of organisms or parts of organisms. The trilobite fossil shown in the bottom photograph is an example of this type of fossil. Impressions or other evidence of an organism preserved in rock are also fossils.

Very rarely, people find fossils that are original remains of entire organisms. Explorers have found the frozen bodies of animals called woolly mammoths that lived about 10,000 years ago preserved in ice. The bodies of insects have been found preserved in sap from plants.

Bones, such as this jaw-bone, are a common type of fossil.

Fossil Formation

Conditions have to be just right for a fossil to form in rock. The organism or trace of the organism must be preserved before it decomposes or disappears. Usually, the soft parts of an organism decay too quickly to be preserved in rock. For that reason, many rock fossils reveal traces or shapes of only the hard parts of animals or plants. Hard parts, such as shells, bones, teeth, and stems or tree trunks, decompose slowly. They are more likely to be preserved as fossil evidence. Most organisms that lived in the past died and decomposed without leaving any traces. An organism that has no hard parts, such as a mushroom or a slug, rarely leaves fossil evidence.

Rock fossils form in sedimentary rock. Remember that sedimentary rock forms from layers of sediment, such as sand or mud. Sometimes, the sediment builds up around the remains of an organism. A fossil can then form in the rock. If sedimentary rocks are changed by heat or pressure, their fossils can be destroyed. Igneous rocks never contain fossils. The heat of the molten rock—from which igneous rock cools—destroys any traces of plants or animals.

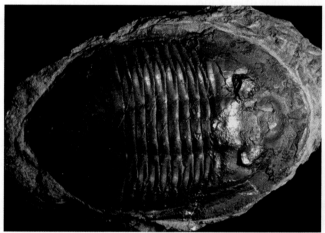

This fossil trilobite formed as minerals replaced the remains of the organism.

VISUALIZATION
CLASSZONE.COM

Explore how a fossil can form.

○ **CHECK YOUR READING** Why do rock fossils form in sedimentary rock rather than in igneous rock?

Fossils in Rocks

If an organism is covered by or buried in sediment, it may become a fossil as the sediments become rock. Many rock fossils are actual body parts, such as bones or teeth, that were buried in sediment and then replaced by minerals and turned to stone.

RESOURCE CENTER
CLASSZONE.COM

Learn more about fossils.

Some fossils are not original remains or actual body parts that have turned to stone. Instead, these fossils are impressions or traces made of rock and provide indirect evidence that the organisms were there, just as a shoeprint can reveal much about the shoe that made it. Rocks can contain detailed shapes or prints of plants, animals, and even organisms too small to see without a microscope. Fossils in rock include molds and casts, petrified wood, carbon films, and trace fossils.

1 **Molds and Casts** Some fossils that form in sedimentary rock are mold fossils. A mold is a visible shape that was left after an animal or plant was buried in sediment and then decayed away. In some cases, a hollow mold later becomes filled with minerals, producing a cast fossil. The cast fossil is a solid model in the shape of the organism. If you think of the mold as a shoeprint, the cast would be what would result if sand filled the print and hardened into stone.

These ancient logs in the Painted Desert Wilderness in Arizona have been preserved as petrified wood for around 225 million years. Minerals replaced the wood to make the stone logs.

2 **Mineral Replacement** The stone fossil of a tree is called petrified wood and is an example of mineral replacement. In certain conditions, a fallen tree can become covered with sediments. Over time, water passes through the sediments and into the tree's cells. Minerals that are carried in the water take the place of the cells, producing a stone likeness of the tree.

3 **Carbon Films** Carbon is an element that is found in every living thing. Sometimes when a dead plant or animal decays, its carbon is left behind as a visible layer. This image is called a carbon film. Carbon films can show details of soft parts of animals and plants that are rarely seen in other fossils.

4 **Trace Fossils** Do you want to know how fast a dinosaur could run? Trace fossils might be able to tell you. These are not parts of an animal or impressions of it, but rather evidence of an animal's presence in a given location. Trace fossils include preserved footprints, trails, animal holes, and even feces. By comparing these clues with what is known about modern animals, scientists can learn how prehistoric animals may have lived, what they ate, and how they behaved. For instance, dinosaur tracks can be studied to learn how fast dinosaurs ran.

CHECK YOUR READING What do carbon film fossils show that trace fossils do not show?

Fossils in Rocks

Rock fossils show shapes and traces of past life.

① Molds and Casts

A mold and cast are formed in the steps below.

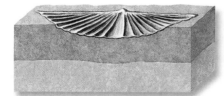

An organism dies and falls into soft sediment.

Over time, the sediment becomes rock and the organism decays, leaving a mold.

Minerals fill the mold and make a cast of the organism.

② Mineral Replacement

In this close-up, you can see the minerals that replaced the wood, forming petrified wood.

③ Carbon Films

This carbon film of a moth is about 10 million years old. Carbon films are especially useful because they can show details of the soft parts of organisms.

④ Trace Fossils

A trace fossil, such as this footprint of a dinosaur in rock, can provide important information about where an animal lived and how it walked and ran.

READING VISUALS What is similar about mold-and-cast fossils and petrified wood?

Original Remains

Fossils that are the actual bodies or body parts of organisms are called **original remains.** Soft parts of organisms usually decay and disappear. But they can become fossil evidence if they are sealed in a substance that keeps out air and tiny organisms. Original remains are found in places where conditions prevent the decay that normally occurs. Original remains give direct evidence of forms of life that lived long ago.

① Ice	② Amber	③ Tar
		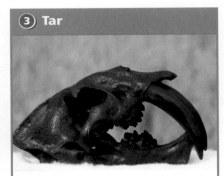
This frozen mammoth body was found in Siberia.	These insects were trapped and preserved in amber.	This saber-toothed cat skull, found in the La Brea Tar Pits, was preserved in tar.

①　Ice Ice is one of the best preservers of the remains of prehistoric life. Huge ice fields in Siberia and North America contain the bodies of 10,000-year-old mammoths and prehistoric rhinos, with bones, muscle, skin, and even hair still in place.

②　Amber A sticky substance inside trees, called resin, flows like syrup and protects the tree by trapping insects. If the tree gets buried after it dies, the resin can harden into amber. Amber can contain the remains of insects and other small organisms.

③　Tar A thick, oily liquid called tar can also preserve remains. Saber-toothed cats and other animals were trapped in pools of tar and have been preserved for thousands of years.

Fossils and other natural evidence show changes in life and the environment.

Fossils reveal that Earth has undergone many changes over billions of years. Scientists study fossils to learn what organisms and animals once lived in places where the fossils were found. Today Antarctica is mostly covered by ice, but fossils show that crocodiles, dinosaurs, and palm trees once lived on that land. The land was once much closer to the equator.

The earliest fossils are of tiny one-celled organisms that lived in an environment without oxygen. Three billion years ago, humans or the land animals we know today could not have breathed the air on Earth. Fossils also record the disappearance of many species.

Ice Cores

In Greenland and Antarctica, snowfall has built up gigantic layers of ice that can be much deeper than the height of a skyscraper and as much as 530,000 years old at the bottom. Scientists drill into the ice and remove ice cores for study. An **ice core** is a cylindrical sample that shows the layers of snow and ice that have built up over thousands of years. Like rock layers, the layers of ice serve as a vertical timeline of part of Earth's past.

Scientists analyze the ice to learn how the atmosphere has changed. Increases in ash in the ice show when major volcanic eruptions occurred. Differences in the oxygen atoms in ice at different levels show how long ice ages and warm periods lasted. This information helps scientists understand how Earth's climate might change in the future.

CHECK YOUR READING How does an ice core provide information about Earth's history?

These scientists are removing an ice core from a thick ice sheet in Antarctica. Ice at the bottom end is oldest.

Tree Rings

The rings in tree trunks are also a tool for studying the past. The widths of tree rings vary, depending on how much the tree grows in various years. Tree rings are thin when growing conditions are poor. A thick ring is a sign of a good year for growth, with enough rainfall. By analyzing the tree rings of many old trees, scientists can develop an accurate history of overall weather patterns over time.

INVESTIGATE Learning from Tree Rings

What do tree rings tell about the past?

1. Examine the photograph of a cross section of a tree trunk.

2. Count the rings in the cross section. Each combination of light and dark represents one ring.

3. Compare the rings with one another. Record your observations.

WHAT DO YOU THINK?

- Rings in a tree trunk form as the tree grows each year.
  The number of rings tells the tree's age. A light ring forms in the early part of the growing season, and a dark ring in the later part.
  How old was the tree when it was cut down?

- In what year did the tree first grow?

- During dry years, trees don't grow as much. Which year was very dry where this tree grew?

CHALLENGE During what part of the growing season was this tree probably cut down? How do you know?

SKILL FOCUS
Observing (7.4.e)

MATERIALS
- Tree Cross Section Datasheet
- hand lens

TIME
20 minutes

Finding the Age of Fossils

The 130-million-year-old theropod dinosaur skeleton shown here was made from both the hard parts and soft parts of the original organism. The fossil is about a meter (3 ft) long.

The fossil of the dinosaur on the left is about 130 million years old. How can scientists tell how old a fossil is? Remember that there are two ways to determine the age of rocks—relative dating and absolute dating. These are also the two ways of determining the age of fossils. A fossil is usually the same age as the rock it formed in.

Remember that sedimentary rocks form in layers and fossils form in sedimentary rocks. Any clue to the age of the fossil or to the age of the rock layer provides information about the area and relative ages of rocks and fossils found there. It takes many clues for scientists to determine relative ages. The pattern of layers gives clues to the age of each layer. Newer fossils are usually found in the younger, top layers while older fossils are found in the older, lower layers of rock. Also, index fossils can help match layers of the same age from many different locations.

If some of the original material of the organism still exists, scientists study the amount of radioactive elements found in the fossils. Radiometric dating may tell the age of the fossil directly. However, radiometric dating, using carbon 14, does not work on very old fossils, because the radioactive elements have decayed completely. For older fossils, radiometric dating is used on nearby layers of rock.

By using a combination of absolute and relative dating of rocks and fossils, scientists are continuing to put together pieces of Earth's past. Look again at the fossil in the photograph. Information from volcanic and sedimentary rock and other fossils found in the same location provided scientists with the information needed to determine the age of this dinosaur.

 CHECK YOUR READING What are the two ways scientists can determine the age of fossils?

5.3 Review

KEY CONCEPTS

1. What can rock fossils and original remains show about Earth's past? (7.4.e)

2. Why do rock fossils form in sedimentary rock and not in igneous rock? (7.4.e)

3. How do tree rings and ice cores help scientists understand how Earth has changed over time? (7.3.c)

CRITICAL THINKING

4. **Infer** If you uncovered fossils of tropical fish and palm trees, what could you say about the environment at the time the fossils formed?

5. **Synthesize** Why might ancient lake and sea beds be rich sources of fossils?

⬥ CHALLENGE

6. **Rank** Which evidence—a fossil, tree rings, or an ice core—would be most helpful to a historian studying how the Pilgrims grew food at Plymouth Colony in 1620? Explain your reasoning.

CONNECTING SCIENCES

Could *T. Rex* Win a Race?

> 7.4.e Students know fossils provide evidence of how life and environmental conditions have changed.

If you want to know how fast a dinosaur ran, study a chicken. John Hutchinson and Mariano Garcia at the University of California, Berkeley, did just that. They wanted to know if *Tyrannosaurus rex* was actually as fast on its feet as some people said it was.

To find the answer, the scientists worked to figure out how strong the dinosaur's legs were. They needed to know how much muscle the giant dinosaur had in its legs. Yet there are no complete remains of dinosaur muscle, just bones. So they used a chicken as a model for *T. rex*.

Fossils and Fowls

The bone fossils of dinosaurs suggest that birds and dinosaurs have some similarities. The scientists found that a chicken needs at least one-tenth of its body mass to be leg muscle. They measured chickens and found they have even more than that, about one-fifth.

The scientists used a computer program to learn if a chicken the size of a 5900 kilogram (10,000 lb) *T. rex* would be able to run. The computer model showed that a chicken that size would need 90 percent of its body mass in its legs to run fast. The scientists inferred that *T. rex* was not a fast runner.

The scientists calculated that an animal with 2.5 meter (8 ft) legs could travel at about 24 kilometers per hour (15 mi/h). In other words, *T. rex* could run about as fast as many humans can today.

EXPLORE

1. **SYNTHESIZE** Based on what you have read, how might the size and speed of an animal be related?

2. **DRAW CONCLUSIONS** Why do you think some scientists think that *T. rex*, a meat eater, mostly ate animals that were already dead instead of live prey?

Chapter Review

the BIG idea

Rocks, fossils, and other types of natural evidence tell Earth's story.

CONTENT REVIEW CLASSZONE.COM

KEY CONCEPTS SUMMARY

1 **Rocks provide a timeline for Earth.**

younger

older

Sedimentary rock layers show the order in which rocks formed. The order of the layers is used to determine the **relative ages** of fossils found in the rock.

Radiometric dating can be used to determine the **absolute age** of igneous rock.

Scientists combine information about the relative and absolute ages of rocks and fossils to construct a timeline of Earth.

VOCABULARY

relative age p. 151
rock cycle p. 152
index fossil p. 155
absolute age p. 156
half-life p. 156

2 **The geologic time scale shows Earth's past.**

The **geologic time scale** divides Earth's history into eons, eras, periods, and epochs. The divisions are based on major changes or events that occurred in Earth's history.

■ Phanerozoic eon ■ Paleozoic era ■ Mesozoic era ■ Cenozoic era

Hadean eon	Archean eon	Proterozoic eon
	Precambrian time	

4.6 bya*	3 bya	2 bya	1 bya	500 mya†	today

*bya = billion years ago   †mya = million years ago

EON → ERA → PERIOD → EPOCH

VOCABULARY

uniformitarianism p. 161
geologic time scale p. 163

3 **Earth's past is revealed in rocks and fossils.**

Fossils are traces or remnants of past life. Many fossils are found in rock. Rocks, fossils, and other natural evidence provide information about how Earth and life on Earth have changed over time.

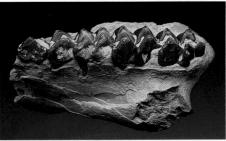

VOCABULARY

original remains p. 174
ice core p. 175

Vocabulary

Make a concept definition map for each of the vocabulary terms listed below. Write the term in the center box. Fill in the other boxes by answering the questions. A sample is shown below.

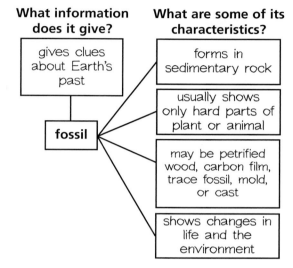

What information does it give?

gives clues about Earth's past

What are some of its characteristics?

forms in sedimentary rock

usually shows only hard parts of plant or animal

may be petrified wood, carbon film, trace fossil, mold, or cast

shows changes in life and the environment

fossil

1. index fossil

2. ice core

3. original remains

Reviewing Key Concepts

Multiple Choice *Choose the letter of the best answer.*

4. Which of the following is most likely to show evidence of a year with low rainfall? (7.4.e)
   a. tree rings
   c. original remains
   b. index fossils
   d. sedimentary rock

5. In which time span did dinosaurs live? (7.4.g)
   a. Cenozoic era
   c. Paleozoic era
   b. Mesozoic era
   d. Precambrian time

6. Half-life is a measurement of (7.4.d)
   a. fossil age
   b. radioactive breakdown
   c. cold climates
   d. relative age

7. What is the age of Earth? (7.4.d)
   a. 570 million years
   c. 4.6 billion years
   b. 1.1 billion years
   d. 9.5 billion years

8. What was the earliest form of life? (7.4.d)
   a. a fish
   c. a one-celled organism
   b. a fern
   d. a reptile

9. Which statement best describes the theory of uniformitarianism? (7.4.a)
   a. Earth continues to change as it always has.
   b. Earth is changing, but not as quickly as it used to.
   c. Earth is changing, but faster than it used to.
   d. Earth is no longer changing.

10. How does petrified wood form? (7.4.e)
   a. A log falls into water that freezes.
   b. Insects become trapped in the resin of a tree.
   c. Igneous rock covers a log and heats it.
   d. Water seeps through a log, replacing its cells with minerals.

11. A cast fossil is formed from (7.4.e)
   a. igneous rock
   c. amber
   b. a mold
   d. wood

12. Which of these substances best preserves soft parts of an organism? (7.4.e)
   a. sedimentary rock
   c. amber
   b. igneous rock
   d. air

13. Which part of an ancient reptile would you be most likely to see in a rock fossil? (7.4.e)
   a. eye
   c. heart
   b. bone
   d. muscle

14. Which type of fossil would be most likely to show the complete outline of a leaf? (7.4.e)
   a. petrified wood
   c. cast fossil
   b. carbon film
   d. trace fossil

Short Answer *Write a few sentences to answer each question.*

15. Why are no fossils found in igneous rocks? (7.4.e)

16. Why is radiometric dating not useful for determining the absolute ages of sedimentary rocks? (7.4.d)

Thinking Critically

APPLY *Refer to the illustration below to answer the next four questions.*

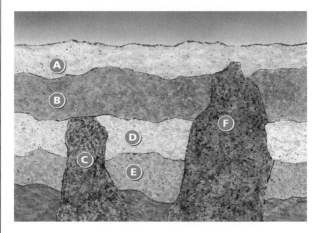

The illustration above is a side view of formations of sedimentary and igneous rock. *C* and *F* are igneous rock.

17. For which of the labeled rock formations could the absolute ages be determined? Why? (7.4.c)

18. Which of the labeled rock formations is the youngest? How do you know? (7.4.c)

19. Which rock is younger, *C* or *D*? Why? (7.4.c)

20. Which of the labeled rock layers is the oldest? Why? (7.4.c)

21. **INFER** Why do you think the Hadean, Archean, and Proterozoic eons are not divided into eras, periods, or epochs? (7.4.g)

22. **COMPARE AND CONTRAST** How is the geologic time scale like a calendar? How is it different? (7.4.g)

23. **CONNECT** Copy the concept map below. Use the geologic time scale on pages 164–165 to complete the map. (7.4.g)

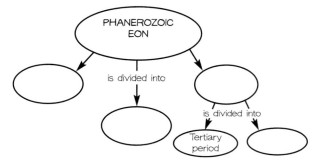

24. **APPLY AND GRAPH** Copy the graph below on your paper. Plot a point on the graph above each of the half-life numbers to show what percentage of the original unstable element remains. Note that the first point has been placed on the graph to show that all of the original element remains at the beginning, when no half-lives have passed. (7.4.d)

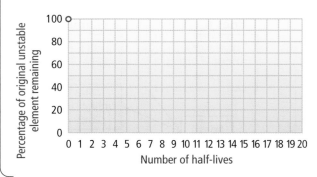

the BIG idea

25. **SYNTHESIZE** Look at the geologic time scale and think about the major events in the history of Earth and the changes in life forms that it shows. How do rocks, fossils, and other natural evidence tell Earth's story? (7.4.g)

26. **PREDICT** What do you think will remain as evidence of today's world 100,000 years from now? How will the types of evidence differ from those that remain from 100,000 years ago? (7.4.a)

UNIT PROJECTS

If you are doing a unit project, make a folder for your project. Include in your folder a list of the resources you will need, the date on which the project is due, and a schedule to keep track of your progress. Begin gathering data.

Analyzing a Diagram

7.4.c, 7.4.e

This diagram shows a cross section of rock layers. All of the layers are sedimentary, except for the area marked as igneous. Use the diagram to answer the questions below.

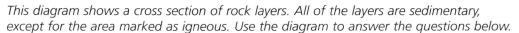

1. What is the approximate age of the oldest ammonite fossil shown in the diagram?

   a. 65 million years   **c.** 480 million years

   b. 248 million years   **d.** 540 million years

2. When did trilobites live on Earth?

   a. within the last 65 million years

   b. between 65 million years ago and 248 million years ago

   c. between 248 million years ago and 544 million years ago

   d. more than 544 million years ago

3. Which fossils are most common in the rock that is 500 million years old?

   a. brachiopods   **c.** ammonites

   b. trilobites   **d.** theropods

4. What is the best estimate of the age of rock I?

   a. less than 300 million years old

   b. 300 million years old

   c. more than 300 million years old

   d. more than 544 million years old

5. Which point shows where a fossil that is 500 million years old would most likely be found?

   a. E   **c.** G

   b. F   **d.** H

Extended Response

Answer the two questions below in detail.
Include some of the terms shown in the word box.
In your answers, underline each term you use.

index fossils	original remains	igneous rock
layers	folded	bent
ice core	tree ring	trilobite

6. Azeem is part of a team of scientists studying the natural history of a region. What types of natural evidence might he and his team look for? Why?

7. In studying fossils found in her community, Yvette noticed a pattern in their ages. People found older fossils close to the surface and younger fossils at greater depths. Explain how that might be.

CHAPTER

Evolution of Living Things

the **BIG** idea

Species develop and change over time.

Key Concepts

SECTION

1 Earth has been home to living things for about 3.8 billion years.
Learn how fossils help explain the development of life on Earth.

SECTION

2 Species change over time.
Learn how species develop and change.

SECTION

3 Environmental changes can affect populations.
Learn how changes in the environment affect the sizes and survival of populations.

SECTION

4 Many types of evidence support evolution.
Learn about the evidence that supports evolution.

 California ClassZone

CLASSZONE.COM

Chapter 6 online resources: Simulation, three Resource Centers, Math Tutorial, Test Practice

How do scientists learn about the evolution of living things?

EXPLORE (the BIG idea)

What Can Rocks Show About Earth's History?

7.4.e Students know fossils provide evidence of how life and environmental conditions have changed.

Look closely at two rocks from different places or at the two rocks shown below. What are the characteristics of each rock? Consider the shape of the rock, its color, and its texture. What have you learned about how rocks are formed that might help you infer which rocks might contain fossils? Can you see evidence of living things in one of them?

Observe and Think
How could the evidence you gathered from your observations help you describe Earth's history?

Internet Activity: Matching Finch Beaks

7.3.b Students know the reasoning used by Charles Darwin in reaching his conclusion that natural selection is the mechanism of evolution.

Go to **ClassZone.com** to match different finch beaks with the foods the birds eat. Learn how each type of beak functions.

Observe and Think
Can you think of any other types of beaks birds have and how they relate to the food these birds eat?

NSTA
scilinks.org
SCiLINKS

The Fossil Record **Code: MDL036**

Getting Ready to Learn

◀ **CONCEPT REVIEW**

- Earth was formed more than 4 billion years ago.
- Living things interact with their environment.
- Fossils are deposited in rock layers.

◀ **VOCABULARY REVIEW**

DNA p. 74

See Glossary for definitions.

cell, genetic material, niche, organism, species, theory

CONTENT REVIEW
CLASSZONE.COM

Review concepts and vocabulary.

▶ **TAKING NOTES**

MAIN IDEA AND DETAILS

Make a two-column chart. Write the main ideas, such as those in the blue headings, in the column on the left. Write details about each of those main ideas in the column on the right.

VOCABULARY STRATEGY

Write each new vocabulary term in the center of a **frame game** diagram. Decide what information to frame it with. Use examples, descriptions, and parts of sentences that use the term in context or pictures. You can change the frame to fit each item.

See the Note-Taking Handbook on pages R45–R51.

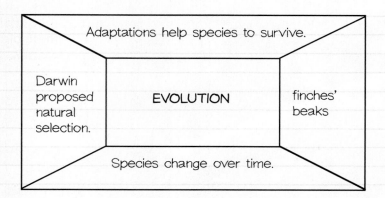

SCIENCE NOTEBOOK

MAIN IDEAS	DETAILS
1. Fossils provide evidence of earlier life.	• Bones, prints, minerals • Relative dating compares fossils • Absolute dating uses the level of radioactivity

Adaptations help species to survive.

Darwin proposed natural selection.

EVOLUTION

finches' beaks

Species change over time.

KEY CONCEPT

Earth has been home to living things for about 3.8 billion years.

CALIFORNIA
Content Standards

7.4.b Students know the history of life on Earth has been disrupted by major catastrophic events, such as major volcanic eruptions or the impacts of asteroids.

7.4.e Students know fossils provide evidence of how life and environmental conditions have changed.

VOCABULARY

extinction p. 189
mass extinction p. 189

◀ **BEFORE, you learned**

- Living things are diverse
- Living things share common characteristics
- A species is a group of living things that can produce off-spring that also can reproduce

▶ **NOW, you will learn**

- How scientists use fossils to learn about the history of life
- How organisms evolved more complex forms over time
- About mass extinctions

EXPLORE Fossils (7.4.e)

What can you infer from the marks an object leaves behind?

PROCEDURE

① Press a layer of clay into the petri dish.

② Choose a small object and press it into the clay to make an imprint of your object.

③ Remove the object carefully and trade your imprint with a classmate.

WHAT DO YOU THINK?

- What object made the imprint?
- What do your observations indicate to you about how the imprint was formed?

MATERIALS
- clay
- petri dish
- small object

Fossils provide evidence of earlier life.

> **REMINDER**
>
> Layers of rock are deposited on top of each other. This means that the oldest layers are at the bottom of a sequence, while the newer layers are near the top.

You have learned that changes recorded in rocks over time tell us about the history of Earth and its organisms. Layers of rock tell us about climate shifts. Layers can also tell us about the movements of continents and resulting events such as volcanic eruptions. Traces of organisms within the rock layers also tell us about changes in the environment.

The information provided by fossils and their location in rocks is called the fossil record. The fossil record lets scientists identify periods during which different species existed. By looking at rock layers, scientists can tell when species disappeared and when new species appeared. This is because fossils were left in a rock layer during the time that layer was formed.

 CHECK YOUR READING What is the fossil record?

More complex organisms developed over time.

Scientists study the fossil record to understand how organisms evolved into more complex forms. Fossil evidence shows that the first living things were simple prokaryotes. Recall that a prokaryote is a unicellular, or single-celled, organism without a nucleus. The earliest prokaryotes were able to survive in the environment of the early Earth. As Earth itself changed over time, so did the organisms that lived on it. In fact, some of these organisms helped to change the conditions on Earth itself.

READING TIP

Uni- means "single," and *multi-* means "several" or "many."

Early Forms of Life

When Earth first formed about 4.5 billion years ago, it was too hot to support life. But Earth's surface cooled and a solid crust formed. Gases such as methane and carbon dioxide formed an atmosphere. There was little nitrogen or oxygen as in today's atmosphere. Gradually, Earth's surface cooled enough for oceans to form.

By 3.8 billion years ago, conditions were still harsh compared to today. But Earth had changed enough to support simple life forms. The earliest known organisms in the fossil record are simple prokaryotes called cyanobacteria (SY-uh-noh-bak-TEER-ee-uh).

Stromatolites are the oldest known fossils on Earth. They were formed by mats of cyanobacteria that were glued to each other in layers.

The cyanobacteria lived in huge groups that formed enormous mats. Some mats floated on the surface of the ocean. Others covered parts of the sea floor. The bacteria produced minerals and substances that "glued" the mats to each other in layers. The fossils of these layered mats of bacteria and minerals are called stromatolites.

Cyanobacteria lived well in Earth's early conditions. They contained chlorophyll and used photosynthesis to make sugars from carbon dioxide. The bacteria produced oxygen as a by-product of photosynthesis. Because there were so many cyanobacteria, oxygen levels in the atmosphere increased.

Gradually, Earth's atmosphere changed. Oxygen increased, while methane and ammonia levels decreased. By 2 billion years ago, there was enough oxygen to support a new life form—eukaryotes.

CHECK YOUR READING How did Earth's oxygen levels get to their current level?

Multicellular Organisms

When the oxygen levels on Earth increased, organisms that used oxygen thrived. Some organisms had structures that helped them use the oxygen efficiently. They used oxygen to release the energy stored in sugars. These structures were mitochondria.

Many scientists think that mitochondria were once free-living cells. They might have become joined with larger prokaryotes into a new type of organism with a nucleus. These cells became the first eukaryotes. Within the larger cells, the mitochondria used oxygen to get energy from sugars. The oldest known fossils of eukaryotes are from algae that lived about 2 billion years ago.

The first eukaryotes were single-celled. Most likely, different types of eukaryotes were better at certain tasks—for example, movement or digestion. Many cells probably grew in colonies. At some point, cells from different colonies may have fused together, forming the first multicellular eukaryotic organisms. Over time these evolved into larger organisms. Scientists are not sure exactly how multicellular organisms arose, but they have a good idea about when they evolved. The oldest fossils of multicellular organisms are from tiny algae that lived about 1.5 billion years ago. By 600 million years ago the first multicellular animals—jellyfish-like organisms—had evolved.

▼ **REMINDER**

A symbiotic relationship is one in which two organisms exist and function together.

CALIFORNIA Focus

California fossil hunters can collect fossils of trilobites, which were early ocean animals, near Amboy in the Mohave Desert. The trilobites lived about 560 million years ago. These multicellular animals were among the first to have eyes and skeletons.

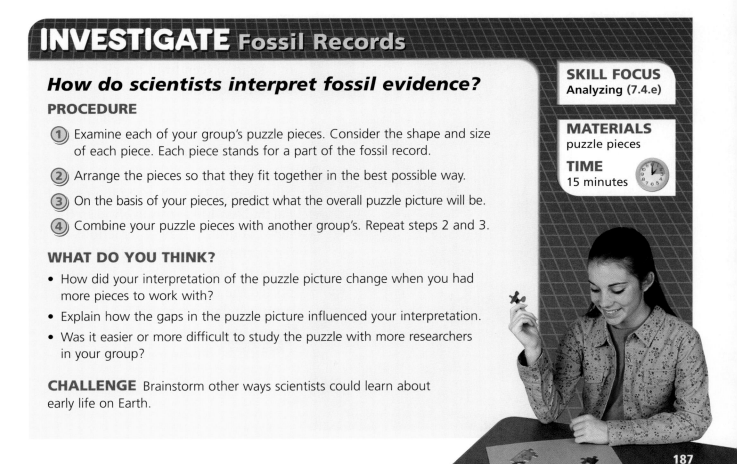

INVESTIGATE Fossil Records

How do scientists interpret fossil evidence?

PROCEDURE

1. Examine each of your group's puzzle pieces. Consider the shape and size of each piece. Each piece stands for a part of the fossil record.

2. Arrange the pieces so that they fit together in the best possible way.

3. On the basis of your pieces, predict what the overall puzzle picture will be.

4. Combine your puzzle pieces with another group's. Repeat steps 2 and 3.

WHAT DO YOU THINK?

- How did your interpretation of the puzzle picture change when you had more pieces to work with?

- Explain how the gaps in the puzzle picture influenced your interpretation.

- Was it easier or more difficult to study the puzzle with more researchers in your group?

CHALLENGE Brainstorm other ways scientists could learn about early life on Earth.

SKILL FOCUS
Analyzing (7.4.e)

MATERIALS
puzzle pieces

TIME
15 minutes

Life on Land

Liverworts are tiny nonvascular plants. The liverworts shown here are life-size.

All of the events you have just read about took place in water. Life on Earth arose in the seas. About 460 million years ago, the first living things began to live on dry land.

Before you learn about these pioneers, consider the challenges of living on dry land. Recall that cells need water to carry out their life processes. Cells in water don't dry out. Organisms that lived on land needed new ways to help them get water. Organisms that lived in water did not have these problems because their cells and bodies were surrounded by water.

The first organisms to wash ashore and survive had features that helped them survive a drier habitat. These pioneers would have lived most easily in moist areas such as shorelines. Bacteria and algae were the first life forms to survive on land. The first plants, similar to those shown below, probably evolved from algae. The leaves of these plants were covered with a waxy substance that prevented them from drying out. Fungi probably evolved around the same time as plants.

The first terrestrial, or land-dwelling, animals were primitive insects. They colonized land about 400 million years ago. These insects probably evolved from hard-shelled aquatic animals such as crabs. The insects' bodies had a tough waxy covering that protected them from drying out. They were able to take in oxygen from the air instead of from the water.

Over time, bacteria, algae, plants, fungi, and insects began to spread to new habitats. Conditions in these habitats changed as the movement of tectonic plates changed the face of Earth. New life forms evolved in the new conditions. The interactions of living things also changed the face of Earth. These changes, in turn, supported the rise of more complex multicellular organisms.

 CHECK YOUR READING What were the first organisms to live on dry land?

Earth's history includes mass extinctions.

Even before the first living things began to live on dry land, many new life forms were developing in the oceans. Many new forms of marine, or ocean-dwelling, invertebrates evolved during the Cambrian period (544–505 million years ago). The first sharks and other fish also appear in the fossil record during this time. This period is sometimes called the Cambrian Explosion because so many species evolved in such a short time.

Just as species can arise, however, they also can go extinct. **Extinction** is the loss of all of the members of a species. During Earth's history, there have been several periods when huge numbers of species have become extinct in a very short time. These events are called **mass extinctions.** The fossil record shows a pattern of at least five mass extinctions during Earth's history. Of these, the Permian extinction and the Cretaceous extinction are the best studied.

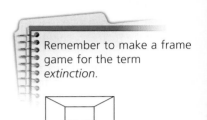

Remember to make a frame game for the term *extinction*.

Permian Extinction

The explosion of new species that began during the Cambrian period continued over the next several hundred million years. By the Permian period (286–248 million years ago), Earth was teeming with species. The oceans contained a great diversity of animals, including corals, jawless fish, and fast-swimming squidlike animals.

By the the end of the Permian period, however, roughly 95 percent of the species on Earth had become extinct. This was the largest mass extinction in Earth's history. Many hypotheses have been put forth to explain the Permian extinction. Some evidence shows that both carbon dioxide levels and global temperatures began to rise in the late Permian. This would have lowered sea levels, destroying marine ecosystems. Other studies point to high levels of volcanic activity in the late Permian. Many major volcanic eruptions would have sent large amounts of volcanic ash into Earth's atmosphere. If the ash prevented sunlight from reaching Earth, even for a short period, many species would have died off as temperatures dropped.

Many simple animals, such as worms and sponges, lived on the seafloor during the Permian period. Algae, mossy plants, and animals resembling modern snails and clams covered coastal areas.

CHECK YOUR READING Why is the Permian extinction so important?

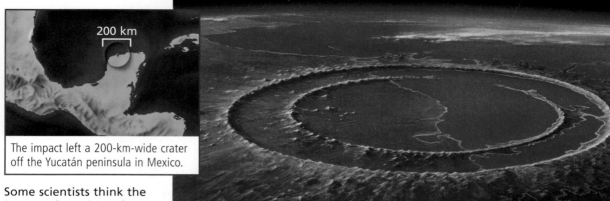

Chicxulub Crater

The impact left a 200-km-wide crater off the Yucatán peninsula in Mexico.

Some scientists think the impact of an object from space off the coast of Mexico caused the Cretaceous extinction.

RESOURCE CENTER
CLASSZONE.COM

Find out more about mass extinctions.

Cretaceous Extinction

By the start of the Cretaceous period some 145 million years ago, Earth was again teeming with different species. Land habitats had changed as organisms evolved and interacted. Many types of plants had evolved. Animals had become a widespread and highly diverse group. The earliest mammals had evolved, as had many other vertebrates. The dominant group of land animals, however, was dinosaurs.

Yet 80 million years later, the dinosaurs were gone. The fossil record shows that this group became extinct very quickly, possibly in less than two million years. More than half of the other species on Earth vanished as well. A very large object from space collided with Earth about 65 million years ago. Most scientists think that the collision and its aftereffects wiped out most of the life forms on Earth. This mass extinction ended the Cretaceous period. The impact formed Chicxulub Crater, a 200-kilometer-wide crater that lies off the coast of Mexico.

 CHECK YOUR READING What do scientists think caused the Cretaceous extinction?

6.1 Review

KEY CONCEPTS

1. How do fossils help scientists learn about the history of life? (7.4.e)

2. How do scientists think that the first multicellular organisms arose? (7.4.e)

3. What is extinction? Give an example of a mass extinction and describe its results. (7.4.b)

CRITICAL THINKING

4. **Infer** What does the presence of mitochondria in each cell suggest about multicellular organisms?

5. **Sequence** Draw a timeline connecting three major events in the history of life. Include these terms on your timeline: *cyanobacteria, multicellular, land, mass extinction.*

⬤ CHALLENGE

6. **Summarize** How has the number of species changed over time? Include three events as well as slower changes.

6.2 Species change over time.

CALIFORNIA
Content Standards

7.3.a Students know both genetic variation and environmental factors are causes of evolution and diversity of organisms.

7.3.b Students know the reasoning used by Charles Darwin in reaching his conclusion that natural selection is the mechanism of evolution.

VOCABULARY

evolution p. 191
natural selection p. 195
population p. 196
genetic variation p. 196
adaptation p. 196
environmental factors p. 196
speciation p. 198

◀ BEFORE, you learned

• Fossils are evidence of earlier life
• More complex organisms have developed over time
• Mass extinctions happen rapidly in geologic time

▶ NOW, you will learn

• About early ideas and observations on evolution
• How Darwin developed his theory of natural selection
• How new species arise

THINK ABOUT

How have telephones changed over time?

Today people across the world can communicate in many different ways. One of the most common ways is over the telephone. Looking at the two pictures, can you describe how this form of communication has changed over time?

Scientists explore the concept of evolution.

MAIN IDEA AND DETAILS
Make a chart for the main idea *Scientists explore the concept of evolution.* Include details about scientists' observations.

In a general sense, evolution involves change over time. You could say that the way humans communicate has evolved. Certainly telephones have changed over time. The first telephones were the size of a shoebox. Today a telephone can fit in the palm of your hand and can send images as well as sound.

In biology, **evolution** refers to the process through which species change over time. Unlike changes in telephone technology, changes in species result from a change in the genetic material of an organism. That material is passed from one generation to the next.

CHECK YOUR READING What is evolution?

Early Ideas

READING TIP

The word *acquire* comes from the root meaning "to add to." Acquired traits are those that are "added" after an organism is born.

In the early 1700s many scientists began to see that species changed over time. Their evidence included observations of the natural world and the fossil record. But no one proposed a strong theory for *how* species changed. The first person to do so was the French naturalist Jean Baptiste de Lamarck. In the early 1800s he proposed that during their lifetimes, organisms change in response to their environment. For example, giraffes had long necks because their ancestors had stretched their necks while reaching for leaves high in a tree. If an acquired trait was useful, it was passed on. Traits that were not useful were not passed on. In this way species changed over time. Lamarck's ideas were later rejected by most scientists. However, he was the first to suggest a reasonable explanation for how evolution occurs.

CHECK YOUR READING How did Lamarck explain the process of evolution?

Darwin's Voyage

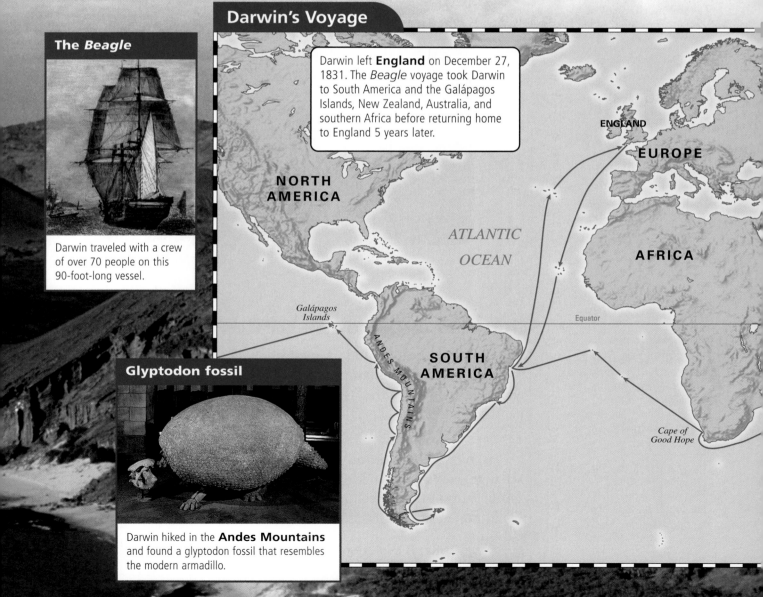

The *Beagle*

Darwin traveled with a crew of over 70 people on this 90-foot-long vessel.

Darwin left **England** on December 27, 1831. The *Beagle* voyage took Darwin to South America and the Galápagos Islands, New Zealand, Australia, and southern Africa before returning home to England 5 years later.

NORTH AMERICA

ATLANTIC OCEAN

ENGLAND

EUROPE

AFRICA

Galápagos Islands

Equator

SOUTH AMERICA

ANDES MOUNTAINS

Cape of Good Hope

Glyptodon fossil

Darwin hiked in the **Andes Mountains** and found a glyptodon fossil that resembles the modern armadillo.

Darwin's Observations

In 1859 the British naturalist Charles Darwin published a book about a voyage he had taken almost 30 years before. He had traveled for five years to many parts of the world. He had served as a naturalist aboard the *Beagle,* a British navy ship. The book described his observations and proposed a new theory for how evolution works.

As he traveled through South America, Darwin studied rock formations and collected fossils. He compared the new plants and animals he was seeing with ones from his own country. Darwin was struck by how different many of these organisms were from those he had seen before. These differences became stronger when he visited the Galápagos (guh-LAH-puh-guhs) Islands. This chain of islands lies about 965 kilometers (600 mi) off the western South American coast. Plants and animals in the Galápagos differed from those Darwin had seen on the mainland. Some even differed from island to island.

Darwin was only 22 when he joined the *Beagle* expedition in 1831.

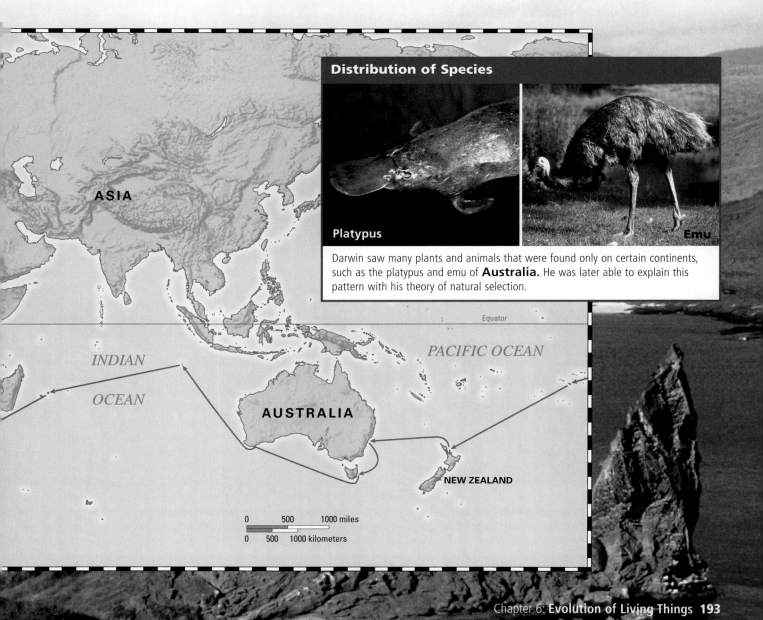

Distribution of Species

Platypus

Emu

Darwin saw many plants and animals that were found only on certain continents, such as the platypus and emu of **Australia.** He was later able to explain this pattern with his theory of natural selection.

ASIA

INDIAN OCEAN

PACIFIC OCEAN

Equator

AUSTRALIA

NEW ZEALAND

0   500   1000 miles
0   500   1000 kilometers

Darwin observed several types of tortoises on the islands. Tortoises with short necks lived in damp areas. These areas had many plants that grew close to the ground. Longer-necked tortoises lived in dry areas. Most of the plants in these areas were cacti and other types of dry shrubs.

Darwin also found many different types of birds called finches living on the islands. Although the finches were similar in many ways, they had some dramatic differences. Some lived in treetops. Others lived in low shrubs. Darwin noticed a variety of beak shapes and sizes among the birds of different islands. Some finches had heavy, short beaks useful for cracking seeds. Other finches had long, thin beaks that could capture insects. These observations puzzled Darwin. Had these birds evolved from similar species? If so, why were there so many variations in their beaks? Did habitat play a role in the variations?

Darwin's Finches

On the Galápagos Islands, Darwin observed closely related finch species with very different beaks suited to different habitats on the islands.

Woodpecker Finch

Vegetarian Finch

The woodpecker finch holds a twig in its long pointed beak to pull insect larvae from trees. The curved beak of the vegetarian finch is suited for plucking berries from a branch.

Large Ground Finch

Cactus Finch

The large ground finch has a large beak that can crack open the hard shells of seeds. The cactus finch has a narrow beak that it uses to cut into a cactus and eat the tissue inside.

Natural selection explains how new species can evolve.

After Darwin returned home to England in 1836, he spent several years analyzing his observations and the specimens he had collected on his voyage. He struggled to develop an explanation for the amazing diversity of species he saw and for the relationships among them. By 1844 he had developed a hypothesis based in part on an insight from one of his hobbies—breeding pigeons.

From personal experience Darwin knew that breeders can produce new varieties of animals over time. For example, breeders can produce a new dog breed by selecting dogs that have certain desired traits. The breeders then mate those individuals with each other. From the resulting litters, they again select and breed only those dogs with the desired traits. By repeating this process generation after generation, a new breed can be produced. This process is called artificial selection.

RESOURCE CENTER
CLASSZONE.COM

Learn more about natural selection.

 CHECK YOUR READING What is artificial selection?

Artificial Selection

Cairn   Airedale   Tibetan

COMPARE AND CONTRAST These dogs are all terriers, but they have been bred through artificial selection to show very specific traits. How are the dogs similar? How are they different?

Darwin's insight was that a similar process happened in nature. He proposed that individuals that are best suited to their environment survive and reproduce at a higher rate than other members of their species in that environment. Darwin called this process **natural selection** and based it on four key principles. These principles are overproduction, variation, adaptation, and selection.

Overproduction

READING TiP

As you read about the principles of natural selection, refer to the diagrams on page 197.

Let's look at Darwin's ideas by studying natural selection in a population of salmon. A **population** is a group of individuals of the same species that live in a particular environment or area. In nature, organisms usually produce more offspring than their environment can support. This is called overproduction. A female salmon may lay several thousand eggs, but only a fraction will hatch. Only a few hundred of those will survive disease and predators. Several dozen of these survivors will live to adulthood. An even smaller number will reproduce.

Variation

REMINDER

The genetic material of an individual or a population is its DNA.

If you looked at thousands of salmon, you would see slight differences among individuals. Some might have larger fins, while others might have stripes on their scales. Many variations result from differences in the DNA of the fish. Differences in DNA in a population make up its **genetic variation.**

Where does genetic variation come from? Offspring get a mix of chromosomes from both parents. Even the chromosomes can change. During meiosis, a pair of chromosomes can exchange segments of DNA. A fish that inherits the new variation may pass it on to its own offspring.

Adaptation

Different traits can offer an advantage in different environments. In a fast-moving river or stream, a slight difference in the shape of a tail fin may increase a fish's chance of survival. The new shape might help it swim faster and avoid predators. An inherited trait that gives an organism an advantage in its particular environment is called an **adaptation.**

Selection

Environmental factors are conditions that affect survival. They include food supply, habitat, predators, and disease, among others. Individuals with an adaptation useful in their environment have a good chance of living long enough to reproduce. They will pass their adaptive traits to their offspring. Over time, the useful trait will become more common in the population. This is called selection. For selection to occur, there must be genetic variation in the population. Selection itself is caused by a population's environmental factors. Individuals without the useful trait are less likely to survive and reproduce. In this way, species evolve, or change over time, through natural selection.

 CHECK YOUR READING What must be present in a population for selection to occur?

Natural Selection

Certain traits become more common in a group of organisms through the process of natural selection.

Overproduction

A fish may lay hundreds of eggs, but only a small number will survive to reach adulthood.

Variation

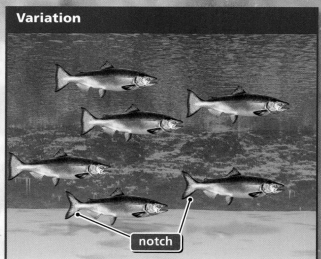

A variation in the genes of some fish may cause their tails to develop a slight notch.

Adaptation

Fish with a notched tail may be able to swim more quickly and escape predators. These fish pass the trait to their offspring.

Selection

With each generation, more fish with notched tails survive to reproduce. Over time, they make up a larger part of the group.

READING VISUALS What are three environmental factors affecting each salmon's chance of survival? What is the adaptation that helps them survive?

New species develop from earlier species.

Darwin's personal observations and the work of another scientist, Alfred Wallace, led Darwin to write about evolution by natural selection. In 1859, after more than twenty years of research, Darwin published his ideas in his book *On the Origin of Species*. This work led the way for our modern understanding of evolution.

Darwin's study of the Galápagos finches also led to an important insight about how species arise. Darwin had noted how isolated each island was from other islands and from the mainland. He observed that finches on each island mated only with other finches on that island. None of the island finches mated with mainland finches. As each finch population adapted to its own environmental factors, it became more and more different from the other island and mainland populations.

Today, when populations are too genetically different to breed and produce offspring, they are considered to be separate species. Darwin's observations inspired scientists to study how the isolation of populations may contribute to the rise of new species. The evolution of a new species from an existing species is called **speciation.** A new barrier—such as a split in a continent due to plate tectonics—can divide a population. A species of fish called cichlids (SIHK-lihdz) shows how a physical barrier can lead to speciation.

Speciation

In this African lake, new species of cichlids have evolved.

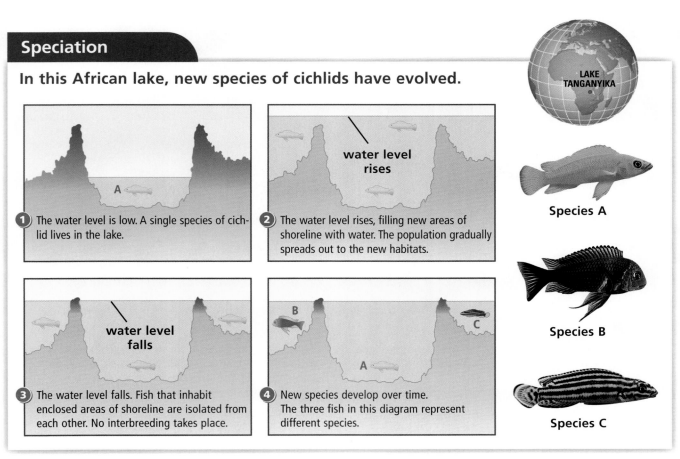

LAKE TANGANYIKA

1. The water level is low. A single species of cichlid lives in the lake.

2. The water level rises, filling new areas of shoreline with water. The population gradually spreads out to the new habitats.

water level rises

3. The water level falls. Fish that inhabit enclosed areas of shoreline are isolated from each other. No interbreeding takes place.

water level falls

4. New species develop over time. The three fish in this diagram represent different species.

Species A

Species B

Species C

Lake Tanganyika (TAN-guhn-YEE-kuh) is one of the largest lakes in the world. It contains at least 200 species of cichlids. Originally, just one population of cichlids lived along the rocky shore. The climate and geology of the area caused the lake's water level to rise and fall many times over thousands of years. As the water level changed, a new, rocky habitat was formed, and some populations of cichlids became isolated from each other.

As the diagram on page 198 shows, the isolated populations could not interact with each other because of barriers between them. As a result, genetic differences began to add up in these populations. The cichlid populations are now different species. They have developed unique characteristics and cannot breed with each other.

Today scientists understand that isolation is a key factor that leads to speciation. For a species to separate, two populations must be prevented from reproducing with each other. A geographic boundary like an ocean or a mountain range or a desert can result in isolation. Two populations of a species can also be isolated from each other if they feed on different things or reproduce at different times of the year.

As the cichlids in Lake Tanganyika show, the variations in one isolated group may differ from another. Two or more populations may evolve differently from each other. The result is speciation, which has contributed to the biodiversity on Earth.

The hills and deserts of Death Valley, California, are both examples of geographic barriers that can isolate populations.

 CHECK YOUR READING Name a key factor that can lead to speciation.

6.2 Review

KEY CONCEPTS

1. How did Lamarck's ideas differ from Darwin's? (7.3.b)
2. What did Darwin observe in the finch populations that supported his idea of natural selection? (7.3.b)
3. Explain how isolation can lead to speciation. (7.3.a)

CRITICAL THINKING

4. **Hypothesize** Two species of grass are separated by a tall mountain range. A third species of grass shares some characteristics with each of the other two species. It inhabits a small valley, surrounded on all sides by mountains. Form a hypothesis for the origin of the third species.

CHALLENGE

5. **Predict** The Arctic hare lives in snow-covered mountains in Canada. The hare is hunted by foxes, wolves, and owls. Which trait is more likely to be inherited by new generations of hares: white fur or black fur? Explain your reasoning.

CHAPTER INVESTIGATION

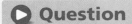

Bird Beak Adaptations

OVERVIEW AND PURPOSE The beaks of most birds are adapted for eating particular types of food. In this lab you will

- use models to imitate how different types of beaks function
- infer how the shape of a bird's beak might affect the food a bird eats

▶ Question

Write It Up

For this lab, you will use a tool as a model of a specialized bird beak. You will try to obtain food with your beak at several different feeding stations. Each station will have a different type of food. Examine the tools that will be used for this lab, as well as the feeding stations. Then write a question about how beak shape might affect the food a bird eats. Your question should begin with *Which, How, When, Why,* or *What.* Keep in mind that you will be asked to answer this question at the end of the lab.

▶ Procedure

1. Make a data table like the one shown on page 201.

2. Complete the title of your data table by writing in the name of the tool you will be using.

3. Before you start collecting food at one of the feeding stations, write a prediction in your data table. Predict how well you think the tool will function with this food and why.

MATERIALS
- tweezers
- eyedropper
- slotted spoon
- pliers
- test tubes in rack
- water
- dried pasta
- millet seeds
- jar of rubber bands
- empty containers
- stopwatch

  7.3.a, 7.7.c

Content Standard
7.3.a Students know both genetic variation and environmental factors are causes of evolution and diversity of organisms.

Investigation Standard
7.7.c Students will communicate the logical connection among hypotheses, science concepts, tests conducted, data collected, and conclusions drawn from scientific evidence.

4 Use the tool to collect as much food as you can in one minute. To collect food, you must move it from the feeding station into a different container. You may only touch the food with the tool.

step 4

5 Describe your results in your data table.

6 Return the food you collected to the feeding station. Try to make it look just like it did when you started.

7 Repeat steps 3–6 at each of the other feeding stations.

Observe and Analyze
Write It Up

1. **INTERPRET DATA** At which feeding station did you have the best results? Why? Explain your answer.

2. **EVALUATE** How accurate were the predictions you made?

3. **APPLY** If you could visit each feeding station again, how would you change the way you used the tool to collect food? Explain your answer.

Conclude
Write It Up

1. **INFER** Answer the question you wrote at the beginning of this lab.

2. **INFER** In what ways do you think the experience you had during this lab is similar to the ways real birds obtain food?

3. **IDENTIFY LIMITATIONS** What unexpected factors or problems might have affected your results?

4. **SYNTHESIZE** What environmental and physical factors can a bird actually control when it is getting food?

5. **APPLY** Examine the beaks of the birds in the photographs below. Write a brief description of the shape of each bird's beak. Then, for each bird, name one type of food its beak might be suited for and one type of food each bird would probably not be able to eat.

INVESTIGATE Further

CHALLENGE How are other parts of birds' bodies specialized for the environments where they live? Investigate the feet of the following birds: ostrich, heron, woodpecker, pelican, and owl.

Bird Beak Adaptations

Question:

Table 1. Collecting Food with_____

Station	Prediction	Results
Water in test tubes		
Dried pasta		
Millet seeds		
Rubber bands in jar		

6.3 Environmental changes can affect populations.

CALIFORNIA
Content standard

7.3.e Students know that extinction of a species occurs when the environment changes and the adaptive characteristics of a species are insufficient for its survival.

BEFORE, you learned

• Species change over time
• Organisms need resources such as energy and space
• Organisms in an ecosystem affect one another

NOW, you will learn

• How populations increase and decrease in size
• What factors affect population size and survival
• How a species can become extinct

VOCABULARY

immigration p. 203
emigration p. 204
limiting factor p. 204

THINK ABOUT

How large can populations grow?

What would happen if a population reproduced without limits? Take fruit flies—one pair can produce 200 eggs in two weeks. If each pair of flies from each generation produced 200 eggs every two weeks, the population would grow to two million flies in six weeks. In less than eight months, the mass of fruit flies would exceed the mass of Earth! Could this really happen? How do resources such as food, water, and space affect population size?

Population size is limited by environmental conditions.

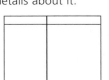

MAIN IDEA AND DETAILS
As you read this section, record each main idea and details about it.

Darwin based his theory of evolution on conclusions he had drawn after observing many populations in nature. Whether the populations were made up of finches, tortoises, or flowers, two things seemed to always hold true.

• All populations have the ability to grow rapidly over time.
• Populations tend to remain about the same size.

This puzzled Darwin. If populations *could* increase greatly in size but *usually didn't*, what was holding them back?

 CHECK YOUR READING What did Darwin notice in all of the populations he observed?

Darwin knew that, just like individual organisms, populations need certain resources to survive. He also knew that these resources—food, water, shelter, mates, and so forth—are limited in nature. Therefore, he reasoned, these resources acted as natural limits to population size.

Populations are like individuals. Both vary in their ability to get and to use resources. Only those who are successful survive. But populations have an extra pressure: to survive, a population's size must be stable. Populations cannot have too many or too few members for very long.

READING TiP

The word *stable* means that little change is occurring. In a stable population, the number of individuals remains fairly constant over time.

Populations increase through births and immigration.

When the environment contains more than enough resources to meet the needs of a population, the population increases in size. High birth rates are a key factor. If the number of births is greater than the number of deaths in a given time period, population size increases.

Immigration is another way population size increases. **Immigration** is the movement of individuals into a population. For example, if wind blows plant seeds from one area into another, the seeds are said to be immigrating into the new area. If they have plenty of sunlight, water, and other resources, the immigrants will survive and reproduce. The population's size will increase because of the immigrant seeds as well as their offspring. Immigration also helps a population that is decreasing in size to become stable.

CHECK YOUR READING How does immigration affect population size?

Each fuzzy particle of a dandelion's head is attached to a seed. The seeds are adapted to be carried by wind to an area away from the parent. The movement of seeds into a new area is called immigration.

Many factors limit population size.

When there are too many population members and not enough resources for each, population size decreases. There are two ways this decline can happen. A large number of deaths is one way. If there are more deaths than births during a given time period, population size falls.

Population size also decreases if members leave. **Emigration** is the movement of individuals out of a population. Individuals may emigrate to areas with more resources or fewer individuals. Emigration can help stabilize a population that is growing too quickly.

Environmental factors that limit population size are called **limiting factors.** These factors include resources such as food, water, light, space, shelter, and air. Other organisms also act as limiting factors. Sudden changes in the environment, such as those caused by a huge storm or fire, can become limiting factors.

READING TiP

The prefix *im-* in *immigration* means "into." The prefix *e-*, as in *emigration*, means "out" or "away."

Competition

Competition for resources is a natural part of life. When your parents shop for tomatoes, they are competing with all the other shoppers at the market. If there are plenty of tomatoes, competition isn't too rough. But if tomatoes are scarce, some shoppers may leave for another store. Others may go home empty-handed.

Competition can occur between different species or between members of the same species. These wolf cubs will compete for food, shelter, mates, and other resources.

When resources are scarce in the natural world, competition can become a matter of life and death. Competition can occur between members of the same species or between different species. The wolf cubs pictured here will compete for food, shelter, and other resources. If the population size grows too large, more and more wolves will compete for the same resources. Some wolves may emigrate to another area. Others, such as those that are unhealthy, very young, or very old, may starve to death or fall prey to predators.

Predators

Predators are animals that prey on other animals. They play a major role in limiting population size. Sharks, for example, play a key role in keeping certain fish populations stable. Without sharks, the fish populations might quickly outgrow their food supplies. Raptors such as owls and hawks keep field-rodent populations in check.

Raptors, such as the eagle pictured here, are birds that prey on small animals, such as rodents, rabbits, reptiles, and other birds.

Disease

Disease also plays a role in limiting population size. As populations grow, closer contact among members increases the chances for diseases to spread. Individuals that have not developed natural defenses against some diseases will become ill, and many will die. In the early 1900s American chestnut trees were infected by a fungus. By 1950 almost every American chestnut tree in the United States had been destroyed.

Catastrophic Events

Events such as wildfires, hurricanes, floods, and droughts are called catastrophic events. Such events can almost wipe out a population. For example, a drought on the Galápagos Islands in 1977 caused a severe drop in the population of one species of finch. The drought reduced the quantity of seeds on which the finch species feeds. The finch population dropped from about 1400 to about 200 individuals. Although the drought ended in 1978, it was many years before the finch population increased to a healthy size again.

 Name four types of limiting factors in populations.

Natural disasters, such as wildfires, can change environmental conditions in very short periods of time.

INVESTIGATE Natural Selection

How do species survive?

PROCEDURE

1. Place 5 large red paper clips, 5 small red paper clips and 5 small blue paper clips on a sheet of blue construction paper. Each type of paper clip represents a different population of a single species of fish.

2. Roll the number cube. If you roll a 1, remove a small blue paper clip. If you roll a 2 or 3, remove a small red paper clip. If you roll a number between 3 and 6, remove a large red paper clip.

3. Continue rolling the number cube until only one type of fish population (paper clip) remains.

WHAT DO YOU THINK?

- What did rolling the number cube represent in this activity? How did this activity model natural selection?

- Why do you think a small population of blue fish might survive in an ecosystem when populations of small red fish and large red fish would not?

CHALLENGE Make your own game that models natural selection. Explain how your game models the process of natural selection.

MATERIALS
- 5 large red paper clips
- 5 small red paper clips
- 5 small blue paper clips
- sheet of blue construction paper
- number cube

TIME
15 minutes

The survival of a species depends on its ability to adapt to change.

Over the millions of years that life has existed on Earth, new species have appeared and others have disappeared. Recall from Section 1 that the disappearance of all members of a species is known as extinction. Species become extinct when they are unable to survive in their environmental conditions.

Just how does extinction happen? A species becomes extinct only after all of its populations have perished. That is, most extinctions happen one population at a time. Individuals that are better adapted to change are more likely to survive and produce offspring. Genetic variation in a population makes it more likely that some individuals will be able to survive environmental changes.

CHECK YOUR READING When does a species become extinct?

How Extinction Happens

Individuals do not become extinct—species do. This happens when all populations of a species die out. A change in the environment may cause individuals to die off quickly. When that happens, population size decreases. The loss of population members decreases the amount of genetic variation in the population. The population may become so small that there are not enough members for each one to find a mate. When the last member dies, the population dies out.

Most populations of a species live fairly close to one another. This means that changes in the environmental conditions of one population may affect other populations. Between 2002 and 2004, an outbreak of Ebola fever killed more than 80 percent of the world's western lowland gorillas. Ebola fever is caused by a deadly virus that also infects humans. Western lowland gorillas live in the rainforests of central and western Africa. They live in scattered populations. However, all of their populations have contact with humans.

The presence of the Ebola virus changed the gorillas' environmental conditions. When the virus appeared in each population, some individuals probably had a natural resistance to the virus. This was because of variations in their genes. Those gorillas survived the outbreak. Gorillas without resistance died. Today the species is not extinct, but it is gravely endangered. Fewer than 100,000 western lowland gorillas exist in nature. It is unlikely that their population sizes will increase rapidly. This is because gorillas are slow to reproduce. These small populations are now even more likely to decrease if their environment changes. Another disease outbreak or the loss of too much habitat could cause the species to go extinct.

When populations become too small, it is difficult for adult members to find mates. Then the population is in danger of dying out.

Extinction and Species Replacement

The loss of a species seems tragic. However, extinction is part of the cycle of life on Earth. The extinction of one species often makes room for other species to thrive. When a species goes extinct, it leaves behind an empty niche in its ecosystem. Other living species or groups with suitable traits can fill this niche.

Mass extinctions often are followed by the sudden appearance of many new species. For example, during the 150 million years before the Cretaceous mass extinction, dinosaurs dominated Earth. The dinosaurs occupied many niches. Mammals also existed during this time. The mammals were not very diverse, however. They occupied few niches. Most mammals were smaller than opossums and fed on insects.

Most scientists think that the Cretaceous extinction began when an object from space struck Earth. Such an impact may have triggered earthquakes and volcanic eruptions. These events would have sent great amounts of dust into the atmosphere. There may have been enough dust to block out sunlight. The dust could have had two key effects. First, photosynthesis would have decreased. This would have caused most plants and algae to die. The loss of plants and algae would have affected the food supply of almost all organisms. Second, global temperatures would have dropped. The dinosaurs were not well adapted for lower temperatures. When they evolved, Earth was fairly warm. Mammals also evolved when Earth was warm. But unlike dinosaurs, the mammals' fur helped them adapt to cooler climates. Other adaptations helped them survive on the decreased food supply. As the dinosaurs died off, the mammals filled the empty niches the dinosaurs left behind.

 CHECK YOUR READING How does the extinction of a species affect its ecosystem?

6.3 Review

KEY CONCEPTS

1. Name two factors that increase population size and two factors that decrease population size. (7.3.e)

2. What factors limit population size? Be specific. (7.3.e)

3. How can a species become extinct? (7.3.e)

CRITICAL THINKING

4. **Analyze** Can you predict population increase based only on birth rate? Why or why not?

5. **Infer** Before 1900 several moth species fed only on the leaves of American chestnut trees. What effect would the deaths of these trees have had on the moth species?

● CHALLENGE

6. **Synthesize** Suppose a newspaper reports an oil spill in Monterey Bay. Six months later you read that the bay's populations of seals, sea otters, and sea birds have declined. What factors may have caused this change? Give reasons for your answer.

Back from the Brink

In 1998 biologists feared that the loggerhead shrike of San Clemente Island was about to become extinct. Scientists could find only 14 birds remaining in the wild. The number of shrikes on the island had begun to drop in the 1880s. At that time ranchers introduced goats, sheep, and pigs to the island. These animals destroyed much of the shrikes' habitat by eating grass and shrubs. The last grazing animals were removed in the 1980s, but the shrike numbers continued to drop. The San Clemente loggerhead shrike has different genes from other North American shrikes. If the last loggerhead shrike dies, the subspecies will be gone forever.

> **7.3.e** Students know that extinction of a species occurs when the environment changes and the adaptive characteristics of a species are insufficient for its survival.

Studying Wild Shrikes

Biologists studied the shrikes to find out what they needed to survive. Shrikes often hunt by waiting on perches until they see an insect or lizard. Then they attack. Scientists installed perches in areas where shrikes had not been seen. This encouraged shrikes to expand their hunting area.

San Clemente Island is the southernmost of the eight California Channel Islands. It lies off the coast of southern California.

Biologists also saw that shrikes tear their prey apart by wedging it between shrub thorns or branches. So the scientists built wedging stations for the birds to use.

The biologists took steps to make it harder for shrikes to be preyed upon by other animals. They collected seeds from native shrubs and planted them around the island. As the shrubs grow, they provide cover for shrikes to nest in and make it easier for them to evade predators.

Captive Breeding Program

Researchers also began raising the shrikes in captivity at the San Diego Zoo. After establishing a captive population, the scientists began to release shrike families into the wild. By 2001 the shrike population on San Clemente had grown to 44. By 2004 almost 200 loggerhead shrikes had been released. Biologists hope to raise that to 700 shrikes—the greatest number of shrikes the island can probably support.

WRITING ABOUT SCIENCE

Write a cause-and-effect essay in which you explain how the introduction of grazing animals nearly led to the extinction of the loggerhead shrike.

This loggerhead shrike chick is 10 to 13 days old. An identification band has been placed around its leg, and it will be returned to the wild.

Many types of evidence support evolution.

CALIFORNIA
Content Standards

7.2.e Students know DNA (deoxyribonucleic acid) is the genetic material of living organisms and is located in the chromosomes of each cell.

7.3.c Students know how independent lines of evidence from geology, fossils and comparative anatomy provide the bases for the theory of evolution.

VOCABULARY

theory p. 211
ancestor p. 211
vestigial organ p. 212

◀ BEFORE, you learned

- Natural selection explains how evolution can occur
- New species develop from earlier species
- The survival of a species depends on how well it adapts to change

▶ NOW, you will learn

- How scientists develop theories
- About the evidence Darwin used to support the theory of natural selection
- About additional evidence most scientists use today

EXPLORE Evidence (7.3.c)

How can observations supply evidence?

PROCEDURE

1 Consider this statement: It rained tonight.

2 Examine the statements below and the photograph to find evidence that supports the statement in step 1.
- There are puddles on the ground.
- The weather report predicted scattered showers for tonight.
- Your sister says that traffic on Hollywood Boulevard was delayed tonight because of rain.

WHAT DO YOU THINK?
- What evidence is the same in both a statement and the photograph?
- Could any of this evidence be misleading? Explain.

MATERIALS
- paper
- pencil

Observations provide evidence for theories.

You have learned that scientists use observations to understand the history of life on Earth. Darwin, too, used observations to describe his ideas about evolution.

Like all good scientists, Darwin was skeptical about what he observed. He took many years to draw conclusions about what he had seen. He did not publish his theory of natural selection until 1859—more than 20 years after the *Beagle* voyage had ended. To understand how Darwin formed his ideas, it is important to understand the meaning of the term *theory*.

Evidence and Theories

Evidence: information from observations and experiments

evidence for evolution

fossil evidence

biological evidence

genetic evidence

theory of natural selection

Theory: a widely accepted statement based on scientific evidence that helps explain natural phenomena

RESOURCE CENTER
CLASSZONE.COM

Examine evidence to support evolution.

In everyday life, people use the word *theory* to suggest an idea or hunch. In science, a **theory** is an explanation of natural phenomena based on a wide range of scientific evidence. A theory is supported by observation and experiment. A theory is widely accepted. It can be used to make and test new hypotheses. The illustration here shows how theories are used in science. It shows what evidence supports evolution. It also shows how evidence supports the theory of natural selection.

VOCABULARY
Remember to make a frame game for *theory* and *ancestor*.

 CHECK YOUR READING   How do scientists support theories?

Fossil evidence supports evolution.

You have read that Darwin collected many fossils on his trip. These fossils provided evidence that species in the past were very similar to species living in Darwin's time. For example, the fossil of an extinct animal called the glyptodon resembles the modern armadillo, an animal found today in Central and South America.

The locations of many fossils are evidence that two species with a common ancestor can develop differently in different locations. An **ancestor** is an early form of an organism from which later forms descend. Common ancestors are key to the theory of natural selection. For example, scientists have compared modern plants and modern algae to fossils of algae. All share a common ancestor.

Biological evidence supports evolution.

Today scientists use both fossil evidence and biological evidence to learn more about evolution. Some have even returned to the Galápagos to further investigate Darwin's work. They have found support for the theory of natural selection that Darwin proposed nearly 150 years ago. Returning year after year, these scientists can follow and record evolutionary changes as they unfold. The evidence they study includes the structure and development of living things. This work helps scientists identify relationships among organisms that exist today. In addition, their observations suggest how modern organisms are related to earlier species.

Similarities in Structure

READING TiP

The root of the word *vestigial* means "footprint." A vestige refers to visible evidence that is left behind—such as a footprint.

Evidence for evolution can be seen within the physical structures of adult organisms. Scientists who study evolution are especially interested in two types of evidence in the structures—vestigial (veh-STIHJ-ee-uhl) organs and similar structures with different functions.

Vestigial organs Some structures seem to be left over from an ancestor of the species. **Vestigial organs** are structures that were fully developed in ancestral organisms but are reduced and unused in later species. Whales have small leg bones that are vestigial. Snake skeletons also have tiny leglike structures that are not used. Vestigial organs show how some modern organisms are related to ancestors that had similar structures.

Similar structures with different functions Scientists who study anatomy have noticed that different species may have similar structures. However, each species uses these structures differently. For example, the forelimbs of lizards, bats, and manatees have similar bone structures. In the diagram on page 213, notice that the forelimbs all have one short bone (green) that goes from the shoulder to the elbow. They have two long bones (orange) that go from the elbow to the wrist. And they have five jointed bones that extend from round wrist bones (yellow).

These similar limb structures suggest that these animals shared a common ancestor. Later generations of this ancestor lived in different environments. Different traits were more useful in these different environments. For lizards, limbs helped them to travel on land. For bats, wings allowed them to fly. For manatees, flippers helped them to swim. In all of these cases, the environment selected for the variations in the form and function of their forelimbs that we see today.

 CHECK YOUR READING What are two types of structural evidence for evolution?

Biological Evidence for Evolution

Scientists learn about common ancestors by looking at physical structures.

Vestigial Structures

The small, leglike bones in modern whales indicate that an early ancestor may have had legs.

Ambulocetus, an extinct whalelike animal with four legs

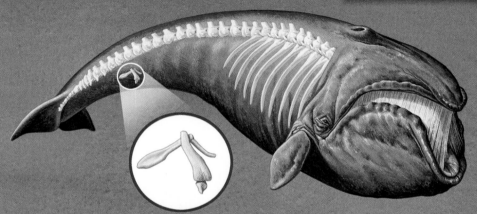

modern whale

Similar Structures, Different Functions

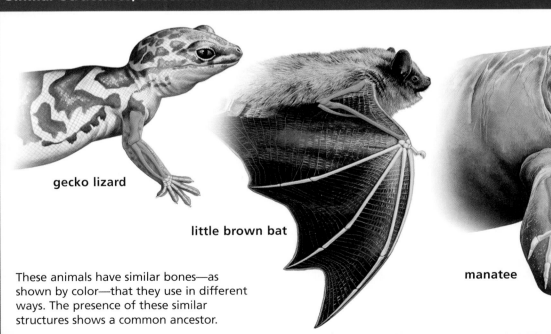

gecko lizard

little brown bat

manatee

These animals have similar bones—as shown by color—that they use in different ways. The presence of these similar structures shows a common ancestor.

READING VISUALS All five animals pictured above share a common ancestor. What evidence shown here supports this statement?

Similarities in Development

READING TiP

An organism that is in an early stage of development is called an *embryo*.

Even before Darwin, scientists were fascinated by the fact that adult animals of widely different species are similar as embryos. Today, scientists consider similarities in development as evidence that they came from a common ancestor.

Stages of the development of a chicken, a rabbit, and a salamander are shown below. During early development, the embryos of all three organisms look similar. As they develop, each organism begins to show its own characteristics. The chicken starts to develop a beak. The salamander begins to look as if it is adapted for life near water.

As adults, these species no longer resemble each other. So why do they look alike as embryos? Remember that genes determine the way an organism looks. Similar genes in different species can make these species look similar. This similarity can happen at any stage of development. That is, different species closely resemble each other as embryos because each species inherited genes controlling this stage from a common ancestor.

Similarities in Development

The study of embryos shows that animals that appear to be very different as adults are similar during early development.

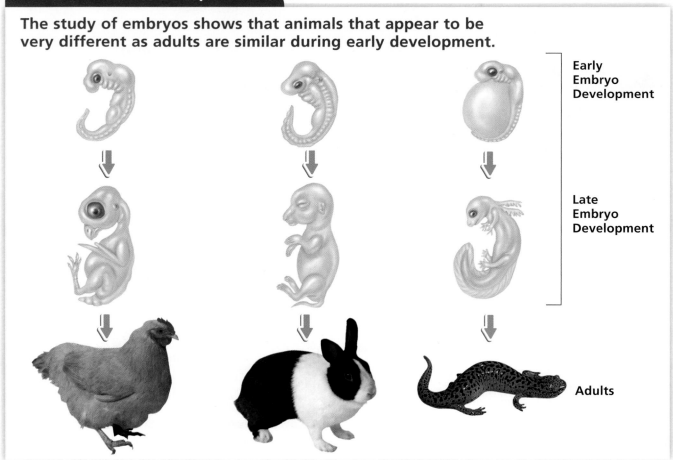

Early Embryo Development

Late Embryo Development

Adults

How can a sequence communicate information?

PROCEDURE

① From your pile of letters (A, D, E, R), spell out the word RED.

② Working with a partner, use the letters to spell two more three-letter words.

WHAT DO YOU THINK?

How does rearranging the letters change the meaning of the words?

CHALLENGE Cut out words from a newspaper. Arrange these words to form different phrases. How do these phrases communicate different messages?

SKILL FOCUS
Sequencing (7.2.e)

MATERIALS
letter cards

TIME
20 minutes

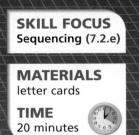

Genetic evidence supports evolution.

The study of DNA offers an important key to understanding how traits are passed from one generation to the next. Recall that DNA is the genetic material found in all living things. DNA contains the information that organisms need to grow and to maintain themselves. When organisms reproduce, they pass on their genetic material to their offspring.

DNA contains a code that a cell uses to build materials it needs to function. The code is determined by the arrangement of four chemical subunits called bases. The bases are represented by the four letters A, T, C, and G. A cell's activity is controlled by its genes. A gene is a DNA segment that controls a trait or a function. Each gene consists of a particular sequence of bases. The code formed by this sequence is translated into proteins. These proteins form structures and perform functions that the organism needs.

One gene scientists are studying is called the clock gene. It is found in many mammals. The clock gene relates to the functions of sleeping and waking. As scientists learn more about the gene, they can identify patterns of behavior in different organisms. The chart on page 216 compares the DNA sequence of part of the clock gene in both humans and mice.

REMINDER

When referring to DNA, the letters G, A, T, and C refer to the chemical bases **g**uanine, **a**denine, **t**hymine, and **c**ytosine.

CHECK YOUR READING How are traits passed from one generation to the next?

Comparing Genes

Humans and mice look very different, but the DNA that makes up their genes is surprisingly similar.

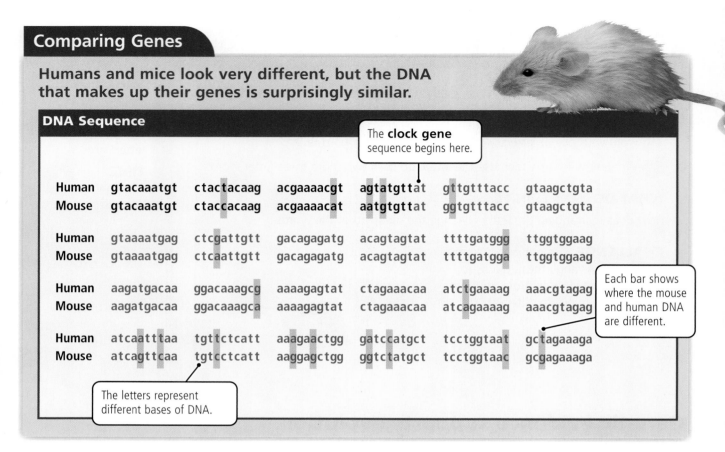

DNA Sequence

The **clock gene** sequence begins here.

Human	gtacaaatgt	ctactacaag	acgaaaacgt	agtatgttat	gttgtttacc	gtaagctgta
Mouse	gtacaaatgt	ctaccacaag	acgaaaacat	aatgtgttat	ggtgtttacc	gtaagctgta
Human	gtaaaatgag	ctcgattgtt	gacagagatg	acagtagtat	ttttgatggg	ttggtggaag
Mouse	gtaaaatgag	ctcaattgtt	gacagagatg	acagtagtat	ttttgatgga	ttggtggaag
Human	aagatgacaa	ggacaaagcg	aaaagagtat	ctagaaacaa	atctgaaaag	aaacgtagag
Mouse	aagatgacaa	ggacaaagca	aaaagagtat	ctagaaacaa	atcagaaaag	aaacgtagag
Human	atcaatttaa	tgttctcatt	aaagaactgg	gatccatgct	tcctggtaat	gctagaaaga
Mouse	atcagttcaa	tgtcctcatt	aaggagctgg	ggtctatgct	tcctggtaac	gcgagaaaga

Each bar shows where the mouse and human DNA are different.

The letters represent different bases of DNA.

Scientists can tell how closely organisms are related by comparing their DNA. The more matches there are in the base sequences of two organisms, the more closely related they are. For example, almost all the genes found in mice are also found in humans. Even though the two organisms appear so different, their cell functions are very similar. Similar DNA, and similar genes with similar functions in very different species, are strong evidence for common ancestors.

CHECK YOUR READING What evidence suggests that mice and humans share a common ancestor?

6.4 Review

KEY CONCEPTS

1. Describe in your own words how scientists use the word *theory*. (7.3.c)

2. What type of evidence did Darwin use to support his theory of natural selection? (7.3.c)

3. Identify three different types of evidence that scientists today use to study evolution. (7.3.c)

CRITICAL THINKING

4. **Analyze** Describe three characteristics of a scientific theory. Explain how Darwin's theory of natural selection is an example of a scientific theory.

5. **Predict** If you were looking at a DNA sequence within the genes of two species, what evidence would you look for that the species are related?

CHALLENGE

6. **Evaluate** The human appendix is a tiny structure in the intestine that has no function. Animals such as horses have a similar, much larger structure called the cecum. The cecum helps these animals digest vegetation. Are the appendix and cecum evidence of a common ancestor? If so, why are they so different?

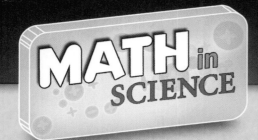

MATH TUTORIAL

CLASSZONE.COM

Click on Math Tutorial for more help with percents and fractions.

Math 7.NS.1.3

Differences Between Species

Does it surprise you to learn that roughly 50 percent of the DNA in your cells is nearly identical to the DNA in the cells of a banana? You probably know from experience that 50 percent is the same as one-half. But you can also convert any percent to a fraction by using the number 100 to represent the whole. Fifty parts out of 100 is the same as one-half. Another example is shown below.

Example

Comparing the cells of two species, scientists find that 40 percent of the DNA is identical. How can you show what fraction that is?

(1) Rewrite the percent as a numerator with a denominator of 100.

$$40 \text{ percent} = \frac{40}{100}$$

(2) Reduce the fraction. Use the greatest common factor (GCF) to write the numerator and the denominator as products.

$$\frac{40}{100} = \frac{2 \cdot 20}{5 \cdot 20}$$

(3) Divide the GCF by itself to get $\frac{1}{1}$, or 1.

$$\frac{2}{5} \cdot \frac{20}{20} = \frac{2}{5} \cdot 1 = \frac{2}{5}$$

ANSWER: 40 percent $= \frac{2}{5}$

Rewrite each sentence, changing the percent to a fraction.

1. About 98 percent of the DNA in human cells is similar to the DNA in mouse cells.

2. The tooth of a modern great white shark can be 55 percent of the length of a fossil tooth from a prehistoric shark.

3. There are about 15 percent as many penguin species as there are pine tree species in the world today.

4. There are about 8 percent as many bear species as pine tree species.

CHALLENGE Choose one example or exercise on this page. Tell whether the comparison works better as a fraction or a percent. Explain why.

Chapter Review

6

the BIG idea

Species develop and change over time.

CONTENT REVIEW
CLASSZONE.COM

◀ KEY CONCEPTS SUMMARY

1 ## Earth has been home to living things for about 3.8 billion years.

Fossil records tell us about the development of life on Earth. Information from fossils can help scientists reconstruct Earth's history.

VOCABULARY
extinction p. 189
mass extinction p. 189

2 ## Species change over time.

Darwin's theory of natural selection explains evolution.

Four principles of natural selection
- overproduction
- variation
- adaptation
- selection

The beak of this cactus finch provides an example of an adaptation.

VOCABULARY
evolution p. 191
natural selection p. 195
population p. 196
genetic variation p. 196
adaptation p. 196
environmental factors p. 196
speciation p. 198

3 ## Environmental changes can affect populations.

- Populations increase through births and immigration and decrease through deaths and emigration.
- Limiting factors such as food, shelter, disease, and the effects of sudden events control population size.
- Most extinctions occur population by population over time.

VOCABULARY
immigration p. 203
emigration p. 204
limiting factor p. 204

4 ## Many types of evidence support evolution.

Three different types of evidence provide a bigger picture of evolution.

fossil evidence   biological evidence    genetic evidence

VOCABULARY
theory p. 211
ancestor p. 211
vestigial organ p. 212

Reviewing Vocabulary

Place each vocabulary term listed below at the center of a description wheel diagram. Write some words describing the term on the spokes.

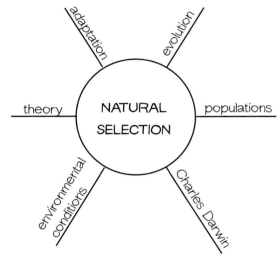

1. evolution
2. immigration
3. limiting factors
4. genetic variation
5. emigration
6. extinction

Reviewing Key Concepts

Multiple Choice *Choose the letter of the best answer.*

7. What advantage did having mitochondria give eukaryotes? (7.1.d)
   a. They gained the ability to photosynthesize.
   b. It helped them use oxygen very efficiently.
   c. They were able to synthesize stromatolites.
   d. It helped them get energy from methane.

8. Which is a possible reason for the Cretaceous mass extinction? (7.3.e)
   a. Earth had no water.
   b. An object collided with Earth.
   c. The continents separated.
   d. The atmosphere had very little oxygen.

9. Darwin's theory that species pass useful traits to offspring and change over time is known as (7.3.b)
   a. natural selection
   b. extinction
   c. emigration
   d. adaptation

10. A rabbit born with a better ability to hear its predators has (7.3.e)
    a. an adaptation
    b. a vestigial structure
    c. an environmental condition
    d. a limiting factor

11. Which of the following directly affect population size? (7.3.e)
    a. immigration, adaptation, and births
    b. isolation, acquired traits, and adaptations
    c. acquired traits and genetic variation
    d. immigration, birth, emigration, and death

12. Which statement best describes why extinction occurs? (7.3.e)
    a. A change in the environment prevents speciation.
    b. A species lacks the adaptations needed to survive a change in the environment.
    c. All species at some point are outcompeted by larger species.
    d. All species must die within a certain amount of time.

13. Genetic evidence is based on the study of (7.3.c)
    a. embryonic development
    b. vestigial structures
    c. common ancestors
    d. DNA sequences

14. Which of the following statements helps explain why the theory of evolution by natural selection is widely accepted by the scientific community? (7.3.c)
    a. It has been proven by experiments.
    b. The fossil record is complete.
    c. It is supported by scientific evidence.
    d. Lamarck's theory was correct.

Short Answer *Write a short answer to the questions below.*

15. Explain the difference between artificial selection and natural selection. (7.3.b)

16. How do vestigial structures in two species indicate common ancestry? (7.3.c)

17. How can extinction occur?

Thinking Critically

18. **COMMUNICATE** Name two things that scientists have learned about past life on Earth from the fossil record. (7.4.e)

19. **PROVIDE EXAMPLES** Explain the principle of overproduction. Give an example. (7.3.b)

20. **SYNTHESIZE** How might the extinction of dinosaurs have made it possible for many new species of mammals to develop? (7.3.e)

21. **HYPOTHESIZE** Using Darwin's theory of natural selection, form a hypothesis about how modern giraffes came to have long necks. (7.3.b)

Think about a population of cichlids in Africa's Lake Tanganyika to answer the next six questions.

22. **COMPARE** Suppose the changing water level in the lake divides one population of cichlids into two. The populations can no longer interact. Just after the population is divided, how similar do you think the two new populations would be? (7.3.a)

23. **PROVIDE EXAMPLES** List some ways in which individual cichlids in one population might differ from one another. (7.3.a)

24. **ANALYZE** Suppose one population now lives among dark-colored rocks, and that there are predators that eat eggs. What would be the advantage of dark-colored eggs? (7.3.a)

25. **PREDICT** Suppose just a few of the cichlids in question 24 had the trait of producing darker eggs. How do you think natural selection will change the population over time? (7.3.a)

26. **INFER** Suppose a population of cichlids lives among dark-colored rocks, but none of the predators in this environment eats cichlid eggs. Would dark-colored eggs be an advantage? Explain your answer. (7.3.a)

27. **INFER** After a great many years, two isolated populations of cichlids may look very different. What might scientists compare to determine that the cichlids started as one population? (7.3.c)

28. **ANALYZE** How is geographic isolation related to the formation of a new species? (7.3.a)

29. **INFER** Other than hunting, how could the presence of humans in the western lowland gorillas' habitat lead to the extinction of the gorillas? (7.3.e)

30. **APPLY** In the mountains of the Sierra Nevada range in California, mountain lions prey on bighorn sheep and other animals. The sheep eat grasses and other plants. In 1990, it became illegal for people to hunt mountain lions in California. How might the results of the law affect a population of bighorn sheep? How might it affect a population of grasses in the mountains?

the **BIG** idea

31. **INFER** Look again at the picture on pages 182–183. Now that you have finished the chapter, how would you change or add details to your answer to the question on the photograph?

32. **SYNTHESIZE** The beaks of hummingbirds are adapted to fit into long, thin flowers. Hummingbirds can feed on the nectar inside the flower. Write an explanation for this adaptation that Lamarck might have proposed. Then write an explanation for this adaptation based on Darwin's ideas. Use the terms *acquired traits* and *natural selection* in your answer. (7.2.e)

UNIT PROJECTS

If you need to create graphs or other visuals for your project, be sure you have grid paper, poster board, markers, or other supplies.

Analyzing Data

7.1.f, 7.3.e

Reef-building corals are animals that live in clear, warm ocean water. As a coral grows, it produces a hard external skeleton. If corals grow on the skeletons of earlier generations, over time their accumulated skeletons form a structure called a reef. Many ocean life forms live in and around coral reefs. This table shows the maximum growth rates of five species of reef-building corals.

Choose the letter of the best response.

Coral Species	Rate of Growth (mm per year)	Time to Grow a 1400-m Reef (years)
1	143	9,790
2	99	14,100
3	120	11,700
4	100	14,000
5	226	6,190

1. Which has the fastest rate of growth?
   a. Species 2
   b. Species 3
   c. Species 4
   d. Species 5

2. What is the growth rate for Species 2?
   a. 99 mm per year
   b. 120 mm per year
   c. 143 mm per year
   d. 14,100 mm per year

3. Which takes the shortest amount of time to grow a 1400-meter reef?
   a. Species 2
   b. Species 3
   c. Species 4
   d. Species 5

4. Which have about the same rate of growth?
   a. Species 1 and 3
   b. Species 2 and 4
   c. Species 3 and 5
   d. Species 4 and 5

5. How many years does it take Species 1 to grow into a 1400-m reef?
   a. 143
   b. 226
   c. 9,790
   d. 14,000

6. Based on the information in the table, which statement is true?
   a. The coral species with the fastest growth rate takes the greatest amount of time to grow.
   b. The coral species with the slowest growth rate takes the least amount of time to grow.
   c. Coral species have different rates of growth that affect how long it takes them to grow.
   d. Coral species that grow more than 100 mm per year take the longest to grow.

Extended Response

Answer the two questions below in detail. Include some of the terms from the word box. In your answers, underline each term that you use.

adaptation	advantage	extinct
resource	limiting factor	natural selection
	environmental factor	

7. Corals are sessile animals—they live attached to one place. Other ocean-dwelling animals are mobile and can move about their environment. Write a paragraph in which you describe what advantages corals might have from their adaptations of being sessile and producing reefs.

8. Pollution and changing ocean temperatures have slowed the growth of some coral reefs and even killed the corals. How might the change in coral growth affect other organisms?

TIMELINES in Science

LIFE Unearthed

How do scientists know about life on Earth millions of years ago? They dig, scratch, and hunt. The best clues they find are hidden in layers of rock. The rock-locked clues, called fossils, are traces or remains of living things from long ago. Some fossils show the actual bodies of organisms, while others, such as footprints, reveal behavior.

Before 1820, most fossil finds revealed the bodies of ocean life. Then large bones of lizard-like walking animals began turning up, and pictures of a new "terrible lizard," or dinosaur, took shape. Later, discoveries of tracks and nests showed behaviors such as flocking and caring for young. Even today, discoveries of "living fossils," modern relatives of prehistoric species, have offered us a rare glimpse of the activity of early life.

1825

Giant Lizards from Fragments

In 1824 William Buckland described *Megalosaurus*, a giant crocodile-like animal he studied from only a few bits of jaw, teeth, ribs, pelvis, and one leg. A year later, fellow Englishman Gideon Mantell assembles *Iguanodon*, a similar animal, from fossil bones.

EVENTS

1800   1810   1820

APPLICATIONS AND TECHNOLOGY

TECHNOLOGY

Removing Fossils with Care

The technology for removing fossils from rock beds has not changed much since the 1820s. Paleontologists still work by hand with hammers, chisels, trowels, dental picks, and sieves. Gideon Mantell used these when he chiseled out *Iguanodon* bones embedded in one large rock called the "Mantell-piece."

Fossil hunters also use hand lenses and microscopes. Sometimes a protective layer is built up with glue, varnish, or another finish. For larger samples, a plaster cast often supports the fossil. Most fossils are packed using a technology found in any kitchen—a sealable plastic bag.

1909
Burgess Shale Shows Soft Bodies

In the Burgess Pass of the Canadian Rocky Mountains, Charles Walcott finds fossils preserved in shale, a soft rock that preserves lacelike details, such as the soft tissues of the Marella. This glimpse of life 505 million years ago is the earliest yet seen.

1948
New Dawn for the Dawn Redwood

In 1944, a Chinese scientist discovered the dawn redwood, or metasequoia, growing beside a small temple. Common in fossil specimens 100 million years old, the tree had not been seen alive in recorded history. The 1944 find starts a search, and in 1948, scientists find a small wild grove in China as well.

1938
African Fisherman Hauls in History

A South African fisherman pulls up a five-foot fish he has never seen. He calls the local museum, whose curator, a naturalist, has also never seen the species. To her surprise, biologists identify it as a coelacanth (SEE-luh-kanth), a prehistoric fish thought to be extinct for more than 50 million years.

| 1900 | 1910 | 1920 | 1930 | 1940 |

APPLICATION

Protecting Fossils and Dig Sites

The United States Antiquities Act of 1906 preserves and protects historic and prehistoric sites. The act requires collectors to have a permit to dig for or to pick up fossils on public lands, such as national parks. It also requires that any major find be publicly and permanently preserved in a museum.

The United Nations also now designates World Heritage sites. For example, the original Burgess Shale find in Yoho National Park in Canada is now protected by international law. Since 1906, many states and provinces in Canada have enacted their own laws about land rights and the excavation and transport of fossils.

1974
"Lucy" and Upright Kin Found

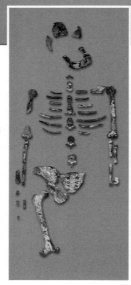

Digging in Ethiopia, Donald Johanson finds an almost complete hominid skeleton. He names the fossil Lucy after a song by the rock group the Beatles. Lucy, who is over 3 million years old, is three and one-half feet tall and has an upright stance or posture. A year later, Johanson's crew finds "The First Family," a group of 13 skeletons of the same species as Lucy.

1990
Largest Tyrannosaurus, *"Sue"*

Out on a walk with her dog in the South Dakota badlands, amateur fossil hunter Sue Hendrickson discovers three huge bones jutting out of a cliff. Hendrickson's find is the largest and most complete *T. rex* skeleton yet. The 67-million-year-old "Sue" is now on display in the Field Museum in Chicago, Illinois.

1953
Piltdown Man No Neanderthal

Scientists once applauded the discovery in 1912 of a "Neanderthal" skull in the Piltdown gravel pit, but a few had their doubts. In 1953, radioactive potassium dating proves the Piltdown fossil to be nothing more than the jaw of an orangutan placed beside human skull fragments.

1950   **1960**   **1970**   **1980**   **1990**

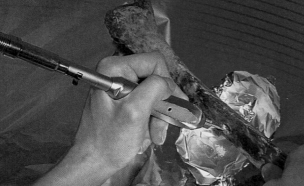

TECHNOLOGY

How Old Is a Fossil?

Before 1947, scientists used a method of fossil dating called relative dating. They assigned a date to a fossil according to the rock layer in which it was found. The deeper, or older, the layer, the older the fossil.

Since the development of radiometric dating in 1947, a fossil's material can be used to find its age. Radioactive elements decay at a constant rate. You can tell the age of the matter from the amount of decay. Carbon-14 dating can be used to tell the age of a fossil that is less than 70,000 years old. Most fossils are older than that, so scientists must also use other methods.

Radioactive potassium 40 decays more slowly than carbon 14. It can be used to date even very old rock layers. However, all types of fossil dating have margins of error, or limits to accuracy.

1993

Oldest Fossils Are Too Small to See

Fossils discovered up to this point date back about 550 million years, to the dawn of the Cambrian Period. J. William Schopf identifies fossils of microorganisms scientifically dated to 3.4 billion years ago. His startling find near Australia's Marble Bar opens up a vast period of time and once again reshapes theories about life's beginnings.

RESOURCE CENTER
CLASSZONE.COM
Discover more about the latest fossil and "living-fossil" finds.

2000

TECHNOLOGY

Fossil Classification and DNA

There are many ways to classify fossils. Scientists look at bone structure, body posture, evidence of behavior, and environment. Microscopes are used to identify organisms too small for the eye to see. Study of DNA molecules helps to identify species when soft tissues remain intact, such as in fossils formed in amber or crystallized tree sap. In 1985, polymerase chain reaction (PCR) became the simplest method for studying the DNA extracted from fossils. In PCR, parts of DNA can be copied billions of times in a few hours.

SPOTLIGHT on
MEE-MANN CHANG

Mee-Mann Chang is a top paleontologist in China, where she was the head of Beijing's Institute of Vertebrate Paleontology and Paleoanthropology from 1983 to 1991. Chang and her team have focused their research on ancient fish. Her most important discoveries include fossils of primitive lungfish. Lungfish are freshwater fish that have lunglike organs as well as gills and can breathe air.

Chang's work has shaped current thinking about the origins of lungfish and early land animals. In 2002 it was announced that a fossil had been found in China that proved an evolutionary link between birds and dinosaurs. It was named *Sinovenator changii* in honor of Dr. Chang. The fossil was of a small, feathered dinosaur.

ACTIVITIES

Writing About Science: Film Script

Write your own version of the story of a fossil. Include drawings, photographs, or video clips to illustrate your story.

Reliving History

Think about the equipment archaeologists and paleontologists use on excavations. Think about their goals. Write a proposal to a local university or museum asking them to fund your excavation.

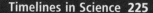

CHAPTER 7

Classification of Living Things

the BIG idea

Scientists have developed a system for classifying the great diversity of living things.

Key Concepts

SECTION 1
Scientists develop systems for classifying living things.
Learn about how scientists classify and name living things.

SECTION 2
Branching diagrams show biological relationships.
Learn how branching diagrams show evolutionary relationships among living things.

SECTION 3
Classification systems change as scientists learn more.
Learn how classification systems have changed based on features of cells.

California ClassZone

CLASSZONE.COM

Chapter 7 online resources: Content Review, Simulation, three Resource Centers, Math Tutorial, Test Practice

How many different types of organisms do you see and how would you group them?

EXPLORE (the BIG idea)

How Would You Sort Pennies?

> **7.3.d** Students know how to construct a simple branching diagram to classify living groups of organisms by shared derived characteristics and how to expand the diagram to include fossil organisms.

Place 20 pennies in a plastic cup. Place your hand over the cup and shake it. Gently pour the pennies onto a table. Without flipping the pennies over, use one trait of the pennies to sort them into groups A and B. Again, without flipping them over, use a second trait to sort the pennies in group A into groups A1 and A2.

Observe and Think What traits do the pennies in each group share? Which group has the largest numbers of pennies?

Internet Activity: Linnaeus

> **7.3.d** Students know how to construct a simple branching diagram to classify living groups of organisms by shared derived characteristics and how to expand the diagram to include fossil organisms.

Go to **ClassZone.com** to learn more about Carolus Linnaeus. Over 200 years ago, Linnaeus laid the groundwork for how today's scientists classify things.

Observe and Think What evidence did Linnaeus use to classify organisms?

NSTA
scilinks.org

SCiLINKS

Classification Systems **Code: MDL037**

Getting Ready to Learn

◀ CONCEPT REVIEW

- Species change over time.
- Fossils and other evidence show that species change.
- The evolution of a new species from an existing species is called speciation.

◀ VOCABULARY REVIEW

evolution p. 191
ancestor p. 211

See Glossary for definitions.
species, trait, DNA

CONTENT REVIEW
CLASSZONE.COM

Review concepts and vocabulary.

▶ TAKING NOTES

SUPPORTING MAIN IDEAS

Make a chart to show main ideas and the information that supports them. Copy each blue heading. Below each heading, add supporting information, such as reasons, explanations, and examples.

VOCABULARY STRATEGY

Place each vocabulary term at the center of a **description wheel** diagram. Write some words describing the term on the spokes.

See the Note-Taking Handbook on pages R45–R51.

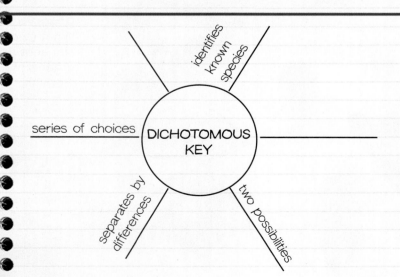

SCIENCE NOTEBOOK

Scientists provide a key for identifying species.

Scientists look for similarities and differences among species.

A dichotomous key helps identify a known organism.

Dichotomous keys use choices for identification.

DICHOTOMOUS KEY

identifies known species

series of choices

two possibilities

separates by differences

Scientists develop systems for classifying living things.

CALIFORNIA
Content Standard

7.3.d Students know how to construct a simple branching diagram to classify living groups of organisms by shared derived characteristics and how to expand the diagram to include fossil organisms.

BEFORE, you learned

- Natural selection helps explain how new species develop
- Evidence shows that species change over time
- New species develop from ancestral species

NOW, you will learn

- How to use a dichotomous key
- How scientists classify and name living things
- About seven levels of classification

VOCABULARY

dichotomous key p. 231
classification p. 232
taxonomy p. 232
binomial nomenclature p. 233
genus p. 233

EXPLORE Classification (7.3.d)

What data do you need to identify objects?

PROCEDURE

1. Think of a secret object and tell your team one characteristic (shape, color, size, type) of that object.

2. Ask your team members to guess the object's identity. Each time someone guesses incorrectly, give one new characteristic of the object. Record characteristics and guesses as you go.

3. When the object is guessed correctly, have another student repeat steps 1 and 2.

WHAT DO YOU THINK?

- How many characteristics did it take to guess the object each time?
- What did you learn about identifying organisms?

Scientists provide a key for identifying species.

When you find a beetle, how do you know what type of beetle it is? Over 300,000 species of beetles have been discovered around the world. With millions of species on Earth, how can a specific one be identified? How can scientists communicate to each other about an organism? Scientists had to come up with a system of classification.

To classify organisms, scientists use similarities and differences among species. Some differences are easy to see, such as fur, feathers, or scales. At other times, special technology, such as equipment to study DNA, is needed to see differences.

Dichotomous Key

Use the dichotomous key below to discover on what tree the circled leaf is found.

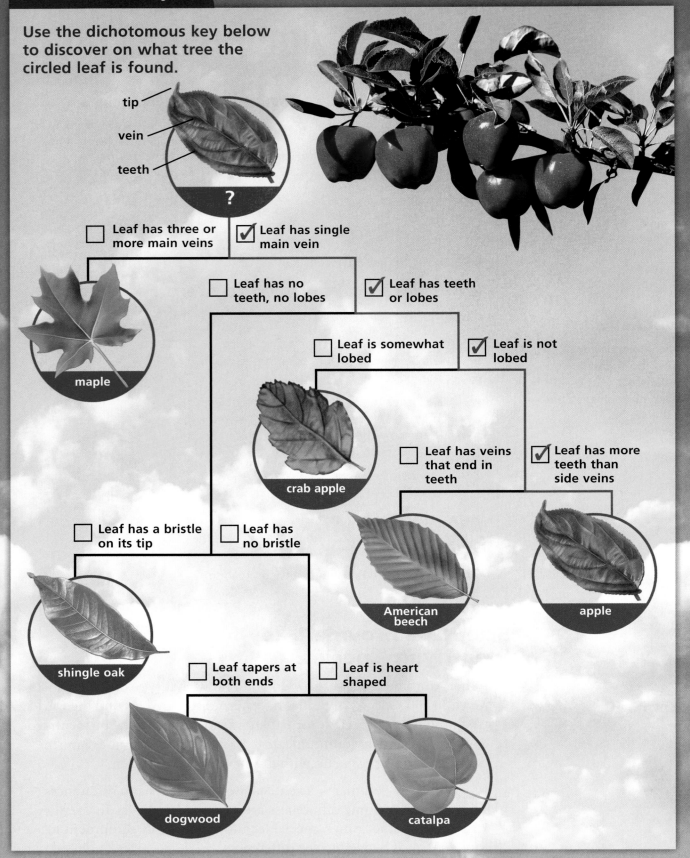

tip

vein

teeth

?

☐ Leaf has three or more main veins

☑ Leaf has single main vein

maple

☐ Leaf has no teeth, no lobes

☑ Leaf has teeth or lobes

☐ Leaf is somewhat lobed

☑ Leaf is not lobed

crab apple

☐ Leaf has veins that end in teeth

☑ Leaf has more teeth than side veins

☐ Leaf has a bristle on its tip

☐ Leaf has no bristle

American beech

apple

shingle oak

☐ Leaf tapers at both ends

☐ Leaf is heart shaped

dogwood

catalpa

Scientists have come up with a method to identify species of organisms such as beetles. A **dichotomous key** (dy-KAHT-uh-muhs) is an identification tool that gives a series of choices. The choices in the key gradually narrow down the list of possible species. Your choice each time leads you to two more possibilities. After working through each pair of choices, you can identify the species. An example of a dichotomous key for trees is shown on page 230.

A dichotomous key is useful only when you know what type of organism you are observing. The purpose is to make identifying a species as easy as possible. The choices can focus on any trait that shows differences between species. The dichotomous key for trees, for example, gives choices only about the traits of the leaves. Leaves are used because they are usually easy to get. Leaves show many characteristics that can be used to tell trees apart.

 When would someone use a dichotomous key?

SIMULATION
CLASSZONE.COM
Use an interactive dichotomous key.

READING TIP

The prefix *di-* means "two." A dichotomous key always gives two choices.

Linnaeus named more than 11,000 species.

Before the 1700s, scientists had no rules or system for naming and grouping organisms. They used long Latin names, sometimes describing an individual plant with as many as seven Latin words. The Latin names were confusing. Worse, any scientist studying the species could change its name. Even the common names for plants and animals were confusing, because they were not the same for everyone. For example, in Great Britain the national bird is called the robin. But Britain's robin is only distantly related to the bird we call the robin in the United States, even though both have red feathers on their chests.

Biologists needed both a system for organizing and a system for naming. Each name would refer to only one type of organism. That way, when scientists used the species name, everybody would know exactly which type of organism they were talking about.

Carolus Linnaeus was a scientist who lived in Sweden in the mid-1700s. He started as a botanist, a scientist who studies plants. Later he studied medicine and became a professor. Linnaeus tried to organize the study of plants and animals by developing systems for both naming species and grouping them. His students traveled the world and sent him samples of plants and animals. Linnaeus named more than 11,000 species of plants and animals. He used physical appearance to put species into groups.

Today, scientists have named over a million species. Modern scientists also use physical appearance, along with other types of evidence, to group species. Linnaeus' system for naming species became the basis of modern classification.

Classification and Taxonomy

Two scientific processes are used to classify and name living things. **Classification** is the process of sorting organisms into groups based on similarities. **Taxonomy** is the science of naming and classifying organisms. Linnaeus' system of classification allows scientists to organize a large amount of information so that it is easy to find and to understand. The system provides a tool for comparing very large groups of organisms as well as smaller groups. A large group might include all animals. Smaller groups might include birds, reptiles, or mammals.

Using Classification

A classification system can help you identify unfamiliar organisms. For example, suppose you have never heard of a caracal. If someone told you it was a kind of cat, you would already know many things about it. It has fur, fangs, and sharp claws. It is a meat eater, not a plant eater. You would know these things because the caracal shares those characteristics with all members of the cat family. A caracal, a pet cat, and all the cats below are different in size, habitat, and other characteristics. But they also have many similarities, and all belong to the cat family, Felidae.

Like other cats, a caracal has fur and sharp fangs and is a meat eater. Its tall tufts of hair look like horns.

Different Species in the Cat Family

Jaguars are muscular cats that may be over two meters long.

Ocelots are small hunters and tree climbers.

Some **lynx** have thick hair and live in colder climates.

READING VISUALS COMPARE What traits do these cats have in common?

Naming Species

Linnaeus' system for naming species is called binomial nomenclature (by-NOH-mee-uhl NOH-muhn-KLAY-chuhr). Binomial means "two names," and nomenclature means "a system of names." So **binomial nomenclature** is a system of naming things using two names each. Most scientific names are Latin terms.

The two names used in binomial nomenclature are the genus and the species. A **genus** (JEE-nuhs) is a group of species that have similar characteristics. For example, the genus *Ursus* groups many of the animals known as bears. This genus includes the species *Ursus arctos* (grizzly bears) and *Ursus maritimus* (polar bears). Species within the same genus are closely related.

People follow certain rules when they write scientific names. The genus name comes first, and its first letter is capitalized. The species name follows the genus name, and its first letter is written in lowercase. The entire name is written in italics.

RESOURCE CENTER
CLASSZONE.COM

Find out more about taxonomy.

CHECK YOUR READING What is the difference between a genus and a species?

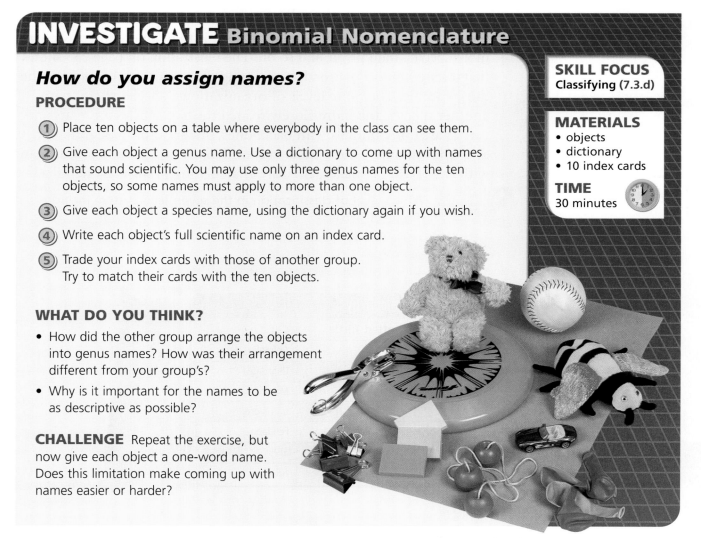

INVESTIGATE Binomial Nomenclature

How do you assign names?

PROCEDURE

1. Place ten objects on a table where everybody in the class can see them.

2. Give each object a genus name. Use a dictionary to come up with names that sound scientific. You may use only three genus names for the ten objects, so some names must apply to more than one object.

3. Give each object a species name, using the dictionary again if you wish.

4. Write each object's full scientific name on an index card.

5. Trade your index cards with those of another group. Try to match their cards with the ten objects.

WHAT DO YOU THINK?

- How did the other group arrange the objects into genus names? How was their arrangement different from your group's?

- Why is it important for the names to be as descriptive as possible?

CHALLENGE Repeat the exercise, but now give each object a one-word name. Does this limitation make coming up with names easier or harder?

SKILL FOCUS
Classifying (7.3.d)

MATERIALS
- objects
- dictionary
- 10 index cards

TIME
30 minutes

Organisms can be classified into seven levels.

SUPPORTING MAIN IDEAS
Make a chart to show information that supports the main idea that organisms can be classified into seven levels.

You've read about species and genus, the most specific levels of the classification system. The system that Linnaeus created has five other levels that describe a species. In Section 3 you will learn about yet another level of classification that was recently added. The seven levels of traditional classification for a house cat are listed below.

1. Kingdom (Animalia—the animals)
2. Phylum (Chordata—animals with backbones)
3. Class (Mammalia—mammals, or furry animals that nurse their young)
4. Order (Carnivora—carnivores, or animals that kill and eat other animals)
5. Family (Felidae—the cat family)
6. Genus (*Felis*—house cats, cougars, and many others)
7. Species (*catus*—all house cats, no matter what their breed)

Like the cat, the turtle is also classified into seven levels. However, only the two highest levels, Animalia and Chordata, are the same levels as those for a house cat. Phyla are more specific than kingdoms, classes are more specific than phyla, and so on. The illustration on page 235 shows that a kingdom is the broadest grouping of organisms. A species is the most specific. The more levels of organization a species shares with another species, the more closely related the two species are. Cats and turtles are both animals with backbones, but are otherwise different. Spotted turtles have more traits in common with snakes and lizards than with cats. Lizards, snakes, and turtles all belong in the class Reptilia.

READING TiP

Phyla is the plural form of *phylum*.

CHECK YOUR READING Which level of classification in the seven-level system includes the most species?

Classification Hierarchy		
	Spotted Turtle	**Cat**
Kingdom	Animalia	Animalia
Phylum	Chordata	Chordata
Class	Reptilia	Mammalia
Order	Testudines	Carnivora
Family	Emydidae	Felidae
Genus	*Clemmys*	*Felis*
Species	*guttata*	*catus*

Clemmys guttata

Felis catus

Classifying Organisms

Moving from kingdom to species, each level includes a smaller set of organisms.

1 Kingdom
Animalia:
Animals

2 Phylum
Chordata:
With backbone or
similar structure

3 Class
Reptilia:
Reptiles

4 Order
Testudines:
Turtles

5 Family
Emydidae:
Water turtles

Spotted turtle
Clemmys guttata

6 Genus
Clemmys:
North American
pond turtles

7 Species
guttata:
Spotted turtle

British Daddy Longlegs		American Daddy Longlegs
Animalia	**Kingdom**	Animalia
Arthropoda	**Phylum**	Arthropoda
Insecta	**Class**	Arachnida
Diptera	**Order**	Opiliones
Trichoceridae	**Family**	Leiobunidae
Trichocera	**Genus**	*Leiobunum*
annulata	**Species**	*rotundum*

The classification system helps separate organisms that have similar common names and look alike. Notice that the common names of the organisms in the photographs above are both daddy longlegs. They may look somewhat similar, but they are classified very differently. They are both members of the phylum Arthropoda. However, British daddy longlegs are members of the class Insecta, which includes all insects. American daddy longlegs are members of the class Arachnida, which includes spiders, ticks, and scorpions.

Scientists can compare very broad categories of organisms, such as Arthropoda. Or they can compare very specific categories, such as species. If scientists wish to compare all the different types of spiders, then they will compare the organisms in the class Arachnida. But if scientists only want to compare American daddy longlegs, then they would compare organisms in the family Leiobunidae.

You can remember the classification levels and their order with this memory aid: **K**ings **P**lay **C**hess **O**n **F**at **G**reen **S**tools. The first letter of each word is the same as the first letter in each level of classification: **K**ingdom, **P**hylum, **C**lass, **O**rder, **F**amily, **G**enus, and **S**pecies. A classification of humans goes like this: kingdom Animalia, phylum Chordata, class Mammalia, order Primates, family Hominidae, genus *Homo*, species *sapiens*.

7.1 Review

KEY CONCEPTS

1. What are dichotomous keys used for? (7.3.d)

2. What is binomial nomenclature? (7.3.d)

3. Write the names of the seven levels of classification. Use the beginning letters to write your own memory aid for the names. (7.3.d)

CRITICAL THINKING

4. **Summarize** What were Carolus Linnaeus' main contributions to taxonomy?

5. **Analyze** Why do scientists need a universal system of naming organisms?

⬤ CHALLENGE

6. **Synthesize** Predict what differences you might find among organisms in the same species.

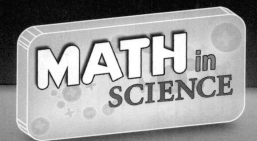

MATH TUTORIAL
CLASSZONE.COM

Click on Math Tutorial for more help dividing by decimals.

Math 7.NS.1.2

Comparing Species

The leatherback sea turtle is one of the largest reptiles alive. In the same family as the spotted turtle, it is a different genus and species: *Dermochelys coriacea*. Full-grown adult leatherbacks have a mass of 880 kilograms, but they start out at just 44 grams.

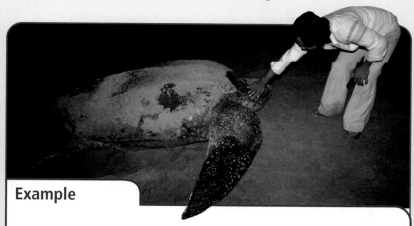

Example

How many times more massive is the 880 kg adult than the 44 g hatchling?

(1) Convert the units so they are all in kilograms.
   44 g × 0.001 kg/g = 0.044 kg

(2) Divide 880 kg by 0.044 kg to get the answer.

(3) To divide by a decimal, multiply the divisor and the dividend by a multiple of 10. Since the decimal number is in thousandths, multiply by 1000.

$$0.044\overline{)880} \qquad\qquad 44\overline{)880,000}^{\,20,000}$$

ANSWER The adult leatherback is 20,000 times heavier than the leatherback hatchling.

Answer the following questions.

1. An adult leatherback has been measured as 1.5 m from nose to tail. The same animal measured just 6 cm as a hatchling. How many times longer is the adult?

2. A typical spotted turtle grows to 12.4 cm long. How many times longer is the adult leatherback than the adult spotted turtle?

3. Suppose the spotted turtle hatched with a length of 2.5 cm. By how many times has its length increased by adulthood?

4. How many times longer is the leatherback hatchling than the spotted turtle hatchling?

CHALLENGE What fraction of its adult mass is the leatherback hatchling in the example?

Family: Emydidae: water turtles
Genus: *Dermochelys*
Species: *coriacea*

7.2 Branching diagrams show biological relationships.

CALIFORNIA
Content Standard

7.3.d Students know how to construct a simple branching diagram to classify living groups of organisms by shared derived characteristics and how to expand the diagram to include fossil organisms.

BEFORE, you learned

- Dichotomous keys are used to identify species
- Binomial nomenclature is used to name species
- Organisms can be classified into seven levels

NOW, you will learn

- How taxonomists study biological relationships
- About evidence used to classify organisms
- How branching diagrams show relationships among organisms

VOCABULARY

cladogram p. 243
derived characteristic p. 244

THINK ABOUT

How are these organisms similar?

Worms and caterpillars both have long, skinny bodies that are divided into segments. But an earthworm moves underground, has no legs or eyes, and can grow back segments that are lost. A caterpillar crawls above ground and is just one part of a butterfly's life cycle. As you read this chapter, think about whether you would classify these animals together or separately.

Taxonomists study biological relationships.

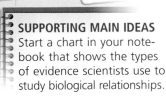

SUPPORTING MAIN IDEAS
Start a chart in your notebook that shows the types of evidence scientists use to study biological relationships.

Scientists need a simple, standard way of arranging all of the different species. The science of taxonomy is related to the Greek word *taxis*, which means arrangement. Taxonomists are scientists who classify and name organisms based on their similarities and differences. A taxon is a group of organisms that share certain traits. *Taxa* is the plural of taxon. Taxa can be broad, like animals and plants, or more specific, like cats and roses.

In order to classify organisms, scientists compare a variety of traits. A trait is a characteristic or behavior that can be used to tell two species apart, such as size or bone structure.

Biological Relationships

Leafy Sea Dragon

The **sargassum fish** and the sea dragon are both fish with wavy fronds.

Both the **sea horse** and sea dragon have the same basic body shape.

This **sargassum seaweed** and the sea dragon both have leafy fronds.

Look at the photographs above. To which organisms is a leafy sea dragon more closely related? The leafy sea dragon shares traits with all of the other organisms. For example, the sea dragon and the sargassum seaweed both have greenish leafy fronds. But the leafy sea dragon is an animal that moves. It gets food from other organisms and breathes oxygen. The sargassum seaweed is not an animal; it is a type of algae.

The sea dragon shares more traits with the sargassum fish. But the sargassum fish's body has a different shape. The leafy sea dragon seems more closely related to a sea horse. Both have heads and bodies with similar shapes. Neither has scales. The leafy sea dragon shares more traits with the sea horse than with the other two organisms.

Taxonomists use evidence like this to figure out the evolution of a species. They try to find out how species are related through a common ancestor. Then they place the species in the classification system. Scientists use physical evidence, such as fur, bones, and teeth. They also use genetic evidence, which is found within an organism's DNA.

CHECK YOUR READING   What types of evidence are used to classify organisms?

Physical Evidence

Physical differences among birds include size, shape, posture, bill shape, and specific color patterns.

Steller's Jay
- Lives only west of the Rocky Mountains
- Has a solid black head and neck and almost no white feathers

Blue Jay
- Lives mostly east of the Rocky Mountains
- Has blue, black, and white feathers on its wings and neck

Physical Evidence

The main tools early scientists used for taxonomy were their eyes and measuring devices. They collected examples of organisms. Then they studied traits such as color, size, weight, and how the organisms get energy. Scientists studied both the animals' internal structure and outward appearances. These physical features are still important today.

Individuals of two species, such as the two jays shown above, can have many similarities as well as some differences. One obvious difference is the color pattern. Another is the area of the world in which they live. Blue jays live east of the Rocky Mountains. Steller's jays live west of the Rockies. The common names and the scientific names show both the species' differences and their common ancestor: blue jay (*Cyanocitta cristata*) and Steller's jay (*Cyanocitta stelleri*).

Skeletons, shells, and other hard parts of organisms become fossilized more easily than soft parts do. Scientists can observe and measure fossilized bones and compare them with each other. They can also compare bones of extinct species with bones of modern living species. From such studies, scientists can learn much about an organism. Physical evidence gives clues about how an organism may have lived, how it moved, or what type of food it ate.

All of this evidence helps scientists see that all living organisms are related by evolution. Some are more closely related than others. Usually, the more traits two species share, the more closely related they are.

 CHECK YOUR READING How could comparing fossilized bones with a modern animal's bones help you see the modern animal's evolutionary history?

Genetic Evidence

In the early 1900s scientists discovered that organisms inherit their traits through structures called genes. In the early 1950s they found that genes are made of DNA and that DNA stores coded information. Today scientists can use laboratory machines to sequence the bases of DNA in an organism. Using a computer, scientists can compare the genes in one organism to the genes in another.

▼ **REMINDER**

Recall that DNA is composed of four bases: adenine, cytosine, guanine, and thymine.

Genetic evidence usually supports physical evidence, but not always. Consider the example shown below. For years, taxonomists argued about how to classify this small, reddish animal found in the mountain forests of the Himalayas. Its scientific name is *Ailurus fulgens,* and its common name is red panda.

Later, scientists discovered a larger, bearlike animal in China, which they called the giant panda. Both pandas eat bamboo, share a common name, and have similar faces. Scientists concluded that they were related to each other and to raccoons. However, genetic evidence has shown that the red panda is closely related to raccoons. The giant panda is more closely related to bears than to raccoons or to red pandas.

CHECK YOUR READING What does genetic evidence tell scientists about two organisms?

Genetic Evidence

Both of these pandas live in the same habitat, have similar faces, and eat bamboo. But genetic evidence shows that red pandas and giant pandas are only distant relatives.

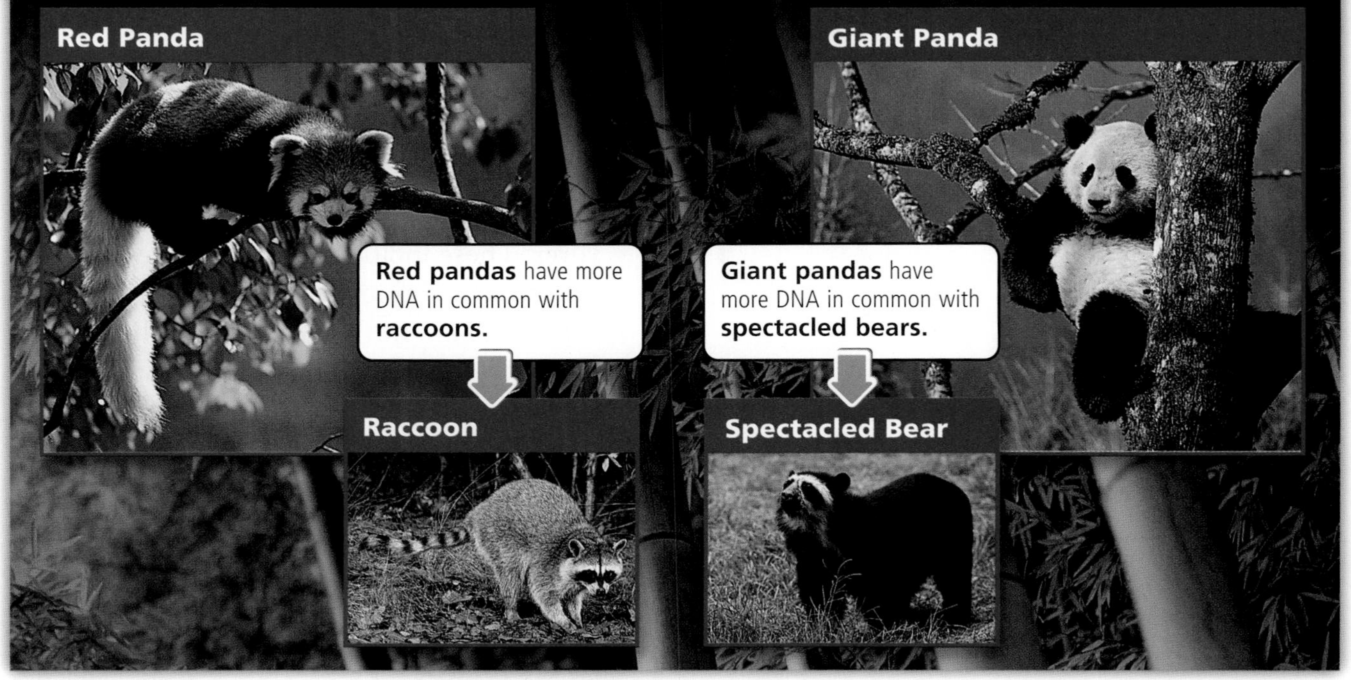

Red Panda

Giant Panda

Red pandas have more DNA in common with raccoons.

Giant pandas have more DNA in common with spectacled bears.

Raccoon

Spectacled Bear

Branching diagrams show how organisms evolved.

Scientists use diagrams to show the relationships they discover using physical and genetic evidence. By putting their results into a diagram, scientists can see the bigger picture of evolution.

The diagram below shows the relationships among the red panda, raccoon, giant panda, and spectacled bear. This diagram shows more than just which animals are more closely related to which others. It also shows when they most likely shared common ancestors.

Common Ancestors

Recall that the giant panda and the spectacled bear have many similarities in their DNA. Scientists consider these animals to be members of the same family, Ursidae. All the members of Ursidae are thought to have evolved from a common ancestor. That ancestor passed down components of its DNA.

The common ancestor of all bears and giant pandas is shown on the diagram at one of the nodes. The node is the part of a stem where a new branch begins to grow. This node is labeled on the diagram as *A*. As you can see from the scale on the left of the diagram, this common ancestor is thought to have lived over 20 million years ago.

Bears, giant pandas, red pandas, and raccoons also share a common ancestor. This common ancestor lived even longer ago. It is shown on the diagram as point *B*. All the types of animals shown shared this ancestor. The ancestor is thought to have passed down the traits common in carnivores. These include its skull shape and prominent canine teeth. Other branches of Carnivora are not shown on this diagram.

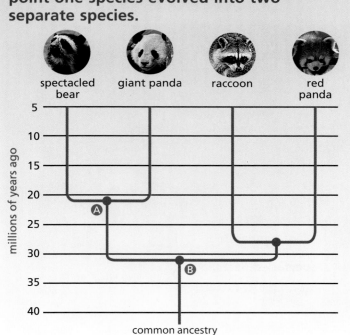

Branching Diagram

A branching diagram shows at what point one species evolved into two separate species.

spectacled bear   giant panda   raccoon   red panda

millions of years ago

common ancestry

 CHECK YOUR READING How are common ancestors represented on branching diagrams?

Diagramming Taxa

Branching diagrams show when organisms shared common ancestors. They also can show how all the members of a taxonomic group are related. These diagrams are like a family tree for the members of the group.

The diagram on page 242 shows when bears and giant pandas evolved into separate groups. It focuses on only a few species. The diagram below shows most of the major families in the order Carnivora. All of the animals listed at the top of the diagram represent families. Spectacled bears and giant pandas are both members of the family Ursidae. Therefore, they are grouped together in this diagram.

The diagram below contains information about other members of Carnivora. You can see that the red pandas are also related to skunks, weasels, and otters. The nodes on this diagram represent common ancestors just as they do on other branching diagrams.

Branching Diagram: Carnivora

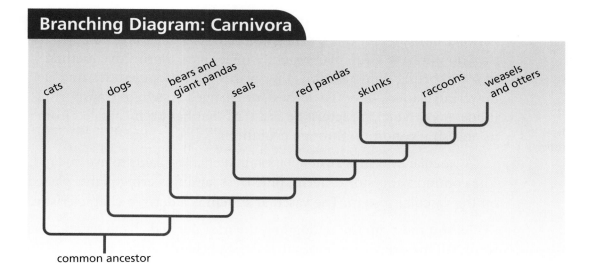

cats   dogs   bears and giant pandas   seals   red pandas   skunks   raccoons   weasels and otters

common ancestor

Cladograms

A **cladogram** (KLAD-uh-GRAM) is a branching diagram based on traits that are passed down from common ancestors. Although they look simple, cladograms carry a lot of information.

A cladogram is a little like a dichotomous key. Each branch on a cladogram shows two possibilities. The possibilities are two versions of an inherited trait. But cladograms differ from dichotomous keys in an important way. Dichotomous keys are based on any observable trait that can help people tell species apart. Cladograms are based only on traits that give information about how organisms evolved.

Plant Cladogram

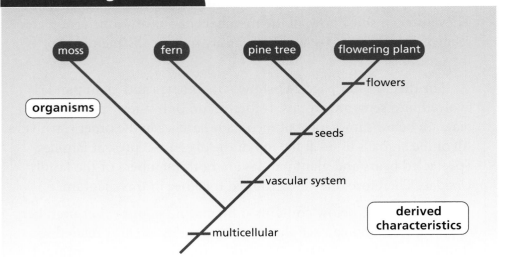

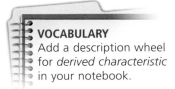

This rhododendron in the Redwood National Park is a flowering plant.

VOCABULARY
Add a description wheel for *derived characteristic* in your notebook.

Look at the cladogram above. A vascular system is a trait that all of the plants shown have in common, except mosses. A vascular system is a network of tissues for transporting fluids. Mosses are nonvascular plants; they do not have a vascular system. Mosses have a primitive method of transporting fluids. All the other plants— ferns, pine trees, and flowering plants—have the derived, or changed system of transporting fluids. A **derived characteristic** is a trait that has been changed from its ancestral condition through evolution.

A vascular system is an adaptation that enables plants to live on land. The common ancestor of ferns, pine trees, and flowering plants passed on the vascular system. The vascular system is a derived characteristic.

As you move up the cladogram, the next derived characteristic is seeds. All the organisms above that derived characteristic on the cladogram have seeds. Pine trees and flowering plants evolved from a common ancestor that had seeds. Pine trees, and flowering plants' common ancestor is closest to them on the diagram. That shows that they are the most closely related of the plants shown here.

Cladograms focus on traits that tie organisms together through history. They do not show every trait that has evolved in organisms. When organisms appear lower on a cladogram, it does not mean they have stopped evolving or that they are less evolved. It means that they shared a common ancestor with the other organisms a very long time ago.

CHECK YOUR READING What characteristic is shared by all of the plants shown in the cladogram?

Branching diagrams help scientists test their hypotheses.

The diagrams that you have just seen are hypotheses about how organisms are related. Depending on the types of evidence used, different scientists may produce different diagrams for the same organisms.

The cladogram on the left below shows one hypothesis about the evolution of the leafy sea dragon. In this cladogram, leafy fronds were thought to be a derived characteristic. The hypothesis suggests that the sargassum fish and the leafy sea dragon inherited the trait of leafy fronds from a common ancestor. That ancestor was not shared by the sea horse. For this hypothesis to be accepted, physical and genetic evidence would have to support it.

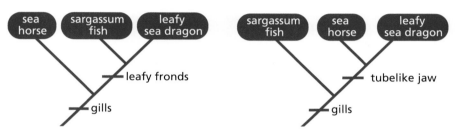

However, the hypothesis shown in the left-hand cladogram is not supported by evidence. The leafy sea dragon and sea horse share traits, such as body shape, bony rings around the body, and a tubelike jaw. It is more likely that those traits are a result of a shared history. A tubelike jaw is more likely to be a derived trait than leafy fronds. Therefore, the cladogram on the right is more likely the better hypothesis about the evolution of the sea dragon.

 CHECK YOUR READING How do cladograms show hypotheses?

7.2 Review

KEY CONCEPTS

1. Why do taxonomists study biological relationships? (7.3.d)

2. Describe two types of evidence that scientists use to classify organisms. (7.3.d)

3. How do branching diagrams show how organisms are related to one another? (7.3.d)

CRITICAL THINKING

4. **Compare and Contrast** Compare a cladogram with a dichotomous key. Explain how they are alike and different.

5. **Predict** The prehistoric flying animal, *Archaeopteryx*, has the same derived characteristic of feathers as modern-day birds. What can you infer about their common ancestor?

○ CHALLENGE

6. **Apply** Your classmate says that the organism at the end of a cladogram is the most evolved. Explain why your classmate is incorrect.

CHAPTER INVESTIGATION

Constructing a Cladogram

OVERVIEW AND PURPOSE Scientists use cladograms to show relationships among organisms based on characteristics the organisms have in common. For example, scientists look at holes in prehistoric animals' skulls to hypothesize about how they are related to one another. In this activity you will use what you have learned about cladograms to

- construct a cladogram based on animals' shared characteristics
- make inferences about how the animals are related to each other

▶ Problem

> Write It Up

How do scientists construct cladograms?

▶ Procedure

1. Copy the table below in your notebook.

Table 1. Characteristics of Vertebrates

Characteristic	Domestic Cat	Hummingbird	Shark	Tree Frog	Goldfish
Jaws	X	X	X	X	X
Lungs or swim bladder	X	X		X	X
Four Limbs	X	X		X	
Sac around embryo	X	X			

2. Calculate the number of X's in each column and write the total in your notebook. The number of X's represents how many characteristics the organisms have in common with each other.

3. Begin to construct your cladogram like the one shown on the sample notebook page. Use different colored pencils for different animals or different derived characteristics. Find the organism that has the fewest characteristics in common with the other organisms. Place this organism on the lowest branch of the cladogram. At the bottom of the branch, label the characteristic that the organism has. Every organism that comes above this on the cladogram should have this characteristic.

MATERIALS

- 4 colored pencils
- 7.3.d, 7.7.d

Content Standard
7.3.d Students know how to construct a simple branching diagram to classify living groups of organisms by shared derived characteristics and how to expand the diagram to include fossil organisms.

Investigation Standard
7.7.d Construct scale models, maps, and appropriately labeled diagrams to communicate to scientific knowledge.

4. Find the organism that has the second lowest number of characteristics in common with the other organisms. Place this organism on the second branch of your cladogram and label the side of the branch with the new characteristic this organism has.

5. Complete the construction of your cladogram by making a separate branch for each organism in Table 1 and labeling the side of the branch with the appropriate characteristic. Remember, as you move towards the top end of the cladogram, each organism should have all of the features of the organism that is on the branch before it.

▶ Observe and Analyze
Write It Up

1. **ANALYZE** Which characteristics are present in tree frogs? Which characteristics are absent?

2. **IDENTIFY** Which animals have four limbs?

3. **INFER** The more characteristics that two organisms have in common, the more closely related they are thought to be. Based upon your cladogram, which two animals are the most closely related?

▶ Conclude
Write It Up

1. **CLASSIFY** A lamprey is a type of fish that does not have jaws. It does not have any of the other characteristics listed in Table 1. Where would you place a branch for a lamprey on your cladogram? Why?

2. **APPLY** The saber-toothed tiger, an extinct cat, is a member of the same family as the domestic cat. It has all of the same characteristics as a domestic cat. Where would you place the saber-toothed tiger on your cladogram? (**Hint:** Side branches can be added onto the main branches of a cladogram.)

▶ INVESTIGATE Further

CHALLENGE Study the table below. Make a cladogram that shows the relationships among the insects in the table.

Table 2. Characteristics of Insects

Characteristics	Mayfly	Butterfly	Grasshopper
Wings	X	X	X
Folding wings		X	X
Distinct development stages		X	

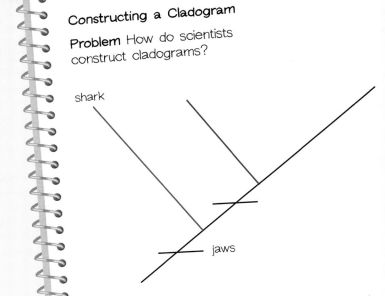

Constructing a Cladogram

Problem How do scientists construct cladograms?

shark

jaws

Classification systems change as scientists learn more.

CALIFORNIA
Content Standard

7.3.d Students know how to construct a simple branching diagram to classify living groups of organisms by shared derived characteristics and how to expand the diagram to include fossil organisms.

◁ BEFORE, you learned

- Scientists give each species a unique scientific name
- Organisms can be classified into seven levels
- Dichotomous keys help us identify organisms

▷ NOW, you will learn

- About the connection between new discoveries and taxonomy
- About the two familiar kingdoms of plants and animals
- About four less familiar kingdoms

VOCABULARY

domain p. 249
vertebrate p. 253
invertebrate p. 253

THINK ABOUT

How do scientists define kingdoms?

Look at this photograph of a sea urchin. It lives its life on the ocean floor. The sea urchin's mouth is on its underside. It eats bits of food right off the ocean floor. The sea urchin doesn't seem to have much in

common with a tiger, an alligator, even a human. Yet all of these organisms belong in the same kingdom, called Animalia. Why do you think scientists group these organisms together?

Taxonomy changes as scientists make discoveries.

The list of species keeps getting longer as scientists find new ones. Also, taxonomists keep learning more and more about species that have already been discovered. As you read in Section 2, new data may cause scientists to reclassify species such as the giant panda. Both the names of species and their groups may change because of discoveries about their evolution.

Early scientists sorted all organisms into two large groups—plants and animals. Anything that was green and stayed in one place was a plant. Anything that moved was an animal. Most scientists today use a system that includes six kingdoms. And, in addition, another level of organization has been added above the kingdom level.

Three Domains

You remember that prokaryotes are single-celled organisms without a nucleus. Scientists now separate prokaryotes into two groups: bacteria and archaea. The differences between these two cell types were greater than scientists had thought. To make room for these groups in the classification system, another level was added. A **domain** is the highest level of classification, higher than kingdoms. Now, the domain Bacteria consists of bacteria. The domain Archaea consists of archaea. The domain Eukarya contains the protists, fungi, plants, and animals.

RESOURCE CENTER
CLASSZONE.COM
Find out more about modern classification.

Domains and Kingdoms

Domain	Bacteria	Archaea	Eukarya			
Kingdom	Bacteria	Archaea	Protista	Fungi	Plantae	Animalia
Cell type	no nucleus	no nucleus	with nucleus	with nucleus	with nucleus	with nucleus
Cell number	unicellular	unicellular	mostly unicellular	mostly multicellular	multicellular	multicellular
How organisms get energy	varies	varies	varies	absorbs materials	uses sunlight	consumes food

The photographs below show examples of cells from each domain. Notice the nucleus in the cell from Eukarya. There are no nuclei in cells from Bacteria and Archaea. The domains Bacteria and Archaea include only organisms with prokaryotic cells. The domain Eukarya includes only organisms with eukaryotic cells.

 CHECK YOUR READING How many kingdoms does the Eukarya domain contain?

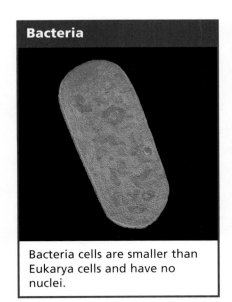

Bacteria

Bacteria cells are smaller than Eukarya cells and have no nuclei.

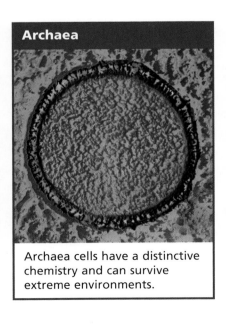

Archaea

Archaea cells have a distinctive chemistry and can survive extreme environments.

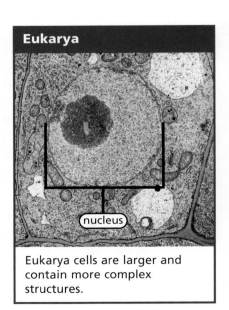

Eukarya

nucleus

Eukarya cells are larger and contain more complex structures.

All living things on Earth can be classified in six kingdoms.

Plantae
- Plants are multicellular, and most live on land.
- Plants obtain energy from sunlight.
- A plant cell has a nucleus, a cell wall, and chloroplasts.

Animalia
- Animals are multicellular and able to move.
- Animals obtain energy by eating food.
- An animal cell has a nucleus but no cell wall or chloroplasts.

Protista
- Most protists are single celled.
- Multicellular protists lack complex structure.
- A protist cell has a nucleus.

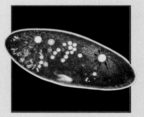

Fungi
- All fungi except yeasts are multicellular.
- Fungi obtain energy by absorbing materials.
- A fungus cell has a nucleus and a cell wall but no chloroplasts.

Archaea
- Archaea are unicellular organisms without nuclei.
- Archaea cells have different chemicals than bacteria.
- Archaea can live in extreme conditions.

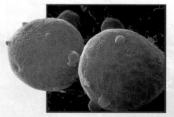

Bacteria
- Bacteria are unicellular organisms.
- A bacterial cell has no nucleus.
- Bacteria reproduce by dividing in two.

Six Kingdoms

Domains are divided into kingdoms. Today's classification system has six kingdoms. Every known species on Earth is sorted into one of these six kingdoms.

- **Plantae** (PLAN-tee) includes plants such as trees, grass, and moss.
- **Animalia** (AN-uh-MAL-yuh) includes animals, from lions and tigers and bears to ants and tiny mites.
- **Protista** (pruh-TIHS-tuh) includes organisms that are not easily classified as animals, plants, or fungi. They are mostly unicellular organisms though some have a simple multicellular structure.
- **Fungi** (FUHN-jy) includes mushrooms, molds, and yeasts.
- **Archaea** (ahr-KEE-uh) contains unicellular organisms that are similar to bacteria, but have a different cell structure.
- **Bacteria** (bak-TIHR-ee-uh) are unicellular organisms with no nucleus.

This system may change as scientists learn more about the species in each kingdom. Before 1990 most scientists used a five-kingdom system. That system put Archaea and Bacteria into one kingdom. However, as scientists learned of chemical differences between these cells, they split them into two kingdoms. Many scientists agree that a system of three domains and six kingdoms is the best way right now to sort organisms. However, some scientists think that the kingdom Protista should be broken into smaller kingdoms. These scientists have found many differences among its species.

 CHECK YOUR READING Which of the six kingdoms include unicellular organisms?

The two most familiar kingdoms are plants and animals.

Carolus Linnaeus put all of the species he knew about into two large groups: plants and animals. These two kingdoms include many common living things. But they also include many unfamiliar organisms.

Humans, elephants, termites, ducks, fish, and worms are very different from each other. It might seem odd that they are all part of the same group. However, all of these animals share some general traits, just as all plants share their own set of general traits.

Clematis viticella
(Italian clematis)

READING TiP

For more detail about the plant kingdom, see pages R66-69 in the Appendix.

Plantae

Over 250,000 plant species live on Earth. They range from tiny mosses to giant sequoia trees, one of the largest organisms on Earth. The oldest living organism is a plant called the bristlecone pine. Some bristlecone pines have been alive since the Egyptians built the pyramids, about 4000 years ago.

All plants are multicellular. All plants store their DNA in the nucleus of their cells. All plants are able to make sugars using the Sun's energy. Unlike animals, plants cannot move around. However, they can grow around objects, turn toward light, and grow upward. Plant cells have tough cell walls outside their cell membranes. Vascular plants have a system of long tubelike tissues. These tissues move water and nutrients to parts of the plant. Nonvascular plants do not have such a system.

Plants are grouped into three main types.

- **Bryophytes** are nonvascular; they were the first plants to live on land. Bryophytes include mosses, hornworts, and liverworts.

- **Vascular seedless plants** have a vascular system but no seeds. Vascular seedless plants include horsetails and ferns.

- **Vascular seed plants** have vascular systems. They also have seeds for protecting and dispersing embryos.

Vascular seed plants include conifers, or evergreen trees, ginkgo trees, and flowering plants. Most of the plants you can think of, such as grass or apple trees, are flowering plants. Most familiar plants are vascular seed plants.

Horsetails

Equisetem telmateia,
a vascular seedless plant

Bristlecone Pine

Pinus aristata,
a vascular seed plant

Orchids

Vanilla planifolia,
a vascular seed plant

Animalia

Scientists have already named a million species in the kingdom Animalia. Many different types of animals live on Earth, but more than 90 percent of the named species are insects. The animal kingdom also has familiar animals such as whales, sharks, humans, bears, dogs, and fish.

All animals get their energy by eating other organisms. All animals can move around for at least part of their life. Most animals have mouths and some type of nervous system. Unlike plant cells, animal cells have no cell walls. Animals are classified by their body types, which vary widely. **Vertebrates** are animals with backbones. **Invertebrates,** the group that contains the most individuals, have no backbone.

About one million invertebrate species live on Earth. Invertebrates can be found just about everywhere, from frozen tundra to tropical forests. Some invertebrates live in water, while others survive in deserts where there is almost no water. Many invertebrates live inside other organisms. Most invertebrate animals are small. Crickets, oysters, sea stars, earthworms, ants, and spiders are some examples of invertebrates. The fact that invertebrates do not have backbones for support tends to limit their size. However, some ocean-dwelling invertebrates can be quite large. For example, the giant squid can grow to 18 meters (59 feet) in length and can weigh over 450 kilograms (992 lb).

The phylum Chordata is made up almost entirely of animals that have backbones. Many of the animals that you are most familiar with are chordates. Fish, amphibians, reptiles, birds, and mammals are all chordates.

READING TIP

For more detail about the animal kingdom, see pages R70–77 in the Appendix.

Jumping Spider

Salticus scenicus,
an invertebrate

Giraffe

Giraffa camelopardalis,
a vertebrate

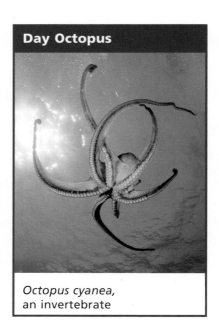

Day Octopus

Octopus cyanea,
an invertebrate

How can you classify leaves?

PROCEDURE

1. Decide, as a class, what traits you will use to classify leaves. You may use size, shape, color, vein patterns, texture, or anything else that you observe.

2. Work with a few classmates. Sort your leaves into four or five taxa, based on the characteristics chosen in step 1. Give each taxon a name that describes its common traits.

3. Compare your classification scheme with those of other groups.

WHAT DO YOU THINK?

- How did you arrange the leaves into groups?
- Did your methods of classifying leaves match those of other student groups?

CHALLENGE How does your group's classification scheme compare with the scheme scientists use for classification?

SKILL FOCUS
Classifying (7.3.d)

MATERIALS
- leaves
- hand lens

TIME
20 minutes

Other organisms make up four more kingdoms.

Carolus Linnaeus' classification system included the organisms he knew about in the late 1700s. Some of the organisms Linnaeus called plants—the mushrooms, molds, and their relatives—turned out to be very different from plants in the plant kingdom. Biologists now put fungi in a kingdom of their own.

Three other kingdoms consist mainly of microscopic organisms. These are Protista, Archaea, and Bacteria. Most organisms on Earth are classified as bacteria or archaea. These prokaryotic organisms are small, simple cells without nuclei.

Although bacteria are tiny, they outnumber every other kingdom of organisms. One shovelful of soil contains trillions of bacteria. They perform important functions, both helpful and harmful to humans. Helpful bacteria break down the matter in dead bodies and waste materials. Other bacteria allow plants to use nitrogen. Bacteria can also be harmful, causing disease in humans and other organisms.

 CHECK YOUR READING What are the four kingdoms besides Plantae and Animalia?

Protista

The kingdom Protista includes a wide variety of organisms. Most protists are unicellular. The multicellular protists are too simple to be classified as animals, plants, or fungi. All protists have large, complex cells with true nuclei. Some eat other organisms as animals do. Some get energy from sunlight as plants do. Some protists resemble fungi. However, multicellular protists are still much simpler than plants, animals, and fungi.

Many protists live in ponds or the ocean. Even the largest of the unicellular species can just be seen with a microscope. However, large organisms such as seaweeds are also classified as Protista. Some seaweeds, such as the giant kelp pictured at right, can grow hundreds of meters in one year.

Different groups of protists evolved from different ancestors. Scientists still debate whether Protista should be classified as one kingdom or should be split into several. The kingdom seems to be a grab bag for organisms that don't fit into other kingdoms.

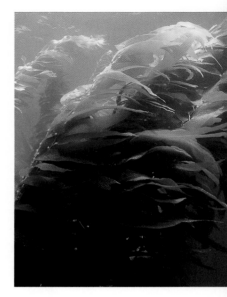

Macrocystis pyrifera
(giant kelp)

CALIFORNIA Focus

Up and down the coast of California lie huge beds of *Macrocystis pyrifera,* the kelp pictured above. These kelp forests serve as filters. They also slow the Pacific currents and are home to thousands of organisms.

Fungi

If you've ever baked a loaf of bread, you probably used a fungus to make the dough rise. One group of fungi called yeasts makes it possible for us to make bread and many other food products. Another type of fungi that people eat includes mushrooms. A mushroom grows in thin threads underground, and only the small cap breaks above the ground.

Some well-known fungi include mushrooms, molds, and yeasts. Both plants and fungi remain rooted in one place. Most fungi have cell walls like the cells walls of plants. Unlike plants, fungi do not use sunlight to make food. Fungi do not "eat" in the same way that animals do. Instead they use chemicals to break down food outside of their bodies. Then they absorb, or take in, that food. Many fungi act as decomposers. They break dead or decaying matter into simpler parts.

READING TiP
Fungi is the plural form of *fungus.*

Penicillium
(bread mold)

Lepiota procera
(parasol mushroom)

Bacteria

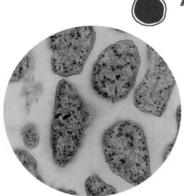

All bacteria are unicellular. They have small, simple cells without a nucleus. Most bacteria have a cell wall outside the cell membrane. This wall, however, is not the same as the cell wall of plants. Bacteria reproduce by dividing in two, and can produce many new generations in a very short time.

Bacteria live nearly everywhere on Earth. They are usually grouped by what tasks they do. Some produce energy from sunlight. Others break down materials in dead or decaying organisms. Some can cause human disease and spoil food, such as *E. coli,* pictured at left. Some bacteria live in a very close relationship either inside or on the surface of other organisms. They can help, harm, or have no effect their hosts.

Escherichia coli (E. coli)

Archaea

Archaea are single-celled. They do not have nuclei, but their cell structure is different from that of bacteria. Like bacteria, they live in many environments, especially in the ocean. But they also live in some very extreme environments: very hot, very cold, or extremely salty places. Other organisms cannot live in such places.

Archaea can live in boiling mud near geysers. They can live in hot vents at the bottom of the ocean. Some, such as those pictured at the left, live in frigid temperatures with little oxygen in Antarctica. The genus name, *Methanococcoides,* shows that it produces methane, a natural gas. Other methane producers live in the dense mud of swamps and marshes. Some live in the guts of cows and termites. They help these plant-eaters digest the cellulose in the plant cell walls. Other archaea live in very salty ponds and lakes. They die if the water is not salty enough.

Methanococcoides burtonii

 CHECK YOUR READING Which traits classify an organism as part of the kingdom Archaea?

7.3 Review

KEY CONCEPTS

1. What caused scientists to change the way they classify species? (7.3.d)

2. What are the two most familiar kingdoms? (7.3.d)

3. Briefly name and describe the other four kingdoms. (7.3.d)

CRITICAL THINKING

4. **Communicate** Make a table with columns titled Animalia and Plantae. Using as many rows as needed, list characteristics that differ between these two kingdoms.

5. **Analyze** Explain how fungi differ from plants.

⬥ CHALLENGE

6. **Analyze** One bacterium has a membrane surrounding its DNA. Should this organism be classified with the eukaryotes? Why or why not?

SKILL: EVALUATING HYPOTHESES

What Is a Pterosaur?

> **7.7.c** Communicate the logical connection among hypotheses, science concepts, tests conducted, data collected, and conclusions drawn from the scientific evidence.

The **pterosaur** illustrated below is from the late Jurassic period. This prehistoric animal is not a dinosaur, although it is related to dinosaurs. How do scientists determine which organisms are related to which others? Scientists use organisms' characteristics to propose a cladogram. Cladograms are hypotheses about how groups of organisms are related to one another.

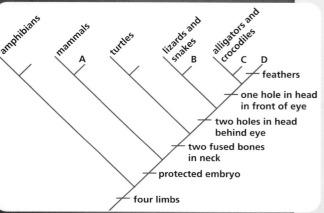

▶ Hypothesis

The diagram at the left is a current, simplified cladogram showing the proposed relationships of tetrapods. Tetrapods have two pairs of limbs, such as legs or wings. Each tetrapod is listed along the top of the cladogram. Derived characteristics, thought to be inherited from a common ancestor, are listed along the side. All of the animals above a derived characteristic have that characteristic. According to this cladogram, all of the animals listed have evolved from a common ancestor that had four limbs.

▶ Observations

The pterosaur has four limbs, but where does it fit into the tetrapod cladogram? Scientists made observations about pterosaur fossils:

	Present in Pterosaur?
Four limbs	Yes
Protected embryo	Yes
Two fused bones in neck	Yes
Two holes in head behind eye	Yes
One hole in head in front of eye	Yes
Feathers	No

▶ Interpret Observations

On your own Study the data presented in the table. Which letter on the cladogram shows where the pterosaur should be placed, A, B, C, or D?

As a group Explain how the pterosaur is related to other, living tetrapods according to this cladogram.

CHALLENGE Snakes are considered tetrapods even though most snakes do not have any legs. How do you think scientists explain this?

Chapter Review

the **BIG** idea

Scientists have developed a system for classifying the great diversity of living things.

CONTENT REVIEW
CLASSZONE.COM

KEY CONCEPTS SUMMARY

1 **Scientists develop systems for classifying living things.**

Spotted turtle
Clemmys guttata

Classification: Spotted turtle	
Kingdom	Animalia
Phylum	Chordata
Class	Reptilia
Order	Testudines
Family	Emydidae
Genus	*Clemmys*
Species	*guttata*

VOCABULARY
dichotomous key
  p. 231
classification p. 232
taxonomy p. 232
binomial
  nomenclature p. 233
genus p. 233

2 **Branching diagrams show biological relationships.**

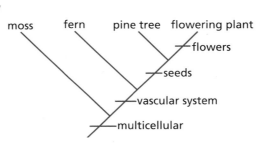

VOCABULARY
cladogram p. 243
derived
  characteristic p. 244

3 **Classification systems change as scientists learn more.**

The most popular system of classification in use today is a three-domain system that includes six kingdoms of organisms.

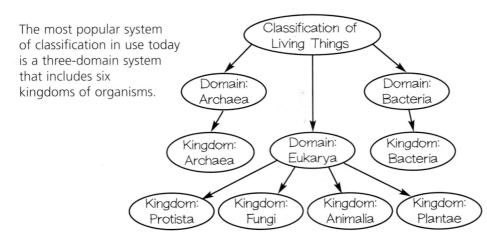

VOCABULARY
domain p. 249
vertebrate p. 253
invertebrate p. 253

Reviewing Vocabulary

Make a frame like the one shown for each vocabulary term listed below. Write the term in the center. Decide what information to frame it with. Use definitions, examples, descriptions, parts, or pictures.

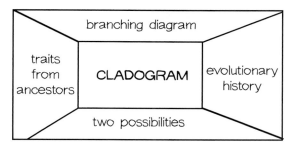

branching diagram

traits from ancestors

CLADOGRAM

evolutionary history

two possibilities

1. binomial nomenclature

2. taxonomy

3. domain

4. vertebrate

Reviewing Key Concepts

Multiple Choice *Choose the letter of the best answer.*

5. The scientific process of arranging organisms into groups based on similarities is (7.3.d)
   a. observation
   b. classification
   c. binomial nomenclature
   d. dichotomy

6. The system of naming organisms developed by Carolus Linnaeus is called (7.3.d)
   a. binomial nomenclature
   b. taxonomy
   c. dichotomous nomenclature
   d. classification

7. Which group includes the most species? (7.3.d)
   a. kingdom
   b. family
   c. domain
   d. phylum

8. The science of taxonomy allows scientists to (7.3.d)
   a. identify unfamiliar organisms
   b. classify and name organisms
   c. refer to one specific type of organism
   d. determine similar traits of organisms

9. Which allows scientists to use genetic information to classify organisms? (7.3.d)
   a. physical traits
   b. DNA
   c. behaviors
   d. habitats

10. A dichotomous key contains a series of choices that people use to
   a. find similar organisms
   b. identify organisms
   c. name organisms
   d. describe organisms

11. What are the names of the three domains?
   a. Plantae, Animalia, Protista
   b. Bacteria, Protista, Fungi
   c. Bacteria, Archaea, Eukarya
   d. Protista, Archaea, Eukarya

12. Which is an example of a physical trait? (7.3.d)
   a. bone structure
   b. DNA information
   c. fossil records
   d. habitat

Short Answer *Write a short answer to each question.*

13. What are the rules for creating a scientific name for an organism? (7.3.d)

14. Why are cladograms considered to be scientists' hypotheses? (7.3.d)

15. What caused scientists to add the level of domain to the system of classification?

Reading a Diagram *Look at the part of a cladogram below and answer the four questions that follow.*

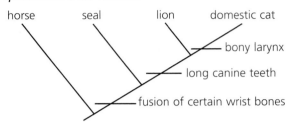

horse   seal   lion   domestic cat

— bony larynx

— long canine teeth

— fusion of certain wrist bones

16. **INTERPRET** What are the derived characteristics shown in this cladogram? (7.3.d)

17. **INTERPRET** What trait does the seal have that the horse does not? (7.3.d)

18. **INTERPRET** Which animal has all of the characteristics shown on the diagram? (7.3.d)

19. **CONCLUDE** What does this cladogram show about all the animals named? (7.3.d)

20. **ANALYZE** How do scientists use fossils to classify organisms? (7.3.d)

21. **APPLY** Scientists once classified American vultures and African vultures together in the falcon family. Since then, scientists have learned that the two vultures belong to different families and that American vultures are more closely related to storks. What type of evidence might scientists have used to come to this conclusion? Explain your answer. (7.3.c)

22. **EVALUATE** Which two of these species are more closely related: *Felis catus, Felis concolor, Picea concolor?* How do you know? (7.3.d)

23. **INFER** A scientist is studying the following organisms. What conclusions can you draw about the organisms based on their scientific names? (7.3.d)
    - *Ursus americanus*
    - *Ursus arctos*
    - *Ursus maritimus*

24. **ANALYZE** Two organisms you are studying are in the same class, but in different orders. What does this information tell you about the two organisms?

25. **RANK** Which of these has more groups of organisms: phylum or family? Explain your answer. (7.3.d)

26. **SUMMARIZE** Describe how you would use a dichotomous key to identify this leaf.

27. **SYNTHESIZE** Linnaeus classified all organisms into two groups. Why did later scientists add more groups? (7.3.c)

28. **CLASSIFY** Suppose you discover a new organism that is single-celled, has a nucleus, lives in the water, and uses sunlight to produce its energy. In which kingdom would you classify this organism? Explain. (7.3.d)

the BIG idea

29. **INFER** Look again at the picture on pages 226–227. Now that you have finished the chapter, how would you change or add details to your answer to the question on the photograph?

30. **PROVIDE EXAMPLES** Imagine that you are a scientist studying a variety of organisms in a South American rain forest. You have classified one organism in the kingdom Animalia and another organism in the kingdom Plantae. Give examples of the characteristics that would enable you to classify each organism in those kingdoms.

UNIT PROJECTS

Evaluate all the data, results, and information from your project folder. Prepare to present your project. Be ready to answer questions posed by your classmates about your results.

Standards-Based Assessment

Interpreting Diagrams

7.3.d

Choose the letter of the best answer.

This diagram shows how groups of carnivores are related to one another. In this diagram, each Y indicates a common ancestor.

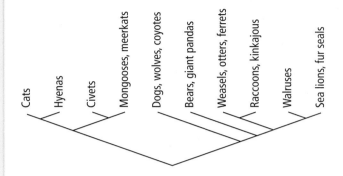

1. Hyenas are most closely related to which group?

  a. cats

  b. civets

  c. mongooses and meerkats

  d. raccoons and kinkajous

2. Weasels, otters, and ferrets are most closely related to

  a. bears and giant pandas

  b. sea lions and fur seals

  c. raccoons and kinkajous

  d. mongooses and meerkats

3. Sea lions and fur seals share their closest common ancestor with

  a. walruses

  b. raccoons and kinkajous

  c. mongooses and muskrats

  d. civets

4. Which statement is true based on the information in the diagram?

  a. Dogs, wolves, and coyotes do not share a common ancestor with any of the groups.

  b. Raccoons are more closely related to weasels than they are to giant pandas.

  c. None of the groups shown in the diagram share a common ancestor.

  d. Mongooses and meerkats are the same as civets.

5. The branches on the diagram indicate where

  a. mass extinctions might have occurred

  b. speciation took place

  c. groups acquired traits and passed them onto their offspring

  d. there are gaps in the line of evolution

Extended Response

6. A scientist has discovered a new type of animal in the tundra area near the North Pole. Write a paragraph describing the type of evidence the scientist might use to classify the animal by its evolutionary history. Use the terms in the box in your paragraph. Underline each term in your answer.

DNA	common ancestor
physical evidence	fossil

7. Draw a small diagram like the one shown above to describe how you think green beans, peas, and broccoli might be related. Write a short paragraph to explain the thinking behind your diagram.

Structure and Function in Living Systems

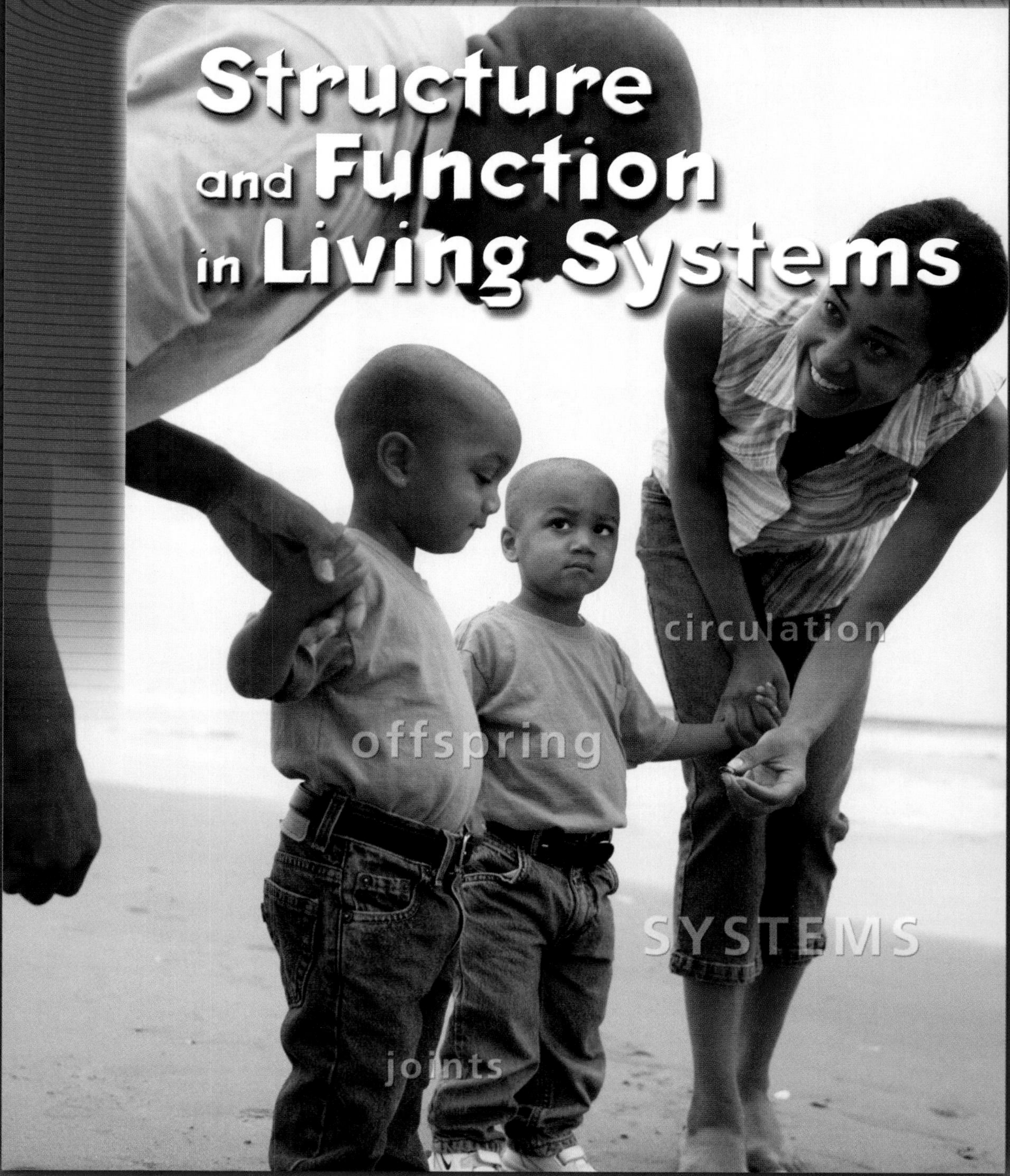

circulation

offspring

SYSTEMS

joints

Contents Overview

Surprising Senses

California Content Standards

7.5.b Students know organ systems function because of the contributions of individual organs, tissues, and cells. The failure of any part can affect the entire system.

SCIENTIFIC AMERICAN FRONTIERS

Learn more about how the brain and senses work. See the video "Sight of Touch."

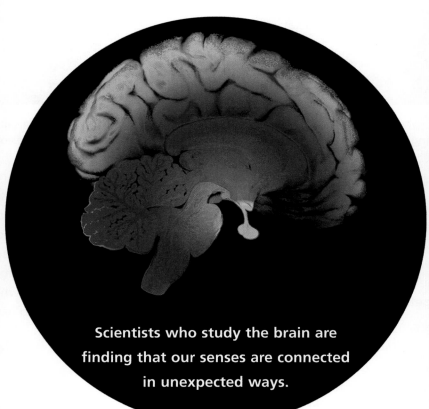

Scientists who study the brain are finding that our senses are connected in unexpected ways.

Senses and the Brain

One of the great mysteries still unsolved in science is what happens inside the brain. What is a thought? How is it formed? Where is it stored? How do our senses shape our thoughts? There are far more questions than answers. One way to approach questions about the brain is to study brain activity at times when the body is performing different functions.

Most advanced brain functions happen in the part of the brain called the cerebral cortex (suh-REE-bruhl KOR-tehks). That's where the brain interprets information from the senses. The cerebral cortex has many specialized areas. Each of the senses is controlled by a separate area of the brain. Scientists are mapping these areas. At first, they studied people with brain injuries. A person with an injury to one area might not be able to speak. Someone with a different injury might have trouble seeing. Scientists mapped each area in which damage usually produced one type of problem.

Now scientists have even more tools to study the brain. One tool is called functional magnetic resonance imaging, or fMRI. Scientists put a person into a machine that uses radio waves to produce images of the person's brain. Scientists then ask the person to do specific activities, such as looking at pictures of faces or listening for specific sounds. The fMRI images show what parts of the person's brain are most active during each activity.

These PET scans show areas of the brain active during particular tasks. Braille is a textured alphabet read using the fingers. Braille reading activates areas associated with touch, vision, hearing, and problem solving.

Double Duty

Using fMRI and other tools, scientists have identified the parts of the cerebral cortex that are responsible for each of the senses. The vision area is located at the back of the brain. The smell, taste, touch, and hearing areas are all close together in the middle part of the brain.

People don't usually use just one sense at a time. Scientists have found some unexpected connections. In one study, Marisa Taylor-Clarke at University College London poked the arms of volunteers with either one or two pins. Then she asked how many pins they felt. Taylor-Clarke found that people did better when they looked at their arms before the test. The fMRI showed that the part of their brains responsible for touch was also more active when they used their sense of sight.

These connections in the brain show up even when one sense doesn't work. Many people who have hearing impairments read lips to understand what other people are saying. Scientists using fMRI discovered that these people use the part of the brain normally used for hearing to help them understand what they see. This is true even for people who have never been able to hear.

Scrambled Senses

Some people have more connections between their senses than most people have. They may look at numbers and see colors, or associate smells with shapes. Some even get a taste in their mouth when they touch something. All these are examples of synesthesia (SIN-ihs-THEE-zhuh). About 1 in 200 people have some kind of synesthesia.

View the "Sight of Touch" segment of the Scientific American Frontiers video to learn about another example of connections between the senses.

IN THIS SCENE FROM THE VIDEO ⊙ Michelle, a research subject, reads Braille with her fingers after wearing a blindfold for three days.

SEEING BY TOUCHING Many blind people read using Braille, a system of raised dots used to represent letters. Some, such as Braille proofreader Gil Busch, can read Braille at astonishing speeds. Scientist Alvaro Pascual-Leone used MRI to study Gil's brain. The visual area of Gil's brain was active while he read Braille.

Gil has been blind since birth, so his brain has had a long time to adjust. Pascual-Leone wanted to know whether the brain could rewire itself in a shorter time. He asked volunteer Michelle Geronimo to wear a blindfold for a week. During that time, she learned to read Braille and experienced the world as a blind person does. At the end of the week, Pascual-Leone was able to demonstrate that Michelle's brain had rewired itself. Her visual center was active when she read Braille.

The use of fMRI has made it possible for scientists to learn more about synesthesia. One group of scientists studied people who saw colors when they heard words. The fMRI showed that the visual areas of their brains were active along with the hearing areas. (For most people, only the hearing area would be active.)

But why does synesthesia happen? Some scientists think that people with synesthesia have extra connections between areas of their brains. Every person has extra connections when they're born, but most people lose many of them in childhood. Perhaps people with synesthesia keep theirs. Or perhaps their brains are "cross-wired" so that information goes in unusual directions.

Some people with synesthesia see this colorful pattern when they hear a dog bark.

As scientists explore synesthesia and other connections between the senses, they learn more about how the parts of the brain work together. The human body is complex. And the brain, along with the rest of the nervous system, has yet to be understood fully.

UNANSWERED Questions

Scientists have learned a lot about how the brain processes different types of information. Their research leads to new questions.

- How does information move between different areas of the brain?
- How and why does the brain rewire itself?
- How does cross-wired sensing (synesthesia) happen?

UNIT PROJECTS

As you study this unit, work alone or in a group on one of the projects below.

Your Body System (7.5.b)

Create one or several models showing important body systems.

- Draw the outline of your own body on a large piece of craft paper.
- Use reference materials to help you place everything correctly. Label each part.

The Brain: "Then and Now" (7.5.b)

Compare and contrast past and present understandings of the brain.

- One understanding is that each part of the brain is responsible for different body functions. This understanding has changed over time.
- Research the history of this idea.
- Prepare diagrams showing then and now. Share your presentation.

Design an Experiment (7.7.e)

Design an experiment to test one of the senses. You should first identify a problem you want to explore.

- The experiment should include a written introduction, materials, procedure, and a plan for recording and presenting outcomes.
- Prepare a blank written experiment datasheet for your classmates to use.

CAREER CENTER
CLASSZONE.COM

Learn more about careers in neurobiology.

CHAPTER

8 Systems in Organisms

the **BIG** idea

Organisms are made of different parts that work together to perform life functions.

Key Concepts

SECTION

1 Systems help organisms meet their needs.
Learn how unicellular and multicellular organisms meet their needs.

SECTION

2 Plants have several levels of organization.
Learn about tissues and organs in plants.

SECTION

3 Animals have several levels of organization.
Learn about tissues and organ systems in animals.

SECTION

4 Human health depends on a balance among systems.
Learn how human body systems maintain homeostasis.

 California ClassZone

CLASSZONE.COM

Chapter 8 online resources: Content Review, one Simulation, three Resource Centers, Math Tutorial, Test Practice

What do these people have in common with this giant sequoia?

EXPLORE (the BIG idea)

How Is a Bird Like a Frog?

> **7.5.b** Students know organ systems function because of the contributions of individual organs, tissues, and cells. The failure of any part can affect the entire system.

Fish, frogs, snakes, birds, dogs, and humans are all vertebrate animals. Choose two vertebrates and quickly sketch them. Make an outline of their bodies and try to locate these parts within them: brain, heart, lungs, stomach, backbone.

Observe and Think Compare the placement of the inner structures in your two animals. How is their organization similar, and how does it differ?

Internet Activity: The Human Body

> **7.5.a** Students know plants and animals have levels of organization for structure and function, including cells, tissues, organs, organ systems, and the whole organism.

Go to **ClassZone.com** to explore the different systems in the human body.

Observe and Think Compare the structures and systems in the human body to the structures and systems in a tree. How are they similar, and how are they different? Compare the human systems to those in a fish. What do they have in common, and how do they differ?

NSTA scilinks.org
SCiLINKS
Homeostasis **Code: MDL072**

Getting Ready to Learn

◀ CONCEPT REVIEW

- The cell is the basic unit of living things.
- Systems are made of interlocking parts that share matter and energy.
- Animals and plants belong to different kingdoms within the domain Eukarya.

◀ VOCABULARY REVIEW

invertebrate p. 253

vertebrate p. 253

multicellular p. 11

unicellular p. 11

CONTENT REVIEW
CLASSZONE.COM

Review concepts and vocabulary.

▶ TAKING NOTES

MAIN IDEA WEB

Write each new blue heading in a box. Then write notes in boxes around the center box that give important terms and details about that blue heading.

VOCABULARY STRATEGY

Write each new vocabulary term in the center of a four square diagram. Write notes in the squares around each term. Include a definition, some features, and some examples of the term. If possible, write some things that are not examples of the term.

See the Note-Taking Handbook on pages R45–R51.

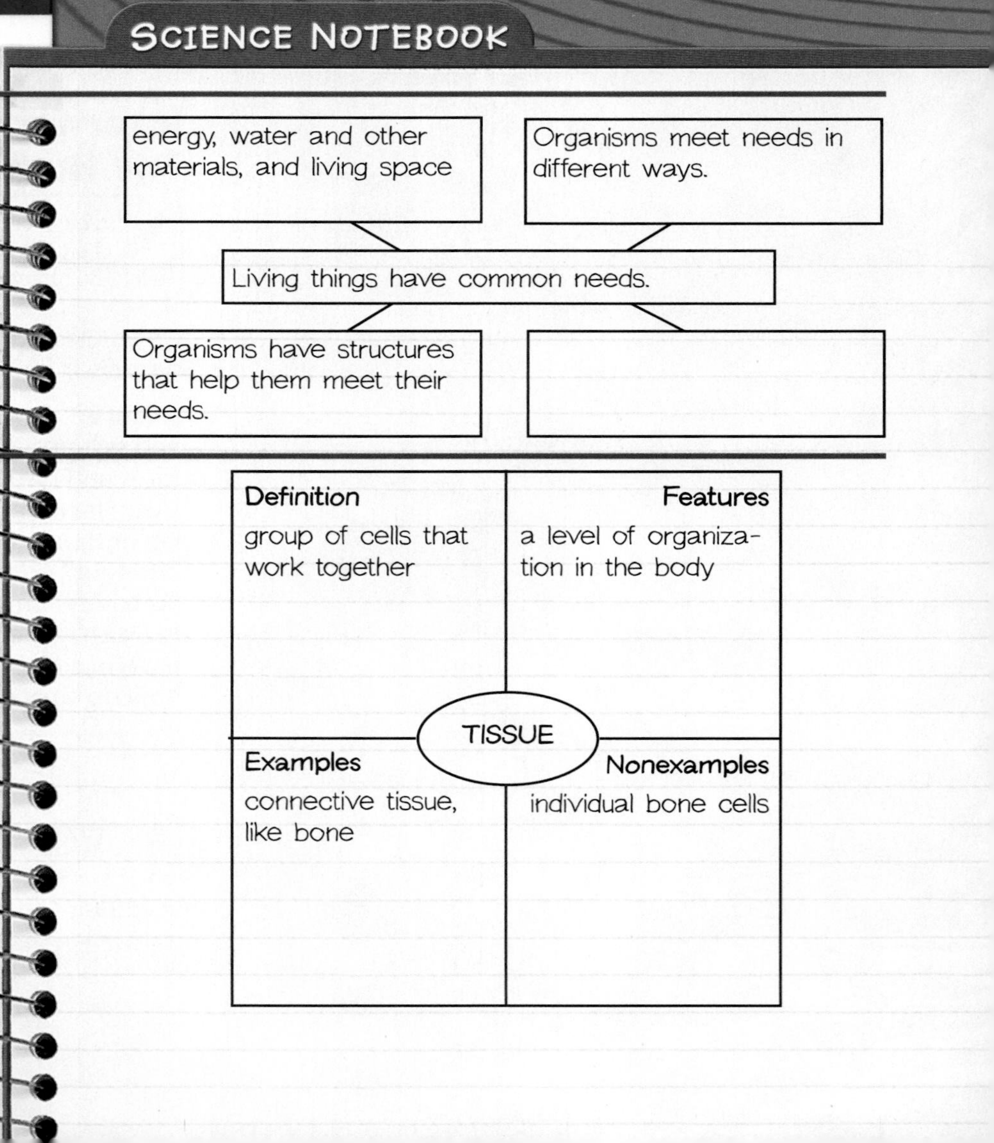

SCIENCE NOTEBOOK

energy, water and other materials, and living space	Organisms meet needs in different ways.

Living things have common needs.

Organisms have structures that help them meet their needs.	

Definition	Features
group of cells that work together	a level of organization in the body

TISSUE

Examples	Nonexamples
connective tissue, like bone	individual bone cells

8.1 Systems help organisms meet their needs.

CALIFORNIA
Content Standards

7.1.f Students know that as multicellular organisms develop, their cells differentiate.

7.5.a Students know plants and animals have levels of organization for structure and function, including cells, tissues, organs, organ systems, and the whole organism.

7.5.b Students know organ systems function because of the contributions of individual organs, tissues, and cells. The failure of any part can affect the entire system.

VOCABULARY

tissue p. 272
organ p. 272
organ system p. 272
hibernation p. 275

BEFORE, you learned

- Some organisms are unicellular and some are multicellular
- In a multicellular organism, cells specialize
- Organisms that have a common ancestor share some traits

NOW, you will learn

- About the needs of living things
- About tissues, organs, and organ systems in multicellular organisms
- How some plants and animals respond to stimuli

THINK ABOUT

People coming to a restaurant are usually seeking the same thing—a good meal. Groups of people working at the restaurant are each doing something different in order to produce and serve the meals. In a complicated process like this one, it helps to have different people doing different tasks at the same time. If everyone made salads, for example, how do you think the process would fail?

Living things have common needs.

All organisms require energy, water and other materials, and living space to survive. They meet these needs in many different ways. Plants use energy in sunlight to make and store sugars. Other organisms use the sugar stored in plants to meet their energy needs. Plants live where they can receive enough sunlight and not be crowded out by other plants or damaged by animals. Animals live where they can find protection and access to materials. Organisms live in every type of environment, from wetlands to deserts, and even deep inside other organisms. Wherever they live, organisms have structures that allow them to use energy and materials and to find living space suited to their needs.

Tiny organisms made of a single cell have the structures to perform all the activities of life—to grow, to respond to the environment, and to reproduce. Larger, multicellular organisms also have structures to help them perform these life processes. In these organisms, the structures are made of many specialized cells.

INVESTIGATE Specialization

What are some advantages of specialization?

PROCEDURE

① Form two teams, each representing an organism. The single-celled team will be made up of just one person; the multicellular team will be made up of three. Each team should obtain a box of materials from the teacher.

② Each team must do the following tasks as quickly as possible: make a paper-clip chain, write the alphabet on both sides of one piece of paper, and make a paper airplane from the second piece of paper. The members of the three-person team must specialize, each person doing one task only.

WHAT DO YOU THINK?

- What are some advantages to having each person on the three-person team specialize in doing a different job?

- Why might efficiency be a factor in the activities done by cells in a multicellular organism?

CHALLENGE Suppose the success of the multicellular team depended on the ability of one person to make a paper airplane. How would specialization be a disadvantage if that person were not at school?

SKILL FOCUS
Making models
(7.5.b)

MATERIALS
- two boxes, each containing 20 paper clips, 2 pieces of paper, and 1 pencil

TIME
10 minutes

Multicellular organisms have organ systems.

Animals and plants are multicellular organisms. As animals and plants develop, their cells differentiate into specialized types. Cells of the same type do the same type of job.

Levels of Organization

In animals, specialized cells include skin cells, nerve cells, and muscle cells. Cells of the same type are organized into tissues. A **tissue** is a group of many similar cells that work together to perform a particular function. Skin tissues, for example, provide protection, nerve tissue carries signals, and muscle tissue provides movement.

An **organ** is a structure that is made up of two or more types of tissue that work together to carry out a function. The brain, the lungs, and the heart are organs. In the heart, muscle tissue contracts at a signal from nerve tissue. This action pumps blood to the lungs and the rest of the body.

An **organ system** is a group of organs that together perform a function. In the circulatory system, the heart pumps blood through blood vessels. The blood transports nutrients to the rest of the body and carries back wastes. Cells, tissues, organs, and organ systems make up an organism.

Organ Systems

The circulatory system and the respiratory system work together.

The blood vessels of the circulatory system carry oxygen-rich blood to the body and oxygen-poor blood to the lungs.

The lungs of the respiratory system remove carbon dioxide from the blood and refresh the blood with oxygen.

The heart of the circulatory system pumps oxygen-poor blood to the lungs and oxygen-rich blood to the rest of the body.

How an Organ System Works

Each part has a role to play in the smooth operation of a system such as the circulatory system. The heart pumps the blood that the vessels carry. A failure of any of these can cause a failure of the system as a whole.

Now think about the human digestive system. Its function is to break down food to release nutrients in a form the body can use. Food travels through the mouth, esophagus, stomach, small intestine, and large intestine. Other organs, such as the pancreas, liver, and gall bladder, release chemicals that are necessary for digestion.

When the system is working smoothly, food is chewed and mixed with saliva in the mouth. Strong muscles in the stomach further mix and mash food particles. The stomach also uses chemicals to break down food. Partially digested food moves from the stomach to the small intestine, where nutrients are absorbed and passed into the blood. In the large intestine, water and some other nutrients are absorbed. Waste material is compacted and moved through.

A failure in one of the digestive organs can affect the rest of the system. For example, acids in the stomach may back up, causing pain in the esophagus. If the problem occurs repeatedly, the esophagus may be damaged. At the other end of the digestive system, some diseases of the large intestine cause pain, fever, nausea, and vomiting. When food cannot be digested, the digestive system and the entire body are affected.

MAIN IDEA WEB
Make a main idea web to take notes about organs and organ systems in multicellular organisms.

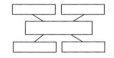

 CHECK YOUR READING How can a problem in one organ cause a problem in another organ?

Organs and systems respond to changes in conditions.

Plants and animals respond to conditions in their environment, which are constantly changing. Systems and organs make adjustments that help the organisms meet their needs.

Plant Responses to Stimuli

A stimulus is something that causes a response from an organism. You hear a loud sound, and you jump. Plants grow and move in response to many stimuli, including light, gravity, moisture, temperature, and touch.

The leaves of a Venus flytrap capture insects, which provide the plant with nutrients.

In plants, leaves are the organs that hold the chloroplasts in position to capture sunlight. Many plants move their leaves during the day in response to changes in light. The broad, flat surfaces of the leaves are presented to the sunlight early and late in the day. At midday, however, the leaves may hang more vertically. When sunlight comes from high in the sky, its heat is most intense. The vertical leaves still receive enough solar radiation, but they avoid damage that could result from getting too hot. These leaf movements are caused by changes in the cells of the joint where the leaf meets the stem.

A stem is the organ that supports a plant. By placing an indoor plant near a window, you can see that stems and leaves grow toward light. After several days, the stems start to bend toward the window. If you turn the plant around, the stems will turn back toward the light. This effect is the result of a plant hormone, or chemical messenger, called an auxin. Auxins are produced in the growing tip of the stem. They flow down the dark side of the stem, where they collect in the cells. Auxins cause these cells to grow faster than the cells on the light side. This bends the stem toward the light.

The Venus flytrap, shown on the left, grows in areas where the soil lacks materials that the plant needs. Venus flytraps get some important nutrients by eating insects. The method relies on the stimulus of touch. The leaves of the Venus flytrap fold in the middle and have long teeth-like spines all around the edges. When an insect lands on an open leaf, the two sides of the leaf fold together, forming a trap. The leaf produces fluids that digest the insect's body.

CHECK YOUR READING   What is the result of a stimulus?

Animal Responses to Stimuli

Animals respond to many stimuli, including a new environment or a change of season. Some frogs, fish, and octopi are able to change the color and patterns of their skin to blend in with new surroundings. This adaptation hides them from predators and from their own prey. Chameleons, like the one on the right, change color in response to mood, temperature, and light, but not usually in response to a change in environment. Their color can communicate anger or willingness to mate, for example, to other chameleons. These color and pattern changes are possible because of several layers of specialized cells in the skin of these organisms.

When winter cold reduces the food supply, some animals hibernate. **Hibernation** is a sleeplike state that lasts for an extended time period. The body systems of hibernating animals slow down, so the animal needs less energy to survive. Many mammals hibernate, including raccoons, skunks, woodchucks, chipmunks, hamsters, hedgehogs, and bats. Bears, however, are probably the best known hibernating animals.

Before going into a cave or other safe place to hibernate, bears eat rich foods and put on weight. They stop eating before they begin hibernating, however, so that no undigested food remains in their digestive organs. They lie in a tight ball, with their thick fur and layers of fat keeping them warm. Their heartbeat slows down, from about 40–50 beats per minute to about 8. Their metabolism, or the chemical reactions in their cells and organs, also slows way down. They require only a fraction of the oxygen they need when they are awake. Bears may hibernate as long as 100 days. During that time, they don't eat or drink.

A chameleon's skin contains color cells that allow it to change appearance in response to mood, temperature, or light.

8.1 Review

KEY CONCEPTS

1. What are three things that all living things need?

2. Put these terms in order, from smallest to largest: organ system, cell, organism, tissue, organ. (7.5.a)

3. How and why do houseplants respond to light in a window?

CRITICAL THINKING

4. **Explain** Give an example of how the failure of one part of the digestive system can affect the whole system.

5. **Compare and Contrast** How is hibernation similar to sleep, and how is it different?

◆ CHALLENGE

6. **Summarize** In animals the respiratory system and the circulatory system can be referred to as a single larger system. Explain how this is so.

Think SCIENCE

What the Body Needs to Survive

> **7.7.c** Communicate the logical connection among hypotheses, science concepts, tests conducted, data collected, and conclusions drawn from the scientific evidence.

In 1914 Ernest Shackleton and 27 men set sail for Antarctica. Their goal was to cross the continent by foot and sled, but they never set foot on Antarctica. Instead, the winter sea froze around their ship, crushing it until it sank. They were stranded on floating ice over 100 miles from land. How long could they survive? How would their bodies respond? What would they need to stay alive?

You can begin to answer these questions by making inferences. First you need to recall what you know. Then you need new evidence. What was available to the explorers? Did they save supplies from their ship? What resources existed in the environment?

▶ Prior Knowledge

- The human body needs air, water, and food.
- The human body needs to maintain its temperature; the body can be harmed if it loses too much heat.

▶ Observations

Several of Shackleton's explorers kept diaries. From the diaries we know the following.

- The crew hunted seals and penguins for fresh meat.
- The temperature was usually below freezing.
- Tents and overturned lifeboats sheltered the crew from the wind.
- Their clothes were made of thick fabric and animal skins and furs.
- They melted snow and ice in order to have fresh water.

▶ Make Inferences

On Your Own Describe how the explorers met each of the needs of the human body.

As a Group Was there anything essential that the explorers did not have? What do you think would have been their biggest challenge?

CHALLENGE How might survival needs differ for sailors shipwrecked in the tropics compared to in the Antarctic?

RESOURCE CENTER
CLASSZONE.COM

Learn more about Shackleton's expedition.

8.2 Plants have several levels of organization.

CALIFORNIA Content Standards

7.5.a Students know plants and animals have levels of organization for structure and function, including cells, tissues, organs, organ systems, and the whole organism.

7.5.b Students know organ systems function because of the contributions of individual organs, tissues, and cells. The failure of any part can affect the entire system.

VOCABULARY

stomata p. 278
vascular system p. 278
root system p. 280
shoot system p. 281

BEFORE, you learned

- Multicellular organisms have tissues, organs, and organ systems that work together to serve their needs
- The failure of one part of a system can affect the entire system

NOW, you will learn

- About tissues in plants
- About plant systems
- How some plant organs and systems are adapted to different environments

---

EXPLORE Leaf Characteristics (7.5.a)

What does a leaf look like up close?

PROCEDURE

1. Examine each leaf carefully. Notice as many details as you can.

2. Make a drawing of both sides of your leaves. Label as many parts as you can, describing each part's function.

3. Compare your diagrams and notes with those of your classmates.

WHAT DO YOU THINK?

- What characteristics did both of your leaves have?
- How would you describe your leaves to someone who could not see them?

MATERIALS
- two leaves
- hand lens

Plants are a diverse group of organisms.

Earth is home to an amazing variety of plant life. Think about grass, wildflowers, vegetables, bushes, vines, trees, water lilies, and cacti. Each is suited to its own environment. In the cold and harsh tundra, birch trees are shrubs that can be only a few centimeters tall. In the warm and rich environment of central California, giant sequoias grow 90 meters (about 300 ft) tall. In dry climates, plants tend to have thick leaves and stems that conserve moisture. In dense tropical rain forests, where tall trees prevent sunlight from reaching the forest floor, orchids grow on the trunks of trees.

Yet all these plants have several important things in common. They are multicellular organisms, their cells have cell walls, and they capture energy from sunlight in the process of photosynthesis.

Plants have three main types of tissue.

As with all multicellular organisms, plant cells are grouped into tissues, tissues into organs, and organs into systems. Although some plants like mosses are nonvascular, you are most familiar with vascular plants. Specialized plant cells form three basic tissues in vascular plants.

- dermal tissue for protection and exchange
- vascular tissue for support and transport
- ground tissue for photosynthesis, storage, and support

Dermal Tissue

Open Stomata

214×

Closed Stomata

214×

Dermal tissue covers a plant just like skin. Its primary function is to protect the underlying tissue from injury or drying out. Dermal tissue can be thin and flexible, as in a blade of grass, or rigid and tough, as in the bark of trees. At the root ends, dermal tissue is only one cell thick. This allows the roots to absorb water and nutrients from the soil. Dermal tissue is thicker in the stems and leaves.

For photosynthesis to occur, a plant needs to allow enough carbon dioxide to enter without too much water moving out and evaporating. Plants have different ways of maintaining this balance. The outermost layer of dermal cells on the leaves and stems of many plants secrete, or give off, a waxy coating. This coating protects against water loss and repels bacteria and fungi. **Stomata** are openings in dermal tissue that control the plant's exchange of water vapor, oxygen, and carbon dioxide with the atmosphere. Most stomata are on the undersides of leaves, but they also occur on stems. When the air is dry, the stomata can close. This can help to prevent water loss.

Salt glands are another special structure in the dermal layer of some plants. Mangroves and other plants that grow in salty environments use these glands to get rid of extra salt.

CHECK YOUR READING What are two ways that dermal tissue helps prevent water loss in plants?

Vascular Tissue

VOCABULARY
Remember to add a four square diagram for *vascular system* to your notebook.

Vascular (VAS-kyuh-lur) tissue provides both support and transport in vascular plants. It is made up of specialized cells that move water, nutrients, and the products of photosynthesis to and from all living parts of the plant. In most plants, the **vascular system** is made up of two types of long, tubelike cells—the xylem and the phloem. Xylem (ZY-luhm) transports water and dissolved nutrients from the roots up a stem to the leaves. Phloem (FLOH-em) carries the energy-rich sugars and carbohydrates down a stem and to the roots.

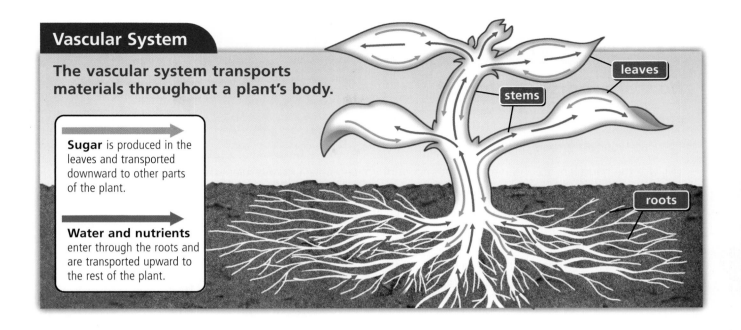

Vascular System

The vascular system transports materials throughout a plant's body.

Sugar is produced in the leaves and transported downward to other parts of the plant.

Water and nutrients enter through the roots and are transported upward to the rest of the plant.

leaves

stems

roots

The cells in xylem tissue are long and hollow, like pipes. Most xylem tissue cells mature and then die, remaining in place. Their cell walls are fortified, or thickened, for strength. Xylem cells have openings in their end walls. With the cells stacked end to end, they are like straws bundled together. The main job of xylem is to move water and minerals up through the plant.

Phloem tissue runs parallel to xylem tissue. Also long and hollow, mature phloem cells are living, although they no longer have a nucleus. They are smaller in diameter than xylem cells. Phloem tissue contains specialized cells to help transport sugars from the leaves, where they are produced, to the rest of the plant.

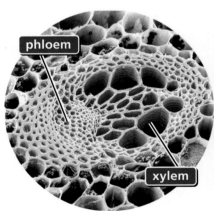

phloem

xylem

This vascular bundle from the stem of a buttercup plant has been magnified 113 times.

Ground Tissue

Ground tissue makes up the bulk of a plant. Despite its name, ground tissue does not mean tissue underground. Instead, it is the tissue between vascular bundles and dermal tissue in all parts of the plant. Ground tissue serves three main functions.

- Cells in the ground tissue contain most of the chloroplasts in the plant. Therefore, most of the photosynthesis takes place in the ground tissue layer.
- Some ground tissue cells are specialized for storing sugars and starches. This tissue is found in stems, roots, fruits, and seeds.
- Another type of ground cell provides support for the plant.

 CHECK YOUR READING What are three functions of ground tissue in plants?

INVESTIGATE Roots

How are roots structured?

PROCEDURE

1 Place your plant roots on a piece of paper towel.

2 Use the hand lens to observe the root system of your sample. Use the ruler to measure the longest root and some of the shorter roots.

3 In your notebook, sketch the root system and label the roots you measured.

WHAT DO YOU THINK?

- Describe how the roots are arranged. For example, tell whether your plant has one main root, several main roots with many offshoots, or some combination of these two arrangements.

- What might be the advantage to a plant of having a single main root that goes deep? What might be the advantage of having a more shallow root system with many offshoots?

CHALLENGE Examine the roots from two different plants. Compare the root systems. Describe the differences, including length of roots, diameter of roots, and number of offshoots.

SKILL FOCUS
Observing (7.5.b)

MATERIALS
- clean plant roots
- paper towel
- hand lens
- ruler
for Challenge
- additional plant roots

TIME
10 minutes

Plant tissues work together in systems.

RESOURCE CENTER
CLASSZONE.COM

Learn more about plant systems.

You could say that plants live in two worlds. Their roots anchor them underground. Above ground, their stems and leaves reach toward the Sun. Most plants have three main organs—roots, stems, and leaves. These organs make up two organ systems, the root system and the shoot system, which are subsystems of the vascular system. In addition, plants have reproductive organs and a reproductive system, which you will read about in Chapter 9.

The Root System

The **root system** anchors a plant and allows the exchange of materials with the soil. Roots anchor the plant by spreading out to the sides or growing down into the ground. The root system absorbs water and nutrients from the soil. It also stores excess sugars, in the form of starch, produced by photosynthesis. Beets, turnips, and carrots are examples of root storage structures.

 How does the root system help keep the plant upright?

The Shoot System

Stems and leaves make up the **shoot system,** which includes structures for photosynthesis, support, storage, and the exchange of materials with the atmosphere. Stems can be short or long, rigid or flexible. They provide support for plants above ground, and they are pathways of the vascular system. The stems of some plants are modified for food storage. A potato is a swollen, underground stem called a tuber. Taro, yams, garlic, and onions are other examples of modified stems.

Leaves are the organs of photosynthesis. In most plants, the majority of chloroplasts are in the leaves. The chloroplasts produce sugars. They use the energy from sunlight, water provided by the root system, and carbon dioxide absorbed from the air through the stomata.

System Failure

Damage to any part of the plant can affect the entire organism. Trees, for example, can be seriously hurt by both natural and human causes. Strong winds, lightning, ice storms, and heavy snow can break limbs. Deer and other animals seeking food may strip the bark off trees. Flooding may drown a tree. Lightning may damage a tree's roots, causing it to die some time after it was struck. Construction equipment may injure a tree's trunk or roots, even if it only compresses the soil above the roots. Over time, an injured tree may show signs of weakening. New leaves and shoots may be smaller, and twigs and branches may die. Healthy trees can repair small wounds. Weakened trees cannot. A wound becomes an entry place for viruses, fungi, and insects.

Houseplants can suffer injuries as well. For example, sometimes the roots of a potted plant can outgrow their space. Instead of growing out and down, they grow around and around into a tangled ball. They can no longer absorb enough water for the plant, and the plant weakens.

Crowded roots cannot absorb enough water and nutrients to keep a plant healthy.

CHECK YOUR READING How does damage to roots affect the entire plant?

Plants have adapted to their environments.

This prickly pear cactus has leaves and stems that have become modified to suit the desert climate.

Even though most plants have similar tissues and organs, these structures do not always serve the same functions. The differences are the results of adaptations the species have made to their environments.

Modified Stems

Desert plants, such as the cactus at left, often have thick, leathery dermal tissue covering their stems. This protective layer helps them resist the drying effects of sunlight and wind. Their stems are swollen with water. They store this water to use when rain is scarce. A jade plant is a common houseplant with water-storing stems.

A stem has joints along its length, called nodes, from which shoots and buds can grow. A root does not have these nodes. This is an important difference between underground roots and stems. Potatoes are underground stems that have nodes, called eyes, from which new plants can grow. The stored starches in the potato provide energy for the new plant.

Irises have another kind of underground stem called rhizomes. Rhizomes are horizontal stems just below the surface of the ground.

Onion bulbs are examples of a third kind of underground stem. The short, central part of the bulb is the stem. The layers of flesh around the stem are actually modified leaves.

Some stems are soft, and some are hard. The soft stems and leaves of many weeds, wildflowers, garden flowers, and vegetables die when the environment they live in becomes too cold or too dry. In many climates, this happens once a year as winter begins. Some plants, such as trees and shrubs, have tough, thick stems that do not die each year. These stems keep growing taller and thicker. As the stems grow, they develop a type of tough xylem tissue that is not found in soft stems. This tough tissue is called wood.

A tendril on this morning glory is a modified leaf that wraps itself around a support.

Modified Leaves

Some plants develop long, thin organs called tendrils. Most tendrils are modified leaves. Peas, morning glories, tropical vines, grape vines, and other plants develop tendrils. A tendril grows out from the plant. When it touches a source of support, the tendril winds itself around it. The support, perhaps a fence or another plant, helps the plant grow upward, where it can get more sunlight.

If the large, flat paddles in the photograph of the prickly pear cactus are its stems, where are its leaves? The leaves of the cactus have become modified into spines, and the chloroplasts are in the stem. Spines have several advantages. Ordinary leaves would dry out in the desert climate, but spines do not. The spines also help protect the plant from animals in search of water and food. Cacti can become very wrinkled and dehydrated, but when rain comes they quickly take up water and regain their original appearance.

Modified Roots

The roots of cacti and other desert plants are very long, but they don't usually go deep. Instead they remain close to the surface. A shallow, broad root system allows the plant to capture as much water as possible from a quick rain.

Some plants have roots that never reach the ground. These roots are adapted to being exposed to air and are called aerial roots. For example, some orchids grow on the trunks of the very tall trees in rain forests. This puts them high enough to receive the sunlight they need for photosynthesis. Their long roots absorb nutrients from the water that runs off the leaves and trunks of the trees. The orchids use the structural support of the tree trunks, so they don't need to build their own supporting structures from the ground up.

Orchids do not harm their host trees. Other plants, like mistletoe, have specialized roots that grow into the vascular tissue of tree branches to obtain water and nutrients. These plants are parasites, meaning they take nutrition from the trees, and they can harm their hosts.

orchid roots

CALIFORNIA Focus

Joshua Tree National Park is named for a tree that appears throughout the Mojave Desert in southern California. Joshua trees have two root systems. A shallow root system absorbs water from the soil. The other system stores water and produces bulbs from which new plants can grow.

 CHECK YOUR READING How can orchids grow on trees without harming them?

8.2 Review

KEY CONCEPTS

1. What are the three main types of tissue in plants? (7.5.a)
2. What organs make up the shoot system? (7.5.b)
3. Describe three ways in which plant structures are sometimes adapted to different environments. (7.5.b)

CRITICAL THINKING

4. **Predict** What might happen to a plant adapted to damp conditions if it were moved to desert conditions?
5. **Infer** Why might damage to a tree take awhile to become obvious?

◯ CHALLENGE

6. **Compare and Contrast** In what ways are stems and roots similar, and how do they differ?

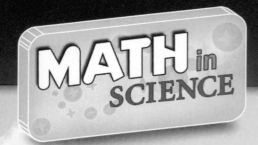

MATH TUTORIAL
CLASSZONE.COM
Click on Math Tutorial
for more help with
perimeter and area.

Math 7.MR.2.1

Chloroplast Math

You can't count all of the chloroplasts in a leaf very easily, but you can estimate their number. For example, if you know the number of chloroplasts in a small area, you can estimate the number of chloroplasts in a whole leaf.

Example

Suppose you are studying how lilacs make food from sunlight. You read that there are 50 million chloroplasts for every square centimeter of a leaf. You want to know the number in a whole leaf.

(1) Trace the leaf on to a sheet of centimeter grid paper.

(2) Count the number of whole squares covering the leaf (1 square = 1cm²). 7 cm²

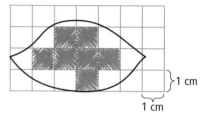

(3) Match pairs or sets of partly covered squares that add up to a whole square. 7 cm² + 5 cm² = 12 cm²

(4) Add on any remaining 0.5 (half), 0.25 (quarter), or 0.75 (three-quarters) of a square. 12 cm² + 0.5 cm² = 12.5 cm²

(5) Multiply the number of chloroplasts in one square (50,000,000) by the number of squares.

ANSWER $\dfrac{50,000,000 \text{ chloroplasts}}{\text{cm}^2} \times 12.5 \text{ cm}^2 = 625,000,000$ chloroplasts.

Give estimates for the following amounts.

1. Trace the beech leaf shown on this page on to a sheet of centimeter grid paper. What is the leaf's approximate area in cm²?

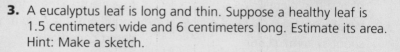

2. About how many chloroplasts are in this beech leaf?

3. A eucalyptus leaf is long and thin. Suppose a healthy leaf is 1.5 centimeters wide and 6 centimeters long. Estimate its area. Hint: Make a sketch.

4. What is the approximate number of chloroplasts in the eucalyptus leaf described above?

CHALLENGE Collect two leaves. Trace the leaves on centimeter grid paper. Label each tracing with the leaf's name, its estimated area, and the approximate number of chloroplasts.

 Animals have several levels of organization.

CALIFORNIA
Content Standards

7.5.a Students know plants and animals have levels of organization for structure and function, including cells, tissues, organs, organ systems, and the whole organism.

7.5.b Students know organ systems function because of the contributions of individual organs, tissues, and cells. The failure of any part can affect the entire system.

7.5.c Students know how bones and muscles work together to provide a structural framework for movement.

VOCABULARY

exoskeleton p. 288
endoskeleton p. 289

BEFORE, you learned

- Plants have tissues for protection, support, and transporting materials
- Plants have root systems and shoot systems
- The failure of a plant organ can damage the organism

NOW, you will learn

- About the types of tissues in animals
- How animal tissues work together in organs
- How organs work together in organ systems

EXPLORE Animal Movement (7.5.b)

What good are legs?

PROCEDURE

MATERIALS
meter stick

1. Measure and record your height in meters.

2. Jump as far as you can, and have your partner record the distance.

3. Divide the distance you jumped by your height.

4. Some frogs can jump a distance that's equal to 10 times their body length. Calculate the distance you would be able to jump if you were a frog.

WHAT DO YOU THINK?
How might the ability to jump help a frog survive on land?

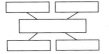

MAIN IDEA WEB
Make a main idea web to begin taking notes about systems in animals.

Animalia is a diverse kingdom.

Animals are extremely varied and live under a wide range of conditions. For example, sponges live attached to the ocean floor, while migrating butterflies may travel hundreds of kilometers in a short lifetime. The giraffe's long neck and long tongue make it possible for it to reach and eat leaves from tall acacia trees. The frog's large leg muscles are specialized for leaping on land and moving swiftly through water. Jellyfish, hydras, and worms are animals, as are snails, insects, fish, amphibians, reptiles, birds, and mammals.

All animals are multicellular organisms. Their specialized cells are organized into tissues, organs, and systems, as in plants. Unlike plant cells, animal cells do not have cell walls. Typically, animals have more differentiated cell types than plants do, but these differentiated cells form only four types of tissues.

 How are animals similar to plants, and how are they different?

Most animals have four types of tissue.

A few animals, such as sponges, have specialized cells but no tissues. Others, such as jellyfish, have simple tissues but no organs. Most animals, both vertebrates and invertebrates, are more complex. They have four basic types of tissue.

The lizard, a reptile, has thick skin that helps prevent water loss. The spotted salamander, an amphibian, has thin skin. It cannot live far from water.

Epithelial Tissue

Epithelial (EHP-uh-THEE-lee-uhl) tissue provides protection and allows for absorption and secretion. Epithelial tissue covers the outside of most animals as skin, much as dermal tissue covers the outside of plants. The epithelial tissue on the surface of animals varies from soft and thin, as in worms and frogs, to very tough, as in alligators and elephants.

In animals, epithelial tissue also covers the surface of internal cavities, passageways, and organs. The mouth, esophagus, stomach, and intestines are lined with epithelial tissue. It absorbs nutrients and secretes enzymes for digesting food. Its secretions also lubricate the passageways. Lungs are lined with epithelial tissue that allows for the exchanges of gases—the movement of oxygen into, and carbon dioxide out of, the organism.

Nerve Tissue

Nerve tissue transmits, or sends, electrical impulses from one part of the body to another. It coordinates and controls many body activities. In vertebrates, the brain, spinal cord, and nerves are made of nerve tissue. Some nerve tissue sends impulses to the brain in response to stimuli. The brain interprets these impulses as sights, sounds, tastes, and other sensory input. Other nerve tissue sends signals to stimulate muscle contractions. Some simpler animals, such as sea stars and sea anemones, do not have a brain or a spinal cord. Their nerves are arranged in a nerve net.

There are two main types of nerve tissue cells—neurons and glial cells. Neurons are the cells that conduct nerve impulses. Extensions on one end of a neuron, called dendrites, receive signals from other neurons. An extension on the other end of the neuron, called an axon, carries impulses to the next neuron. Glial cells do not conduct nerve impulses. They provide support, nourishment, and protection for the neurons.

CHECK YOUR READING   What type of nerve cell transmits impulses?

The lion tenses its muscles in response to the porcupine. The porcupine's muscles raise its quills in defense.

Muscle Tissue

Muscle tissue consists of bundles of long and narrow cells that can contract, or shorten. Muscle tissue makes all animal movement possible. It moves a shark through water and a rabbit through grass. Muscle tissue is also responsible for movement inside the animal. It causes the beating of the heart and the contractions of the digestive organs that move food and wastes through the body. Muscle tissue also can produce needed heat by contracting rapidly and repeatedly, as when you shiver.

Muscles that move when the animal directs them are called voluntary muscles. Muscles that manage the movement of the internal organs are called involuntary muscles. These muscles work continuously.

Connective Tissue

Connective tissue joins body parts together, providing protection and support. Tendons and ligaments are connective tissues that bind other tissues together. In a lion, for example, tendons connect the muscles to the bones and the cartilage of the internal skeleton. These connections make it possible for the lion to move. Ligaments connect the bones and cartilage together, creating a unified structure. This structure provides support, protects inner organs, stores calcium and phosphate, and produces blood cells. Tendons and ligaments function the same way in animals with an outer skeleton, such as a lobster, and animals with a protective shell, such as a snail.

Fat is another type of connective tissue. Fat stores energy, insulates the body, and provides protective padding for some organs. Blood is also a connective tissue. Blood serves many functions. It delivers oxygen, food molecules, and other nutrients; it removes wastes such as carbon dioxide; and it moves chemical messengers throughout the body.

Animals are adapted to many environments.

Almost all animals share the same four types of tissue. Yet the organization of those tissues into organs and organ systems shows a wide range of adaptations to many environments.

Eyes

Eyes are organs that respond to light and are part of an animal's nervous system. Some animals, like those that filter food from the earth or water, can survive with eyes that are little more than a cluster of nerve cells mounted on muscular and connective tissues. For example, a worm or a starfish can react to the presence or absence of light. But it relies more on other senses to interact with the environment.

Other animals have compound eyes that are adapted to respond to motion in the environment. These eyes have many tiny lenses that produce a pattern of light and dark dots, like a mosaic. The compound eyes of an insect make it possible for the animal to see in all directions at once. Other animals—octopus, squid, and most vertebrates such as owls—have eyes that can focus and provide much sharper images. An optic nerve carries impulses from the eye to the brain. This process produces a camera-like image of the environment.

 CHECK YOUR READING What is an advantage of compound eyes?

Owls hunt at night. Their large eyes provide excellent vision in the dark. Their feathers are slightly ragged on top, which reduces the sound they make as they dive toward their prey.

Skin

Skin is a large organ that includes all four types of tissue and shows a wide variety of adaptations. For example, mammals have hair, birds have feathers, and fish have scales. Skin provides protection and support, and often helps an animal regulate its body temperature.

Skeletal Systems

Animals are broadly divided into vertebrates, animals that have a skull and a backbone, and invertebrates, those that don't. Many invertebrates have an exoskeleton. An **exoskeleton** is a strong but flexible outer covering that supports and protects the animal and also prevents it from drying out.

The exoskeleton completely covers the body and legs of this shrimp.

An exoskeleton is jointed, often divided into segments. Muscles are attached to the inside of the exoskeleton. Arthropods are a large group of animals that have a segmented exoskeleton. This group includes spiders, lobsters, crabs, and shrimp, as well as all insects—for example, beetles, bees, and ants. These animals have segmented legs, which are often adapted for specialized functions. Lobsters and beetles have front claws for grasping. Water bugs have paddlelike legs for swimming. Many arthropods also have wings for flying.

The exoskeleton cannot grow along with the animal. As the animal grows, it must discard its exoskeleton from time to time and replace it. The process of shedding the exoskeleton is called molting.

CHECK YOUR READING Why must an animal like a shrimp or a crab replace its exoskeleton?

Vertebrate animals have an internal support system called an endoskeleton. An **endoskeleton** is typically made of the connective tissues—bones, cartilage, ligaments, and tendons. The endoskeleton grows along with the animal. Once the animal has reached full size, the skeleton continues to be renewed. Muscles attached to the bones allow the animal to move.

You can see how the endoskeleton supports the cheetah in the diagram below. The backbone protects the spinal cord, and the ribs protect the internal organs. Powerful muscles attached to large bones allow the animal to run very fast.

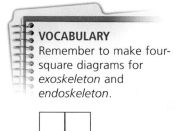

VOCABULARY
Remember to make four-square diagrams for *exoskeleton* and *endoskeleton*.

Vertebrate Skeleton and Muscles

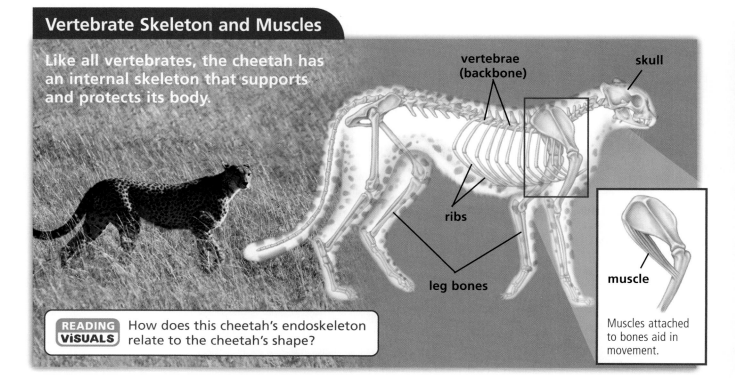

Like all vertebrates, the cheetah has an internal skeleton that supports and protects its body.

vertebrae (backbone)

skull

ribs

leg bones

muscle

Muscles attached to bones aid in movement.

READING VISUALS How does this cheetah's endoskeleton relate to the cheetah's shape?

Organ systems work together.

READING TiP

See the appendix for descriptions and illustrations of all the human organ systems.

Except for simple organisms like sponges and jellyfish, all animals have organ systems. These organ systems, working together, make up the whole organism.

Respiratory System Through the respiratory system, oxygen enters the body and carbon dioxide exits. In many vertebrates, including mammals, this exchange takes place in the lungs.

Circulatory System The circulatory system transports blood throughout the body. Blood carries materials to and from the cells and organs. In many animals, the heart pumps blood continuously throughout the body. The circulatory system works closely with the respiratory system, which adds oxygen to the blood.

Skeletal System The skeletal system in animals provides support and protection. It helps animals move in a variety of ways. Arthropods have exoskeletons to which their muscles attach from the inside. Snakes have long central backbones with as many as several hundred pairs of ribs attached. Sharks have skeletons made entirely of cartilage, which gives them great flexibility in the water.

Lymphatic System The lymphatic system includes the immune system. It has vessels that collect the fluid outside the cells, or plasma, and return it to the blood. Organs in the lymphatic system produce chemicals that help regulate many body processes. The immune system defends the body against invading viruses and bacteria.

Endocrine System The endocrine system releases hormones into the blood. Hormones control the activities of cells and manage water and chemical balances in the body. The endocrine system works together with the circulatory, digestive, and reproductive systems.

Digestive System The digestive system processes the food and liquid taken in by the organism and prepares it for use by the body. Biting, chewing, and mashing begin to process food. Chemicals break down food further. Nutrients and water are absorbed through the intestinal walls into the blood stream, and undigested waste is excreted.

Most fish, like this queen angelfish, have bony skeletons and are covered with scales.

Birds like these tanagers feed their offspring food that they have partially digested.

Nervous System The nervous system detects and responds to external and internal stimuli. It connects the systems of the body together. In vertebrates, the brain and spinal cord are the central nervous system (CNS). The nerves going out from the spinal cord to the rest of the body are the peripheral nervous system (PNS).

Muscular System The muscular system allows animals to move and to change shape. Muscle and other tissues can produce movement by pulling parts of a skeleton into different positions. Muscles also protect the bones and the internal organs of animals with endoskeletons.

The muscular system of the snail pulls the animal along beneath its shell. The shell is part of the animal's integumentary system.

Integumentary System The integumentary system protects the body from the external environment. It helps to regulate body temperature by controlling the flow of fluids such as blood and sweat. Sweat glands, hair, feathers, and scales are part of the integumentary systems of different animals.

Urinary System The urinary system helps keep the amounts of fluids and the materials in them balanced. In vertebrates, kidneys remove wastes, salt, and excess water from the blood plasma. These wastes and water are stored in the bladder and eliminated as urine.

Reproductive System The reproductive system consists of the organs necessary for the animals to produce offspring. In humans, these include the ovaries and the uterus in females, and the testes and the penis in males. It is the only system that is not essential to the survival of the individual organism.

CHECK YOUR READING What do kidneys remove from blood plasma in vertebrates?

8.3 Review

KEY CONCEPTS

1. Name the four types of tissue that animals have. (7.5.b)
2. What types of tissue is skin made of? (7.5.b)
3. How do the circulatory system and the respiratory system work together? (7.5.b)

CRITICAL THINKING

4. **Analyze** Look again at the porcupine on page 287. To what system do you think the quills belong? Why?
5. **Compare and Contrast** Blood is classified as connective tissue. How does it seem similar to other connective tissues, and how is it different?

CHALLENGE

6. **Synthesize** Do you think it is possible for an organ to function as part of more than one system? Why or why not?

CHAPTER INVESTIGATION

Comparing Plant and Animal Tissues

OVERVIEW AND PURPOSE Plants and animals are multicellular organisms. They have levels of organization that range from cells (the smallest level) to the whole organism (the most complex level). In this investigation you will

- look at plant and animal cells, tissues, and organs
- compare the structures and functions of plant and animal tissues

▶ Procedure

1 Break a piece of lettuce leaf in half. Use the forceps to peel a piece of the thin, clear layer of tissue from the lower surface of the leaf. This is the epidermis of the leaf.

2 Place the piece of epidermis in the center of a microscope slide. Place one drop of water on the tissue and cover with a cover slip. Remove excess water with a paper towel. (See p. R15 for more detailed directions.)

3 Observe the tissue under the low power and the high power of the microscope. Identify the stomata. Draw and label the stomata in the epidermis of the leaf in your notebook.

4 Study the leaf diagram below. Add labels to your sketch for any additional parts of the leaf you can identify.

MATERIALS
- lettuce leaf
- forceps
- slide
- cover slip
- eyedropper
- water
- paper towel
- microscope
- hand lens
for Challenge:
- prepared leaf slide

7.1.b, 7.5.a, 7.7.a, 7.7.d, 7.7.e

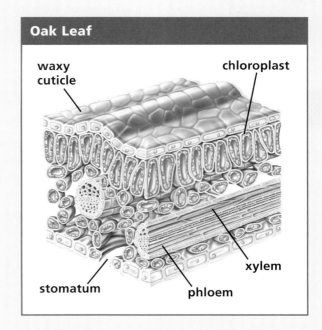

Oak Leaf

waxy cuticle

chloroplast

stomatum

phloem

xylem

Content Standard
7.5.a Students know plants and animals have levels of organization for structure and function, including cells, tissues, organs, organ systems, and the whole organism.

Investigation Standard
7.7.d Construct scale models, maps, and appropriately labeled diagrams to communicate scientific knowledge (e.g., motion of Earth's plates and cell structure).

5 Use the hand lens to observe the details of the skin on the back of your hand. Draw and label the structures you can see.

6 Study the diagram of human skin at the bottom of the page. Add labels to your sketch for any parts you can identify.

▶ Observe and Analyze

Write It Up

1. **RECORD** Using the leaf diagram, describe the appearance of the cells and structures in the leaf.

2. **RECORD** Using the skin diagram, describe the appearance of the cells and structures in the skin.

3. **COMPARE AND CONTRAST** How are the cells, tissues, and structures of the epidermis in the leaf tissue similar to the cells, tissues, and structures of the epidermis of the skin? How are they different?

4. **EXPLAIN** How are the functions of the structures and tissues in leaves (such as the xylem, phloem, and stomata) similar to the functions of the structures and tissues in the skin (such as blood vessels and pores)?

▶ Conclude

Write It Up

1. **ANALYZE** Why is a leaf considered to be an organ?

2. **ANALYZE** Why is the skin considered to be an organ?

3. **IDENTIFY** To which organ system does the skin belong? What are the functions of this system? How do its parts help it do its function?

4. **APPLY** Sun blocks prevent harmful ultraviolet radiation from reaching the skin. Why do you need to reapply a sun block several times during a hot day when you are in sunlight?

▶ INVESTIGATE Further

CHALLENGE Examine a prepared slide of a cross-section of a leaf under low power and high power of the microscope. Draw the structures you observe on the slide. Compare what you observe on the slide to the diagram of the leaf. Identify and label as many structures from the slide as possible.

Human Skin

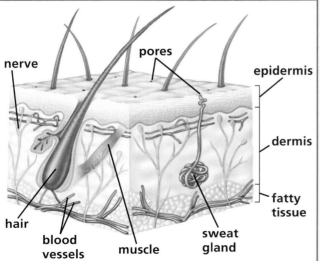

nerve · pores · epidermis · dermis · fatty tissue · hair · blood vessels · muscle · sweat gland

Comparing Plant and Animal Tissues
Stomata Sketch

Skin Sketch

Oak Leaf Description

Skin Description

Human health depends on a balance among systems.

CALIFORNIA
Content Standards

7.5.b Students know organ systems function because of the contributions of individual organs, tissues, and cells. The failure of any part can affect the entire system.

VOCABULARY

homeostasis p. 295
hormone p. 297
gland p. 298

BEFORE, you learned

- Animals have epithelial, muscle, nerve, and connective tissues
- Organs and organ systems are made of specialized tissues
- Many interrelated systems perform vital functions in animals

NOW, you will learn

- How human organ systems maintain homeostasis
- About the role of the endocrine system in homeostasis
- What happens when homeostasis fails

THINK ABOUT

How is the human body like a city?

A city is made up of many parts that perform different functions. Buildings provide places to live and work. Transportation systems move people around. Electrical energy provides light and heat. Similarly, the human body is made of several sys-

tems. The skeletal system, like the framework of a building, provides support. The digestive system works with the respiratory system to provide energy and materials. What other systems in your body can you compare to a system in the city?

The body's systems work all the time.

A city's smooth operation can be interrupted if the buses stop running, the streets are flooded, or the garbage is not collected. People can't get to work, supplies can't get to people, and waste piles up. Similarly, the smooth functioning of the human body depends on processes that don't stop. The body needs to breathe and to circulate blood. It needs to take in food, to digest it, and to eliminate waste materials. Even during sleep, your organ systems remain active. The body's many levels of organization, from cells to organ systems, work constantly to maintain the balance needed to survive.

 CHECK YOUR READING What are two of the functions your body must perform without stopping?

INVESTIGATE Exercise

How does exercise affect body systems?

How much do you think exercise, such as seated jumping jacks, might raise your temperature? How quickly? What other effects do you think exercise may have on your body? How could you test your predictions?

DESIGN — YOUR OWN — EXPERIMENT

PROCEDURE

1. List changes you think may happen when you exercise. Think about how different body systems could be affected.

2. Design a procedure to test one of your predictions. Specify the exercise and tell how you will detect the change. Write up your procedure.

3. Carry out your procedure to test for one type of change.

WHAT DO YOU THINK?

- Were you able to detect a change? If so, what were your measurements?

- If you were not able to detect a change, why do you think that happened? How could you improve your procedure?

SKILL FOCUS
Designing experiments (7.5.b)

MATERIALS
- thermometer
- stopwatch
- other materials requested and approved

TIME
30 minutes

Body systems maintain homeostasis.

The ability of the body to maintain internal conditions within normal ranges is called **homeostasis** (HOH-mee-oh-STAY-sihs). When your body is in homeostasis, conditions are in equilibrium, or balanced. Conditions inside and outside the body are always changing in small ways. Therefore the body systems must constantly work to maintain the equilibrium. Your body systems regulate such things as body temperature, the amount of sugar in your blood, oxygen and carbon dioxide levels, and water and salt balance in body fluids.

READING TiP

The word *equilibrium* comes from the Latin *aequi-*, meaning "equal," and *libra*, meaning "balance."

Body Temperature

Your body's normal internal temperature is about 37°C (98–99°F). The integumentary, circulatory, muscular, respiratory, and nervous systems are all involved in maintaining that temperature. A temperature much above or below 37°C shows that the homeostatic systems are having trouble maintaining your usual temperature.

When you are active, your temperature may rise. Your body responds to bring your temperature down again. If it is a hot day, or you are working very hard, you will begin to sweat. The evaporation of sweat from your skin helps to cool your body.

Ion Concentrations

Your kidneys help keep the volume of water in your body constant. If you drink a lot of water, your kidneys will release more water in urine. If you do not drink enough water, the kidneys will make less urine. By maintaining the volume of water, the kidneys maintain the proper concentrations of ions and other substances in the blood. *Concentration* refers to the amount of one substance that is dissolved in another substance. The less water there is, the higher the concentration of dissolved substances. The more water, the lower the concentration.

Evaporating sweat helps to cool the body during exercise. Water helps replace the fluid lost in sweat.

An ion is an atom of an element that has gained or lost one or more electrons. Ions are charged particles. They are important to many body processes, including the movement of substances across cell membranes and the sending of nerve impulses. Sodium, potassium, chloride, and calcium are four important ions in the body. These ions are also called electrolytes.

Sodium and chloride ions together make up common table salt. Similar combinations of ions are also called salts. You can tell that you have lost some salts when you sweat because your skin tastes salty afterwards. Many sports drinks contain salts, such as sodium chloride and potassium chloride, to help restore the ions you lose when you exercise.

 CHECK YOUR READING Why is sweat salty?

Oxygen and Carbon Dioxide Concentrations

The respiratory system and the circulatory system maintain a balance of oxygen and carbon dioxide concentrations in the blood. These dissolved gases are carried by the blood and delivered to and from the tissues in plasma. When you are exercising, your muscle cells use more oxygen and give off more carbon dioxide than when you are at rest. Your respiratory system responds to the increased need by increasing your breathing rate and your breathing volume. To keep up with the demand, your heart pumps faster so that your circulatory system increases blood supply to the limbs. When you are resting, your breathing is shallower, and your heart pumps more slowly.

Other Nutrients

Your liver is very important for maintaining homeostasis. It is part of the digestive system. The liver breaks down large food molecules—carbohydrates, fats, and proteins—into nutrients that the body can use. It stores glucose, vitamins, and iron. It produces bile, a fluid used in digestion. And the liver breaks down alcohol, drugs, and other toxic chemicals. The liver filters, stores, and releases materials as needed.

Blood glucose levels rise after a meal. A balance is maintained when excess glucose is absorbed out of the blood.

The pancreas is an organ that functions in both the digestive and endocrine systems. It helps maintain blood glucose levels at an optimum, or ideal, range. The pancreas releases a substance called insulin when blood glucose levels rise after a meal. Insulin signals the body's cells to remove glucose from the blood. The blood glucose level decreases between meals or when you are exercising. Then the pancreas releases more and more of a substance called glucagon. Glucagon signals the liver to release stored glucose back into the blood. This balance of hormones helps to maintain homeostasis.

The endocrine system helps regulate body conditions.

Maintaining homeostasis is a very important function of the endocrine system. The endocrine system controls the conditions in the body by making and releasing chemicals that are transported throughout the body. These chemicals are called hormones. **Hormones** are chemicals that are made in one organ, travel through the blood, and produce an effect in target cells. The insulin and glucagon produced in the pancreas are hormones. The hormone adrenaline makes your heart beat faster in exciting situations like a roller coaster ride.

Hormones are made at one location and function at another location. Hormones are often called chemical messengers. Target cells have special structures, called receptors, that allow them to respond to the chemical messenger.

Hormones and Glands

The main structures of the endocrine system are groups of specialized tissues called **glands.** Many glands in the body produce hormones and release them into your circulatory system. Endocrine glands can be found in many parts of your body, as you can see in the illustration on page 299.

Pineal Gland The pineal (PIHN-ee-uhl) gland is a tiny organ about the size of a pea. It is near the center of the brain. The pineal gland is sensitive to light, and it produces a hormone that is essential to body rhythms, such as sleep. The gland also plays a role in maintaining body temperatures, in reproducing, and in aging.

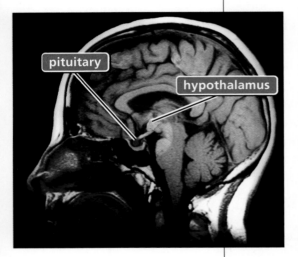

The hypothalamus and the pituitary are important endocrine glands.

Hypothalamus The hypothalamus (HY-poh-THAL-uh-muhs) connects the nervous and endocrine systems. It produces hormones that control the release of hormones produced by another gland, the pituitary.

Pituitary Gland The pituitary (pih-TOO-ih-TEHR-ee) gland is located at the base of the brain. It can be thought of as the director of the endocrine system. It produces many important hormones, including those hormones that control growth, sexual development, and the absorption of water into the blood by the kidneys.

Thyroid Gland The thyroid (THY-ROID) gland releases hormones necessary for growth and metabolism. It also releases a hormone involved in the regulation of calcium in the body.

Thymus Gland The thymus (THY-muhs) helps the body fight disease by controlling the production of white blood cells called T cells.

Adrenal Glands The adrenal (uh-DREE-nuhl) glands secrete about 30 different hormones. These hormones regulate carbohydrate, protein, and fat metabolism and water and salt levels in the body. These glands also produce adrenaline, the hormone that is released in response to stress. Adrenaline makes your heart beat faster and allows you to react quickly in dangerous or exciting situations.

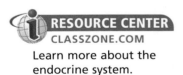

RESOURCE CENTER
CLASSZONE.COM

Learn more about the endocrine system.

Pancreas The pancreas is part of both the digestive system and the endocrine system. It secretes insulin and glucagon that regulate the levels of glucose in the blood.

Ovaries and Testes The ovaries in females and testes in males are glands that secrete hormones that control sexual development. Although the ovaries and testes make the same hormones, ovaries make more estrogen and testes make more testosterone. The different amounts of hormones produced give males and females different characteristics.

 What glands are different in males and females?

Endocrine System

The endocrine system is made of a group of glands. These glands produce and release hormones, or chemical messengers.

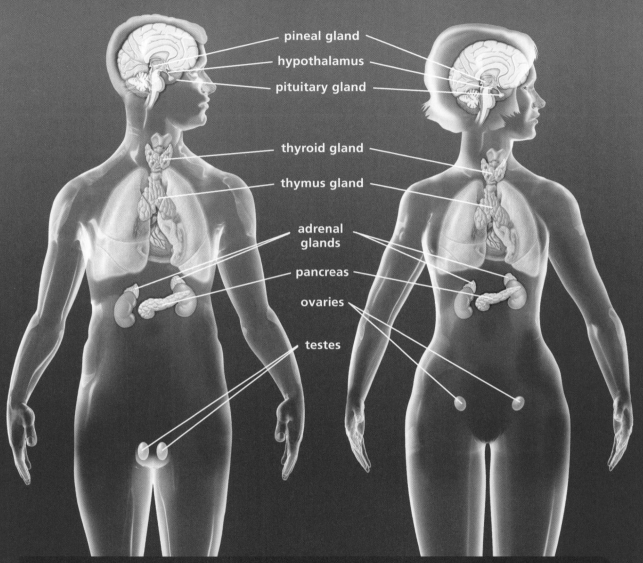

pineal gland
hypothalamus
pituitary gland
thyroid gland
thymus gland
adrenal glands
pancreas
ovaries
testes

Some Glands and Hormones

Gland	Hormone	Function of Hormone
Pituitary gland	growth hormone	stimulates cell division, the making of proteins, bone growth
	antidiuretic hormone	promotes reabsorption of water into the blood, reducing the volume of urine
Thyroid	thyroxine	stimulates chemical processes in cells and digestion, and affects energy levels
Adrenal glands	adrenaline	triggers faster, stronger heartbeat; rise in blood pressure; rise in blood sugar
Pancreas	insulin	stimulates sugar metabolism and removal of sugar from the bloodstream
	glucagon	triggers sugar production and addition of sugar to the bloodstream
Ovaries	estrogen	stimulates sexual maturation, influences female characteristics
Testes	testosterone	stimulates sexual maturation, influences male characteristics

Negative Feedback

Hormone levels in the body are regulated mostly by negative feedback. What is negative feedback? Suppose you are adjusting the volume on a sound system. Your friend tells you it's now just right. In response to that feedback, you stop changing the volume. You are acting as a control center and your friend is acting as a sensor. Feedback is information coming back to a control center from a sensor that tells the control center what it needs to do to maintain a level within an ideal range. In hormone regulation, negative feedback signals to a gland that hormone levels are correct and no more of the hormone is needed.

Homeostasis may be disrupted.

Hormones from the endocrine system help your body systems maintain homeostasis. Yet the delicate balance in and among the body's systems can be disrupted. Signs of imbalance range from the mild sniffles of a cold, to dangerous overheating of the body, to serious and even fatal diseases.

Sneezing, as shown on the left, is one way the respiratory system defends the body from foreign substances. Viruses, bacteria, and other disease agents are called pathogens. When a cold or flu virus does enter your body, it multiplies rapidly. This calls the immune system into action. You develop symptoms, such as a sore throat, a runny nose, and a cough. Your muscles and joints may ache. After a few days, however, your immune system begins to kill the virus. The symptoms in your respiratory, muscular, and skeletal systems gradually fade away as homeostasis is restored.

The immune system also goes to work when a pathogen enters the body through a wound in the skin. The skin around a wound may become red, swollen, and warm to the touch. Those are signs that the immune system is increasing blood flow to the wound and flooding the area with disease-fighting agents.

Sometimes the body's normal ways of maintaining temperature are not enough. On a very hot day or when exercising, a person normally sweats. He or she may lose too much water from the body, however, and become dehydrated. Dehydration—or too great water loss—along with dizziness, nausea, fainting, and a dangerous drop in blood pressure are signs of heat exhaustion. If the person stops sweating, it is a sign of a worse condition called heat stroke. The person's internal temperature climbs and can very quickly reach a dangerous level. People running in distance races sometimes experience this problem. They can collapse and may even die if they are not treated right away. Ice packs or an ice-water bath may be used to cool the body rapidly. Then the person should receive medical attention.

cilia

foreign materials

Cilia are hairlike protrusions that trap materials entering your respiratory system (600×).

Hypothermia is the opposite condition, in which a person's body temperature falls too low. This can happen in a cold environment, especially in cold water. Hikers, boaters, skiers, and other people outdoors in cool or cold weather are at risk. A person with hypothermia can be warmed gradually with warm clothing, hot liquids, and a heat source, such as a nearby fire.

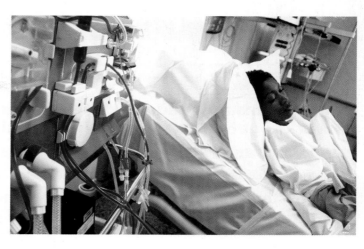

When kidneys can no longer filter the blood, a patient may need dialysis.

Sometimes glands produce too much or too little of a hormone. The resulting hormone imbalances can cause serious diseases. For example, the pancreas normally maintains glucose balance in your blood by releasing insulin and glucagon as needed. If the pancreas cannot produce the needed hormones, the result may be diabetes. A person with diabetes may need to monitor the glucose level in his or her blood and take insulin to control the glucose level. Diabetes can also lead to the failure of other organs, in the form of heart disease, blindness, and kidney damage.

Kidneys continually filter the blood, taking out waste products. Kidneys may be damaged by diabetes and other diseases, injury, high blood pressure, toxic chemicals, drugs, cancer, and other causes. If a person's kidneys fail, he or she may need to undergo kidney dialysis. In this process, the person is connected to an artificial kidney machine. The person's blood is circulated through the machine from an arm or leg. The machine filters out the wastes. A typical patient needs three sessions of dialysis every week.

CHECK YOUR READING What function does a kidney dialysis machine perform?

8.4 Review

KEY CONCEPTS

1. What is homeostasis and how is it important? (7.5.b)
2. How does the endocrine system do its job? (7.5.b)
3. How does a cold virus disrupt homeostasis in the body? (7.5.b)

CRITICAL THINKING

4. **Apply** Suppose you exercise on a warm day. What are two things you could do to help your body maintain homeostasis?

5. **Compare and Contrast** How are the hormones produced by your endocrine glands similar? How are they different?

CHALLENGE

6. **Infer** A person with diabetes may need to take insulin. In addition, the person needs to control his or her diet very closely. Why do you think controlling the diet is important?

Chapter Review

the BIG idea

Organisms are made of different parts that work together to perform life functions.

CONTENT REVIEW
CLASSZONE.COM

◀ KEY CONCEPTS SUMMARY

1 Systems help organisms meet their needs.

- Multicellular organisms have cells, tissues, organs, and organ systems.
- Organs and systems respond to changing conditions.

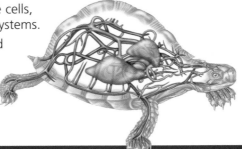

VOCABULARY
tissue p. 272
organ p. 272
organ system p. 272
hibernation p. 275

2 Plants have several levels of organization.

- Vascular plants have dermal, vascular, and ground tissues.
- Plants have root systems and shoot systems.
- Plants have adapted to many varied environments.

VOCABULARY
stomata p. 278
vascular system p. 278
root system p. 280
shoot system p. 281

3 Animals have several levels of organization.

- Animals have epithelial, nerve, muscle, and connective tissues.
- Tissues work together in organs, and organs work together in systems.
- Systems have adapted in different ways in different animals.

VOCABULARY
exoskeleton p. 288
endoskeleton p. 289

4 Human health depends on a balance among systems.

- Body systems maintain homeostasis.
- Body temperature, ion concentrations, oxygen and carbon dioxide concentrations, and concentrations of other nutrients are kept at certain levels
- The endocrine system helps regulate body conditions.

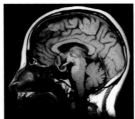

VOCABULARY
homeostasis p. 295
hormone p. 297
gland p. 298

Reviewing Vocabulary

Draw a word triangle for each of the terms below. On the bottom row, write the term and your own definition of it. Above that, write a sentence in which you use the term correctly. At the top, draw a small picture to remind you of the term. A sample is completed for you.

Sample:

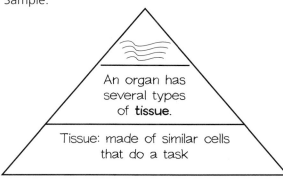

An organ has several types of **tissue**.

Tissue: made of similar cells that do a task

1. organ
2. organ system
3. hibernation
4. stomata
5. vascular system
6. root system
7. shoot system
8. endoskeleton
9. exoskeleton
10. gland

Reviewing Key Concepts

Multiple Choice *Choose the letter of the best answer.*

11. Which of these can an individual organism survive without?
    - **a.** energy
    - **b.** offspring
    - **c.** materials
    - **d.** living space

12. What is one difference between a plant and an animal? (7.5.a)
    - **a.** a plant's cells have cell walls, an animal's cells do not
    - **b.** a plant is unicellular and an animal is multicellular
    - **c.** a plant does not need energy but an animal does
    - **d.** a plant eats soil but an animal eats plants or other animals.

13. Which of these structures includes all of the other structures listed? (7.5.a)
    - **a.** cell
    - **b.** organ system
    - **c.** organ
    - **d.** tissue

14. How are the roots, stems, and leaves of a plant arranged? (7.5.b)
    - **a.** the roots and stems are part of the shoot system
    - **b.** the stems and leaves are part of the shoot system
    - **c.** the roots and leaves are part of the shoot system
    - **d.** the roots, stems, and leaves make up the shoot system

15. Which type of tissue carries electrical impulses from the brain of an animal? (7.5.b)
    - **a.** epithelial tissue
    - **b.** muscle tissue
    - **c.** nerve tissue
    - **d.** connective tissue

16. Connective tissues provide (7.5.b)
    - **a.** support and strength
    - **b.** communication and control
    - **c.** movement
    - **d.** hormones

Short Answer *Write a short answer to each question.*

17. What are the three common needs of all living things?

18. How are the wood of some plants and the ability of some animals to hibernate similar?

19. The prefix *homeo-* means "same" and the suffix *-stasis* means "stand still." How do these word parts relate to the definition of homeostasis? (7.5.b)

20. Why are hormones called chemical messengers? (7.5.b)

21. How are a plant's vascular system and an animal's circulatory system similar? (7.5.b)

Thinking Critically

Use the diagrams of plant and animal organs below to answer the next seven questions.

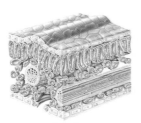 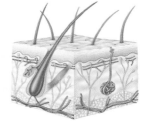

leaf   human skin

22. COMPARE AND CONTRAST How are the two types of tissue similar? different? (7.5.a)

23. COMPARE What structures in animal skin are similar to stomata? Explain how their functions are similar. (7.5.a)

24. APPLY How do these types of tissues help organisms respond to their environments? (7.5.b)

25. INFER Describe the structures in plants and animals that circulate liquids. (7.5.a)

26. HYPOTHESIZE What would happen to a plant and to an animal if these types of tissues had small cuts? (7.5.b)

27. ANALYZE How does the structure of a leaf relate to its function? (7.5.b)

28. APPLY How do the four types of tissue in animal skin help it function? (7.5.b)

29. ANALYZE Some animals, such as sponges, are anchored in place. How are they different from plants?

30. APPLY Plants have three things in common. Copy the chart and use the hints to fill out the second column.

Hint	Characteristic
number of cells	
borders of cells	
capture energy	

31. SUMMARIZE Describe three important functions of a skeletal system. (7.5.b)

32. APPLY How would all four types of animal tissue be involved in a simple activity, such as raising your hand? (7.5.b)

33. INFER What type of tissue helps an animal blend into its environment? (7.5.a)

34. PROVIDE EXAMPLES Give an example of several organs working together to serve a function. (7.5.b)

35. APPLY How does drinking water after you sweat help you maintain homeostasis? (7.5.b)

36. COMPARE How are a vascular system, an endoskeleton, and an exoskeleton similar? (7.5.b)

37. SUMMARIZE What are some of the ways your body maintains homeostasis when you exercise? (7.5.b)

38. EVALUATE Do you think plants maintain homeostasis? Explain your reasoning. (7.5.b)

39. APPLY How do several of your organ systems work together to provide your cells with nutrients? (7.5.b)

the BIG idea

40. INFER Look again at the picture on pages 268–269. Now that you have finished the chapter, how would you answer the question about the people and the sequoia? (7.5.a)

41. SYNTHESIZE Your brain receives signals about balance and position from many parts of your body. It sends nerve signals to your muscles to help you keep your balance. How is this similar to your endocrine system? (7.5.b)

UNIT PROJECTS

If you are doing a unit project, make a folder for your project. Include in your folder a list of the resources you will need, the date on which the project is due, and a schedule to track your progress. Begin gathering data.

Standards-Based Assessment

Analyzing Diagrams

Read the text and study the diagram, and then choose the best response for the questions that follow.

7.5.b

Vertebrates, such as birds, fish, and mammals, have endoskeletons. This internal skeleton is made up of a system of bones that extends throughout the body. Muscles can attach directly to the bones, around joints—the place where two bones meet. As shown in the generalized diagram of a vertebrate leg below, at least two muscles are needed to produce movement. One of the muscles contracts, or shortens, pulling on the bone, while the other muscle extends, or is stretched.

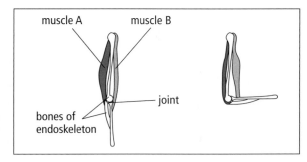

1. Endoskeletons are made up of
   a. contracting muscles
   b. extending muscles
   c. internal bones
   d. external bones

2. A muscle produces movement by
   a. pulling
   b. relaxing
   c. bending
   d. rotating

3. A joint is where
   a. one muscle connects to another
   b. one bone connects to another
   c. a muscle connects to a bone
   d. a bone bends

4. The leg in the diagram bends when
   a. muscle A contracts
   b. muscle A relaxes
   c. muscle B contracts
   d. muscles A and B contract

5. What is the main point of the diagram and the text above?
   a. Two muscles are needed to produce movement in vertebrates.
   b. Vertebrates have internal skeletons.
   c. The muscular system is more important than the skeletal system.
   d. Movement in vertebrates is the result of the interaction of muscles and tendons.

Extended Response

Use terms from the word box to answer the next question. Underline each term you use in your answer.

contract	pull	exoskeleton
extend	muscle	

6. Many fish go forward by moving their tails from side to side. Describe the action of the muscles on each side of the fish as the tail moves from one side to the other.

7. Describe what must happen for an arthropod with an exoskeleton to bend a leg. Compare that process with the process shown in the diagram.

SEEING INSIDE the Body

A chance discovery in a darkened room provided a glimpse inside of a hand. Today, technology allows people to produce clear and complete pictures of the inside of the human body. From x-rays to ultrasound to the latest computerized scans, technologies have provided new ways to study and diagnose the inner workings of the human body.

Being able to see inside the body without cutting it open would have seemed unthinkable in the early 1890s. But within a year of the discovery of the x-ray in 1895, doctors were using this technology to see through flesh to bones. In the time since then, techniques for making images have advanced to allow doctors to see soft tissue, muscle, and even how body systems work in real time. Many modern techniques use x-rays. Others use sound waves or magnetic fields.

1895

Accidental X-Ray Shows Bones

Working alone in a darkened lab to study electric currents passing through vacuum tubes, Wilhelm Konrad Roentgen sees a mysterious light. He puts his hand between the tubes and a screen, and an image appears on the screen—a skeletal hand! He names his discovery the x-ray, since the images are produced by rays behaving like none known before them. Roentgen uses photographic paper to take the first x-ray picture, his wife's hand.

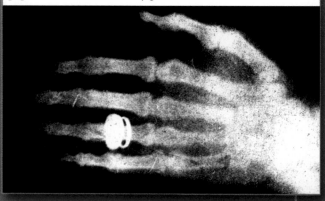

EVENTS

1880   1890

APPLICATIONS AND TECHNOLOGY

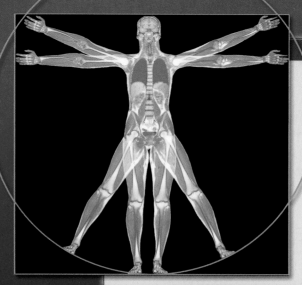

APPLICATION

Doctor Detectives

Within a year of Roentgen's discovery, x-rays were used in medicine for examining patients. By the 1920s, x-ray use was widespread. Modern-day x-ray tubes are based on a design by William Coolidge. Around 1913, Coolidge developed a new x-ray tube that, unlike the old gas tube, provided consistent exposure and quality. X-ray imaging changed the practice of medicine by allowing doctors to look inside the body without using surgery. Today, x-ray images and other technologies, such as the MRI used to produce this image, show bones, organs, and tissues.

1914–1918

Radiologists in the Trenches

In World War I field hospitals, French physicians use x-ray technology to diagnose war injuries quickly. Marie Curie trains the majority of the female x-ray technicians. Following the war, doctors return to their practices with new expertise.

1898

Radioactivity

Building on the work of Henri Becquerel, who in 1897 discovered "rays" from uranium, physicist Marie Curie studies other substances. She uses the property of radioactivity to discover two new elements, polonium and radium.

1955

See-Through Smile

X-ray images of the entire jaw and teeth allow dentists to check the roots of teeth and also wisdom teeth that are completely below the gum line.

1900   **1910**   **1950**

APPLICATION

Better Dental Work

In the 1940s and 1950s, dentists began to use x-rays. In x-ray photographs of teeth, cavities and decay show up as dark spots on a white tooth. Photographing below the gum line shows dentists the pattern of growth of new teeth. By 1955, dentists could take a panoramic x-ray, which shows the entire jaw. In the early years of dental x-rays, little was known about the dangers of radiation. Today, dentists use a lead apron to protect the patient from the potentially harmful radiation.

1976

New Scans Show Blood Vessels

The first computerized tomography (CT) systems scanned only the head, but now whole-body scanners are available. With the CT scan, doctors see clear details of blood vessels, bones, and soft organs. Instead of sending out a single x-ray beam, a CT scanner sends several beams from different angles. Then a computer joins the images, as shown in this image of a heart.

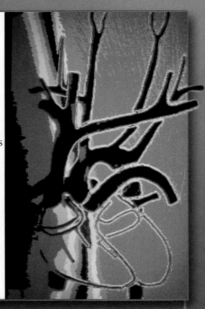

1977

Minus the X-Ray

Doctors Raymond Damadian, Larry Minkoff, and Michael Goldsmith develop the first magnetic resonance imaging (MRI) machine. They nickname it "Indomitable," as many people had told them such a machine could not be made. MRI allows doctors to "see" soft tissue, such as the knee below, in sharp detail without the use of x-rays.

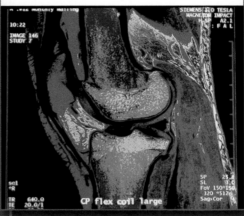

1973

PET Shows What's Working

The first positron emission tomography (PET) machine is called PET Scanner 1. A small amount of radioactive dye is injected and travels through a patient's bloodstream. A PET scan then shows the distribution of the dye.

1960   **1970**   **1980**

TECHNOLOGY

Ultrasound: Moving Images in Real Time

Since the late 1950s, Dr. Ian Donald's team in Scotland had been viewing internal organs on TV monitors using sound waves of frequencies too high to hear—ultrasound. In 1961, while examining a female patient, Donald noticed a developing embryo. Now ultrasound imaging is widely used to monitor the growth and health of fetuses. Ultrasound captures images in real time. It shows movement of internal tissues and organs. The technology uses ultrasound waves to produce images of structures inside the body. High-frequency sound waves bounce off the structures. A computer converts the data into changing images on a television monitor.

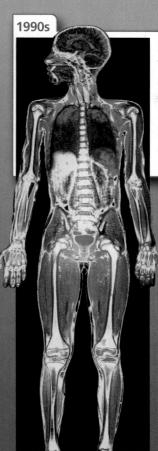

1990s

Filmless Images

With digital imaging, everything from x-rays to MRIs is now filmless. Data move directly into 3-D computer programs and shared databases.

2003

Multi-Slice CT

By 2003, 8- and 16-slice CT scanners offer greatly increased detail and speed. A multislice scanner reduces exam time from 45 minutes to less than 10 seconds.

 RESOURCE CENTER
CLASSZONE.COM

Find more on advances in medical imaging.

1990　　　**2000**

TECHNOLOGY

3-D Images and Brain Surgery

In operating rooms, surgeons are beginning to use another type of 3-D imaging known as interventional MRI. They watch 3-D images in real time and observe details of tissues while they operate. These integrated technologies now allow scientists to conduct entirely new types of studies. For example, 3-D brain images of many patients with one disease can now be integrated into a composite image of a "typical" brain of someone with that disease.

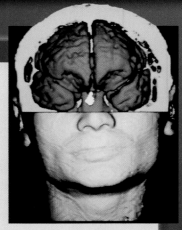

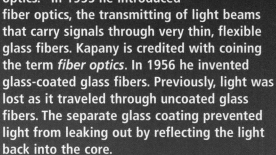

SPOTLIGHT on
NARINDER S. KAPANY

The physicist Narinder S. Kapany is known as the "father of fiber optics." In 1955 he introduced fiber optics, the transmitting of light beams that carry signals through very thin, flexible glass fibers. Kapany is credited with coining the term *fiber optics*. In 1956 he invented glass-coated glass fibers. Previously, light was lost as it traveled through uncoated glass fibers. The separate glass coating prevented light from leaking out by reflecting the light back into the core.

Fiber optics has been used in the field of medicine to observe the inside of the body without surgery or x-rays. Optical fibers can also deliver laser light to specific points inside the body to help surgeons perform delicate surgery.

Kapany's research and inventions involve not only fiber optics but also lasers, biomedical instrumentation, solar energy, and pollution monitoring. He holds more than 100 patents for his inventions.

ACTIVITIES

Writing About Science: Brochure

Make a chart of the different types of medical imaging used to diagnose one body system. Include an explanation of how the technique works and list the pros and cons of using it.

Reliving History

X-rays use radioactivity, which can be dangerous. However, you can use visible light to shine through thin materials that you can't normally see through. Try using a flashlight to illuminate a leaf. Discuss or draw what you see.

Reproduction

the **BIG** idea

Reproductive systems allow the production of offspring.

Key Concepts

SECTION

1 Organisms reproduce in different ways.
Learn why some organisms need partners to reproduce, while others do not.

SECTION

2 Plants can reproduce in several ways.
Learn about the role seeds, pollen, and fruit play in plant reproduction.

SECTION

3 Human reproduction is a complex process.
Learn how fertilization and pregnancy occur in humans.

California ClassZone

CLASSZONE.COM

Chapter 9 online resources: Content Review, three Visualizations, Resource Center, Math Tutorial, Test Practice

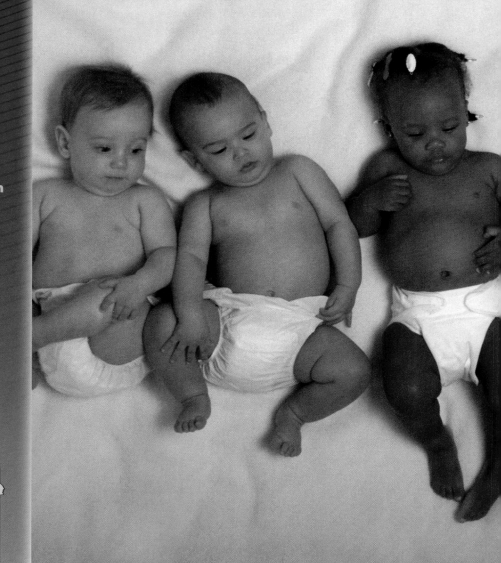

How do living things produce offspring?

EXPLORE (the BIG idea)

What's Inside a Chicken Egg?

> **7.5.a** Students know plants and animals have levels of organization for structure and function, including cells, tissues, organs, organ systems, and the whole organism.

Examine a raw chicken egg. Describe the appearance of the outside shell. Break it open into a small dish and note the different parts inside. Wash your hands when you have finished.

Observe and Think If this egg had been fertilized, which part do you think would have served as the food for the growing chicken embryo? Which part would protect the embryo from impact and serve to cushion it?

Internet Activity: Sprouting Seeds

> **7.5.f** Students know the structures and processes by which flowering plants generate pollen, ovules, seeds, and fruit.

Go to **ClassZone.com** to watch a time-lapse video of a seed sprouting. Pay attention to the thick, light-colored lines of the roots and the shoots.

Observe and Think If plants come from seeds, where do seeds come from?

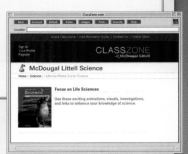

NSTA
scilinks.org

SCI LINKS

Reproductive System **Code: MDL047**

Getting Ready to Learn

◀ CONCEPT REVIEW

- Both sexual and asexual reproduction involve cell division.
- Meiosis is a special form of cell division.
- Organisms inherit DNA from their parents.

◀ VOCABULARY REVIEW

specialization p. 28

mitosis p. 81

cytokinesis p. 81

egg p. 118

sperm p. 118

meiosis p. 119

CONTENT REVIEW
CLASSZONE.COM

Review concepts and vocabulary.

▶ TAKING NOTES

OUTLINE

As you read, copy the headings on your paper in the form of an outline. Then add notes in your own words that summarize what you read.

VOCABULARY STRATEGY

Write each new vocabulary term in the center of a **frame game** diagram. Decide what information to frame the term with. Use examples, descriptions, pictures, or sentences in which the term is used in context. You can change the frame to fit each term.

See the Note-Taking Handbook on pages R45–R51.

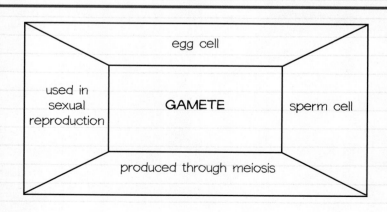

SCIENCE NOTEBOOK

OUTLINE

I. Sexual reproduction always involves an exchange of DNA.
   A. Sexual reproduction between males and females
      1. External fertilization
         a.
         b.
         c.
      2. Internal fertilization
         a.
         b.
         c.

egg cell

used in sexual reproduction | GAMETE | sperm cell

produced through meiosis

Organisms reproduce in different ways.

CALIFORNIA Content Standards

7.2.a Students know the differences between the life cycles and reproduction methods of sexual and asexual organisms.

7.2.b Students know sexual reproduction produces offspring that inherit half their genes from each parent.

VOCABULARY

gamete p. 317
fertilization p. 317
zygote p. 317

 BEFORE, you learned

- In asexual reproduction, it takes only one parent to produce offspring
- Sexual reproduction requires two parents that exchange genetic material

NOW, you will learn

- About several forms of asexual reproduction
- About different types of sexual reproduction
- How asexual and sexual reproduction compare

THINK ABOUT

How is new life made?

All living things produce offspring. Many single-celled organisms reproduce by simple cell division. Some plants produce seeds and fruit. In other plants, seeds are carried by wind or water. Most amphibians and mosquitoes lay their eggs in water, while birds and reptiles build nests to hold their eggs and young. Humans and other mammals give birth to live offspring that have developed inside the mothers. Why are there so many ways to reproduce? Is one method better than the others?

There are many forms of asexual reproduction.

OUTLINE
Use the blue headings in each section as the main ideas in your outline. The red headings form the supporting ideas, and the black headings make up the numbered details.

I. Main idea
 A. Supporting idea
  1. Detail
  2. Detail
 B. Supporting idea

Despite the huge differences between a lizard and a bacterium, or a dandelion and a tiger, all living things must perform the basic tasks of life to survive—obtain energy, grow and develop, exchange materials with the environment, and reproduce. The first three tasks help keep individuals alive. Reproduction ensures that future generations will live. Without reproduction, life on Earth could not continue.

You have already learned that there are two main types of reproduction. Some species reproduce asexually—that is, without a partner. In sexual reproduction, two individuals come together to reproduce. It may surprise you to learn that many species can reproduce either way.

 CHECK YOUR READING What is asexual reproduction?

VISUALIZATION
CLASSZONE.COM

Observe the process of binary fission.

In asexual reproduction, only one parent produces offspring. In most cases, the offspring are genetically identical to the parent. This occurs because the offspring gets its DNA only from one parent.

Some organisms that reproduce asexually, such as bacteria, have a simple structure. However, some complex organisms, such as plants and invertebrates, can also reproduce this way. With the exception of one lizard species, asexual reproduction does not occur in vertebrates.

Types of Asexual Reproduction

There are several ways that organisms can reproduce asexually. Asexual reproduction can give species an advantage in many circumstances.

Binary Fission Many single-celled organisms, such as bacteria and certain protists, reproduce by binary fission. This process follows the same steps as cell division. DNA in the parent cell replicates and then separates. The DNA copies attach to the cell membrane at opposite sides of the cell. The cell wall and plasma membrane grow into the center of the cell. The cell divides into two sections that become two daughter cells. Each daughter cell is identical to the parent cell. The photograph on the left shows the final stages of binary fission.

Budding You have learned that many aquatic invertebrates, such as sponges and jellyfish, reproduce by budding. In this process, the parent grows a small bud or branch on its own body. When the bud is large enough to live on its own, it separates from the parent and forms a new individual.

Some yeast reproduce by budding. The process begins when the parent's DNA replicates and the chromosomes separate. The photograph at the left shows how the cell membrane grows into the cell. The membrane pinches off a small section of cytoplasm that contains the duplicate DNA (shown in yellow). This differs from binary fission, which divides the parent cell into two equal parts.

Binary Fission

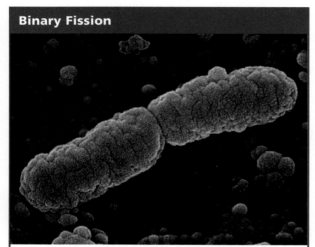

This bacterium is undergoing the final stages of binary fission. Both daughter cells will be the same size.

Budding

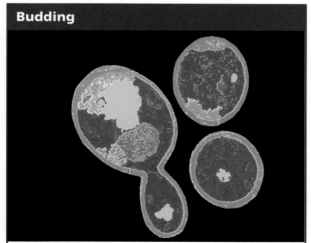

The parent yeast cell on the left is in the last stages of budding. Notice the daughter cell is smaller than the parent cell.

 CHECK YOUR READING How does binary fission differ from budding?

Fragmentation In some organisms, pieces of a parent organism that have broken off can produce a new organism. This is called fragmentation.

Fragmentation is common among planarians, a group of flatworms that live in ponds and streams. Planarians can literally split themselves into two parts to reproduce. The worm attaches its tail end to a solid surface, such as a pond bottom or underwater rock. It then pulls its upper body away from the tail end, causing its body to split crosswise. Within two weeks or so, the tail portion grows an upper half, complete with a head. The upper portion grows a new tail end.

Fragmentation is common in some plants and fungi. For example, if a piece of moss plant lands in a favorable location, it can grow roots and develop into an adult plant.

CHECK YOUR READING What type of flatworms undergo fragmentation?

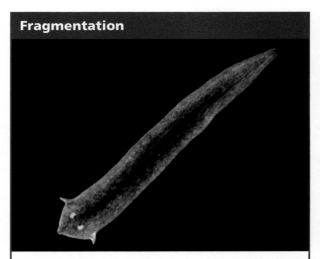
Fragmentation

Some planarian flatworms can split themselves into two halves to reproduce asexually. Each half of the parent worm then regenerates the missing half.

Parthenogenesis In parthenogenesis (PAHR-thuh-noh-JEHN-ih-sihs), females produce eggs that develop without being fertilized. It is the only type of asexual reproduction that produces offspring with genetic variation. Recall that during meiosis, chromosomes can exchange genes while crossing over. This can produce egg cells that are different from each other and from the mother. If these eggs develop without being fertilized, they will produce genetically diverse offspring.

REMINDER
Meiosis produces sex cells with different combinations of the parent's DNA.

Honeybees use both sexual reproduction and parthenogenesis to reproduce. In honeybee colonies, only the queen bee produces offspring. Unfertilized eggs produce drones. These are male bees whose sole job is to mate with the queen. Fertilized eggs produce worker bees. Worker bees are females. They care for the hive and the queen's offspring but do not reproduce. The queen can control the number of drones and workers in her colony by controlling whether or not her eggs are fertilized.

Parthenogenesis

Honeybees use parthenogenesis to control the number of drones and workers in the colony.

Advantages and Disadvantages of Asexual Reproduction

Asexual reproduction is a simpler and more efficient process than sexual reproduction.

- It is simple because it takes place quickly and easily—organisms do not have to find a mate.
- It is efficient because one individual can produce large numbers of offspring in a short time.

Asexual reproduction has one major disadvantage. Offspring do not have much genetic variation. This is because they inherit all of their DNA from one parent. If the environment changes in some way, the offspring may not have the characteristics that will enable them to survive. Suppose a disease-causing bacteria invades a colony of genetically identical insects that lack a gene to resist infection. The disease could destroy the colony. Colonies of insects that reproduce sexually are more likely to be genetically diverse. If bacteria invade these colonies, there is a chance that some insects might have a disease-resisting gene.

Because bananas reproduce asexually, each banana on this tree is genetically identical to the others.

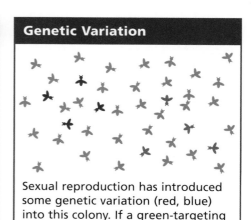

No Genetic Variation

In this asexual colony, all of the insects are genetically identical (green). If a disease that targets green insects infects the colony, the entire population will be destroyed.

Genetic Variation

Sexual reproduction has introduced some genetic variation (red, blue) into this colony. If a green-targeting disease infects the colony, the non-green bugs will survive to reproduce.

In the 1940s and 1950s, a disease attacked and destroyed most of the banana crops on plantations in Central America. Because bananas reproduce asexually, all of the bananas were genetically identical. None of the bananas could resist the disease and crops were devastated. Banana planters later grew a different variety of banana that had resistance to the disease. However, a new disease is now threatening the new variety.

Genetic variation has important benefits. In most cases, genetic variation occurs in offspring only when two individuals share or exchange DNA with one another.

 CHECK YOUR READING What is the main disadvantage of asexual reproduction?

Sexual reproduction always involves an exchange of DNA.

Sexual reproduction involves two parents and the exchange of DNA. In Chapter 4 you learned that organisms that reproduce sexually produce gametes through meiosis. A **gamete** is a specialized reproductive cell. Gametes produced by males are called sperm, while gametes produced by females are called eggs. During **fertilization,** male and female gametes join together to become a zygote. A **zygote** is a fertilized egg cell that will develop into a mature individual.

Some organisms, such as bacteria, do not have true males and females. However, there are distinct differences between sexual partners in these organisms. For example, bacteria have donor and receiver cells. The donor cell contributes DNA to the receiver cell.

VOCABULARY
Add frame game diagrams for the terms *gamete; zygote,* and *fertilization* to your notebook.

Sexual Reproduction Between Males and Females

In animals, as in most organisms that reproduce sexually, a sperm from a male joins with an egg from a female. This forms a zygote. The zygote develops into an individual. The DNA of the offspring is a combination of the DNA from the parents. Depending on the species, eggs are fertilized in one of two ways: external fertilization or internal fertilization.

External Fertilization Most animals that live or reproduce in water fertilize eggs outside of the female's body. This is known as external fertilization. First the female lays her eggs in the water. The male then releases his sperm nearby. The sperm then swim to the eggs and fertilize them.

Almost no parental care is involved among animals that use external fertilization. This means parents can produce large numbers of offspring because they don't have to be involved in caring for each one. When the offspring hatch, they can swim and find food on their own right away. Fish and amphibians are two types of animals that reproduce this way.

sperm

This male fish is releasing sperm into the water near a mass of eggs that have already been laid. The water environment allows the sperm to swim to the eggs and protects the gametes from drying out.

Offspring of most mammals develop inside the mother's body. They require a great deal of care after birth.

Internal Fertilization The eggs of humans and many other animals are fertilized in the mother's body. This is called internal fertilization.

In some species, such as birds and reptiles, the fertilized eggs are laid in a nest. These eggs contain nutrients that nourish the developing offspring. Some species, such as the emperor penguin, give their eggs enormous amounts of care and attention. In contrast, green sea turtles lay their eggs in deep sand pits and return to the sea.

The offspring of most mammals, including humans, develop inside the mother's body after fertilization. The developing animal receives nutrients from the mother's body as it grows. The body of the female, such as the horse pictured on the left, holds and protects the developing young until birth.

Even after birth, parents may need to feed and protect their young until the offspring can survive on their own. Young animals often need to learn certain skills from their parents. Tiger cubs must learn how to hunt. Baby birds must learn the songs that will enable them to signal danger or find a mate. In some species, the parent-offspring relationship lasts months or years.

CHECK YOUR READING   Where do the eggs of mammals develop?

INVESTIGATE Eggs

What are some of the characteristics of eggs?

SKILL FOCUS
Observing (7.5.d)

PROCEDURE

1. Carefully examine the outside of the hard-boiled egg. Try to notice as many details as you can. Write your observations in your notebook.

2. Gently crack the eggshell and remove it. Try to keep the shell in large pieces and the egg whole. Set the egg aside, and examine the pieces of shell. Look for details you could not see before. Write your observations in your notebook.

3. Examine the outside of the egg. Make notes about what you see. Include a sketch.

4. Use the knife to cut the egg in half. Take one half apart carefully, trying to notice as many parts as you can. Use the other half for comparison. Write up your observations.

MATERIALS
• hard-boiled egg
• plastic knife

TIME:
20 minutes

WHAT DO YOU THINK?

• Reptiles, like birds, have eggs with hard shells. What structures does an egg with a shell contain?

• What might the function of each structure be?

CHALLENGE How might the egg's structures support a developing embryo?

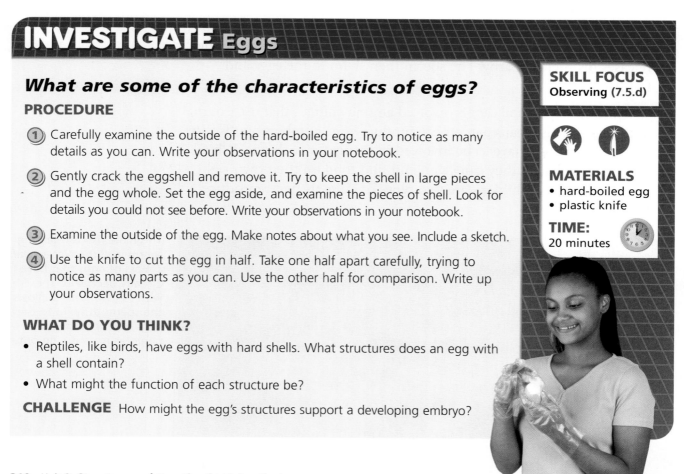

Other Methods of Genetic Exchange

Many organisms have evolved methods of exchanging DNA without actually mating. This means that organisms can produce genetically diverse offspring without spending time and energy to find a mate.

Self-Fertilization Organisms with both male and female sexual organs can produce sperm cells that fertilize their own eggs. Plants that do this are called self-pollinators. Tomatoes, peas, and sunflowers are examples of self-pollinating plants.

The male sex organs in some self-pollinators are contained in catkins. These are the long structures shown at right. The catkins produce pollen grains that contain sperm cells.

The tiny red flower near the bottom of the photograph contains a female sex organ of this plant. Each female flower contains at least one egg cell. When pollen from the catkins falls on the female flower, some sperm cells will enter the flower and fertilize its egg cells. Although fertilization occurs on the same plant, it is not asexual. This is because the zygote receives half of its DNA from the sperm cell and half from the egg cell.

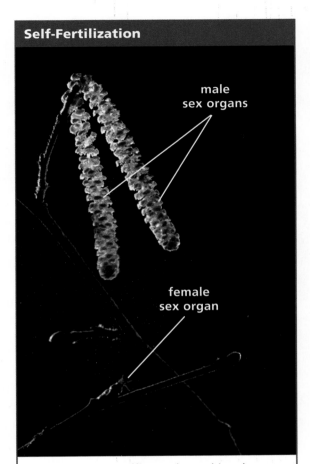

Self-Fertilization

male sex organs

female sex organ

Each tiny green ruffle on the catkins shown here is a separate male flower that produces sperm cells. The female flower sits on a separate branch on the same plant.

○ **CHECK YOUR READING** Why isn't self-fertilization considered a form of asexual reproduction?

Conjugation Many bacteria and protist species exchange DNA through conjugation. The photograph on the right displays an example of this process. The donor cell attaches a special bridge-like structure to a receiver cell. The bridge connecting two individual bacteria is called a pilus. DNA passes through the pilus to the receiver cell, where it joins the cell's own DNA. This DNA exchange introduces new forms of genes to the receiver's DNA. After this exchange is complete, the receiver bacterium reproduces asexually through binary fission.

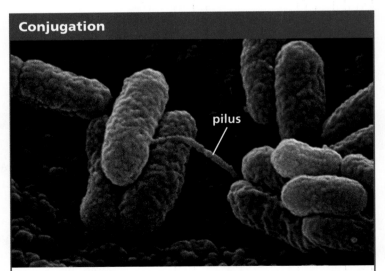

Conjugation

pilus

Although bacteria do not have separate sexes, they do have distinct donor and recipient cells. Only donor cells can form a pilus.

Finding and winning a mate takes time and energy. Some species, such as the California condor, undergo elaborate mating rituals in order to win mates.

Advantages and Disadvantages of Sexual Reproduction

CALIFORNIA Focus

By the 1980s, the California condor was threatened with extinction. In 1987, the last wild condors were captured and put in a captive breeding program. In 1992, the first pair of the captive-bred birds was released into the wild.

Sexual reproduction is more complex than asexual reproduction. Individuals must find partners. This takes time and energy. Because of this, fewer offspring are produced over a given period of time.

Yet sexual reproduction provides one very important benefit—it increases genetic variation. Offspring produced asexually receive their genes from only one parent. Offspring produced sexually receive a new combination of genes from two parents. This means that sexually reproducing populations are more genetically diverse than asexual populations. Genetic diversity helps a species survive changes in the environment.

Many types of organisms can reproduce both sexually and asexually. The ability to reproduce both ways is common in bacteria, fungi, and many plants. This flexibility gives these organisms an advantage under many circumstances.

CHECK YOUR READING What is the main benefit of sexual reproduction?

9.1 Review

KEY CONCEPTS

1. Name two forms of asexual reproduction. Give an example of an organism that undergoes each form. (7.2.a)

2. What is the main advantage of sexual reproduction? (7.2.b)

3. How are asexual and sexual reproduction similar? How do they differ? (7.2.a)

CRITICAL THINKING

4. **Explain** What is fragmentation? Give a description of how it works.

5. **Evaluate** If banana farmers began to breed bananas through sexual reproduction, would this make bananas completely resistant to disease? Explain your answer.

CHALLENGE

6. **Synthesize** Amphibian eggs are soft and slimy. Reptile eggs have a tough leathery shell. Most amphibians lay their eggs in water. Many reptile eggs are laid in nests on dry ground. How are amphibian and reptile eggs each adapted to their own environments?

CONTROLLING REPRODUCTION

Medflies

> 7.2.a Students know the differences between the life cycles and reproduction methods of sexual and asexual organisms.

Since the mid-1970s, California scientists have been struggling to protect California's fruit industry from a destructive pest. The medfly, or Mediterranean fruit fly, is a colorful insect only slightly smaller than the common house fly. The adult flies themselves do not destroy a large amount of fruit. The problem is their offspring.

Food for Larvae

Female medflies lay their eggs by injecting them into ripening fruit. Medflies can lay eggs in apples, oranges, peaches, and many other types of fruit. When the eggs hatch, the larvae begin eating through the fruit. The larvae then move into the soil, where they pupate, or go through the next stage of their development. When they emerge, they are adult medflies. These new adult medflies reproduce, and the cycle of crop destruction begins again.

More Is Less

When scientists find an infestation of medflies, they must act immediately to protect California's fruit. A population of medflies could grow from one mating pair to tens of thousands of flies in just a few weeks. Scientists try to control the medflies by releasing more medflies—medflies that can interrupt the reproductive cycle.

Scientists raise their own medflies and sterilize the males with radiation. The radiation destroys parts of the flies' DNA. So even if these flies mate, their sperm cannot fertilize eggs. Large populations of sterile medflies are released into the area where scientists suspect medflies may be breeding. The females that mate with sterile males can still lay their eggs, but the eggs will never hatch.

Female medflies often mate with more than one male before laying their eggs. Scientists are trying to determine how multiple mating affects the medfly population. Scientists study medflies and their reproductive techniques to improve methods for reducing the medfly population.

Sterilizing the male medfly (shown enlarged above) helps to reduce the medfly population. This protects ripening fruit, such as the nectarines shown at left.

WRITING ABOUT SCIENCE

Many people use pesticides to destroy pests such as flies. Write a few paragraphs comparing the effects of using pesticides with the method described above. Which method might be more effective in eliminating medflies? What side effects might you expect with each method? Organize your comparison to help the reader understand your ideas.

Plants can reproduce in several ways.

CALIFORNIA
Content Standards

7.5.f Students know the structures and processes by which flowering plants generate pollen, ovules, seeds, and fruit.

VOCABULARY

vegetative propagation p. 323

pollen p. 325

seed p. 325

embryo p. 325

ovule p. 327

fruit p. 329

BEFORE, you learned

• Plants can reproduce asexually and sexually
• Asexual reproduction produces many offspring in a short amount of time
• Sexual reproduction increases the genetic variation of a population

NOW, you will learn

• How plants reproduce asexually
• About sexual reproduction in spore-producing plants
• How sexual reproduction in flowering plants produces seeds and fruits

---

EXPLORE Fruit (7.5.f)

What do you find inside fruit?

PROCEDURE

① Place the apple on a paper towel. Carefully cut the apple in half. Find the seeds.

② Place the pea pod on a paper towel. Carefully split open the pea pod. Find the seeds.

③ Both the apple and the pea pod are examples of fruits. In your notebook, draw a diagram of the two fruits you examined. Label the fruit and the seeds.

WHAT DO YOU THINK?
• How many seeds did you find?
• What part of an apple is usually eaten?
• What part of a pea is usually eaten?

MATERIALS
• apple
• paper towel
• plastic knife
• pea pod

Plants can reproduce asexually from different parts.

You have learned that asexual and sexual reproduction each offer advantages and disadvantages. Asexual reproduction is the more efficient method, but offspring lack genetic variation. Sexual reproduction is inefficient, but it increases genetic variation in offspring.

Many plants can reproduce both sexually and asexually. This is an important adaptation. When resources are abundant, asexual reproduction lets the plants spread quickly. However, the plants are genetically the same. A change in the environment could destroy all of these plants.

REMINDER

An *adaptation* is an inherited trait that gives an organism an advantage in its particular environment.

Have you ever noticed a potato or onion in your kitchen that started growing eyes? Each eye on a potato is a site from which a new plant can emerge. In onions, new plants grow out of the middle of the onion bulb. These plants are undergoing vegetative propagation. **Vegetative propagation** (PRAHP-uh-GAY-shuhn) is a form of asexual reproduction in which plants produce offspring from non-reproductive tissues such as leaves, stems, and roots. Although these plants can reproduce sexually, their ability to reproduce asexually has some advantages.

 What is vegetative propagation?

Tubers and Bulbs

Tubers and bulbs are large fleshy underground stems that store nutrients and give rise to new plants. Sugars and starches stored in the stems give the emerging plants energy to grow. The pinkish buds emerging from the potato pictured at right are new stems. If this potato were planted, each of these stems could develop into a new potato plant. Many potato farmers grow potatoes this way instead of using seeds. Potatoes and sweet potatoes are examples of tubers. Plants that grow from bulbs include onions, daffodils, and tulips.

potato

New plant stems

Runners and Rhizomes

Runners and rhizomes (RY-zOHMS) are other specialized stems that grow off an adult plant. Runners are thin stems that grow horizontally above the ground. New shoots called plantlets grow vertically out of the runners. Plantlets get their nutrients from the parent plant until their own roots are established. Strawberry plants grow runners. The plantlets of spider plants look like spiders. Rhizomes are similar to runners but grow underground. Irises grow from rhizomes, as do bananas and many types of grass.

spider plant

runners

plantlets

Fragmentation

Fragmentation occurs when a piece of a leaf or stem breaks off the parent plant and falls to the ground. The plant fragment can grow roots and form a new plant. Many people grow plants from cuttings. These are stems that are cut off of the adult and placed in water. When the stem produces roots, it can be planted in soil. Farmers and greenhouse workers grow many plants from cuttings, since growing plants from seeds takes more time and money.

coleus plant

roots

Some plants need water to reproduce sexually.

Hundreds of millions of years ago, conditions on Earth were very different from the way they are today. Temperatures were higher, and the atmosphere and ground were moister. Under these conditions, sexual reproduction in land plants became an important adaptation. The presence of water—in rainfall, streams, and even puddles—provided a way for gametes to travel from one plant to another.

Mosses and Other Nonvascular Plants

REMINDER

Vascular plants have long tubelike structures that transport water and nutrients from one part of the plant to another. Nonvascular plants lack these structures.

Mosses, liverworts, and other nonvascular plants reproduce using spores. A spore is a single reproductive cell, or gamete, protected by a hard, watertight covering. This covering prevents the gamete from developing when conditions are not right. It prevents the cell from drying out and protects it from harsh conditions.

Spores are small and can be transported through the air. This allows gametes to join together at a distance from their parents. The green moss plants you have seen grew from spores. A clump of moss has both male and female reproductive structures that produce sperm and eggs. When water is present—perhaps as a puddle around the plant—the tiny moss sperm float toward eggs that are on a female reproductive structure. The fertilized egg grows a stalk and capsule. Inside the capsule, thousands of tiny spores are produced by meiosis. When these are released, each can grow into a new plant.

CHECK YOUR READING What is a spore?

capsule

spores

stalk

moss plant

Ferns, Horsetails, and Club Mosses

Ferns and their close relatives, the horsetails and club mosses, also reproduce sexually through spores. Like mosses, they need water for the sperm to travel to the eggs. The gamete-producing structures of these plants are contained in tiny low-lying plants. If enough moisture is present, the sperm fertilize the eggs, which grow into larger spore-producing plants. The leafy spore-producing plant, such as the one pictured on the right, is the plant that you recognize as a fern.

The spores grow in clusters on the underside of a fern's leaves, or fronds. Cells within the cluster undergo meiosis to produce spores. The clusters open to release the spores into the air. If the spores land at a favorable site, they grow into a new generation of egg- and sperm-producing plants, and the cycle begins again.

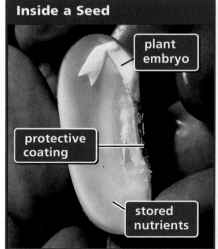

spores

spore cluster

Seeds and pollen are reproductive adaptations.

Because spore-producing plants need a layer of water to reproduce sexually, they are limited to wetter habitats. Over time, conditions on Earth changed. Water was not always available in many land habitats. Some plants could produce gametes that did not depend on water. These plants were able to thrive in drier habitats. Two adaptations allowed this to occur.

Seed plants in dry environments produce sperm in protective structures called pollen. A **pollen** grain is a dry structure that holds a sperm cell and a tube cell. The tube cell produces a tube through which the sperm travels to an egg cell. The hard outer covering of the pollen grain prevents the sperm cell from drying out. Pollen is carried from plant to plant by wind, water, or animals. Some pollen grains land on plants of the same species. Pollination occurs when such a pollen grain attaches to the part of a plant that contains the egg and releases its sperm.

The evolution of seeds was an important turning point in the adaptation of plants to dry habitats. A **seed** is a structure that encloses a plant embryo and stored food in a protective coat. An **embryo** is the immature form of an organism that has the potential to grow and develop. The seed coat protects the embryo until conditions for its survival are good. It allows the embryo to be carried by wind, animals, or water. Seeds can travel great distances and survive harsh conditions. For example, coconuts are large seeds that can float on the ocean until they arrive on land.

Inside a Seed

plant embryo

protective coating

stored nutrients

CHECK YOUR READING What is the difference between a seed and an embryo?

Gymnosperms are ancient seed-producing plants.

Pine trees and spruce trees were among the first plants to reproduce using pollen and seeds. These plants are gymnosperms (JIHM-nuh-SPURMZ), a type of plant that evolved more than 300 million years ago. Gymnosperms produce seeds that are not enclosed in fruit. Conifers, or cone-bearing plants, are the gymnosperms you are probably most familiar with. This group includes pine, fir, spruce, hemlock, cypress, and redwood trees. The pine tree described below is typical.

The pinecones you see hanging on pine branches are the tree's reproductive structures. These are the sites of meiosis. A mature pine tree has both male and female cones. Male cones produce sperm cells that are enclosed in pollen. In female cones, each egg cell is enclosed in a protective compartment within a cone scale.

During reproduction, male cones release large amounts of pollen into the air. When a pollen grain lands on a female cone, the grain produces a tube that grows through the protective compartment surrounding the egg. The sperm cell in the pollen grain then travels through the tube to the egg and fertilizes it. After fertilization, the egg grows into an embryo. The compartment that surrounds the egg develops into the seed coat. The inner compartment contains nutrients that nourish the developing embryo.

When the seeds are mature, the female cone releases its seeds into the air. The seeds have light winglike structures that help them float through the air. The wind carries these winged seeds over long distances. If a seed lands in a favorable location, it may germinate, or sprout, and grow into a new pine tree.

NOTE-TAKING STRATEGY
As you read, remember to use the blue headings as the main points in your outline.

I. Main idea
  A. Supporting idea
    1. Detail
    2. Detail
  B. Supporting idea

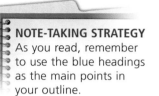

A mature pine tree has both male and female cones. Meiosis occurs inside the cones, producing sperm and egg cells.

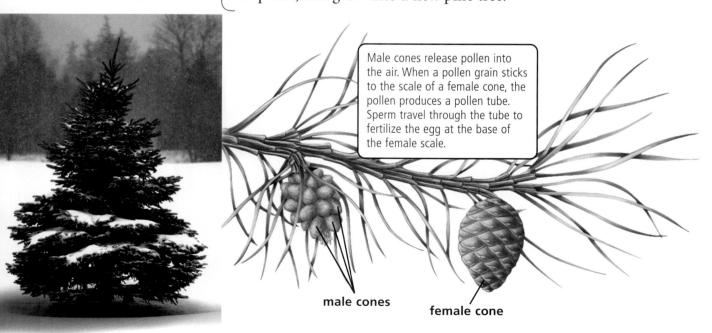

Male cones release pollen into the air. When a pollen grain sticks to the scale of a female cone, the pollen produces a pollen tube. Sperm travel through the tube to fertilize the egg at the base of the female scale.

male cones

female cone

Angiosperms produce flowers and fruit.

Angiosperms (AN-jee-uh-SPURMZ) are plants that produce their egg and sperm cells in flowers, and produce their seeds inside fruit. Angiosperms are not limited to plants we call flowers, such as daisies and poppies. They include most of the plants you see and use every day, from oak trees along the street to corn and beans you eat. In many species, male and female reproductive structures are located on the same flower. Other species produce male flowers and female flowers.

The reproductive organ of an angiosperm is the flower. The diagram below shows the key parts of a flower. The pistil is the female reproductive structure. At its base is the ovary, which contains at least one ovule. An **ovule** is a structure that holds an immature egg cell. Pollen grains enter the pistil through an opening called the stigma. After the egg cell is fertilized, it grows as an embryo inside the ovule.

The stamen is the male reproductive structure of a flower. It includes the anther, which is on a stalk called the filament. The anther produces sperm cells, which are enclosed in pollen grains and transported to egg cells by wind, water, or animals.

The flower's petals are actually colored leaves. They are arranged in a circle around the pistil. The petals open as the reproductive structures of the plant mature. The color, size, shape, and fragrance of the flower are adaptations that help attract animals to pollinate the plant.

> **READING TiP**
> The word *angiosperm* comes from the Greek words meaning "enclosed seed." Angiosperm seeds are enclosed inside a fruit.

CHECK YOUR READING Where are the sperm and egg located in an angiosperm?

Parts of a Flower

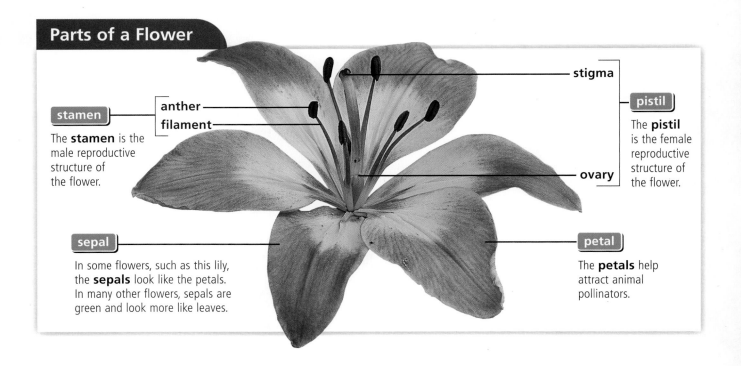

stamen
The **stamen** is the male reproductive structure of the flower.

anther
filament

stigma

pistil
The **pistil** is the female reproductive structure of the flower.

ovary

sepal
In some flowers, such as this lily, the **sepals** look like the petals. In many other flowers, sepals are green and look more like leaves.

petal
The **petals** help attract animal pollinators.

Life Cycle of a Cherry Tree

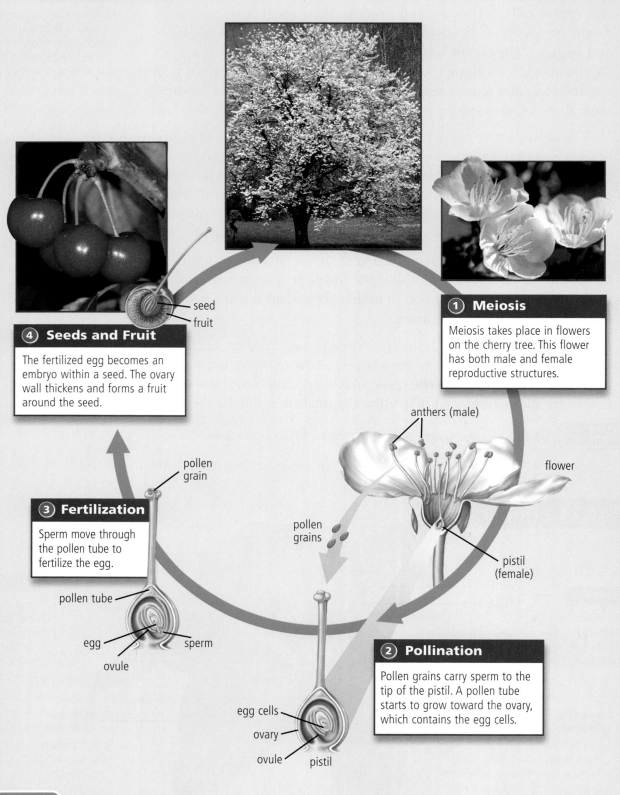

④ Seeds and Fruit

The fertilized egg becomes an embryo within a seed. The ovary wall thickens and forms a fruit around the seed.

seed
fruit

① Meiosis

Meiosis takes place in flowers on the cherry tree. This flower has both male and female reproductive structures.

anthers (male)

flower

③ Fertilization

Sperm move through the pollen tube to fertilize the egg.

pollen grain

pollen grains

pistil (female)

pollen tube

egg   sperm

ovule

② Pollination

Pollen grains carry sperm to the tip of the pistil. A pollen tube starts to grow toward the ovary, which contains the egg cells.

egg cells

ovary

ovule   pistil

READING VISUALS At what point in this cycle does the embryo begin to grow?

A **fruit** is a ripened plant ovary. Some ovaries, such as apples and figs, contain many seeds. Others, like cherries, contain a single seed. Fruits such as apples and cherries are called fleshy fruits because they have juicy flesh. Tomatoes are also fleshy fruits. Some angiosperms produce dry fruits. These include legumes, such as peanuts, and nuts such as walnuts, almonds, and acorns. Some dry fruits, such as the winged fruit of a maple tree, have structures that help the seeds to be carried by the wind.

▼ **REMINDER**

Remember to use frame games for vocabulary terms such as *fruit*.

The life cycle of the sour cherry tree is shown in the diagram on page 328. As you read the numbered paragraphs below, follow the numbers on the diagram.

RESOURCE CENTER
CLASSZONE.COM

Learn more about flowers and fruit.

1. **Meiosis** Sour cherry flowers contain both male and female parts. Meiosis in the anther produces sperm cells, which are then enclosed in pollen grains. Meiosis in the ovary produces egg cells, which are enclosed in ovules.

2. **Pollination** Pollen grains are released. When a pollen grain is caught on the pistil of a flower, the pollen grain produces a tube that grows into the pistil. At that time, an egg cell in the ovary begins to mature.

3. **Fertilization** When the pollen tube reaches the ovary and penetrates an ovule, the sperm cell travels through the tube and fertilizes the egg cell. The fertilized egg grows into an embryo. The embryo remains inside the ovule, which becomes the seed coat. The ovary develops into a fruit.

4. **Seeds and Fruit** The fruit may fall to the ground or it may be eaten by an animal. If the seed inside lands in a place where it can develop, it will grow into a new sour cherry tree.

CHECK YOUR READING   What happens to the plant ovary after fertilization?

9.2 **Review**

KEY CONCEPTS

1. Name three ways plants can reproduce asexually. (7.2.a)
2. What enables some plants to reproduce even in dry conditions? (7.2.a)
3. How are flowers related to seeds? to fruits? (7.5.f)

CRITICAL THINKING

4. **Evaluate** Why do many plants reproduce asexually when their environmental conditions are good?
5. **Compare and Contrast** Use a Venn diagram to show the differences and similarities between gymnosperms and angiosperms.

◇ CHALLENGE

6. **Infer** In a tundra, most plants produce spores. In a rainforest, many plants produce flowers and fruit. What factors might play a role in shaping the plant life in each biome?

CHAPTER INVESTIGATION

Which Seeds Will Grow?

DESIGN
— YOUR OWN —

OVERVIEW AND PURPOSE

Many of the foods you eat come from seed plants. What seeds or parts of seed plants have you eaten lately? What seeds can you find outside in your neighborhood? What conditions do the seeds from these plants need to grow? In this investigation, you will

- plant a variety of seeds
- observe differences in germination and growth among seeds planted in similar conditions

▶ Problem

Write It Up

How successfully will a variety of seeds germinate in conditions that can be provided in your classroom? Define what you mean by "success."

▶ Procedure

1. Make a data table in your **Science Notebook** like the one shown on page 331.

2. Examine the seeds you will use in this investigation. Try to identify them. Record your observations in the data table.

3. Decide where you will keep your seeds while they are growing and how often you will check and water them. Be sure to keep the conditions for all of the seeds the same.

MATERIALS
- assorted seeds
- potting soil
- paper cups
- water
- paper towels
- labels

7.5.f, 7.7.c

RICE
~NEY BEAN
SUNFLOWER SEE~

Content Standard
7.5.f Students know the structures and processes by which flowering plants generate pollen, ovules, seeds, and fruit.

Investigation Standard
7.7.c Communicate the logical connection among hypotheses, science concepts, tests conducted, data collected, and conclusions drawn from scientific evidence.

4. Use the materials provided to plant the seeds. Remember that the planting conditions should be the same for each of the seeds. Label each container. Wash your hands after handling seeds and soil.

5. Observe your seeds for at least ten days. Check and water them according to the plan you made.

step 5

Observe and Analyze
Write It Up

1. **RECORD** In your **Science Notebook**, draw and label a diagram to show how you planted the seeds, the materials you used, and the place where they are being kept.

2. **RECORD** Each time you check on your seeds, record your observations in your data table.

3. **IDENTIFY** Which seeds sprouted? What differences in growth and development did you observe in the different types of seeds?

Conclude
Write It Up

1. **INTERPRET** Based on your definition of success, which seeds were most successful?

2. **INFER** What patterns or similarities did you notice in the seeds that grew most successfully?

3. **IDENTIFY LIMITS** What factors were you unable to control? What other limits might have affected your results?

4. **APPLY** Use your experience to write directions for planting and caring for seeds that a young child could understand. What type of seeds would you suggest?

INVESTIGATE Further

CHALLENGE Some seeds need special conditions, such as warmth or a certain amount of moisture, before they will germinate. Design an experiment in which you test just one type of seed in a variety of conditions to learn which conditions result in the most growth. Include a hypothesis, a materials list, and a procedure when you write up your experiment. Remember to include a control group in your design.

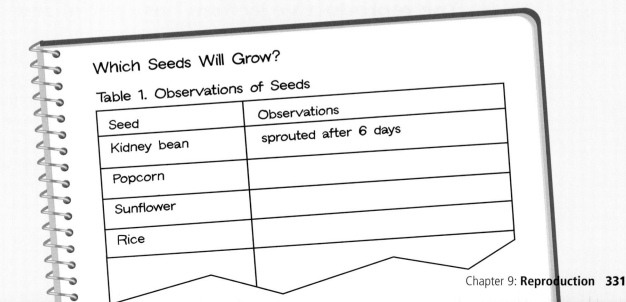

Which Seeds Will Grow?

Table 1. Observations of Seeds

Seed	Observations
Kidney bean	sprouted after 6 days
Popcorn	
Sunflower	
Rice	

9.3 Human reproduction is a complex process.

CALIFORNIA
Content Standards

7.5.a Students know plants and animals have levels of organization for structure and function, including cells, tissues, organs, organ systems, and the whole organism.

7.5.d Students know how the reproductive organs of the human female and male generate eggs and sperm and how sexual activity may lead to fertilization and pregnancy.

7.5.e Students know the function of the umbilicus and placenta during pregnancy.

VOCABULARY

menstruation p. 334
placenta p. 337
umbilical cord p. 338
fetus p. 338

BEFORE, you learned

- Sexual reproduction usually occurs between a mature male and a mature female
- Males produce sperm and females produce eggs
- In humans, eggs are fertilized while inside the mother's body

NOW, you will learn

- About specialized reproductive cells and organs
- How fertilization and pregnancy occur
- How human offspring develop during pregnancy

EXPLORE Reproduction (7.5.d)

How are sperm and egg cells different?

PROCEDURE

1. From your teacher, get slides of egg cells and sperm cells.
2. Examine each each slide under a microscope.
3. Draw a sketch of each cell.
4. With a partner, discuss the differences that you observed between the sperm and the eggs.

WHAT DO YOU THINK?

- What differences did you observe?
- What do the differences suggest about how each functions?

MATERIALS

- slides of egg and sperm cells
- microscope
- paper
- pencil

The reproductive system has specialized cells and structures.

Like all living organisms, humans reproduce. The reproductive system allows adults to produce offspring. Males and females have different reproductive systems, but both systems share an important feature— they both make specialized cells. Remember that a specialized cell is a cell that takes on a special job.

In the female, the specialized cells of reproduction are called egg cells. In the male, they are called sperm cells. Each of these specialized cells provides genetic material from the parent who produced it.

Sperm cells contain genetic material from the male, and egg cells have genetic material from the female. If this sounds familiar to you, it is! Human sperm cells and egg cells play the same roles in humans that plant sperm cells and egg cells play in plants.

The male and female reproductive systems rely on hormones to work properly. Recall that hormones are chemical messengers produced by structures in the endocrine system called glands. Hormones carry signals that control sexual development and reproduction.

NOTE-TAKING STRATEGY
Remember to add the headings in this section to your outline.

I. Main idea
  A. Supporting idea
    1. Detail
    2. Detail
  B. Supporting idea

The Female Reproductive System

The female reproductive system has two functions. The first is to produce egg cells, and the second is to protect and nourish the offspring until birth. The main reproductive organ of the female is the ovary. Every female has two ovaries. Each is about the size of an almond and sits on one side of the uterus. As in other sexually reproducing organisms, the ovaries contain both immature egg cells and maturing unfertilized eggs.

 CHECK YOUR READING How many ovaries does a female have?

Female Reproductive Organs

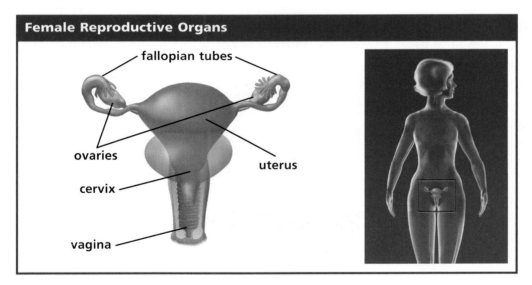

fallopian tubes

ovaries

cervix

uterus

vagina

The female reproductive system contains several other organs and structures. There are two fallopian tubes. These are the sites of fertilization. Each tube connects an ovary to the uterus. The uterus, which is also called the womb, is where the unborn offspring develop until birth. At the base of the uterus is an opening called the cervix. It connects the uterus to the vagina. The vagina is a passageway from the uterus to the outside of the female's body. The male deposits sperm in the vagina during intercourse. During childbirth, the vagina serves as the birth canal.

 CHECK YOUR READING What are the main reproductive organs of the female?

Egg Production

The human female is born with hundreds of thousands of egg cells in each ovary. Each egg cell was produced by meiosis. Recall that meiosis produces gametes that contain half of the genetic material needed to produce a new individual. The egg cells are not active until the female reaches puberty. In humans, most females start puberty sometime between 10 and 14 years of age.

At puberty, a gland in the female's brain releases a hormone that stimulates egg development. Several eggs begin to develop in one ovary. The active ovary produces hormones that cause the uterus lining to thicken with blood. This spongy lining gets the uterus ready for pregnancy. These events are the start of a cycle that will occur every 28 days or so for the next 30 to 40 years.

 CHECK YOUR READING When are eggs produced in the female?

Menstruation

Each month, several eggs in one ovary begin to develop, but only one is released. The released egg moves from the ovary into the nearest fallopian tube. This process is called ovulation. If the egg is not fertilized within the next 12 to 24 hours, both the egg and the lining of the uterus begin to break down. The uterus sheds its bloody lining, which exits the body through the vagina. The monthly shedding of the uterus lining is called **menstruation.**

VOCABULARY
Be sure to add frame games for *menstruation* and other vocabulary terms to your notebook.

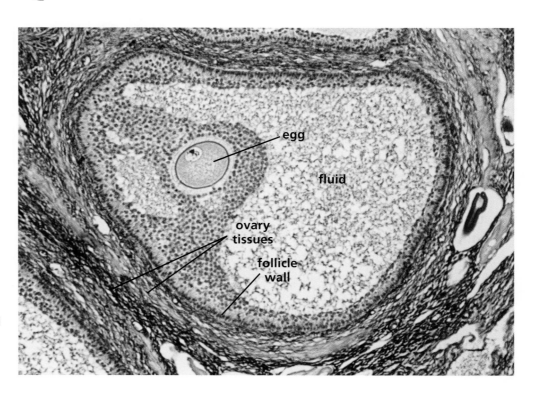

egg

fluid

ovary tissues

follicle wall

In the ovary, the developing egg is enclosed in a follicle. The follicle is a fluid-filled sac enclosed by a wall of several cell layers. When the egg is mature, the follicle wall bursts and the egg is released toward the fallopian tube.

The Male Reproductive System

The male reproductive system produces sperm. Each sperm is a highly specialized cell. The only function of sperm is to carry the male's genetic material to the female's egg. Unlike females, who are born with a lifetime supply of immature eggs, males do not have sperm in their bodies at birth. Sperm production in males begins when the male reaches puberty. In males puberty usually begins sometime between 11 and 14 years of age. This is slightly later than in females. Sperm production continues throughout the male's life. A sexually mature male produces millions of sperm every day.

 When do sperm begin developing in males?

The male reproductive system consists of several structures. The main reproductive organ of the male is the testis. Males have two of these. Inside each testis are tiny coiled tubes hundreds of feet long. Sperm are produced inside these tubes. Each sperm consists of a single cell with a head and a whiplike tail. The sperm head contains the male's genetic material. When sperm are released, the tail helps the sperm swim up the female reproductive tract.

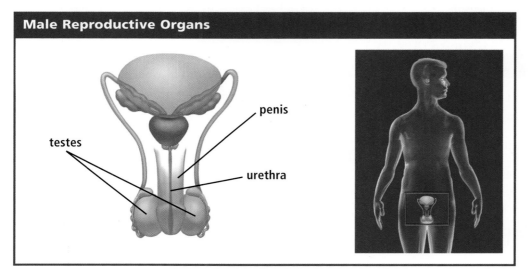

Male Reproductive Organs

testes

penis

urethra

Before they exit the male's body, the sperm cells mix with fluids to form semen. This fluid contains nutrients for the sperm and helps carry them out of the male's body. One drop of semen contains several million sperm cells. Semen exits the body through the urethra when the male ejaculates. The urethra is a tubelike channel that extends through the penis to an opening at the penis tip. The urethra is also connected to the bladder and is the passageway through which urine travels before exiting the body.

The production of offspring includes sexual intercourse, fertilization, pregnancy, and birth.

In order for fertilization to occur, sperm must reach the egg that lies inside one of the female's fallopian tubes. This occurs through sexual intercourse. In this act, the male inserts his penis into the female's vagina and ejaculates. Ejaculation releases semen that contains millions of sperm cells. The sperm enter the vagina and swim rapidly up through the uterus and into the fallopian tubes.

Fertilization

Although sperm travel up both fallopian tubes, usually just one tube holds a mature egg that can be fertilized. Millions of sperm arrive in the tube together, and all of them try to penetrate the egg. However, only one sperm will be successful. Fertilization occurs when a sperm cell joins an egg cell. The numbered steps on page 337 describe the main events of fertilization. As you read them, refer to the diagram below.

CHECK YOUR READING When does fertilization occur?

Fertilization

The egg moves down the fallopian tube following fertilization. Its final destination is the uterus.

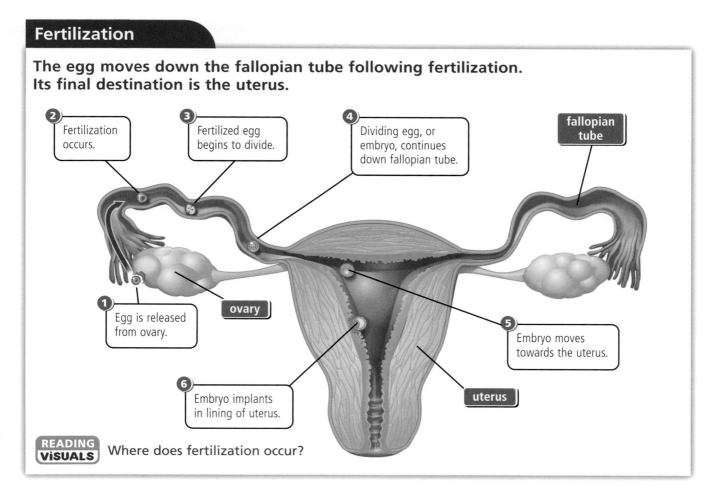

2 Fertilization occurs.

3 Fertilized egg begins to divide.

4 Dividing egg, or embryo, continues down fallopian tube.

fallopian tube

1 Egg is released from ovary.

ovary

5 Embryo moves towards the uterus.

6 Embryo implants in lining of uterus.

uterus

READING VISUALS Where does fertilization occur?

① The ovary releases a mature egg, which enters the nearest fallopian tube.

② Fertilization occurs when one sperm penetrates the egg. A chemical change prevents more sperm from entering the egg. Inside the egg, DNA from the sperm combines with the DNA of the egg.

③ After about 24 hours, the fertilized egg begins dividing. It first divides into two cells through mitosis. Each cell divides, producing four cells. Each of these cells divides, producing eight cells, and so on, forming a ball of cells that is better described as an embryo. In humans, an embryo is the developing organism during the period from the first cell division until eight weeks after fertilization.

④ As it divides, the embryo begins moving down the fallopian tube.

⑤ The embryo continues to divide rapidly as it enters the uterus.

⑥ About one week after fertilization, the embryo attaches itself to the thickened, spongy lining of the uterus. This is called implantation. Once implantation occurs, the mother's body undergoes many chemical changes to prepare it for the next stage—pregnancy.

Fertilization does not always occur. The female's ovary may fail to release an egg. Or, the egg that is released may be damaged in a way that prevents fertilization. Problems with the male's sperm can also cause fertilization to fail. The sperm may be damaged and unable to penetrate the egg. However, even though fertilization can fail, there is always a chance that it will occur following sexual intercourse. Every time two people have sex, there is a chance that the female will become pregnant, even if birth control is used.

VISUALIZATION
CLASSZONE.COM

Follow an egg from fertilization to implantation.

Pregnancy

The nine months of pregnancy can be divided into three periods called trimesters. Each trimester lasts about twelve weeks and marks specific stages of development.

In the week after implantation, the embryo grows rapidly. The embryo and the uterus contribute cells to a new organ called the placenta. The **placenta** is an organ filled with blood vessels that supply the embryo with oxygen and nutrients and remove wastes. It is attached to one side of the uterus. In the placenta, the mother's blood vessels lie next to vessels from the embryo. Nutrients, oxygen, and disease-fighting substances diffuse across the placenta from the mother's blood vessels to the embryo's vessels. Wastes diffuse from the embryo's vessels to the mother's vessels.

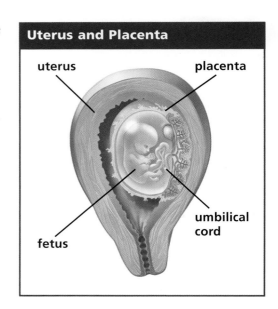

Uterus and Placenta

uterus

placenta

umbilical cord

fetus

The **umbilical cord** is a long tube that encloses the blood vessels connecting the embryo to the placenta. The cord carries nutrients and oxygen from the placenta to the embryo. It also carries carbon dioxide and other waste materials from the embryo to the placenta. These wastes move through the placenta and into the mother's circulation. The mother's body then removes them along with her own waste products. The cord is attached to the embryo at a small opening in its abdomen called the umbilicus.

CHECK YOUR READING What is the difference between the umbilical cord and the umbilicus?

The embryo is called a fetus after about eight weeks of pregnancy. A **fetus** is a developing human from eight weeks after fertilization until birth. Between the eighth and twelfth weeks of pregnancy, the fetus begins developing facial features, major organ systems, and a skeleton. During this time the fetus also develops the sexual traits that will make it either a male or a female.

In the second trimester, between weeks 12 and 24, the fetus continues to grow and its bones develop further. In the last trimester, between weeks 24 and 36, the fetus and all of its organ systems develop fully.

Labor and Delivery

After nine months, the fetus is fully developed and ready to leave the mother's body. The birth of a fetus is divided into three stages. These are labor, delivery of the fetus, and delivery of the placenta.

Labor begins with strong muscular contractions of the uterus. The first contractions occur about every 15 to 30 minutes. Each contraction lasts roughly 40 seconds. With each contraction the mother's cervix widens. This allows the fetus to move closer to the vagina, which is the birth canal. The interval between contractions gradually decreases. When the contractions start occurring about every two minutes, the cervix is wide enough for the fetus to pass through.

During delivery the mother's muscles push the fetus out of the uterus and through the vagina. The fetus remains connected to the mother during delivery by the umbilical cord. Shortly after delivery, the umbilical cord is cut. Once the cord is cut, the fetus becomes a separate individual.

The placenta separates from the uterus within minutes after birth. The mother delivers the placenta with the help of more muscle contractions. Once the placenta is delivered, the delivery process is complete.

READING TiP

An interval is a period of time between two specific points. During labor, the interval between contractions is the period between the end of one contraction and the start of another.

Growth of the Fetus

**An embryo grows and develops from
a cluster of cells to a fully formed fetus.**

4-day embryo

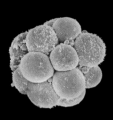

magnification 620x

- Embryo has 16 cells
- Not yet implanted in the uterus

5-week embryo

size < 1 cm

- Heart is beating
- Beginning of eyes, arms, and legs are visible

8-week fetus

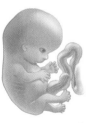

size 2–3 cm

- Embryo is now called a fetus
- Has all basic organs and major body parts

16-week fetus

size 12 cm

- Can move around in the womb
- Hair, eyelashes, and eyebrows are growing

7–8 month fetus shown in this composite image is about 35–40 cm in length and has a mass of 1.5–2.3 kg. The fetus usually gains at least 1 kg during the final month of pregnancy.

Multiple Births

Do you have any friends who are twins or triplets? Perhaps you are one yourself. The birth of more than one offspring at a time is called a multiple birth. Multiple births are fairly uncommon in humans.

Identical twins are produced when one fertilized egg divides in half early in embryo development. Each half forms one complete organism—a twin. Such twins are of the same sex, look alike, and have the same blood type. Identical triplets are produced in much the same way, except that one half of the fertilized egg divides again, producing three identical zygotes.

Fraternal twins are not identical. They are produced when two eggs are released at the same time and are fertilized by two different sperm. Fraternal triplets can result when three eggs are released and fertilized by three different sperm. Fraternal twins and triplets can be the same sex or different sexes. They can be as similar or as different as siblings born at different times.

CHECK YOUR READING Why are some twins identical and some are not?

 Review

KEY CONCEPTS

1. What are the specialized reproductive cells in males and in females? **(7.5.d)**

2. How does sexual intercourse result in pregnancy? **(7.5.d)**

3. How are the placenta and the umbilical cord related? **(7.5.e)**

CRITICAL THINKING

4. **Sequence** Describe the sequence of events between ovulation and menstruation.

5. **Infer** Sperm cells have very little cytoplasm, while egg cells have a lot of cytoplasm. How do these different structures support the different functions of eggs and sperm?

▲ CHALLENGE

6. **Analyze** Children born to mothers who smoke during pregnancy have a higher rate of respiratory disease than children born to nonsmoking mothers. Explain how a mother's tobacco use could affect the fetus during development.

MATH TUTORIAL
CLASSZONE.COM
Click on Math Tutorial for more help with solving proportions.

Math 7.AF.4.2
Science 7.5.d

SKILL: SOLVING PROPORTIONS

Twins and Triplets

Is the number of twins and triplets on the rise? Between 1980 and 2002, twin births in the United States rose from roughly 68,000 to about 125,000 per year. In 1980, there were about 3,600,000 births total. To compare these numbers, you can use proportions. A proportion is an equation. It shows two ratios that are equivalent.

Example

Find the ratio of twin births to the total births in the United States in 1980. Express the number as twin births per 1000 births.

(1) Write the ratio of twin births to total births for that year.

$$\frac{68{,}000 \text{ twin births}}{3{,}600{,}000 \text{ total births}}$$

(2) Write a proportion, using x for the number you need to find.

$$\frac{68{,}000 \text{ twin births}}{3{,}600{,}000 \text{ total births}} = \frac{x \text{ twin births}}{1000 \text{ total births}}$$

(3) In a proportion, the cross products are equal, so

68,000 twin births • 1000 total births = x twin births • 3,600,000 total births

(4) Solve for x:

$$\frac{68{,}000 \text{ twin births} \cdot 1000 \text{ total births}}{3{,}600{,}000 \text{ total births}} = 18.9 \text{ twin births}$$

ANSWER There were 18.9 twin births for every 1000 births in 1980.

Find the following birth ratios.

1. In 2002, there were about 125,000 twin births and about 4,000,000 total births. What was the ratio of twins to total births?

2. In 1980, about 1,350 sets of triplets were born. By 2002, this number had risen to about 6,900. What were the ratios of triplets to total births in 1980 and in 2002?

3. How much did the ratio increase for twin births between 1980 and 2002? for triplets?

4. Find the overall birth ratio of twins and triplets, combined, to the total births in 1980.

CHALLENGE In 1989, there were about 4 million total births, and the ratio of triplets born per million births was about 700. How many triplets were born?

Chapter Review

the **BIG** idea

Reproductive systems allow the production of offspring.

CONTENT REVIEW
CLASSZONE.COM

◀ **KEY CONCEPTS SUMMARY**

1 **Organisms reproduce in different ways.**

- All living things can produce offspring.
- Asexual reproduction is efficient, but offspring lack genetic diversity.
- Sexual reproduction increases genetic variation in offspring.

VOCABULARY
gamete p. 317
fertilization p. 317
zygote p. 317

2 **Plants can reproduce in several ways.**

- Some plants reproduce using spores, while others use pollen and seeds to produce offspring.
- A seed provides protection and nutrients for the plant embryo.
- In angiosperms, flowers produce pollen. Flowers and fruit attract animals.

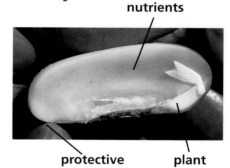

stored nutrients

protective coating

plant embryo

VOCABULARY
vegetative propagation p. 323
pollen p. 325
seed p. 325
embryo p. 325
ovule p. 327
fruit p. 329

3 **Human reproduction is a complex process.**

- The female produces eggs, and the male produces sperm.
- Sexual intercourse can lead to fertilization and pregnancy.
- Following fertilization, the fetus develops over a period of about nine months.

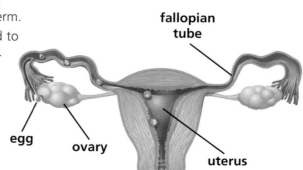

fallopian tube

egg

ovary

uterus

VOCABULARY
menstruation p. 334
placenta p. 337
umbilical cord p. 338
fetus p. 338

Reviewing Vocabulary

Describe how vocabulary terms in the following pairs are related to each other. Explain the relationship in a one- or two-sentence answer. Underline each vocabulary term in your answers.

1. gamete and zygote

2. ovule and fruit

3. embryo and seed

4. fruit and flower

5. menstruation and fertilization

6. embryo and fetus

7. placenta and umbilical cord

Reviewing Key Concepts

Multiple Choice *Choose the letter of the best answer.*

8. What happens in binary fission? (7.2.a)
   a. Two cells combine their DNA.
   b. A parent cell produces two daughter cells that differ.
   c. Material from one cell is divided into two cells.
   d. One cell divides into four egg cells.

9. Which of the following involves an exchange of DNA? (7.2.a)
   a. fragmentation   c. conjugation
   b. binary fission   d. budding

10. An important benefit of asexual reproduction is that (7.2.a)
    a. offspring are genetically diverse
    b. offspring develop outside the organism
    c. it requires water
    d. it can take place quickly and easily

11. Which of these structures do moss and ferns use in reproduction? (7.2.a)
    a. seeds   c. spores
    b. cones   d. flowers

12. Eggs develop in a female reproductive organ called a(n) (7.5.f)
    a. uterus   c. vagina
    b. fallopian tube d. ovary

13. The joining of one sperm cell and one egg cell is an event called (7.2.b)
    a. implantation   c. menstruation
    b. fertilization   d. delivery

14. In humans, fertilization takes place in the (7.5.d)
    a. urethra   c. fallopian tubes
    b. vagina   d. cervix

15. Oxygen and other substances are transported from the mother to the fetus across the (7.5.e)
    a. fallopian tubes c. ovaries
    b. placenta   d. vagina

16. Which of the following is one of the stages of childbirth?
    a. delivery of the placenta
    b. fertilization of the egg
    c. development of the fetus
    d. implantation

Short Answer *Write a short answer to each question.*

17. What is the role of water during sexual reproduction of mosses and ferns? (7.2.a)

18. The bat in these photographs is feeding from the flower. How might this activity help the plant reproduce? (7.5.f)

19. **COMMUNICATE** What process is shown in this photograph? Describe the sequence of events taking place. (7.2.a)

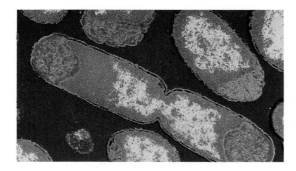

20. **CALCULATE** A bacterium reproduces every hour. Assuming the bacteria continue to reproduce at that rate, how many bacteria will there be after 10 hours? Explain how you found your answer. (7.2.a)

21. **CONNECT** You or someone you know may be allergic to pollen that is in the air during the growing seasons of some plants. What is the advantage for a plant of producing so much pollen? (7.5.f)

22. **PREDICT** If you observed three plants in a forest—a moss, a fern, and a flowering plant—which plant would have the most insects nearby? Explain your answer. (7.5.f)

23. **COMPARE** Make a chart that shows how reproduction in mosses, ferns, pine trees, and cherry trees is similar and how it is different. (7.5.f)

24. **COMPARE** How are the reproductive systems of flowering plants similar to those of humans? Your answer should include specialized cells and organs. (7.5.a)

25. **INFER** Give two reasons why fertilization in humans might not occur. (7.5.d)

26. **SUMMARIZE** Describe the events between fertilization and birth. (7.5.d)

27. **COMPARE AND CONTRAST** How are the functions of the ovaries and the testes alike? How are their functions different? (7.5.d)

28. **CONNECT** Describe the events that occur during the female's 28-day menstrual cycle. Explain how pregnancy can occur during this time. (7.5.d)

29. **INFER** In humans, about how much time goes by between fertilization and implantation, when the mother's body begins its chemical changes? (7.5.d)

30. **SYNTHESIZE** Many species reproduce asexually when conditions are good. Their sexual reproduction becomes more important when survival is more difficult. Why might different forms of reproduction be advantages at different times? (7.3.e)

the BIG idea

31. **SUMMARIZE** Look again at the photograph on pages 310–311. Now that you have finished the chapter, how would you change or add details to your answer to the question on the photograph? (7.2.a)

32. **SYNTHESIZE** Fish use external fertilization to reproduce after laying hundreds of eggs. Gorillas use internal fertilization. They give birth to one or two offspring at a time, which have developed inside the mother's body. Each method of reproduction is an adaptation for the species in its own environment. Use what you know about fish and gorillas to explain how the number of offspring represents an advantage for each species. (7.3.b)

UNIT PROJECTS

Check your schedule for your unit project. How are you doing? Be sure that you have placed data or notes from your research in your project folder.

Analyzing Data

7.5.d, 7.5.e

This chart shows some of the stages of development of a typical fetus.

Week of Pregnancy	Approximate Length of Fetus (cm)	Developmental Changes in Fetus
6	1	Primitive heartbeat
10	3	Face, fingers, and toes are formed.
14	8.5	Muscle and bone tissue have developed.
18	14	Fetus makes active movements.
24	30	Fingerprints and footprints form.
28	37.5	Brain develops rapidly.
36	47.5	Body fat increases
38	50	Fetus is considered full term.

Use the chart to answer the questions below.

1. What is the approximate length of the fetus at 10 weeks?

a. 1 cm   **c.** 3 cm

b. 2 in.   **d.** 3 in.

2. At about which week of development does the fetus begin to make active movements?

a. week 10   **c.** week 18

b. week 14   **d.** week 24

3. At about which week of development does the fetus reach a length of about 30 cm?

a. week 18   **c.** week 36

b. week 24   **d.** week 38

4. Which statement is true?

a. Between weeks 28 and 38, the fetus grows at an average of a little over a centimeter per week.

b. The fetus begins to develop fingerprints at about week 28.

c. During week 10, the length of the fetus is about 7.5 cm.

d. The fetus is about 12.5 cm long when muscle and bone tissue develop.

5. Between which weeks of development does the greatest overall increase in length usually take place?

a. weeks 6 and 10

b. weeks 10 and 14

c. weeks 14 and 18

d. weeks 24 and 28

Extended Response

Answer the following two questions in detail. Include some of the terms from the word box in your answer. Underline each term you use.

homeostasis	placenta	hormones
umbilical cord	fetus	

6. A pregnancy usually lasts 36–38 weeks, roughly 9 months. The development of the fetus can be broken down into three stages, each about 12 weeks long. These stages are referred to as trimesters. Briefly describe changes in length and development that occur during each of these stages.

7. Anything that enters the mother's circulation during pregnancy can be transferred to the fetus through the placenta. Alcohol is known to damage DNA and interfere with other cellular processes, especially when cells are rapidly dividing. Describe some effects you might expect a mother's drinking to have on a developing embryo.

10 Movement and Forces

the BIG idea

Muscles and bones provide forces and levers to move the body.

Key Concepts

SECTION

1 The skeletal system provides support and protection.
Learn how the skeletal system is organized and what it does.

SECTION

2 The muscular system makes movement possible.
Learn about different types of muscles and how they work.

SECTION

3 Muscles exert forces.
Learn how muscles exert forces to move the body.

SECTION

4 Bones and joints act as levers.
Learn how bones and joints act as levers and give the body mechanical advantage.

California ClassZone

CLASSZONE.COM

Chapter 10 online resources: Content Review, two Simulations, two Resource Centers, Math Tutorial, Test Practice

Which body systems is this racer using to get ahead?

EXPLORE (the BIG idea)

How Many Bones Are in Your Hand?

7.5.c Students know how bones and muscles work together to provide a structural framework for movement.

Use a pencil to trace an outline of your hand on a piece of paper. Feel the bones in your fingers and the palm of your hand. At points where you can bend your fingers and hand, draw a circle. Each circle represents a joint where two bones meet. Draw lines to represent the bones of your hand.

Observe and Think How many bones did you find? How many joints?

How Does It Move?

7.5.c Students know how bones and muscles work together to provide a structural framework for movement.

The bones in your body are hard and stiff, yet they move smoothly. The point where two bones meet and move is called a joint. Find a few objects in your home with hard parts that move against each other, such as a door hinge, a joystick, or a pair of scissors.

Observe and Think How are these objects attached so that movement is possible? What parts of your body produce similar movements?

NSTA
scilinks.org
SCI LINKS
Bones and Joints **Code: MDL073**

Getting Ready to Learn

CONCEPT REVIEW

- The cell is the basic unit of living things.
- Systems in living things are made up of interacting parts that share matter and energy.
- In multicellular organisms, cells work together to support life.

VOCABULARY REVIEW

See Glossary for definitions.

cell
system

CONTENT REVIEW
CLASSZONE.COM

Review concepts and vocabulary.

▶ TAKING NOTES

SUPPORTING MAIN IDEAS

Make a chart to show main ideas and the information that supports them. Copy each blue heading. Below each heading, add supporting information, such as reasons, explanations, and examples.

VOCABULARY STRATEGY

Draw a **word triangle** diagram for each new vocabulary term. In the bottom row, write and define the term. In the middle row, use the term correctly in a sentence. At the top, draw a small picture to help you remember the term.

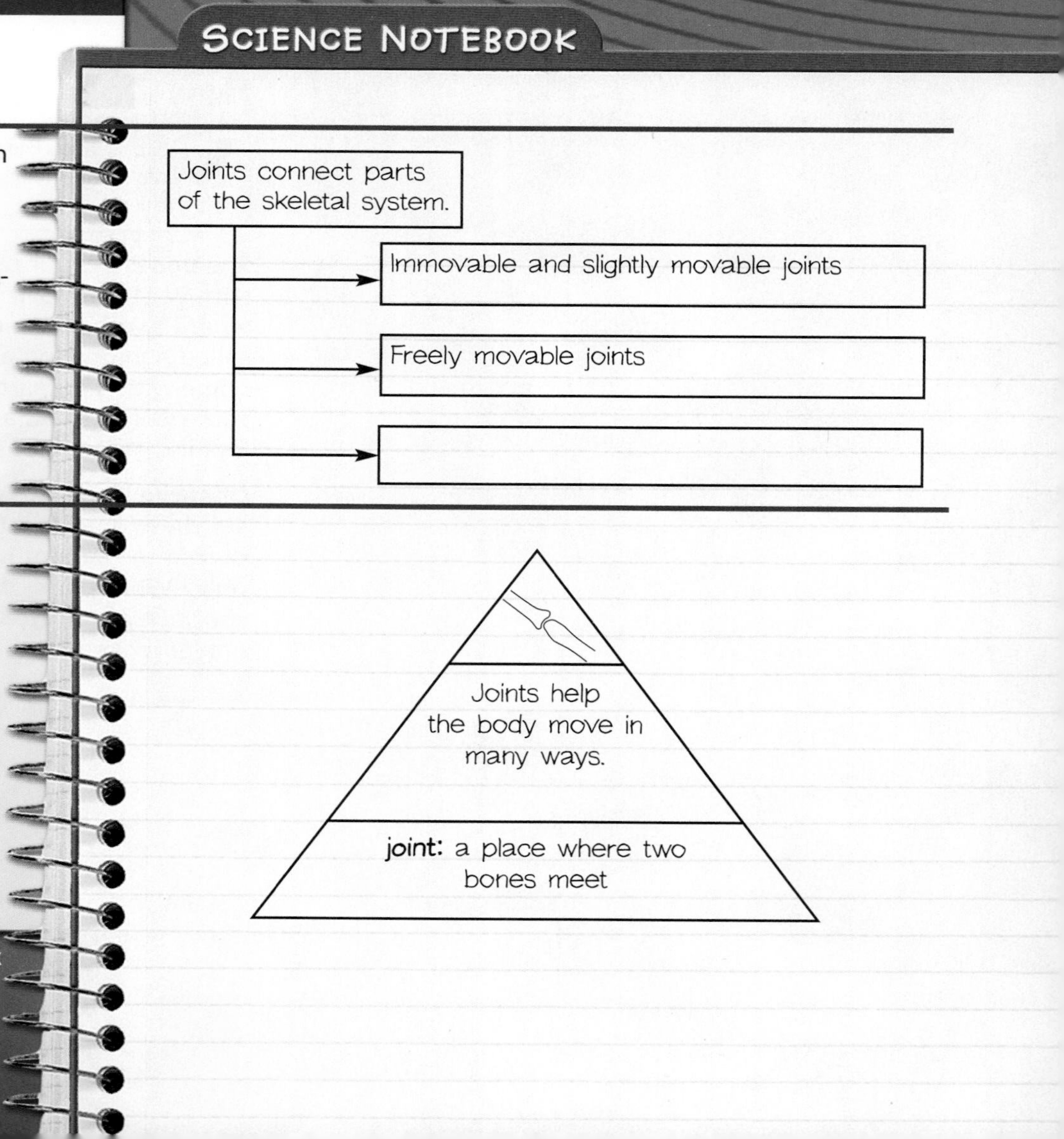

See the Note-Taking Handbook on pages R45–R51.

SCIENCE NOTEBOOK

Joints connect parts of the skeletal system.

→ Immovable and slightly movable joints

→ Freely movable joints

→

Joints help the body move in many ways.

joint: a place where two bones meet

The skeletal system provides support and protection.

CALIFORNIA
Content Standards

7.5.c Students know how bones and muscles work together to provide a structural framework for movement.

7.6.h Students know how to compare joints in the body (wrist, shoulder, thigh) with structures used in machines and simple devices (hinge, ball-and-socket, and sliding joints).

BEFORE, you learned

- The body is made of cells, tissues, organs, and organ systems
- Different organ systems work together
- The muscular and skeletal systems help the body move

NOW, you will learn

- How the human skeleton is organized
- About different types of bone tissue
- How joints allow movement

VOCABULARY

skeletal system p. 349
axial skeleton p. 350
appendicular skeleton p. 350
joint p. 353
cartilage p. 353

EXPLORE Arm Movement (7.5.c)

How does position affect support?

PROCEDURE

1. Hold the bag in your hand and keep your arm straight. Move the bag up and down.

2. Move the handles of the bag over your elbow. Again hold your arm straight and move the bag up and down.

3. Move the bag to the upper part of your arm and repeat the procedure.

MATERIALS
- sports bag

WHAT DO YOU THINK?
- At which position was it easiest to move the bag?
- At which position did the bag move the farthest?

The skeleton is the body's framework.

SUPPORTING MAIN IDEAS
Support the main idea that the skeletal system provides protection and support with examples.

Every movement in your body is possible because of the interaction of muscles with the skeletal system. The **skeletal system** includes the bones, ligaments, cartilage, and tendons. This system anchors the body's movement, provides support, and protects the internal organs.

Bones in the skeletal system can be classified by their shapes: long bones, short bones, flat bones, and irregular bones. Long bones are longer than they are wide. They are found in the arms and legs. Short bones are about as long as they are wide. They include bones in the wrists and ankles. Flat bones are thin and flat or slightly curved. They are found in the ribcage and skull. Irregular bones are shaped differently from those listed above and include bones in the spine and skull.

Like the frame of a building, the skeleton provides the body's shape. The skeleton works with other systems to allow movement. Scientists have classified two main divisions in the skeleton. These are the axial (AK-see-uhl) skeleton and the appendicular (AP-uhn-DIHK-yuh-luhr) skeleton. The **axial skeleton** is the central part of the skeleton that includes the skull, the spinal column, and the ribs. The bones in the appendicular skeleton are attached to the axial skeleton. The diagram on page 351 shows some important bones in your skeleton.

The Axial Skeleton

READING TiP

Axis is a noun meaning "a straight line about which a body rotates." *Axial* is an adjective describing something that has an axis.

Imagine a line straight down your back and think of that line as an axis. Sitting, standing, and twisting are some of the motions that turn around this axis. The axial skeleton is the part of the skeleton that forms the axis in your body. It mainly provides support and protection. In the diagram, the parts of the axial skeleton are shown in red.

At the top of the axial skeleton is the cranium (KRAY-nee-uhm)—the bones that surround the brain. Most of the bones in the cranium do not move. The cranium and the bones in the face—such as the jawbones and cheekbones—make up the skull. The skull connects to the spinal column.

Your spinal column is the main portion of the axial skeleton. The spinal column, or backbone, is made up of many bones called vertebrae (VUR-tuh-BRAY). The vertebrae are stacked one on top of the other in a vertical line. If you run your finger along your back, you will feel your vertebrae. The rib bones and the sternum are also part of the axial skeleton. The ribs protect internal organs, such as the heart and lungs.

 CHECK YOUR READING Where in your body is your axial skeleton?

The Appendicular Skeleton

READING TiP

Note that the word *appendicular* contains the word *append*, which means "to attach." Bones in the appendicular skeleton are attached to the axial skeleton.

The **appendicular skeleton** consists of the bones of the skeleton that function to allow movement. It includes the arms and the legs. Notice that the diagram shows the appendicular skeleton in yellow. The bones in your shoulders help the bones in your arms move. The upper arm bone that connects to the shoulder is the longest bone in the upper body. It connects with two bones of the lower arm. Together, the bones of the shoulders, arms, and hands make up the upper part of your appendicular skeleton.

SIMULATION
CLASSZONE.COM

Assemble a virtual skeleton.

The bones in your hips, legs, and feet make up the lower part of the appendicular skeleton. This part of the skeleton bears all of your body's weight when you are standing. Your leg bones are the strongest in your skeleton. Just as the lower arm includes two bones, the lower leg has two bones.

The Skeletal System

The skeletal system interacts with other body systems to allow this soccer player to stand, run, and kick.

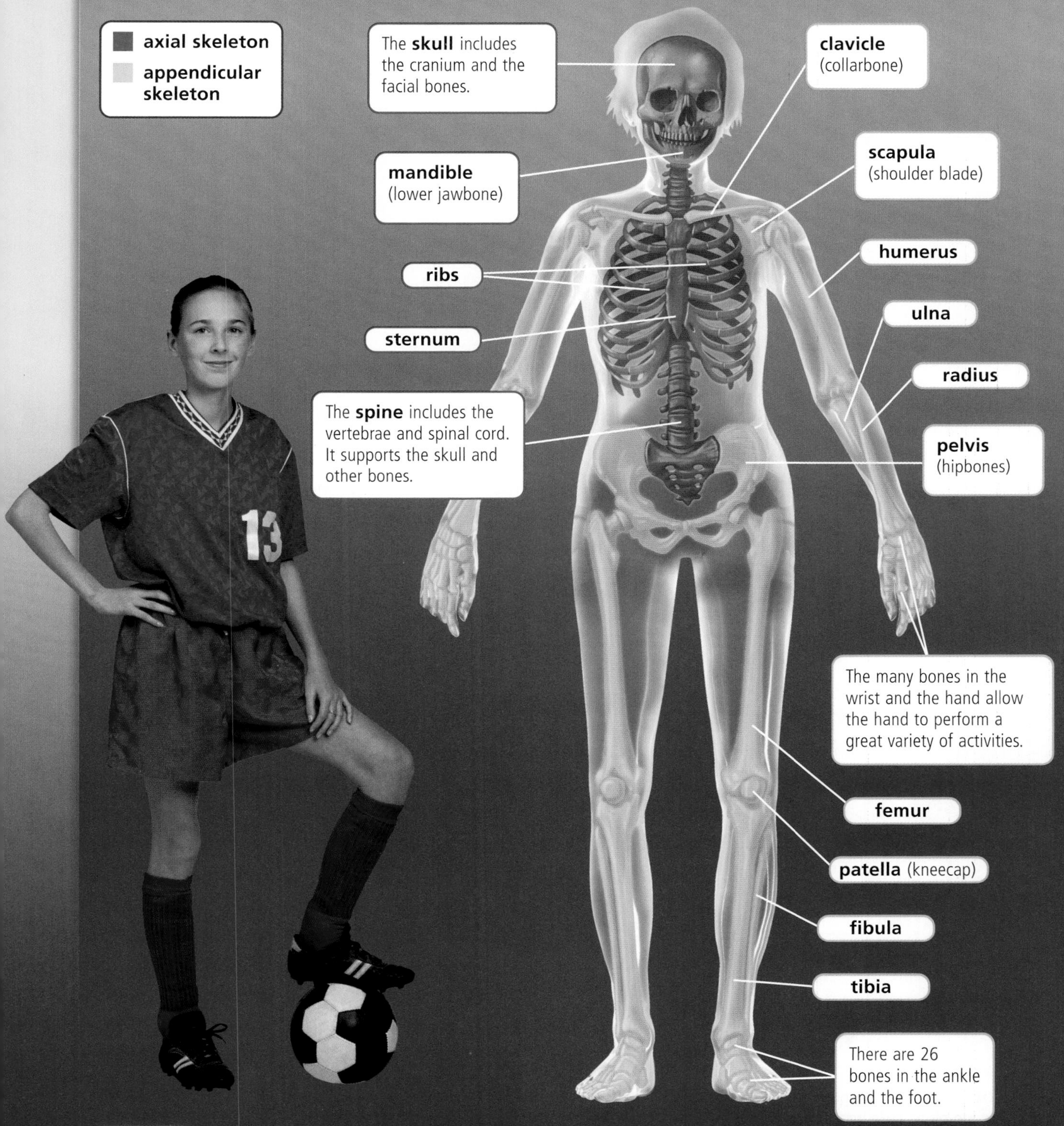

■ axial skeleton
□ appendicular skeleton

The **skull** includes the cranium and the facial bones.

mandible (lower jawbone)

ribs

sternum

The **spine** includes the vertebrae and spinal cord. It supports the skull and other bones.

clavicle (collarbone)

scapula (shoulder blade)

humerus

ulna

radius

pelvis (hipbones)

The many bones in the wrist and the hand allow the hand to perform a great variety of activities.

femur

patella (kneecap)

fibula

tibia

There are 26 bones in the ankle and the foot.

READING VISUALS Which bones might this soccer player use most when playing soccer?

Bones are living tissue.

You might think that bones are completely solid. However, they are not—they have spaces inside. These spaces make your bones lighter in weight. Bones are made up of cells and minerals. They also contain blood vessels. Cells constantly make, maintain, and break down bone tissue in the body. Minerals such as calcium give bones structure and stiffness. Bones serve many important functions. For example, they support and protect the body, produce and store blood cells, and store calcium for the body.

Every bone is made up of two types of bone tissue: spongy bone and compact bone. Spongy bone is a strong but lightweight tissue. The mineral part of the spongy bone looks like a web. This web supports the bone in the same way that beams support a building. Spongy bone can be compressed slightly without damage. The spongy bone tissue near the end of each long bone helps the body absorb forces.

Within the spongy bone tissue is red bone marrow, the part of the bone that produces blood cells. New blood cells travel from the marrow into blood vessels that run throughout the bone. Blood also brings nutrients to bone cells and carries waste materials away.

Compact bone is the tough outer layer of bone that surrounds spongy bone. Compact bone acts as the basic supportive tissue of the body. This dense tissue is organized in layers, so it is very strong.

 CHECK YOUR READING What are the different functions of bones?

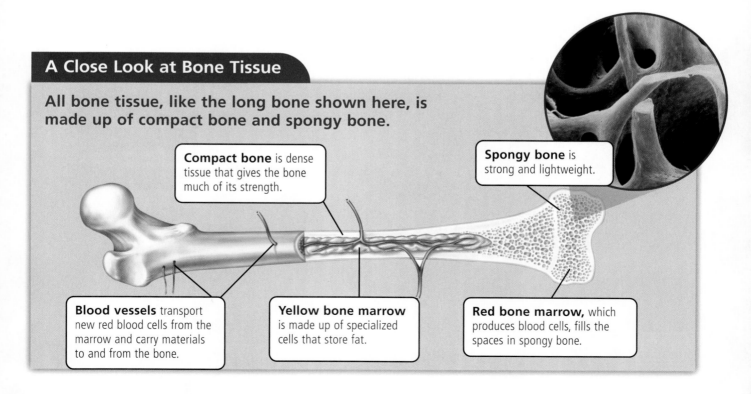

A Close Look at Bone Tissue

All bone tissue, like the long bone shown here, is made up of compact bone and spongy bone.

Compact bone is dense tissue that gives the bone much of its strength.

Spongy bone is strong and lightweight.

Blood vessels transport new red blood cells from the marrow and carry materials to and from the bone.

Yellow bone marrow is made up of specialized cells that store fat.

Red bone marrow, which produces blood cells, fills the spaces in spongy bone.

Joints connect parts of the skeletal system.

A **joint** is a place where two bones in the skeletal system meet. Joints allow the body to be flexible. There are three types of joints in the body: immovable, slightly movable, and freely movable.

Immovable and Slightly Movable Joints

An immovable joint locks bones together like puzzle pieces. The bones in the skull are connected by immovable joints. Inside the cranium these joints are called sutures (SOO-chuhrz) because it appears as though the bones have been stitched together. There is no space between bones at an immovable joint.

Slightly movable joints are able to flex a little. For example, your ribs are connected to your sternum by slightly movable joints. There is no space between the bones, but they can move because the bones are joined by cartilage. **Cartilage** (KAHR-tl-ihj) is a tough but flexible connective tissue. The outermost part of your ear is made of one type of cartilage. Another type of cartilage connects and cushions the vertebrae in your spinal column.

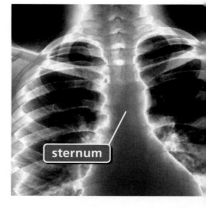
sternum

The sternum is connected to the ribs by slightly movable joints.

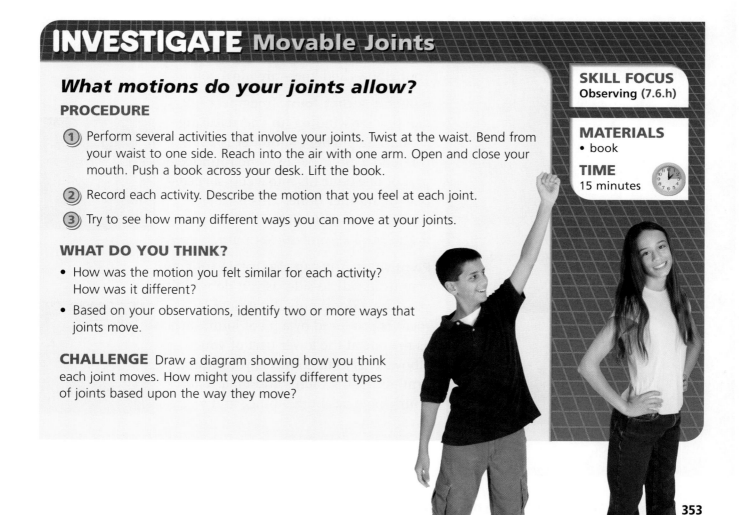

INVESTIGATE Movable Joints

What motions do your joints allow?

PROCEDURE

1. Perform several activities that involve your joints. Twist at the waist. Bend from your waist to one side. Reach into the air with one arm. Open and close your mouth. Push a book across your desk. Lift the book.

2. Record each activity. Describe the motion that you feel at each joint.

3. Try to see how many different ways you can move at your joints.

WHAT DO YOU THINK?

• How was the motion you felt similar for each activity? How was it different?

• Based on your observations, identify two or more ways that joints move.

CHALLENGE Draw a diagram showing how you think each joint moves. How might you classify different types of joints based upon the way they move?

SKILL FOCUS
Observing (7.6.h)

MATERIALS
• book

TIME
15 minutes

353

Freely Movable Joints

Freely movable joints allow you to bend and move. They make up most of the joints in your body. Your wrist, knee, and elbow are all movable joints. The bones of movable joints are separated by a cavity that contains fluid. You will learn more about fluids in Chapter 11.

Tissues called ligaments hold bones together at movable joints. Fluids and other materials between the bones, such as cartilage, cushion the bones and keep them from rubbing together. Tendons, a type of connective tissue, connect the muscles to the bones but are not considered part of the joint. These pieces work together with muscles to produce different types of movement.

Movable joints can be classified by the type of movement they produce. The diagrams show different types of joints and the directions in which the bones can move. Scientists can model the movement of bones at joints using simple devices, like hinges (HIHNJ-uhz).

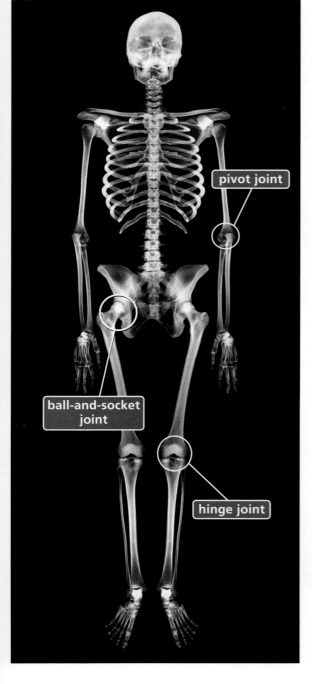

pivot joint

ball-and-socket joint

hinge joint

Hinge Joint Think about the movement of your arm when you eat an apple. Your hand moves towards your face. The angle between your upper arm and lower arm decreases. This is angular movement. The joint that produces this movement is called a hinge joint. Your elbows and knees are hinge joints.

Ball-and-Socket Joint Imagine a softball pitcher winding up and releasing a ball. The pitcher's shoulder is able to rotate in a circle because the rounded part of one bone fits into a cup-shaped part of another bone. This is called a ball-and-socket joint. The hip joint is another ball-and-socket joint.

Pivot Joint You can also rotate your arm from side to side, as you do when you turn a doorknob. Rotational movement is produced by a pivot joint, such as the one at the lower part of your elbow. This joint connects your lower arm bones, the radius and ulna. Thus, your elbow has both a hinge and a pivot joint.

Gliding Joint Some of the joints in your ankles and wrists involve small, flat bones that slide or glide over one another. These are called gliding joints. The gliding joints in the body have limited movement. The vertebrae in your spine can glide and move because of gliding joints.

Saddle Joint Think about a joystick. It can move forward and backward and rock from side to side. This is how a saddle joint allows bones to move. There is only one place in the body that has a saddle joint—the thumb. Try moving your thumb back and forth and side to side. The movement is more limited than the movement of a ball-and-socket joint.

Ellipsoid Joint In your hands and feet, you have ellipsoid joints. They can be found at the base of each finger and toe. These joints allow the bones to move like a hinge in different directions but not to rotate.

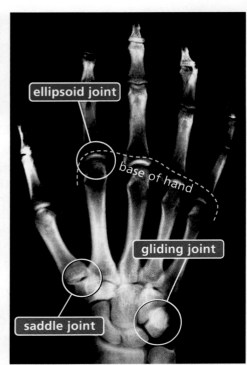

ellipsoid joint

base of hand

gliding joint

saddle joint

At many places in the body, different joints work simultaneously to produce smooth, continuous motion. Wave your hand from side to side so that you are moving your wrist. What types of joints in your wrist and hand are being used? Now think about other kinds of movement: dancing, typing on a computer, playing sports, or playing a musical instrument. Many types of movements are possible because of joints.

CHECK YOUR READING What types of movement do joints allow?

10.1 Review

KEY CONCEPTS

1. What are the main divisions of the human skeleton? (7.5.c)

2. What are the two types of bone tissue? Describe them. (7.5.c)

3. Name three types of joints and give an example of each. (7.6.h)

CRITICAL THINKING

4. **Classify** What types of tissues keep bones together at joints?

5. **Analyze** Which type of movable joint allows the most movement? How does the joint's shape and structure contribute to this?

○ CHALLENGE

6. **Analyze** Find an object that moves like a joint. What type of joint is it most like? Justify your answer.

KEY CONCEPT

10.2 The muscular system makes movement possible.

CALIFORNIA
Content Standard

7.5.c Students know how bones and muscles work together to provide a structural framework for movement.

BEFORE, you learned

- The human skeleton has two main divisions
- There are different types of bone tissue
- Joints function in several different ways

NOW, you will learn

- About the functions of muscles
- About the different types of muscles and how they work
- How some muscles work to produce movement

VOCABULARY

muscular system p. 357
skeletal muscle p. 358
smooth muscle p. 358
cardiac muscle p. 358

EXPLORE Muscles (7.5.c)

How do muscles change as you move?

PROCEDURE

1. Sit on a chair with your feet on the floor.

2. Place your hand around your leg. Straighten one leg as shown in the photograph.

3. Repeat step 2 several times.

WHAT DO YOU THINK?
- How did your muscles change during the activity?
- Record your observations.

Muscles perform important functions.

Every movement of your body—from the beating of your heart to the movement of food down your throat to the blinking of your eyes—occurs because of muscles. Some movements happen automatically, while other movements are under your control. For example, if you are riding a bike, you can control when to push on the pedals to make the bike go faster and when to use the brakes to make the bike stop or slow down. Muscles do more in your body than just produce movement. Muscles also help to regulate your body's temperature and maintain your body's posture.

CHECK YOUR READING What three functions do muscles perform in the body?

Movement

The **muscular system** consists of skeletal muscles—muscles attached to the skeleton. The muscular system works with other systems in the body to produce movement. Most skeletal muscles are attached to bones by tendons. The skeletal muscles are made up of muscle fibers, which are made up of many individual muscle cells. These fibers contract and relax. As they contract, the muscle fibers shorten, or bunch up. As the muscle fibers relax, they lengthen.

Most of the muscles involved in moving the body work in coordinated groups. It may surprise you that muscles do not push. They only exert a force when they pull. Think about bending your leg. Muscles on the back of your leg pull in one direction, while the muscles on the front of your leg relax. So as the muscle contracts, the muscles on the back of your leg shorten, pulling the bones. The opposite muscles work when you straighten your leg.

RESOURCE CENTER
CLASSZONE.COM
Discover more about muscles.

Maintaining Body Temperature

Remember that the balance of conditions in the body is called homeostasis. One function of the muscular system is related to homeostasis. Muscles help maintain body temperature.

When muscles contract, they release heat. You may have observed the way your muscles affect your body temperature when you shiver. The quick muscle contractions that occur when you shiver release heat and raise your body temperature. Without this heat from shivering, the body would have difficulty maintaining its normal temperature.

CHECK YOUR READING How do muscles help maintain homeostasis?

Maintaining Posture

Have you ever noticed that you stand up straight without thinking about it, even though gravity is pulling your body down? Most muscles in your body are always a little bit contracted. This tension, or muscle tone, is even present most of the time you spend sleeping.

Try standing for a few moments on the balls of your feet or on one leg. When you are trying to balance or hold one position for any length of time, you can feel different muscles contracting and relaxing. Your muscles make constant adjustments to keep you sitting or standing upright. You don't have to think about these tiny adjustments; they happen automatically.

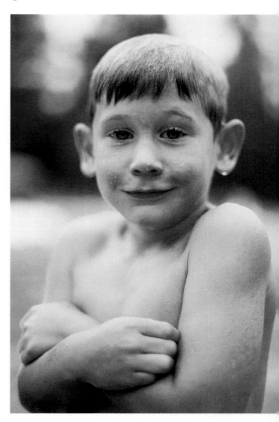
Muscles contract during shivering, raising body temperature.

Your body has different types of muscle.

Your body has three types of muscle. All three types of muscle tissue share certain characteristics. For example, each type of muscle contracts and relaxes. Yet all three muscle types have different functions and are found in different locations.

Skeletal Muscle

CALIFORNIA Focus

Researchers at the University of California at Los Angeles and NASA have been studying the loss of muscle mass in low-gravity environments. The researchers hope their work will help people who are recovering from long periods of limited mobility to regain muscle function and strength.

Skeletal muscle is a type of muscle tissue that is attached to bones in the body. Skeletal muscles help give the body its shape. This type of muscle allows voluntary movement—that is, movement you choose to make. The muscle is often called a voluntary muscle.

Skeletal muscle is made up of long fibers. These fibers are made up of many smaller bundles, as a piece of yarn is made up of strands of wool. These bundles are made up of cells that can have more than one nucleus. The fibers grow in response to use. There are two types of muscle fiber. One type allows your muscles to move slowly, but it can sustain the tension in your muscle for a long period of time. Another type of muscle fiber allows your muscles to move quickly, but it can sustain the tension for only a short period of time. Your skeletal muscles are made up of a combination of these two types of muscle fibers.

 Why are skeletal muscles called voluntary muscles?

Smooth Muscle

READING TiP

The word *voluntary* comes from a Latin word meaning "to choose" or "to wish." In the word *involuntary*, the prefix *in-* means "not." *Involuntary movement* refers to movement you do not control.

Smooth muscle is a type of muscle tissue that contracts without voluntary control. In other words, smooth muscle can work without your control. Smooth muscle is often called an involuntary muscle.

Smooth muscle contracts slowly. It is found in the walls of the stomach and intestines, where it helps push food through the digestive system. Smooth muscle is also found in blood vessels, where it helps regulate blood pressure. You will learn more about blood pressure and the circulatory system in Chapter 11.

Cardiac Muscle

Your heart is made of cardiac muscle. **Cardiac muscle** is a type of muscle tissue that moves without conscious control and is found only in the heart. Each cardiac muscle cell is branched. These cells connect in a chain. The chains form webs and layers that allow cardiac muscle cells to contract together and make the heart beat.

 Compare and contrast the three types of muscle: skeletal, smooth, and cardiac.

Muscle Tissue

The marchers in this band are using all three different types of muscle tissue.

250×

Cardiac muscle allows the hearts of the band members to pump blood as they march to the beat of the music.

150×

Smooth muscle in the air passages of the lungs helps the band members to breathe as they play their instruments.

360×

Skeletal muscle moves the legs of these marchers.

READING VISUALS   Which type of muscle tissue helps these band members hold their instruments?

Skeletal muscles, tendons, and joints allow bones to move.

Many skeletal muscles are attached to your bones by tendons. Tendons are made of extremely strong connective tissue and are connected to muscle on one end and bone on the other. As the fibers in a muscle contract, they shorten and pull the tendon. The tendon, which often passes over a joint, pulls on the bone and makes it move.

You can feel your muscles and tendons moving your bones. Place your left arm, with your palm facing up, in front of you on a table. Place the fingers of your right hand just above your left elbow. Bend your elbow and raise and lower your left arm. You are contracting your biceps. Can you feel the muscle pull on the tendon?

The dancers in the photograph below are using many muscles. Look at the diagrams to see how muscles, tendons, and joints work together. Notice that the muscles are connected to tendons, and these tendons are attached to bones. As the muscle contracts, or shortens, it pulls on the tendon and decreases the angle between the leg bones. The contraction of muscles produces movement—in the case of these dancers, very complicated movement.

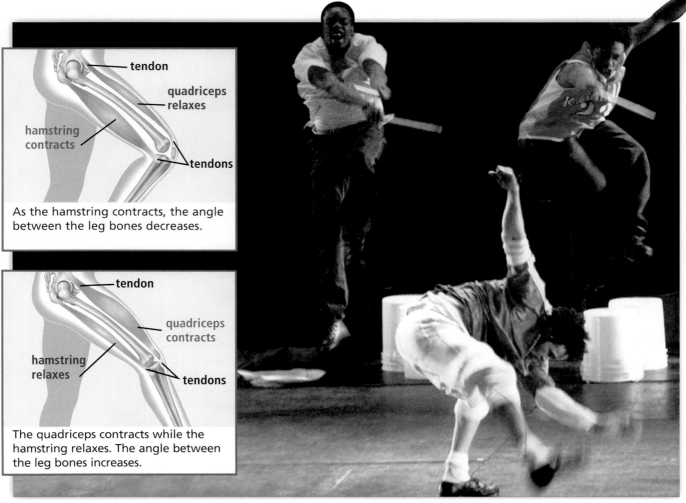

tendon

quadriceps relaxes

hamstring contracts

tendons

As the hamstring contracts, the angle between the leg bones decreases.

tendon

quadriceps contracts

hamstring relaxes

tendons

The quadriceps contracts while the hamstring relaxes. The angle between the leg bones increases.

INVESTIGATE Muscle Movement

How do muscles work together?

PROCEDURE

① Stand up straight and hold the water bottle in your hand. Slowly raise the bottle up to your shoulder. As you raise the bottle, feel both your biceps and triceps at the front and back of your arm.

② With the water bottle in your hand, bend over at the waist. Bend one arm so the upper part of your arm is parallel to the floor. Slowly raise the water bottle as shown in the picture. Keep your upper arm parallel to the floor as you lift. Feel both your biceps and triceps.

MATERIALS
• water bottle
For Challenge:
• cardboard
• string
• tape

TIME
10 minutes

WHAT DO YOU THINK?

• What happened to your biceps and triceps during each step?

• How do the muscles work together so that you can move your arm and lift objects?

CHALLENGE Using cardboard and string, make a model to show how your bones and muscles work together.

Muscles must work together in coordinated groups. One group of muscles moves the bones at a joint in one direction. Another group of muscles moves them in the opposite direction. When a muscle contracts and shortens, it exerts force. At the same time, its counterpart relaxes and lengthens, allowing the bones to move in the direction of the contracted muscle. Look at the diagrams on page 360 again. Which muscles work together to bend and extend your leg?

Now think about lifting your leg without bending your knee. Which muscles must contract in order to keep your knee from bending? Does it make a difference if you point your toes? Some of the muscles in your leg are working to stabilize the joints while other muscles are contracting to produce the controlled movement.

All of these movements depend on the musculoskeletal system—the muscular system and skeletal system—but especially on the brain. Signals from the brain cause the muscles to contract. The brain also regulates muscular coordination—that is, which muscles contract and for how long they stay contracted.

 What controls the musculoskeletal system?

Muscles grow and heal.

An infant's muscles cannot do very much. A newborn cannot lift and hold its head up. The neck muscles are not strong enough to support the baby's heavy head. For the first few months of life, a baby needs extra support until these muscles grow strong. The rest of the skeletal muscles also have to develop and strengthen. During infancy and childhood and into adolescence, humans develop muscular coordination and become more graceful in their movements.

Stretching the muscles before exercise can help prevent injury.

When you exercise regularly, your muscles may get bigger. However, the number of muscle fibers does not increase. Muscles increase in size and strength with some types of exercise, because the thickness of the muscle fibers and surrounding tissues increases.

You may have experienced sore muscles during or after exercise. During exercise, a chemical called lactic acid can build up in the muscles. This chemical can make your muscles cramp or ache. When the muscle cells do not receive enough oxygen for cellular respiration, they switch to fermentation for energy. Fermentation causes the buildup of lactic acid.

The muscle soreness you may feel a day or so after exercise can be caused by damage to the muscle fibers. The muscle fibers are sometimes stretched too much or even torn. Such injuries take time to heal, because the body must remove or repair any injured cells.

 CHECK YOUR READING What causes muscles to ache?

10.2 Review

KEY CONCEPTS

1. What are the three main functions of the muscular system? (7.5.c)
2. Make a rough outline of a human body and label where you could find each of the three types of muscles. (7.5.c)
3. Explain how muscles, joints, and tendons produce movement. (7.5.c)

CRITICAL THINKING

4. **Apply** You are exercising and you begin to feel hot. Explain what is happening in your muscles.
5. **Analyze** Describe what happens in your neck muscles when you nod your head.

CHALLENGE

6. **Infer** The digestive system breaks down food and transports materials. How are the short length and slow movement of smooth muscle tissues in the stomach and intestines related to the functions of these organs?

MATH TUTORIAL
CLASSZONE.COM
Click on Math Tutorial
for help with solving
proportions

Math 7.MR.2.8

SKILL: USING PROPORTIONS

Modeling an Arm

Suppose you wanted to make a scale model that shows where a muscle is attached to the bone in an arm. You know where the muscle is attached in a real arm. You can determine where it should be in your scale model by using a proportion. A proportion is an equation that shows that two ratios are equal.

Example

One person's forearm is about 20 cm long. Suppose the biceps muscle is attached to the forearm 5 cm from the elbow. Where should the muscle be attached on a scale model of the forearm that is 10 cm long?

(1) The ratio of the distance to the length of the forearm in your model must equal the same ratio in the real arm. Write out the information as a proportion.

$$\frac{\text{distance to muscle}}{\text{length of forearm}} = \frac{\text{distance to model muscle}}{\text{length of model forearm}}$$

(2) Substitute the known values into your equation.

$$\frac{5 \text{ cm}}{20 \text{ cm}} = \frac{\text{distance to model muscle}}{10 \text{ cm}}$$

(3) Cross-multiply and solve for the unknown quantity.

$$5 \text{ cm} \cdot 10 \text{ cm} = 20 \text{ cm} \cdot \text{distance to model muscle}$$

$$\frac{50 \text{ cm}^2}{20 \text{ cm}} = \text{distance to model muscle}$$

$$2.5 \text{ cm} = \text{distance to model muscle}$$

ANSWER The model muscle should be 2.5 cm from the model elbow.

Answer the following questions.

1. Keri's arm is 50 cm long. Her elbow is 30 cm from her shoulder. She makes a scale model of her arm that is 20 cm long. How far from the model shoulder should the model elbow be?

2. A sculptor wants to make a statue of a person who is 160 cm tall and whose foot is 25 cm long. If the final statue is 400 cm high, how long is the statue's foot?

CHALLENGE Do all people have the same proportions? Pick two lengths on your body, such as height and foot length, and see if the ratio is the same for other people in your class as it is for you.

Muscles exert forces.

CALIFORNIA
Content Standards

7.5.c Students know how bones and muscles work together to provide a structural framework for movement.

7.6.h Students know how to compare joints in the body (wrist, shoulder, thigh) with structures used in machines and simple devices (hinge, ball-and-socket, and sliding joints).

VOCABULARY

force p. 364
simple machine p. 367

BEFORE, you learned

- The limbs have a wide range of movement
- Groups of skeletal muscles move the limbs
- Skeletal muscles pull bones as they contract

NOW, you will learn

- How muscles exert forces to produce motion
- How the direction of a force can be changed
- How parts of the body can be compared to simple machines

EXPLORE Force and Motion (7.6.h)

How do tools move?

PROCEDURE

① Examine one of the tools closely. Notice where you push or pull and how each part moves.

② Sketch a diagram of the tool. Try to show all of the working parts. Add arrows and labels to show the direction of motion for each part.

WHAT DO YOU THINK?
- How many moving parts does the tool have?
- How do the parts work together?

MATERIALS
- various small tools

Muscles provide forces that produce motion.

Think about pulling a drawer open. When you pull on the drawer, you are applying a force. A **force** is a push or a pull. The forces exerted by your body come from your muscles. As your muscles contract, they pull on your bones and cause movement. The force needed to pull the drawer open came from the muscles in your arms.

If the drawer is stuck, you need to pull harder—that is, you need to use more force. Forces can change the motion of an object. You use forces all day to change the motion of objects around you. From picking up a backpack to throwing a ball to writing with a pencil, your daily activities require varying amounts of force.

 What is a force?

The strength, or size, of a force produced by muscles varies. Not everyone has the same muscle strength. You might be able to lift something that your friend cannot. Remember that your muscles are made of fibers. When the fibers contract and pull, they provide a force. More fibers or larger fibers can provide greater forces.

When you move, your muscles use energy to produce a force. But where does the energy to contract come from? Recall from Chapter 2 that cells get energy through the processes of cellular respiration and fermentation. The energy and chemicals for these processes come from the foods you eat.

The skeletal muscle fibers show the filaments that make contraction possible. (600×)

Forces act along the muscles.

Let one arm hang down relaxed at your side. Grasp the elbow lightly with your other hand. Your fingers should rest across the inside of your elbow. Now bend the arm that is hanging and raise it to your shoulder. You should be able to feel the tendon tighten and move as the muscle contracts. Your tendon and biceps pull, like a string, from your forearm to your shoulder. The direction of the force from your biceps acts along this line parallel to the direction of the contraction. The effect of a force depends on both the size and the direction of the force.

Forces from your muscles can be more or less effective. Think about your arm when it is hanging straight down again. When you first begin to move it toward your shoulder, the muscle is not that effective. Most of the force is stabilizing the joint and holding your arm bones together. At 90 degrees, when your arm is at a right angle, the muscle is more effective. At this point, more of the force is being used to move the arm. When muscles pull in the direction in which the joints move most easily, their effective force is greatest.

Suppose that you need to move a suitcase. If you pull the suitcase handle at an angle, you are not using all of the applied force to move the suitcase forward. The force is not being used effectively. If you instead pull the suitcase handle parallel to the direction in which you want the suitcase to move, most of the applied force is being used to move the suitcase forward.

When the biceps contracts, the tendons and muscles pull the forearm and the shoulder towards each other. The arm pivots about the elbow.

 CHECK YOUR READING How does the direction of a force help a muscle be more effective?

More than one force affects your body.

READING TIP

Gravity is the force that objects exert on each other because of their mass, such as the force that Earth exerts on your arm.

If you hold your arm out in front of you for a long time, your muscles will become tired even though there is no motion. One of the forces acting on the body at all times is weight. Weight is the downward force due to gravity. When you hold your arm out, you apply a force that acts against gravity.

If you hold a rock in your hand while your arm is extended out in front of you, your muscles will tire even faster. With the additional weight of the rock, your muscles must provide more force to keep your arm from moving.

Many forces affect your body's motion, and they often act in opposing directions. Remember, lack of motion does not mean lack of force. Consider what happens when two teams pull on opposite sides of a rope, as shown below. If both sides pull with the same force, as shown in the top photograph, the forces are balanced. Balanced forces have the same effect on an object as no force at all—there is no change in motion. The motion of the rope does not change, and the rope does not move. If one side pulls harder than the other, as shown in the bottom photograph, the forces are unbalanced, and the rope moves toward the stronger team.

If both teams pull with equal forces in opposite directions, the two forces cancel each other. The rope stays at rest, as if no force were acting on it.

balanced forces

If one team pulls with more force than the other team, the forces do not cancel each other. The total force on the rope is the difference between the greater force in one direction and the smaller force in the other direction. The total force on the rope is unbalanced, and the rope moves.

unbalanced forces

INVESTIGATE Changing Force

How can you change the direction of a force?

PROCEDURE

1. Use the 10 cm string to attach the pulley to the ring on the ring stand.

2. Tie one end of the 40 cm string to the 100 g mass. Make a small loop on the other end of the string.

3. Attach the spring scale to the string using the loop. Lift the mass and measure and record the weight of the mass in newtons.

4. Remove the spring scale. Thread the looped end of the string over the pulley as shown. Attach the spring scale to the loop, and pull until the mass is raised. Measure and record the force used to lift the mass.

WHAT DO YOU THINK?

- How does the weight of the mass compare with the force used to raise it?
- What does the pulley do to the force you applied to the string? Why is a pulley useful?

CHALLENGE Let the mass hang over the edge of a table and pull the string parallel along the table to lift the mass. What force do you need?

MATERIALS
- 2 pieces of string (10 cm, 40 cm)
- ring stand with ring
- pulley
- 100 g mass
- spring scale

TIME
20 minutes

Some body parts act like simple machines.

Because there is a limit to how much force your muscles can apply, you often want to find a way to turn a small force into a larger one. Suppose you want to move a large box up a flight of stairs. The box is too heavy to carry up the stairs. How can you move the box?

With the help of a simple machine, you can change the amount of force you need to move it. You could build a ramp and push the box up the ramp. Less force is needed to push the box than to lift it. If the ramp were very long, even less force would be needed because the force would be applied over a greater distance. The ramp is an example of an inclined plane, which is one type of simple machine. A **simple machine** is one of six devices on which all other mechanical machines are based. The six simple machines are the pulley, lever, screw, wheel and axle, wedge, and inclined plane.

Forces can transfer energy from one object to another. In science, the amount of energy that you transfer to an object when you move it is called work. Work is a transfer of energy. You do work on an object only if you exert a force on the object to move it. If you lift a box, you do work on it. Holding the box, or holding a rock in your hand, is not doing work even though your muscles may become tired.

All machines help people do work. However, machines don't change the total amount of work that is required. With the help of a machine, you can use less force over a longer distance to perform the same amount of work. In other words, there is a tradeoff between force and distance. Think about the long ramp. Although you use less force to move the box up the ramp, you have to move it over a longer distance.

Simple machines can be used to model some of the actions of muscles and joints in the body. We usually have to use several simple machines together in order to model the way that limbs work. Physical models of biological systems are not perfect, of course, but they can be a useful way to describe and understand how complex systems interact. The three simple machines that can model movement in the body are pulleys, inclined planes, and levers.

Pulleys

Sometimes you want to change the direction of force. Think of raising a flag on a flagpole. You pull down on the rope, and the flag moves up. There is a fixed pulley at the top, meaning that the pulley is attached to something that holds it steady. You use the pulley to change the direction in which you apply force to raise the object. You haven't changed the distance the flag moves or the force needed to move it. The distance you pull the rope down is the same distance the flag moves upward. The force pulling the flag upward is equal to your downward force. The fixed pulley allows you to take advantage of the downward pull of your weight to move a load upward.

Your muscles, tendons, and joints sometimes work together in a similar way. Recall that muscles in the limbs are attached to two or more bones by tendons. Most of the skeletal muscles are attached to one end of a bone, stretch across a joint, and are attached to another bone. When the muscle passes over a joint, the joint can act as a fixed pulley, changing the direction over which the force is applied. Think of your shoulder as an example. Muscles crisscross the shoulder joint, attaching to the bones at many points and allowing many directions of motion.

Muscles exert force by contracting—pulling their two ends together. Some muscles pull across more than one joint. This happens, for example, at the elbow, where the upper arm bone meets the two lower arm bones. The biceps is attached to the upper arm bone and to the lower arm bones. Bands of connective tissue, as well as other muscles and tendons, can help change the direction in which a muscle pulls.

Pulley

Wrists and hands also are good examples of body parts that act like pulleys. Think about how strong and flexible hands are. Long ligaments and tendons allow the fingers to be moved by muscles far away in the forearm. Wiggle the fingers of your left hand while holding your forearm with your right hand. You should be able to feel the muscles in the forearm contracting.

Inclined Planes

You already read that an inclined plane, or ramp, is a simple machine that decreases the force required to move a heavy object. A gradual incline on a steep hill, such as the zigzag shown in the photograph, decreases the effective weight of a car. The car's engine and brakes don't need to work as hard. Many vehicles couldn't climb a road built straight to the top of a steep hill.

Gliding joints, found in the feet and wrists, have slightly slanted or inclined surfaces where the bones meet. At gliding joints, these nearly flat bone surfaces glide over each other, allowing only limited motion.

Lombard Street in San Francisco is an inclined plane. The road down is longer but less steep than the hill.

Levers

The action of a muscle pulling on a bone can be compared to a simple machine called a lever. A lever is a solid bar, or rod, that moves around a fixed point. The fixed point is called a fulcrum. An example of a lever is a crowbar.

In the human body, muscles supply the force needed to move bones. Scientists can model forces in the limbs by thinking of each bone as a rod and each joint as a fulcrum. You will learn more about how the bones operate as levers in the next section.

10.3 Review

KEY CONCEPTS

1. How do muscles provide forces for the body? (7.5.c)
2. Where and how does a force act when a muscle contracts? (7.5.c)
3. Describe a simple machine and how it can model a part of the body. (7.6.h)

CRITICAL THINKING

4. **Analyze** Give an example of a situation in which forces are balanced.
5. **Synthesize** How do gliding joints resemble inclined planes?

CHALLENGE

6. Suppose you flex your arm so that your biceps muscle contracts. How does this relate to balanced forces?

PHYSICAL SCIENCE AND LIFE SCIENCE

A Running Machine

Marlon Shirley lost his left foot due to an accident at the age of five. He is a champion sprinter who achieved his running records while using a prosthesis (prahs-THEE-sihs), or a device used to replace a body part. Like his right leg and foot, his prosthesis is a combination of simple machines that convert the energy from muscles in his body to move him forward. The mechanical system is designed to match the forces of his right leg.

> **7.6.i** Students know how levers confer mechanical advantage and how application of this principle applies to the musculoskeletal system.

Legs as Levers

Compare Marlon Shirley's prosthesis with his right leg. Both have long rods—one made of bone and the other of metal—that provide a strong frame. These rods act as levers. At the knee and ankle, movable joints act as fulcrums for these levers to transfer energy between the runner's body and the ground.

How Does It Work?

1. As the foot—real or artificial—strikes the ground, the leg stops moving forward and downward and absorbs the energy of the change in motion. The joints in the ankle and knee act as fulcrums as the levers transfer the energy to the muscle in the upper leg. This muscle acts like a spring to store the energy.

2. When the runner begins the next step, the energy is transferred back into the leg from the upper leg muscle. The levers in the leg convert the energy into forward motion of the runner's body.

   The people who design prosthetic legs study the natural motion of a runner to learn exactly how energy is distributed and converted to motion so that they can build an artificial leg that works well with the real leg.

EXPLORE

1. **VISUALIZE** Run partway across a room, paying close attention to the position of one of your ankles and knees as you move. Determine where the fulcrum is in the lever formed by your lower leg.

2. **CHALLENGE** Use the library or the Internet to learn more about mechanical legs used in robots that walk. How do the leg motions of these robots resemble your walking motions? How are they different?

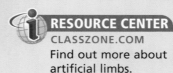 **RESOURCE CENTER**
CLASSZONE.COM
Find out more about artificial limbs.

10.4 Bones and joints act as levers.

CALIFORNIA
Content Standard

7.6.i Students know how levers confer mechanical advantage and how application of this principle applies to the musculoskeletal system.

BEFORE, you learned

- Some muscles exert pulling forces on bones
- Simple machines can change the way a force is applied
- How parts of the body act as simple machines

NOW, you will learn

- About levers in the human body
- How to find the mechanical advantage of a lever
- About three classes of levers

VOCABULARY

lever p. 372
fulcrum p. 372
input force p. 373
output force p. 373
mechanical advantage p. 374

EXPLORE Changing Forces

How can you change a force?

PROCEDURE

1. Lay one pencil on a flat surface. Place the other pencil on top of the first pencil and perpendicular to it, as shown. Place the book on one end of the top pencil.

2. Push down on the free end of the top pencil to raise the book.

3. Change the position of the bottom pencil so that it is closer to the book and repeat step 2. Then move the bottom pencil closer to the end of the pencil you are pushing on and repeat step 2.

WHAT DO YOU THINK?

- How did changing the position of the bottom pencil affect the amount of force you needed to lift the book?
- At which position is it easiest to lift the book? most difficult?

MATERIALS
- 2 pencils
- small book

The body uses levers.

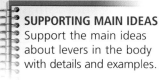

SUPPORTING MAIN IDEAS
Support the main ideas about levers in the body with details and examples.

Imagine that you want to pick up a backpack that is resting on the floor at your feet. It's heavy, but you can do it. Now imagine that a classmate challenges you to lift the same backpack from half a meter away without stepping closer. Will it be harder or easier?

When you lift something close to your body, your shoulder muscles apply less force than when you lift something with your arm stretched out. You may have also noticed that a small movement from your muscles moves the end of your arm a large distance. This is because your arm acts like a lever.

Levers can change the effects of a force.

RESOURCE CENTER
CLASSZONE.COM

Learn more about levers in the body.

Recall that a **lever** is a rod that can pivot, or turn, around a fixed point. You can think of a bone as a rod and a joint as the pivot point. When you bend your arm at the elbow, you are pivoting your forearm around the joint in your elbow. Your arm acts as a lever. Most of the time, several levers work together to move limbs. Limbs are a combination of levers. Picture a person running, or throwing a ball. The runner and the pitcher are using levers that are made of bones and joints and powered by muscles.

Fulcrum

A **fulcrum** is the fixed point around which the rod of a lever turns. In other words, the fulcrum is a lever's pivot point. The fulcrum can be located anywhere along the lever. For instance, if the fulcrum is in the middle of the lever, both ends of the lever can move. If the fulcrum is at the end of the lever, then that end is fixed and the other end of the lever can move.

In a stapler, the fulcrum is at the hinge. If you want to staple just two sheets of paper together, you can probably do it by pushing down on the middle of the stapler. But that takes more force than pressing down on the open end of the stapler. Now imagine stapling five or six sheets together. The stapler probably won't work if you press down on the middle. Pressing the open end of the stapler—farther from the fulcrum—allows you to use less force.

When a force is farther from the fulcrum, it can turn the lever more effectively. The elbow is the fulcrum for the lever of the forearm. Rest your elbow on the edge of your desk or table, and hang a weight from your wrist. Without lifting your elbow from the table, raise your forearm. Now position the weight closer to your elbow and raise your forearm again. Where was the weight more effective at pulling your arm down? When the weight was suspended from your wrist—farther from the fulcrum—it was harder to lift. For both the stapler and the hanging weight, the force is more effective when it is farther from the fulcrum.

 CHECK YOUR READING What is a lever?

The trebuchet, a medieval weapon, is based on the lever. Weights are attached on one end, and then the arm is pulled down and loaded. When the weights drop, the load flies a great distance.

lever

fulcrum

weights

Input Force and Output Force

Input force is the force exerted on a machine. When you press on one end of a lever, you are applying an input force. Often the input force is called the effort force, because the effort you apply to use the machine produces the input force.

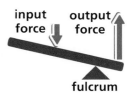

Output force is the force that a machine exerts on an object. The output force often acts on an object that the machine moves. The weight of this object is called the load. Generally, the output force is equal to the load. The output force is also called the resistance force because it resists, or acts against, the load. The load causes the lever to pivot in one direction. The output force acts to balance the load.

The input force on a body limb comes from muscles pulling on bone. Contraction of the biceps exerts an input force on the lever of the forearm. The distance from a fulcrum to a force is called the lever arm. Each lever has a lever arm defined for the input force and another defined for the output force. In the case of your forearm, the lever arm is very short, just a few centimeters from the elbow. That's where your biceps muscle is attached to the bones of your forearm.

Changing Force Size and Movement Distance

People often use machines to reduce the amount of force they need to move an object. A lever can change a small input force into a large output force. A lever can also change the direction of a force. For example, a person trying to lift a heavy rock might put the tip of a shovel under the rock, and then use the handle of the shovel as a lever. The person's small downward force on the shovel handle is changed into a large upward force on the rock. The farther the input force is from the fulcrum, the greater the output force will be.

Reducing the amount of force comes with a price, however. A person lifting a large rock with a shovel must push the handle of the shovel down a large distance to raise the rock only a small distance. The farther away from the fulcrum a load is, the more it will move when a force is applied to the lever.

In contrast, some levers, including many of the levers found in the body, change a large input force into a small output force. You trade off having a larger force for having a larger range of motion. Muscles can move parts of your body over a large distance by applying a larger force that moves a short distance. The force those body parts can apply to other objects is smaller than the force of the muscle.

A rake is a machine that changes a large force over a short distance to a smaller force over a larger distance.

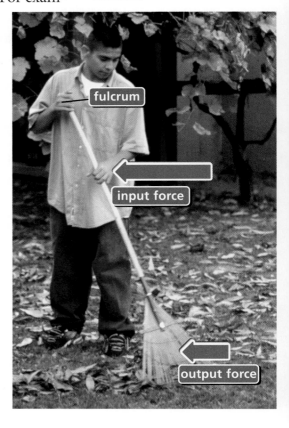

Different lever arrangements serve different purposes.

Every lever consists of a rod and fulcrum. Where the load is placed, where the input force is applied, and where the fulcrum is placed can change from lever to lever. A lever used to pry up a rock has a different arrangement from the lever formed by your arm.

Mechanical Advantage

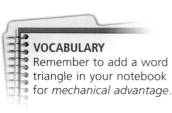

VOCABULARY
Remember to add a word triangle in your notebook for *mechanical advantage*.

Some levers are used to increase the input force. Suppose you are trying to lift a book using two pencils—one as the lever, and one as the fulcrum. What arrangement would make it easiest for you? If you experiment, you will find that the closer the book is to the fulcrum, the less force you have to use. You will also find that the farther from the fulcrum you push, the less force you need. By placing the load close to the fulcrum and the input force far from the fulcrum, you give yourself the largest advantage.

A machine's **mechanical advantage** is the output force divided by the input force. When the input force and output force are equal, the mechanical advantage is 1. When the output force is greater than the input force, the mechanical advantage is greater than 1. A shovel used to pry up a rock has a mechanical advantage that is greater than 1. Some machines have a mechanical advantage that is less than 1. These machines have an output force that is less than the input force. Many of the levers in your body have a mechanical advantage that is less than 1. The body gives up mechanical advantage in exchange for speed and range of motion.

The mechanical advantage of a lever depends on the lever arms. The input lever arm is the distance between the input force and the fulcrum (d_{in}). The output lever arm is the distance between the output force and the fulcrum (d_{out}). The input and output forces are related to these distances by the following formula:

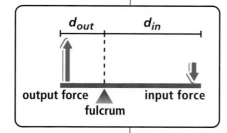

$$\frac{\text{Output Force}}{\text{Input Force}} = \frac{\text{Input Lever Arm}}{\text{Output Lever Arm}}$$

$$\frac{F_{out}}{F_{in}} = \frac{d_{in}}{d_{out}}$$

In this formula, F_{out} stands for the output force, F_{in} stands for the input force, d_{in} stands for the input lever arm (distance from the input force to the fulcrum), and d_{out} stands for the output lever arm (distance from the output force to the fulcrum). The standard unit of force is the newton (N).

Calculating Lever Ratios

▶ **Sample Problem**

A ballet dancer balances on her toes. If the 500 N output force is 20 cm from the ankle joint (the fulcrum), what is the input force from her muscles if it is applied 5 cm from the ankle joint?

What do you know?   Output force = 500 N, output lever arm = 20 cm, input lever arm = 5 cm

What do you want to find out?   Input force

Write the formula: $\dfrac{F_{out}}{F_{in}} = \dfrac{d_{in}}{d_{out}}$

Rearrange the formula: $F_{in} = F_{out} \cdot \dfrac{d_{out}}{d_{in}}$

Substitute into the formula: $F_{in} = 500\text{ N} \cdot \dfrac{20\text{ cm}}{5\text{ cm}}$

Calculate and simplify: $F_{in} = 500\text{ N} \cdot 4 = 200\text{ N}$

Answer: $F_{in} = 200\text{ N}$

▶ **Practice the Math**

1. The output force equals 275 N, d_{out} equals 32 cm, and d_{in} equals 8 cm. What is the input force?
2. The input force equals 150 N, d_{in} equals 10 cm, and d_{out} equals 10 cm. What is the output force?

The formula states the principles of levers in mathematical terms. The closer a force is to a fulcrum, the less effective it is at causing the lever to move. This principle applies to both the load and the input force. A load that is closer to the fulcrum requires less force to move, and a load that is farther from the fulcrum requires more force to move. An input force that is applied close to the fulcrum cannot move as large a load as can an input force applied farther from the fulcrum. If you increase d_{in} you increase the ratio of the output force to the input force. If you increase d_{out} you decrease the ratio of the output force to the input force.

○▼ **REMINDER**

A ratio is the comparison of two numbers. A ratio can be expressed as a fraction.

Think about the example of lifting a backpack. What happens when you lift the backpack from a distance? When the backpack is far away, you need to lift it with your arm straight out. The fulcrum is at your shoulder. When the backpack is closer, you can lift it with your forearm. The fulcrum is at your elbow. In this case, the distance from the output force to the fulcrum (d_{out}) is smaller than when you lift with your arm out. You need less force from your muscles to lift the backpack.

 In a lever, what can you change to use less force?

Classes of Levers

SIMULATION
CLASSZONE.COM

Explore how a lever works.

Just as a fulcrum can be located at different places on a lever, so can the input and output forces. On some levers, such as a seesaw, the input force is on the opposite side of the fulcrum from the output force. On other levers, such as your leg, the input and output forces are on the same side of the fulcrum. Levers are classified as three different types, depending on the arrangement of the output force, the input force, and the fulcrum.

- On first-class levers, the fulcrum is between the input and output forces.
- On second-class levers, the output force is between the fulcrum and the input force.
- On third-class levers, the input force is between the fulcrum and the output force. Third-class levers always decrease the output force in favor of speed or distance.

Your arm is a third-class lever. The fulcrum is your elbow joint, and the input force is applied where your biceps is attached to the bones of your forearm. The output force acts against the weight of your arm to move it. Your arms, hands, legs, and feet can move remarkably fast in a number of directions because they act as third-class levers.

READING TiP

The lengths of the arrows in the diagram represent the size of the force.

Levers

Levers can be classified according to where the fulcrum is.

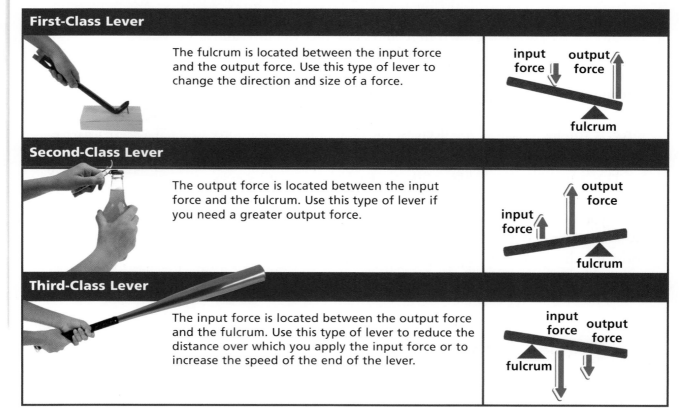

First-Class Lever

The fulcrum is located between the input force and the output force. Use this type of lever to change the direction and size of a force.

input force   output force   fulcrum

Second-Class Lever

The output force is located between the input force and the fulcrum. Use this type of lever if you need a greater output force.

output force   input force   fulcrum

Third-Class Lever

The input force is located between the output force and the fulcrum. Use this type of lever to reduce the distance over which you apply the input force or to increase the speed of the end of the lever.

input force   output force   fulcrum

The body's levers can be used effectively.

As you have read, the body contains many levers. Many of the bones and joints in your arms, legs, hands, and feet act as levers. But so do your hips and shoulders, and even your back. Using a lever puts stress on both the lever and the fulcrum—the bone and the joint. You can use your knowledge of levers to protect your body as well as to make tasks easier or more effective.

You already know that it's easier to lift a heavy object if it is close to your body. Lifting can strain your muscles. Bending over causes your back to become a lever, and puts stress on your spine. Although your back can act as a lever, it has to do so by contracting its muscles and holding the vertebrae tightly together. Lifting with your legs, however, uses the leg bones as levers. The strong muscles in your thighs and calves provide the input force.

Your hand and arm can act as a lever in different ways, depending on the motions you make. Your hand is a lever with the fulcrum at the wrist. Your forearm is a lever with a fulcrum at the elbow. Your upper arm is a lever with a fulcrum at the shoulder. When you swing a baseball bat or use a hockey stick, you are using all these levers in both arms. In general, you shorten the output lever arms and use your strongest muscles when you need a large output force. Of course, you can't shorten your bones. But you can use your body to combine the effects of different levers, or reduce the output lever arm. Athletes try to achieve the best combination of power and speed, using their entire bodies.

COMPARE How is the lever made by the bat and the hand similar to the lever made of the batter's arm and his elbow?

 Describe some of the levers in the body.

10.4 Review

KEY CONCEPTS

1. Describe a lever found in the human body. Where is the fulcrum? (7.6.h)

2. What is mechanical advantage? (7.6.i)

3. Describe the arrangement of the input force, the output force, and the fulcrum in a third-class lever. (7.6.h)

CRITICAL THINKING

4. **Synthesize** Explain how the mechanical advantage of a lever depends on the input lever arm (d_{in}) and the output lever arm (d_{out}).

5. **Infer** What is the mechanical advantage of a lever if the input force is twice the output force?

CHALLENGE

6. **Analyze** Nod your head up and down. How is your skull like a lever? Where is the fulcrum?

Using Levers

OVERVIEW AND PURPOSE Have you used a lever recently? What about this week? Many tools—shovel, broom, wheelbarrow, scissors—act as levers. People use levers to gain a mechanical advantage. They also use levers to move an object in a different direction or faster than they could without the lever. In this investigation you will

- observe how first-, second-, and third-class levers work to move objects and produce mechanical advantages
- find out which class of lever best completes an assigned task

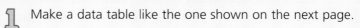

Problem

Which class of lever is best suited to each of three specific tasks?

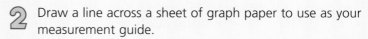

Procedure

1. Make a data table like the one shown on the next page.

2. Draw a line across a sheet of graph paper to use as your measurement guide.

3. You will use the lever to try to accomplish three tasks. For each task, you must follow these rules:

   - push with only one finger *away* from yourself
   - keep your hand in one position on the table
   - keep the pencil eraser in one position

The three tasks are:

Task A: Move a 10 g object a distance of 7 cm away from you.
Task B: Move a 50 g object a distance of 5 cm toward you.
Task C: Move a 500 g object a distance of 3 cm away from you.

MATERIALS
- pencil
- ruler with slots
- graph paper
- 10 g object
- 50 g object
- 500 g object

7.6.h, 7.6.i, 7.7.d

First-Class Lever

Second-Class Lever

Content Standard

⬗ **7.6.i** Students know how levers confer mechanical advantage and how application of this principle applies to the musculoskeletal system.

Investigation Standard

7.7.d Students will construct scale models, maps, and appropriately labeled diagrams to communicate scientific knowledge (e.g. motion of Earth's plates and cell structures).

4 Line up the ruler with your measurement guide. Place the pencil as shown to make a first-class lever.

5 Attempt each task using the first-class lever. Have your partner hold the pencil.

6 Supply the input force by extending one finger to push the ruler away from you at the input point. Record how far this point moved from the line.

7 Have your partner repeat steps 5–7 using a second-class lever. Then repeat steps 5–7 with a third-class lever.

▶ Observe and Analyze
Write It Up

1. **RECORD** Complete your data table and record all of your measurements.

2. **IDENTIFY** Draw the three levers. Label the fulcrum, input point, and output point for each.

3. **ANALYZE** Which class of lever was best for changing the direction of the force?

4. **ANALYZE** Which lever was the best for moving the 500 g object?

5. **ANALYZE** Which lever could move the object the greatest distance?

▶ Conclude
Write It Up

1. **INFER** Explain how you could have achieved a greater mechanical advantage from the first-class lever in your experiment.

2. **INFER** Explain how you can change your second-class lever to increase the mechanical advantage.

3. **APPLY** Name a part of your body that uses a third-class lever. How does it help you?

▶ INVESTIGATE Further

CHALLENGE Calculate the mechanical advantage of each class of lever you used during your experiment. The formula for calculating the mechanical advantage is

$$\text{Mechanical advantage} = \frac{\text{Input Lever Arm}}{\text{Output Lever Arm}}$$

Third-Class Lever

Using Levers

Table 1. Input Distance

Class of Lever	Task A Distance (cm)	Task B Distance (cm)	Task C Distance (cm)
First class			
Second class			
Third class			

10 Chapter Review

Muscles and bones provide forces and levers to move the human body.

CONTENT REVIEW
CLASSZONE.COM

KEY CONCEPTS SUMMARY

1 The skeletal system provides support and protection.

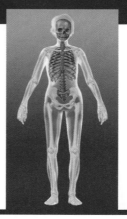

Bones are living tissue. The skeleton is the body's framework and has two main divisions, the **axial skeleton** and the **appendicular skeleton**. Bones come together at joints.

VOCABULARY
skeletal system p. 349
axial skeleton p. 350
appendicular skeleton p. 350
joint p. 353
cartilage p. 353

2 The muscular system makes movement possible.

Type of Muscle	Function
skeletal muscle, voluntary	moves bones, maintains posture and body temperature
smooth muscle, involuntary	moves internal organs, such as the intestines
cardiac muscle, involuntary	pumps blood throughout the body

VOCABULARY
muscular system p. 357
skeletal muscle p. 358
smooth muscle p. 358
cardiac muscle p. 358

3 Muscles exert forces.

- Muscles provide forces that produce motion.
- Parts of the body act as simple machines.

VOCABULARY
force p. 364
simple machine p. 367

4 Bones and joints act as levers.

- A bone acts as a lever with a joint as its fulcrum.
- Levers can be arranged in different ways.

VOCABULARY
lever p. 372
fulcrum p. 372
input force p. 373
output force p. 373
mechanical advantage p. 374

Reviewing Vocabulary

In one or two sentences, describe how the vocabulary terms in each of the following pairs are related. Underline each vocabulary term in your answer.

1. axial skeleton, appendicular skeleton

2. input force, output force

3. skeletal muscle, smooth muscle

4. force, balanced forces

5. lever, fulcrum

Reviewing Key Concepts

Multiple Choice *Choose the letter of the best answer.*

6. Cardiac muscle is found in the (7.5.c)
  a. heart
  b. stomach
  c. intestines
  d. arms and legs

7. The stomach is partly made up of (7.5.c)
  a. cardiac muscle
  b. skeletal muscle
  c. smooth muscle
  d. voluntary muscle

8. Bone cells lie within a network made of (7.5.c)
  a. tendons
  b. calcium
  c. marrow
  d. joints

9. The red bone marrow produces (7.5.c)
  a. spongy bone
  b. red blood cells
  c. compact bone
  d. calcium

10. Which bones are part of the axial skeleton? (7.5.c)
  a. skull, shoulder blades, arm bones
  b. skull, spinal column, leg bones
  c. shoulder blades, spinal column, hip bones
  d. skull, spinal column, ribs

11. Bones of the skeleton connect to each other at (7.6.h)
  a. tendons
  b. ligaments
  c. joints
  d. muscles

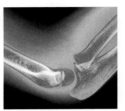

12. How do muscles contribute to homeostasis? (7.5.c)
  a. They keep parts of the body together.
  b. They control the amount of water in the body.
  c. They help the body move.
  d. They produce heat when they contract.

13. To calculate mechanical advantage, you need to know (7.6.i)
  a. time and energy
  b. input force and output force
  c. distance and work
  d. size and direction of a force

14. The rod of a lever turns around a (7.5.c)
  a. fixed point called a fulcrum
  b. solid bar that rotates
  c. wheel attached to an axle
  d. sloping surface called an inclined plane

Short Answer *Write a short answer to each question.*

15. What is the difference between spongy bone and compact bone? (7.5.c)

16. Hold the upper part of one arm between your elbow and shoulder with your opposite hand. Feel the muscles there. What happens to those muscles as you bend your arm? (7.5.c)

17. Name one part of the body that acts as a lever and explain how it works. (7.6.i)

Thinking Critically

18. **APPLY** You are using a board to pry a large rock out of the ground when the board suddenly breaks in the middle. You pick up half of the board and use it to continue prying up the rock. The fulcrum stays in the same position. How has the mechanical advantage of the board changed? (7.6.i)

19. **EXPLAIN** How do your muscles exert forces to produce movement in the body? (7.5.c)

20. **SUMMARIZE** Describe three important functions of the skeleton. (7.5.c)

Use the diagram below to answer the next two questions.

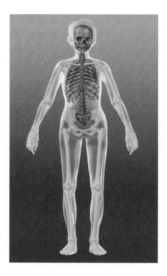

21. **SYNTHESIZE** Identify the types of joints that hold together the bones of the skull. How do these types of joints relate to the function of the skull? (7.6.h)

22. **SYNTHESIZE** Scientists use two main divisions to describe the human skeleton. Which division do the arms and legs belong to? How do the joints that connect the arms to the shoulders and the legs to the hips relate to the function of this division? (7.5.c)

23. **COMPARE AND CONTRAST** How is the skeletal system of your body like the framework of a house or building? How is it different? (7.5.c)

24. **CONNECT** A clamshell is made of a calcium compound. The hard material provides protection to the soft body of the clam. The material is also light-weight. Describe three ways in which the human skeleton is similar to a clamshell. What is one important way in which it is different? (7.5.c)

25. **APPLY** The joints in the human body can be described as allowing three types of movement. Relate these three types of movement to the action of brushing your teeth. (7.6.h)

26. **COMPARE AND CONTRAST** When you stand, the muscles in your legs help keep you balanced. Some of the muscles along the front and back of your leg bones contract. How does this differ from how the muscles behave when you start to walk? (7.5.c)

27. **INFER** Muscles are tissues that are made up of many muscle fibers. A muscle fiber can either be relaxed or contracted. Some movements require very little effort, such as picking up a piece of paper. Others require a lot of effort, such as picking up a book bag. How do you think a muscle produces the effort needed for a small task compared with a big task? (7.5.c)

the BIG idea

28. **INFER** Look again at the photograph on pages 346–347. Now that you have finished the chapter, how would you change or add details to your answer to the question on the photograph? (7.5.c)

29. **SUMMARIZE** Write a paragraph explaining how skeletal muscles, bones, and joints work together to allow the body to move and be flexible. Underline the terms in your paragraph. (7.5.c)

UNIT PROJECTS

Check your schedule for your unit project. How are you doing? Be sure you've placed data or notes from your research in your project folder.

Interpreting Diagrams

7.6.i

In the human body, a muscle supplies the effort needed to move a bone—the lever rod. The joint is the fulcrum, and the load is the weight of the body part being moved. There are three types of levers, which are classified according to the position of the fulcrum, the effort, and the load.

Read the text and study the diagrams, and then choose the best answer for the questions that follow.

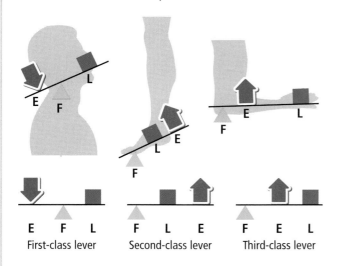

E F L	F L E	F E L
First-class lever	Second-class lever	Third-class lever

1. In a first-class lever,

   a. the load is at the end of the lever opposite the fulcrum

   b. the load is between the effort and the fulcrum

   c. the fulcrum is between the load and the effort

   d. the effort and load are on the same side

2. What is true of all levers?

   a. The fulcrum must be located at the center.

   b. The force of the load and the effort point in the same direction.

   c. The load and the effort are on the same side of the fulcrum.

   d. The lever exerts a force in the opposite direction of the load.

3. What structure in the human body can act as a fulcrum?

   a. joint   **c.** muscle

   b. bone   **d.** ligament

4. The main point of the diagram on this page is to show

   a. why bones are strong

   b. three classes of levers and how they are applied

   c. where to apply a force

   d. the forces involved in moving parts of the body

Extended Response

Use the diagrams above and terms from the word box to answer the next two questions. Underline each term you use in your answers.

fulcrum	load	effort	rod
bone	muscle	joint	

5. Suppose you had a heavy box to lift. Your first thought might be to bend over, stretch out your arms, and grab the box. Your body would be acting as a simple machine. Identify the type of lever this would be and the parts of this machine.

6. A doctor would advise you not to lift a heavy object, such as a box, simply by bending over and picking it up. That action puts too much strain on your back. It is better to bend your knees, hold the box close to your body, and then lift. How does this way of lifting change how you are using your body?

CHAPTER 11

Fluids, Pressure, and Circulation

the BIG idea

The body uses fluid pressure in many ways.

Key Concepts

SECTION

1 **Fluids spread force over an area.**
Learn about fluids and how to calculate pressure.

SECTION

2 **The heart produces blood pressure.**
Learn about blood pressure and circulation.

SECTION

3 **Fluid pressure affects the body in different ways.**
Learn about fluids in the eye, the ear, and other parts of your body.

 California ClassZone

CLASSZONE.COM

Chapter 11 online resources: Content Review, two Visualizations, three Resource Centers, Math Tutorial, and Test Practice

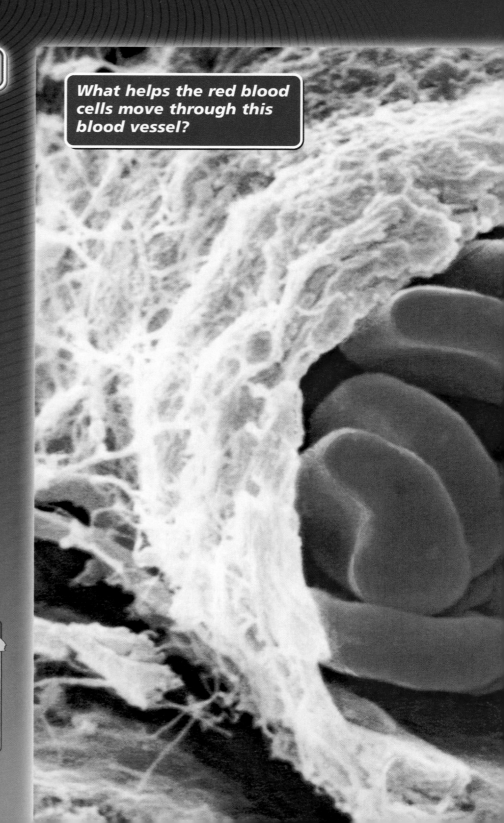

What helps the red blood cells move through this blood vessel?

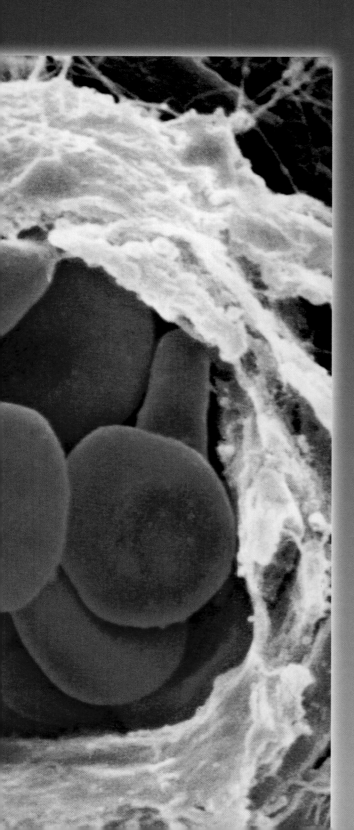

EXPLORE (the BIG idea)

Blood Pressure

> 7.6.j Students know that contractions of the heart generate blood pressure and that heart valves prevent backflow of blood in the circulatory system.

Fill a small, round balloon halfway full with air. Tie off the end. Gently squeeze the balloon in your hand. Observe any changes. Release the pressure and observe any changes. Squeeze again.

Observe and Think
As you apply pressure, what happens to the air in the balloon? What happens as you release the pressure?

Internet Activity: Heart Pumping

> 7.6.j Students know that contractions of the heart generate blood pressure and that heart valves prevent backflow of blood in the circulatory system.

Go to **ClassZone.com** to learn about how the heart pumps blood. See how the valves open and close as the different chambers contract. Notice how pressure in one direction opens a valve, but pressure in the other direction helps push the valve closed.

Observe and Think
Which valves open when the atria contract? when the ventricles contract?

NSTA
scilinks.org
SCiLINKS

Blood Pressure **Code: MDL074**

Getting Ready to Learn

CONCEPT REVIEW

- Cells make up tissues, which make up organs, which make up organ systems.
- The circulatory system transports materials.
- Organ systems work together.

VOCABULARY REVIEW

tissue, p. 272

organ, p. 272

force, p. 364

CONTENT REVIEW
CLASSZONE.COM

Review concepts and vocabulary.

TAKING NOTES

CHOOSE YOUR OWN STRATEGY

Record the main ideas and other notes using one or more of the strategies from earlier chapters—**main idea webs, outlines,** or **supporting main ideas.** You can also use other note-taking strategies that you might already know.

VOCABULARY STRATEGY

Place each vocabulary term at the center of a **description wheel diagram.** Write some words describing it on the spokes.

See the Note-Taking Handbook on pages R45–R51.

SCIENCE NOTEBOOK

Main Idea Web

Outline

I. Main idea
    A. Supporting idea
        1. Detail
        2. Detail
    B. Supporting idea

Supporting Main Ideas

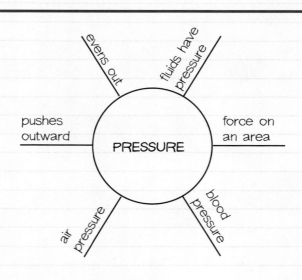

11.1 Fluids spread force over an area.

CALIFORNIA
Content Standards

7.5.b Students know organ systems function because of the contributions of individual organs, tissues, and cells. The failure of any part can affect the entire system.

Background for

7.6.j Students know that contractions of the heart generate blood pressure and that heart valves prevent backflow of blood in the circulatory system.

BEFORE, you learned

- A force is a push or a pull
- Forces can produce or change movement
- Muscles exert forces

NOW, you will learn

- What fluids are
- How to calculate pressure
- About the effects of pressure in fluids

VOCABULARY

fluid p. 387
pressure p. 388

THINK ABOUT

Can gases flow?

You have seen water flow, but can a gas flow? The answer is yes, but it is often hard to see. In the photograph, a cold gas is being poured. Water droplets form a mist that shows where the cold gas is. Perhaps you have seen such a mist forming around dry ice—frozen carbon dioxide—or above liquid nitrogen. The gas and mist usually fall downward, right through the air. A cold, dense gas can be poured through air from one container to another. What other materials do you know that can flow?

VOCABULARY
Make a description wheel for each new vocabulary term.

Fluids are part of your body.

A **fluid** is a material that can flow easily, such as a gas or a liquid. Fluids flow to fit the shape of their containers. Liquid water is a fluid. Air and other gases are fluids. When a mixture of liquids and solids can flow to fit the shape of a container, it is considered a fluid.

Organisms use water, air, and other fluids. Much of a cell's cytoplasm is made of fluids. Your body has many fluids, such as blood and the liquids that help your joints move smoothly. In this section, you will learn about fluid pressure. Later in this chapter, you will learn of the different ways that fluids work in your body.

 CHECK YOUR READING What are fluids?

Fluids push in all directions.

NOTE-TAKING STRATEGY
Remember to choose a strategy to record each main idea, or blue heading. Add notes that support the main idea.

Air, water, and other fluids press in all directions. When you are in a swimming pool, the water pushes inward on you as well as outward on the pool walls. When you move in a pool, the water flows around you—no empty holes are left. The water flows because the fluid pushes on itself as well as on solid objects in and around it. The water fills up spaces in any direction that it can move.

Pushing means that the water exerts a force. The force is not applied in just one place but is spread over an area. **Pressure** is a measure of how much force is acting on a certain area. If the pressure in a fluid is greater in one place and less in another, the fluid will tend to push on itself in all directions until the pressure is the same throughout. Some of the fluid may also move toward the area of lower pressure. Air moves from areas of higher to lower pressure when you breathe.

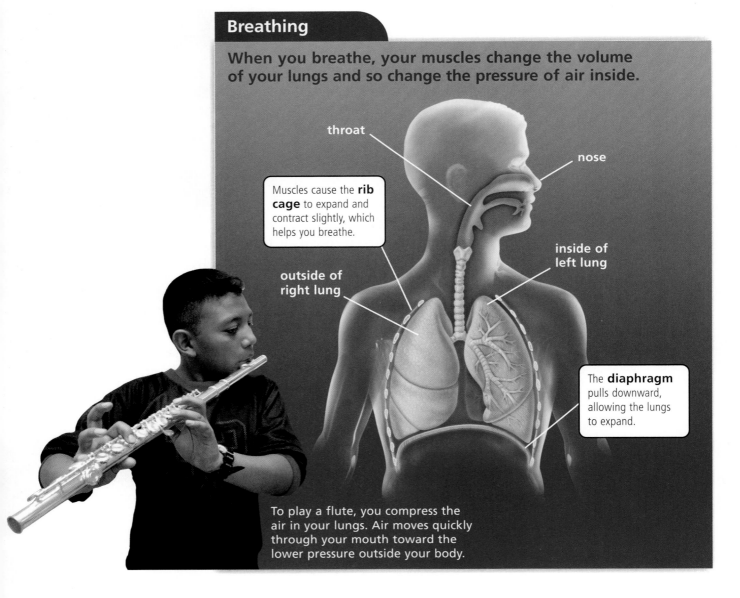

Breathing

When you breathe, your muscles change the volume of your lungs and so change the pressure of air inside.

throat

nose

Muscles cause the **rib cage** to expand and contract slightly, which helps you breathe.

outside of right lung

inside of left lung

The **diaphragm** pulls downward, allowing the lungs to expand.

To play a flute, you compress the air in your lungs. Air moves quickly through your mouth toward the lower pressure outside your body.

Your body is surrounded by air on the outside, pressing inward. You also have air inside your lungs, pressing outward. You make air move by changing the pressure of the air in your lungs. To play a flute, you compress the air in your lungs in order to blow it out through your mouth. Muscles between your ribs pull inward, and muscles in your lower abdomen squeeze the lungs upward. The volume of your lungs becomes smaller, so the air is compressed. The air in your lungs is now at a higher pressure than the air around you. Air rushes out through your open mouth until the pressures are equal.

To fill your lungs again, you inhale using a muscle called the diaphragm (DY-uh-FRAM). When your diaphragm contracts, it flattens and moves down. At the same time, muscles between your ribs pull your rib cage slightly upward and outward. Your lungs are elastic, somewhat like balloons. Your diaphragm and rib cage stretch your lungs, which increases their volume. The air inside expands to fill the larger space. Because of the expansion, the air pressure inside your lungs becomes lower. Then, air at a higher pressure outside your body pushes into your lungs until the pressures are equal. When your diaphragm and other muscles relax, your lungs contract again and air moves gently out—you exhale.

VISUALIZATION
CLASSZONE.COM

See how your diaphragm helps your lungs change volume.

CHECK YOUR READING   What happens when the air pressure outside your body is greater than the air pressure inside your lungs?

INVESTIGATE Lungs

How does air move in and out of lungs?

PROCEDURE

1. Make a model of your lungs by inserting the end of an uninflated balloon into the top of a plastic bottle. While squeezing the bottle to force out some air, stretch the end of the balloon outward over the lip of the bottle as shown. Tape the balloon in place to make a tight seal.

2. Release the bottle so that it expands back to its normal shape. Squeeze and release the bottle several times while observing the balloon. Record your observations.

WHAT DO YOU THINK?

- What happens when you squeeze and release the bottle?

- How do you think your lungs move when you inhale? when you exhale?

CHALLENGE Design an addition to your model that could represent the diaphragm. If possible, test your design.

SKILL FOCUS
Making models
(7.6)

MATERIALS
- medium-sized balloon
- clear plastic bottle with labels removed
- duct tape

TIME
15 minutes

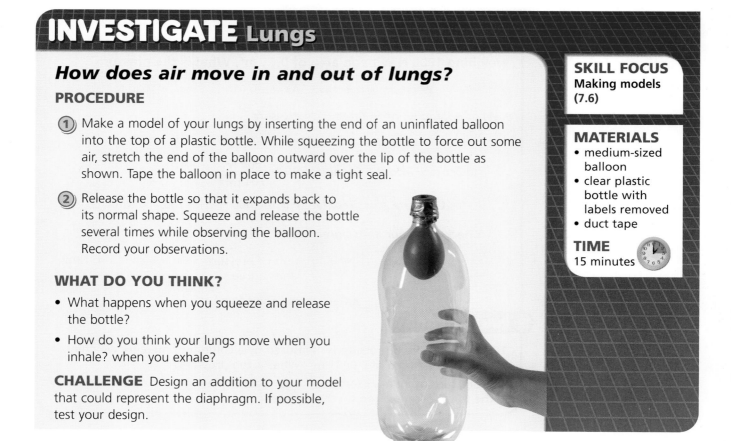

Pressure is force divided by area.

MAIN IDEA WEB
Record the formula for pressure and other notes in a main idea web. Or choose a different strategy for your notes.

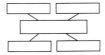

Pressure describes how concentrated a force is. If the force increases, so does the pressure. If the area increases, the force decreases. The formula below shows how pressure depends on force and area. In this formula, P is the pressure, F is the force, and A is the area over which the force is exerted. The unit for pressure is the pascal (Pa). One pascal is the pressure exerted by one newton (1 N) of force on an area of one square meter (1 m^2). That is, one pascal is equivalent to one N/m^2.

$$\text{Pressure} = \frac{\text{Force}}{\text{Area}} \qquad P = \frac{F}{A}$$

Pressure can also be measured in millimeters or inches of mercury (mm Hg or in. Hg). A device lets liquid mercury move up and down in a column, or tube, until the pressure of mercury matches the pressure to be measured. The weight, or downward force, of the mercury and the area across the column can then be used to determine the pressure. A column of mercury 760.0 millimeters high (29.92 in.) produces the same pressure that the atmosphere produces at sea level—101,325 Pa.

CHECK YOUR READING What do the units Pa, N/m^2, and mm Hg have in common?

RESOURCE CENTER
CLASSZONE.COM

Learn more about fluids and pressure.

Calculating Pressure

> **Sample Problem**
>
> **Suppose an air pressure is measured by a column of mercury weighing 1000 N with an area of 0.01 m^2. What is the pressure?**
>
> *What do you know?* Area = 0.01 m^2, Force = 1000 N
>
> *What do you want to find out?* Pressure
>
> *Write the formula:* $P = \dfrac{F}{A}$
>
> *Substitute into the formula:* $P = \dfrac{1000 \text{ N}}{0.01 \text{ m}^2}$
>
> *Calculate and simplify:* $P = 100{,}000 \, \dfrac{\text{N}}{\text{m}^2} = 100{,}000 \text{ N/m}^2$
>
> *Check that your units agree:* Unit is N/m^2.
>
> Unit of pressure is Pa, which is also N/m^2. Units agree.
>
> *Answer:* $P = 100{,}000$ Pa

> **Practice the Math**
>
> 1. Someone's blood pressure is measured by a column of mercury weighing 10 N with an area of 0.0001 m^2. What is the pressure?
>
> 2. A pressure of 3 Pa is exerted on a surface with an area of 20 m^2. What is the total force exerted on the surface?

Fluids both move and transfer forces.

Fluids move smoothly as they respond to forces, such as forces due to gravity or forces due to differences in pressure. Fluids can be pushed aside by solids or by other fluids. Air and other gases change volume to fit their containers. Liquids usually do not expand or contract much. So, a liquid in an open container usually has a distinct surface—it does not expand upward. Fluids in your body can be gases, liquids, and even mixtures of gases, liquids, and solids.

Your body uses fluid pressure in three main ways. Fluids in your body can transfer forces. When fluids move, they can carry materials from place to place. And fluids can spread out forces to protect your body.

The pressure of a fluid can transfer a force from one location to another. Think about the liquid in a syringe. You apply a force to this fluid by pushing on the plunger. The plunger pushes on the liquid. The pressure throughout the liquid increases. The liquid transfers the force from the plunger to the tip of the syringe.

Pressure can also move a fluid. At the small open tip of the tube, the air pressure is lower than the liquid pressure. The liquid moves toward this area of lower pressure. What's the result? Liquid squirts out of the syringe. If you apply a greater force, the liquid moves faster.

Fluid pressure can spread out a force. If you squeeze one end of a very full balloon, the air inside might not move much. It may feel like a solid object. However, the air spreads out the force to the whole balloon. The spread-out force is less likely to break the balloon.

CHECK YOUR READING What are three results of fluid pressure?

11.1 Review

KEY CONCEPTS

1. Give three examples of fluids. What do they have in common? (7.6)

2. What is pressure? Express your answer both in words and in an equation. (7.6.j)

3. What happens when you apply a force to a liquid? (7.6.j)

CRITICAL THINKING

4. **Calculate** A carbonated beverage in a can exerts a force of 40 N on an opening of 2 cm² (0.0002 m²). What is the pressure?

5. **Apply** An inflated balloon exerts an inward force on the air in the balloon. What effect does the pressure have if you release the balloon without tying the end?

● CHALLENGE

6. **Apply** Suppose you squeeze a plastic bottle of ketchup slowly—using a small force. What happens to the fluid in the bottle? What is different if you apply a larger force?

MATH TUTORIAL
CLASSZONE.COM
Click on Math Tutorial for more help converting units.
Math 7.MG.2.4
Science 7.6.j

How Much Pressure?

The standard unit for pressure is the pascal (Pa), which is one newton of force per square meter of area. However, other units of pressure are often used. A tire gauge may measure pounds per square inch (psi). The average air pressure at sea level is called an atmosphere (atm). You can use the chart to convert pressures from one unit to another.

Unit Conversions

1 millimeter of mercury (mm Hg)	=	133 pascals (Pa or N/m^2)
1 atmosphere (atm)	=	760 millimeters of mercury (mm Hg)
1 atmosphere (atm)	=	101,300 pascals (Pa or N/m^2)
1 pound per square inch (psi)	=	51.7 millimeters of mercury (mm Hg)
1 millibar (mb)	=	0.76 millimeters of mercury (mm Hg)
1 millibar (mb)	=	100 pascals (Pa or N/m^2)

Example

A doctor records a patient's maximum blood pressure (systolic pressure) as 120 mm Hg. What is this pressure in pascals?

(1) Use the chart to find out how to convert millimeters of mercury to pascals: 1 mm Hg = 133 Pa.

(2) Set up the conversion as a fraction. The number you are converting to should be on the top. The number you are converting from should be on the bottom: $\dfrac{133\ \text{Pa}}{1\ \text{mm Hg}}$

(3) Multiply the value in the units you have by the conversion fraction to get your answer:

Pressure = 120 m̶m̶ H̶g̶ · $\dfrac{133\ \text{Pa}}{1\ \text{m̶m̶ H̶g̶}}$ = 15,960 Pa.

Notice how the original unit (mm Hg) cancels out, leaving the new unit (Pa).

ANSWER A pressure of 120 mm Hg equals about 16,000 Pa.

Answer the following questions.

1. A pressure gauge measures the pressure in a tire to be 32 pounds per square inch (psi). What is this pressure in millimeters of mercury?

2. The air pressure at the top of Mount Everest, the highest mountain in the world, was measured as 253 mm Hg. What is this pressure in atmospheres?

CHALLENGE What is the conversion factor between pounds per square inch and millibars? Use the conversions given in the table to find your answer.

11.2 The heart produces blood pressure.

CALIFORNIA Content Standards

7.5.a Students know plants and animals have levels of organization for structure and function, including cells, tissues, organs, organ systems, and the whole organism.

7.5.b Students know organ systems function because of the contributions of individual organs, tissues, and cells. The failure of any part can affect the entire system.

7.6.j Students know that contractions of the heart generate blood pressure and that heart valves prevent backflow of blood in the circulatory system.

BEFORE, you learned

- Fluids exert pressure
- Forces can cause fluids to move
- Forces can increase fluid pressure

NOW, you will learn

- How the structures of the circulatory system work together
- What blood pressure is and how it is produced
- Why blood pressure is important

VOCABULARY

circulatory system p. 393
artery p. 394
vein p. 394
capillary p. 397

EXPLORE Blood Pressure (7.6.j)

Is blood flow constant?

PROCEDURE

(1) Hold out one hand with your palm facing up.

(2) Place the first two fingers of your other hand on your wrist near your thumb. Move your fingertips slightly until you can feel your pulse.

WHAT DO YOU THINK?

- What does your pulse tell you about how blood moves through your body?
- Gently press your fingers against the side of your neck. How does this pulse compare with your first observations?

NOTE-TAKING STRATEGY
Take notes on the main idea. *Blood is a fluid that circulates in the body.*

Blood is a fluid that circulates in the body.

Blood is a fluid that includes red and white blood cells and small pieces of cells. These solid pieces are carried in a liquid called plasma. The plasma is made of water, proteins, glucose, and other materials. The liquid and solid particles together behave as a fluid.

Blood moves around the body in the **circulatory system,** which consists of the heart and blood vessels. You can think of the system as a container that holds blood. A change in the container can change the pressure of the fluid inside. The circulatory system of some animals, such as grasshoppers, is like an open container. A grasshopper's heart increases the blood pressure, but then the fluid moves out of the blood vessels and among the cells. The pressure drops. Your own circulatory system is more like a closed container.

 What is blood made of?

Blood exerts pressure on blood vessels.

The blood in your body moves through a network of structures called blood vessels. Blood vessels are flexible, tube-shaped structures of different diameters. Blood flows through these vessels in two types of loops, or circuits, in your body.

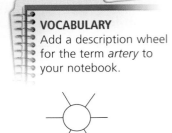

VOCABULARY
Add a description wheel for the term *artery* to your notebook.

1 The heart acts as two separate pumps. The right side of your heart pushes blood into a vessel that splits into two. A vessel that carries blood from the heart toward another part of the body is called an **artery.** An artery carries the blood toward each of your lungs. There, the blood gets rid of carbon dioxide and takes up oxygen. In the diagram on page 395, blue indicates oxygen-poor blood flowing toward the lungs. Oxygen-poor blood is actually dark red, while oxygen-rich blood is brighter red. In the diagram, red indicates oxygen-rich blood flowing from the lungs to the heart and other parts of the body.

2 Blood from each of your lungs is then carried back to your heart by veins. A **vein** is a vessel that carries blood toward the heart. This first loop of blood flow, from the heart to either lung and back to the heart, is called the pulmonary circuit.

READING TiP

The Latin word for lung is *pulmo*. The pulmonary circuit carries blood between the heart and lungs, while the systemic circuit carries blood between the heart and the rest of the body systems.

3 The left side of your heart then pumps the blood to the rest of your body's systems. This begins the second loop, called the systemic circuit. Several large arteries carry blood in different directions. Some blood moves to your heart muscle, some to each arm, and some to your head. Much of the blood moves downward. Vessels carry blood to your internal organs and to each leg.

4 Veins carry blood from each leg and each other location and return it to your heart. Loops of the systemic circuit are then complete.

Blood is pumped into a loop of the pulmonary circuit—one lung—where it exchanges waste carbon dioxide for oxygen. Then it passes again through one loop of the systemic circuit. Blood delivers nutrients and takes up waste products from your cells. It takes up nutrients when it passes to your digestive system. It leaves behind wastes when it passes to your excretory system. Your blood also moves hormones and other materials around your body.

Differences in pressure make blood move. Each time the heart beats, it pushes blood into large arteries. The pressure is high, so the blood moves toward areas of lower pressure. The pressure changes as blood flows through the pulmonary and systemic circuits.

CHECK YOUR READING Does your blood flow through every part of your body before it returns to the heart? Explain.

Circulatory System

The circulatory system allows blood to flow to and from every part of the body.

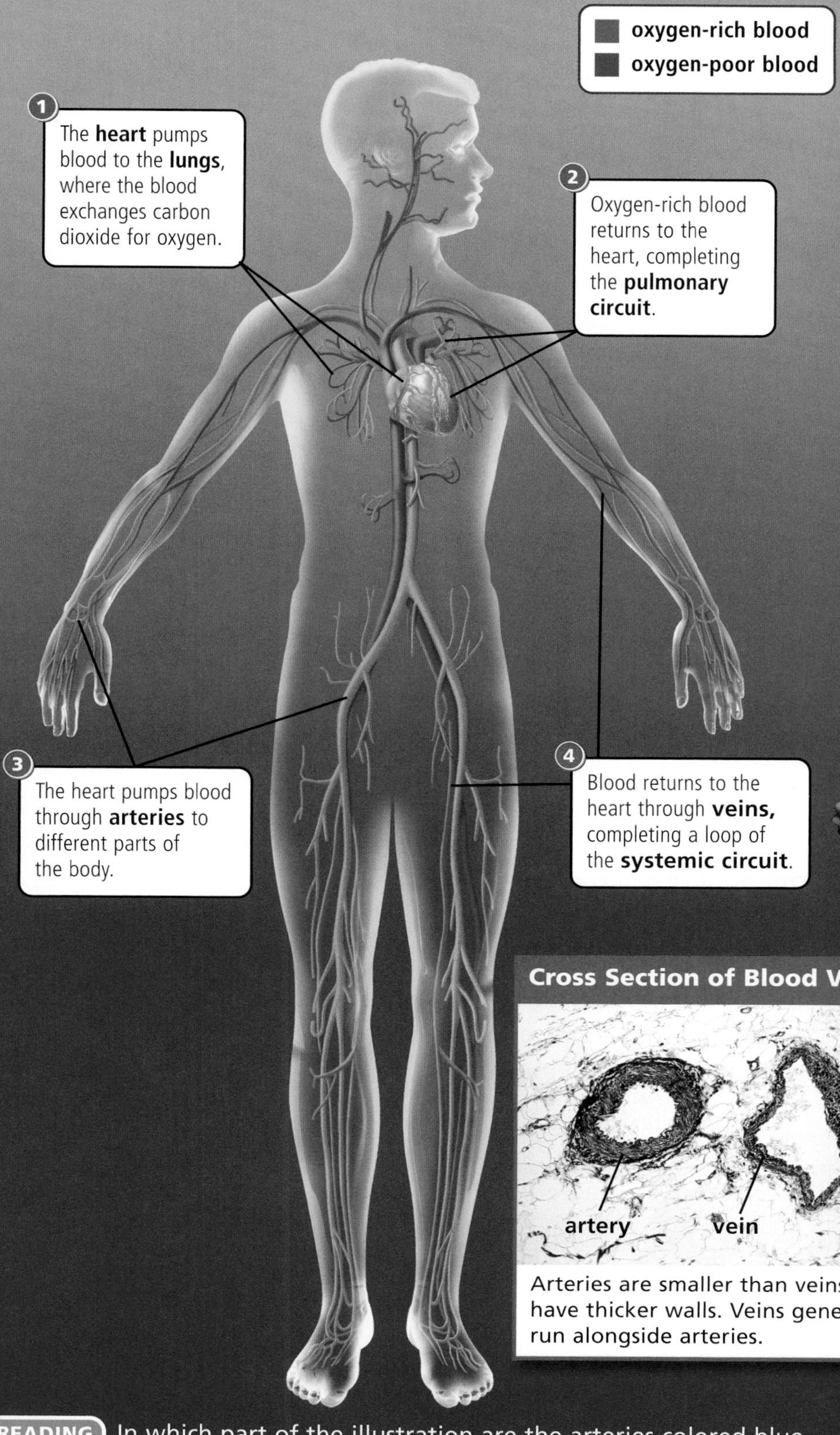

oxygen-rich blood
oxygen-poor blood

1 The **heart** pumps blood to the **lungs**, where the blood exchanges carbon dioxide for oxygen.

2 Oxygen-rich blood returns to the heart, completing the **pulmonary circuit**.

This runner depends on a constant flow of oxygen-rich blood to fuel his cells.

3 The heart pumps blood through **arteries** to different parts of the body.

4 Blood returns to the heart through **veins,** completing a loop of the **systemic circuit**.

Cross Section of Blood Vessels

artery   vein

Arteries are smaller than veins and have thicker walls. Veins generally run alongside arteries.

READING VISUALS In which part of the illustration are the arteries colored blue to show oxygen-poor blood flowing away from the heart?

Blood Pressure

Blood pressure allows materials to travel to all parts of your body.

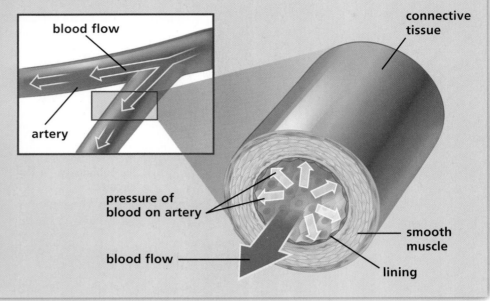

blood flow

artery

connective tissue

pressure of blood on artery

blood flow

smooth muscle

lining

Air pressure in a cuff is increased until the flow of blood through an artery stops. When the air pressure is reduced enough, the blood resumes flowing and can be heard.

RESOURCE CENTER
CLASSZONE.COM

Find out more about the circulatory system.

Arteries

Blood vessels resemble rubber tubing. Blood pushes outward on the blood vessels as it flows. The blood leaving the heart is at a high pressure, so the arteries must have strong walls. An artery wall is thick and elastic and can handle the tremendous force produced when the heart pumps. The artery that carries blood toward most of the body—in the systemic circuit—is called the aorta (ay-AWR-tuh). The vessels that carry blood toward the two lungs—in the pulmonary circuit—are called the pulmonary arteries.

The outside of an artery is a layer of strong, connective tissue. As you can see in the diagram above, it covers a layer of smooth muscle. Inside, surrounding the blood, is a thin lining. The muscle can contract and reduce the diameter of the artery. This action squeezes the blood and increases blood pressure.

Large arteries branch into smaller and smaller arteries. Even though the vessels are small, together they have a large volume. Blood spreads out as it moves into these many smaller vessels. As a result, the pressure is reduced as the blood moves farther from the heart. There is less pressure on the walls of the smaller blood vessels. The smaller blood vessels have thinner walls than larger vessels have.

 CHECK YOUR READING List two of the things that affect the blood's pressure in arteries.

Capillaries

Blood flows through smaller and smaller arteries to reach different parts of your body. **Capillaries** are the smallest blood vessels. They carry blood from the arteries close to every cell in the body. You need more than 100 kilometers of capillaries to reach all your cells. The walls of the capillaries do not have layers of muscle and strong connective tissue. They are very thin, just a single layer of cells. Blood plasma and other materials move right through the capillary walls toward the other cells in your body. The same fluid and waste materials from the cells move through the capillary walls and become part of the blood. The tiny vessels join into larger vessels—the veins—that carry the blood back to the heart.

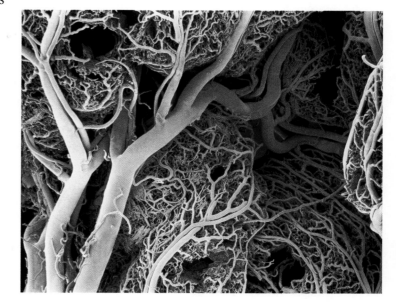
Arteries, capillaries, and veins form a complex web that carries blood to all the cells in the body (30×).

CHECK YOUR READING How are capillaries different from other blood vessels?

Veins

Veins generally have greater diameters than the arteries that are next to them. Blood pressure is much lower in veins than in arteries. So, the walls of veins do not need to be as strong and are thinner than the walls of arteries. Because veins are large, all the veins together have a large volume. At any given time, most of your blood is in your veins.

Think about the veins and arteries in your legs. The two sets of blood vessels lie side by side. The blood coming through your arteries is pushed by your heart and is also pulled downward by gravity. However, blood in the veins has to travel upwards without much pressure. How can that happen? Inside your veins are one-way valves. Blood can flow through them toward your heart. The valves block the blood from flowing backwards. Also, the muscles in your legs help push the blood through your veins when you walk.

Blood flows from capillaries to veins, and then returns to the heart. Then it flows through arteries, capillaries, and veins in the pulmonary circuit. Then the heart pumps the blood again into the arteries, capillaries, and veins of the systemic circuit.

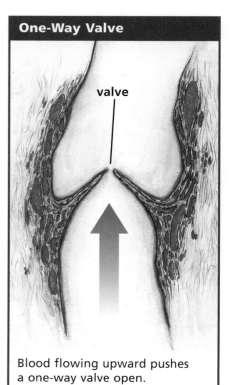
One-Way Valve

valve

Blood flowing upward pushes a one-way valve open.

The heart pumps blood through the body.

READING TiP

The plural of *atrium* is *atria*. *Atrium* comes from the Latin word for forecourt or hall. *Ventricle,* the word for a lower chamber of the heart, comes from the Latin word for belly.

The heart supplies the pressure to move blood through the circulatory system. The human heart acts as two pumps—devices that move fluids—working at the same time. The right side of the heart pumps blood to the lungs. The left side pumps blood to the rest of the body. Each side of the heart—each pump—is divided into two areas called chambers. An upper chamber, called an atrium (AY-tree-uhm), collects blood for pumping. The atria have thin walls of muscle that move the blood quickly. A lower chamber, called a ventricle, does the pumping. The left ventricle is very strong. It pumps blood through the whole body.

Use the diagram below to follow the path of blood. Blood from the upper and lower body flows into the right atrium, and then the right ventricle, and out to the lungs. Oxygen-rich blood flows from the two lungs into the left atrium, and then into the left ventricle, and upward to the arms and head and downward to the lower body.

CHECK YOUR READING How many times does blood pass through the heart before it returns to its starting place?

The Heart

The heart is a pair of pumps that move blood to the lungs and to the rest of the body.

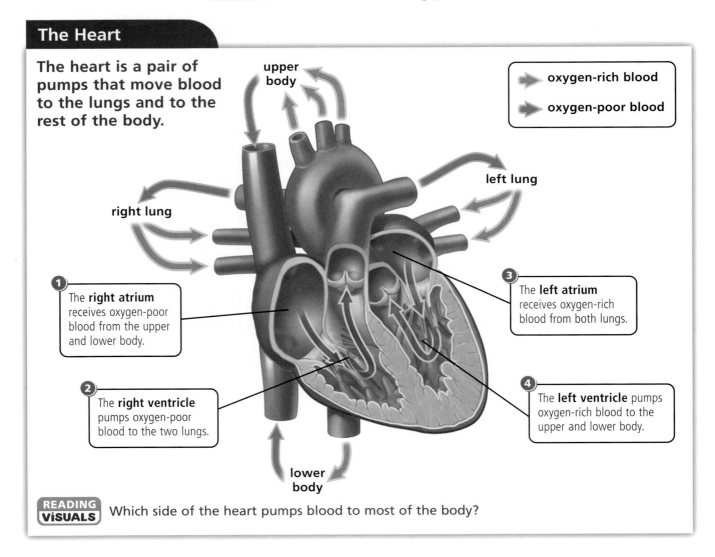

upper body

left lung

right lung

oxygen-rich blood

oxygen-poor blood

1 The **right atrium** receives oxygen-poor blood from the upper and lower body.

2 The **right ventricle** pumps oxygen-poor blood to the two lungs.

3 The **left atrium** receives oxygen-rich blood from both lungs.

4 The **left ventricle** pumps oxygen-rich blood to the upper and lower body.

lower body

READING VISUALS Which side of the heart pumps blood to most of the body?

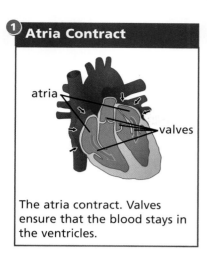

① Atria Contract

The atria contract. Valves ensure that the blood stays in the ventricles.

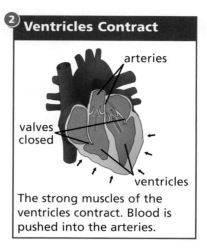

② Ventricles Contract

The strong muscles of the ventricles contract. Blood is pushed into the arteries.

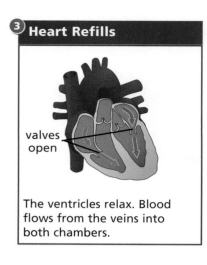

③ Heart Refills

The ventricles relax. Blood flows from the veins into both chambers.

① **Atria Contract** A heartbeat starts when both atria gently contract. The increased pressure moves extra blood into the ventricles.

② **Ventricles Contract** Next, the atria relax and the ventricles contract. One-way valves between the chambers close. The large increase of pressure moves blood quickly into the arteries.

③ **Heart Refills** Finally, the ventricles relax. Blood returning from the veins fills the chambers, and a new heartbeat begins.

With each heartbeat, the pressure in your arteries increases briefly. When your heart beats fast, the pressure increases more. Your body needs this extra pressure and movement of blood when you exercise, because your muscle cells need to get more oxygen and to get rid of waste faster. Your blood pressure returns to normal when you rest. But if a person's blood pressure stays high over a long period of time, the continued pressure can damage the heart and arteries. Low blood pressure can also cause problems. If your blood pressure is too low, blood can't get oxygen and other nutrients to all your cells, especially your brain.

11.2 Review

KEY CONCEPTS

1. What are the structures of the circulatory system? Explain the function of each part. (7.5.b)

2. How is blood pressure produced? (7.6.j)

3. Why can both high and low blood pressure cause problems? (7.5.b)

CRITICAL THINKING

4. **Compare and Contrast** Large highways are sometimes called arteries. How are roads and highways similar to and different from your circulatory system?

5. **Synthesize** What two parts of the circulatory system use one-way valves? In which of these parts is blood pressure high?

⬢ CHALLENGE

6. **Apply** If a person's blood pressure drops, a medical worker may raise the person's feet slightly. Why might this be helpful?

CHAPTER INVESTIGATION

The Human Heart

OVERVIEW AND PURPOSE Different parts of the heart have different purposes. The atria collect blood, the ventricles pump blood out of the heart and to the body, and the valves in between open and close to build up the pressure needed to move the blood. The artificial valve at left has three flaps that open and close, similar to the valve it replaces. In this investigation you will

- use various objects to model the functions of different parts of the heart
- tell how changes in blood pressure are affected by heart valves and contractions of the heart muscle

▶ Problem

Write It Up

What is the difference between atria and ventricles? How do heart valves affect blood flow through the heart?

MATERIALS
- thin-walled pet toy
- tennis ball
- turkey baster
- round balloons
- binder clip
- water bottle with squirt top

7.6.j, 7.7.d

▶ Procedure

PART 1

1. Set aside the binder clip. Examine the other materials. Blow some air into the balloon and then squeeze the balloon while holding it closed. Squeeze the other objects. Record your observations of these model heart chambers.

2. Imagine that each object is filled with water. Which objects could be made to spray water with greater pressure?

3. Look at the illustration of the human heart on page 398. What similarities and differences do you notice between the walls of the four chambers? How might these affect blood pressure or blood flow?

4. Make a data table like the one shown on the sample notebook page to help you compare the characteristics of the atria and ventricles.

5. In your Science Notebook, design a model that would use the available materials to help someone understand the function of each chamber of the heart. For example, you might use tennis balls for two of the chambers. Which chambers would be connected?

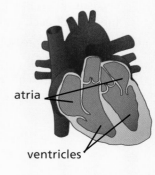

atria

ventricles

Content Standard
7.6.j Students know that contractions of the heart generate blood pressure and that heart valves prevent backflow of blood in the circulatory system.

Investigation Standard
7.7.d Construct scale models, maps, and appropriately labeled diagrams to communicate scientific knowledge (e.g., motion of Earth's plates and cell structure).

PART 2

6 Inflate the balloon partway and hold it closed with your fingers. Then use the binder clip to seal it. Examine the top of the water bottle. Which of these three model valves would hold best when under pressure? Record your observations.

7 In your Science Notebook, add valves to your design to show the function of these parts of the heart. Where does the heart need the strongest valves?

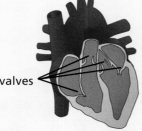

valves

▶ Observe and Analyze | Write It Up

1. **OBSERVE** How does the thickness of a ventricle wall differ from that of an atrium?

2. **COMPARE** Which object did you use to model each heart chamber and valve? What features influenced your decision?

3. **RECORD** Draw your design of a model heart. Label what each part represents. Identify the object you would use for each part.

▶ Conclude | Write It Up

1. **ANALYZE** Ventricles pump blood out of the heart to the lungs and body. Why would thicker walls make this process more efficient?

2. **INFER** Why might you describe the atria as places where blood collects? What function do the thin walls serve?

3. **CONCLUDE** Why is it important for pressure to become higher in the ventricles than in the atria?

4. **COMPARE** Which of the ventricles needs to be stronger than the other? Does one atrium need to be stronger? Explain your answers.

5. **ANALYZE** Where did you place valves in your model? Which of the valves need to be the strongest and why?

6. **INTERPRET** Answer the questions posed in the problem.

7. **APPLY** What other objects have you encountered that have chambers for collecting or squeezing a fluid? that have valves?

▶ INVESTIGATE Further

Design a different type of model to show the shape and structure of the heart instead of the functions. This model does not need moving parts. How would this model differ from the model of the heart functions?

The Human Heart

Problem What is the difference between atria and ventricles? How do heart valves affect blood flow through the heart?

Observe and Analyze

Table 1. Comparing Atria and Ventricles

Chamber	Structure (thin or thick walls)	Pressure exerted (great or small)
Atrium		
Ventricle		

Conclude

KEY CONCEPT
11.3 Fluid pressure affects the body in different ways.

CALIFORNIA
Content Standards

7.5.g Students know how to relate the structures of the eye and ear to their functions.

Extension of

7.5.b Students know organ systems function because of the contributions of individual organs, tissues, and cells. The failure of any part can affect the entire system.

VOCABULARY

mucus p. 403
semicircular canals p. 404

BEFORE, you learned

- Fluids spread force over an area
- Fluids can transfer forces from one place to another
- Liquids change volume much less than gases

NOW, you will learn

- About several functions that fluids have in the body
- How the eye and the ear make use of fluids
- How fluids are important in different organ systems

THINK ABOUT

How much of your body is solid?

When you push on liquid water, the water moves out of the way because it is a fluid. Much of your hand is also made of fluids, but your hand feels solid. How can this be so? Remember that your hand is made of cells. Each cell is filled with cytoplasm, which is mostly fluid. Think about sitting on a plastic chair filled with air. The plastic keeps the air from moving out of the way. When you sit, the chair feels solid even though it is mostly fluid. How are the pieces of the chair similar to your cells?

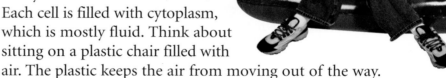

Fluids serve several functions in the body.

NOTE-TAKING STRATEGY
Take notes about the different functions that fluids serve in the body.

Pressure within your cells helps support the cells' shapes. In Section 2, you read about how pressure helps blood circulate and how blood carries materials to and from different parts of your body. Because fluids can be moved easily, your body uses them in many different places to move materials. Your body also uses fluids to transfer forces and to spread out forces. A fluid coating can make various parts slide more easily. A fluid coating can also prevent a material from reaching a layer of tissue by catching the material or moving it sideways. Use the table on page 403 to learn more about the different functions of fluids. Then, as you learn about the different fluids in your body, think about the different functions each fluid serves.

 CHECK YOUR READING What are some of the functions that fluids serve?

Functions of Fluids

A fluid can serve one or more functions in the body.

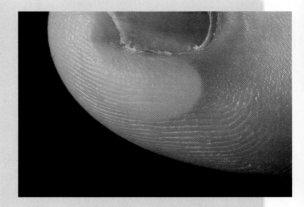

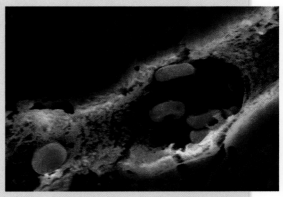

Function	Description	Example	In the Body
Divert and spread forces	Fluid pressure transmits a force to a different location or spreads a force to a bigger area.	In a shoe, a gel insole spreads the forces that are usually concentrated at the heel and ball of the foot to more of the sole of the foot.	Fluid in a blister spreads a damaging force to a larger area and so reduces further damage.
Support	Fluid pressure outward on a closed container makes the container act as a solid.	The air in an inflatable chair supports a person sitting down.	Fluid pressure inside cells makes the cells firm.
Transport materials	A difference in pressure makes a fluid move, which can carry materials to new locations.	People often use rivers to transport materials downstream.	Flowing blood carries nutrients to cells and waste away from cells.
Lubricate	A fluid between two surfaces makes the surfaces slide more easily against one another.	Grease makes machine parts move more smoothly.	Tears help the eyelids glide more easily.
Block materials	Fluid can form a barrier that prevents materials from entering or escaping.	Oil can help prevent rust by keeping oxygen from reaching a metal surface.	Tears help keep dust from reaching the eye's surface and also keep the surface from drying out.

READING VISUALS What functions of fluids are shown in the photographs?

Many fluids serve several functions at the same time. For example, epithelial tissues in several parts of your body produce **mucus,** which is a fluid that forms a protective coating. Mucus lubricates surfaces, helps transport some materials, and blocks other materials from reaching the tissue beneath the coating. Mucus also protects tissue from drying out by reducing the motion of water away from the tissue. The materials in mucus can help destroy harmful bacteria. Cells in your nose, throat, and other places produce mucus.

RESOURCE CENTER
CLASSZONE.COM

Find out more about balance.

The senses make use of fluids.

Your body detects conditions both outside and inside itself. Some of your senses depend on fluids. For example, saliva in your mouth helps move materials to your taste buds. Mucus inside your nose helps move materials to the cells that detect smells. Mucus also protects the cells from small particles in the air.

The Ear

When you think of keeping your balance, you probably don't think of your ears! But fluid inside tiny cavities in your ears helps you sense your position and motion. Three of these cavities, called **semicircular canals,** are shaped like tubes bent partway around a circle. When you move your head, fluid in these tubes moves. Special cells sense the motion of the fluid.

In the diagram below, you can see that each semicircular canal curves in a different direction. One curve helps you feel your head nodding up and down. Another curve helps you feel your head turning side to side. The third curve helps you feel your head tilting to one side or the other. Fluids in two other chambers help you sense which way is up and when you start or stop moving. If you move too violently, as on some theme park rides, you can shake up the fluids.

Balance

The semicircular canals, which are part of the inner ear, help you sense different motions.

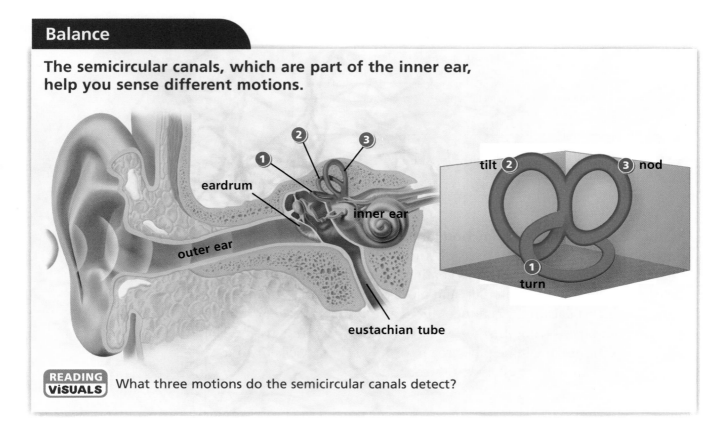

eardrum
inner ear
outer ear
eustachian tube

tilt ② ③ nod
① turn

READING VISUALS What three motions do the semicircular canals detect?

This gives you confusing signals. As a result, you may feel dizzy or sick. A cold or an infection in one ear can cause the signals from your two ears to be different, which can also make you feel dizzy.

Remember that air is a fluid that can be compressed. Sound waves have areas of high and low pressure. When these waves enter your ear, they move through the air in your outer ear to your eardrum.

The middle part of your ear is also filled with air. Your eardrum works best when the air pressure is the same on the outside and the inside. A tube called a eustachian (yoo-STAY-shuhn) tube connects the middle part of your ear to your throat. When you yawn or swallow, both of your eustachian tubes open up and the fluid pressures can balance. A fast change in air pressure can make your eardrum move, and so you may hear a popping sound.

Your ear responds to sound waves by pushing on the innermost part of your ear. This snail-shaped chamber is filled with a liquid. There, special cells respond to pressure and motion in this fluid and send signals to your brain. You will learn more about sound and hearing in Chapter 12.

 CHECK YOUR READING Which two parts of your ear are filled with air? Which part is filled with a liquid?

CALIFORNIA Focus

Researchers at the University of California at Los Angeles have developed a computer-controlled chair in which a patient can be moved around. The chair is used to help doctors understand why a patient is experiencing dizziness. Instruments collect data about how well the patient's eye movements and inner ear work together to maintain balance.

INVESTIGATE Semicircular Canals

How are the semicircular canals arranged?

PROCEDURE

1. Cut 3 pieces of plastic tubing, each 30–35 cm long.

2. Plug one end of a tube with clay. Use the funnel to fill the tube most of the way with colored water. Plug the other end of the tube with clay. Repeat for the other tubes.

3. Tape the tubes to the outside of the box as shown in the photograph below. Then move the box to simulate nodding, turning, and tilting your head.

WHAT DO YOU THINK?

In which tube does the air bubble move most for each motion?

CHALLENGE Which ear does your model represent? How might you model both ears using one box?

SKILL FOCUS
Using models
(7.5.g)

MATERIALS
• clear plastic tubing
• scissors
• modeling clay
• small funnel
• colored water
• small box
• transparent tape

TIME
20 minutes

The Eye

The fluid called tears flows continually from tear ducts at the upper, outer side of each eye. It crosses the eye, lubricating the surface and helping the eyelids move smoothly. At the inner corner of each eye, the fluid drains into the nose. When tiny particles or chemicals get into your eye, tears carry them away—sometimes down your face.

READING TiP

Humor is an ancient word for a fluid of the body. The root of *aqueous* is *aqua*, meaning "water."

Look at the diagram below. Behind the clear front, or cornea, of the eye is a chamber filled with a clear fluid called aqueous humor. This fluid is produced near the lens of the eye and flows right through the open dark area of the eye, the pupil. The fluid is absorbed in an area just behind the cornea. Aqueous humor carries nutrients to the eye's lens and cornea. It also carries away waste material.

If aqueous humor builds up too much, the pressure on the lens can cause damage. The pressure can also be transferred to other parts of the eye, where more damage can occur. This condition is called glaucoma. The fluid pressure can be tested by pushing briefly on your cornea with a special instrument or with a puff of air. You will learn more about eyes and vision in Chapter 14.

Fluids and the Eye

Tears clean and lubricate the outer part of the eye, while aqueous humor nourishes some of the clear parts.

Measuring Pressure

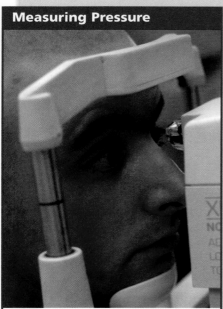

A puff of air is used to measure the pressure of the aqueous humor.

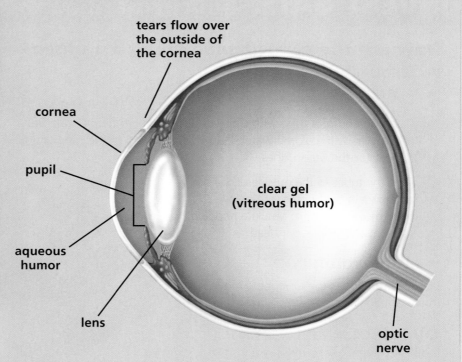

tears flow over the outside of the cornea

cornea

pupil

aqueous humor

lens

clear gel (vitreous humor)

optic nerve

READING VISUALS Where are the fluids of your eye?

Organ systems use different types of fluids.

You have read about the functions of blood and some other fluids in your body. In fact, all of your organ systems use fluids.

REMINDER

The systems of the human body are summarized in the Appendix beginning on page R78.

Circulatory and Lymphatic Systems Remember that blood is made partly of a liquid called plasma. Plasma carries materials through the capillary walls to other cells. However, some of the fluid—up to three liters per day—does not go directly back into the capillaries from the cells. The leftover fluid, now called lymph, is collected by another set of tiny vessels, which are also called capillaries. The lymph capillaries merge into larger and larger vessels, which together form the lymphatic system. Lymph vessels have one-way valves, just as blood veins do. The fluid is collected and returned to the blood.

Respiratory System You have read how air, a fluid, carries materials into and out of your body. Also, your respiratory system produces mucus in your nose and airways. This fluid catches particles, such as dust and bacteria, and prevents them from reaching your lungs.

Digestive and Urinary Systems Your digestive system depends on fluids to move materials. Stomach fluids, which are called gastric fluids, and saliva soften and move the chewed-up food. Enzymes in these fluids help break down the food. The liquid and nutrients are absorbed through blood and lymph capillaries in the walls of the digestive system. Some fluid remains in your digestive system and helps move solid waste. In your urinary system, your kidneys filter out waste materials carried by your blood. Each day, your kidneys process the equivalent of about 180 liters (45 gal.) of blood as the blood goes around and around your body. The waste and a small amount of water make up 1–2 liters of urine.

Nervous System Fluids help protect your fragile brain and spinal cord. Cerebrospinal fluid (CSF) fills the space between these organs and the bones that surround them. It also fills several areas inside your brain. If you shake or bump your head, the fluid spreads out the force, so less damage is done to the tissues. Like lymph, CSF is formed from blood plasma. It carries nutrients to the tissues and carries wastes away as it is returned to the blood.

CHECK YOUR READING What are two functions of the fluid in your nervous system?

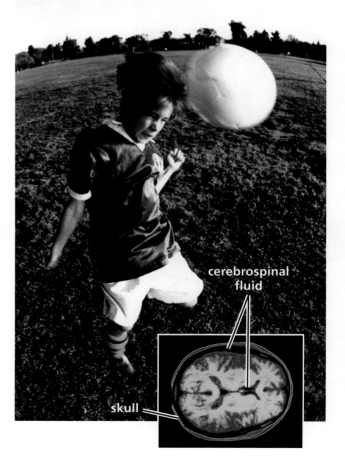

Fluids in the head spread out a force so that the force on each brain cell is smaller.

cerebrospinal fluid

skull

Reproductive System The female and male reproductive systems include many fluids. Just as in other organ systems, fluids in the reproductive system transport nutrients and other materials, lubricate tissues, and give structural support and protection. For example, a fetus develops inside a fluid-filled sac. The fluid performs all these functions, including shock absorption. The watery liquid in the sac is called amniotic (AM-nee-AHT-ihk) fluid.

The same fluids that perform life-giving functions can also transport materials that cause disease. The viruses and bacteria that cause sexually transmitted diseases, such as AIDS, genital herpes, gonorrhea, and syphilis, are transported from one person to another through the fluids of the reproductive system.

Muscular and Skeletal Systems Your muscles need a large supply of oxygen and other nutrients, and they produce a great deal of carbon dioxide and other wastes. Blood and lymph transport these materials. Your skeletal system uses fluids, too. Synovial (sih-NOH-vee-uhl) fluid, a thick and slippery substance, lubricates your joints and nourishes the tissues there. This fluid helps you bend quickly at your wrists, elbows, shoulders, hips, knees, and other freely movable joints. Some joints are cushioned by a thin pad, called a bursa, that is filled with synovial fluid. You may have heard of bursitis. This condition occurs when a bursa becomes inflamed and swells with additional fluid, causing pain.

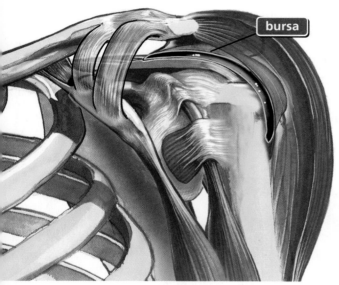

A bursa, which is a sac filled with fluid, cushions this shoulder joint.

bursa

CHECK YOUR READING What are three of the systems in which fluids help protect the body?

11.3 Review

KEY CONCEPTS

1. Describe the functions of fluids in the body. (7.5.b)
2. Which structures of the ear contain fluids? (7.5.g)
3. What functions can mucus serve? (7.6)

CRITICAL THINKING

4. **Classify** Choose a fluid in your body and try to determine which function or functions it serves. Use the chart on page 403 to help you.
5. **Apply** How does fluid pressure help fluids carry out their functions?

CHALLENGE

6. **Analyze** Trace the path of one fluid in your body. Can you tell where it comes from and where it ends up?

Breathtaking Heights

> **7.6.j** Students know that contractions of the heart generate blood pressure and that heart valves prevent backflow of blood in the circulatory system.

About 12,000 people try to climb Mt. Shasta each year. However, only about half make it to the summit.

Air is a fluid. The atmosphere's weight produces air pressure. As a person climbs to a higher elevation, he or she encounters air at lower pressure. The air is also less dense—which means each lungful of air contains fewer molecules. Climbers must inhale more often to get enough oxygen. The heart pumps faster to help the blood pick up the oxygen. This increases a person's blood pressure.

Too High, Too Fast

The rate that a person climbs and the resulting change in elevation can cause him or her to become sick. Most people feel all right below 2500 meters (8200 ft). About one-fifth of climbers feel nauseated, dizzy, or develop a headache above 2500 meters. It is hard to predict who will be affected by the elevation change. Climbers who wish to go to higher elevations should stop partway up. They should camp overnight before they climb the rest of the way up Mt. Shasta. This gives the body a chance to reach homeostasis—a stable internal environment—in the new conditions.

A high-pressure chamber can simulate the conditions of lower altitude for the person inside.

At higher elevations, climbers can develop worse problems. Fluids can cause the brain to swell. Fluids can also leak into the lungs. These conditions can be deadly if the climbers do not return to lower elevations and seek medical care. However, climbers who develop these conditions may not be able to walk back down the mountain. Rangers use helicopters to evacuate sick climbers who are unable to get themselves safely off Mt. Shasta.

WRITING ABOUT SCIENCE

Commercial airplanes usually travel at an altitude of 11,000 meters (35,000 ft). Extra air is pumped into the passenger cabin to keep the air pressure from changing too much. What effects do you suppose the higher pressure helps prevent? In your answer, compare passengers with mountain climbers.

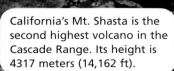

California's Mt. Shasta is the second highest volcano in the Cascade Range. Its height is 4317 meters (14,162 ft).

Chapter Review

the **BIG** idea

The body uses fluid pressure in many ways.

CONTENT REVIEW CLASSZONE.COM

◀ **KEY CONCEPTS SUMMARY**

① Fluids spread force over an area.

$$\text{Pressure} = \frac{\text{Force}}{\text{Area}}$$

Fluids push in all directions. Pressure on a fluid can transfer a force to a different location, spread out a force, and cause the fluid to move.

VOCABULARY
fluid p. 387
pressure p. 388

② The heart produces blood pressure.

The heart acts as two pumps that produce pressure.

Blood flows from the heart through arteries, capillaries, veins, and then back to the heart.

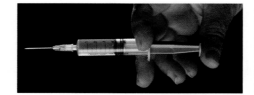

The left side pumps blood through the body in the systemic circuit.

The right side pumps blood through the lungs in the pulmonary circuit.

VOCABULARY
circulatory system p. 393
artery p. 394
vein p. 394
capillary p. 397

③ Fluid pressure affects the body in different ways.

Fluids serve one or more purposes in all major organ systems.

Fluids divert and spread forces, support, transport materials, lubricate, and block materials.

The motion of fluids in the ear gives you a sense of balance.

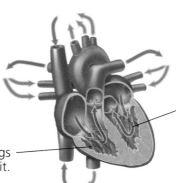

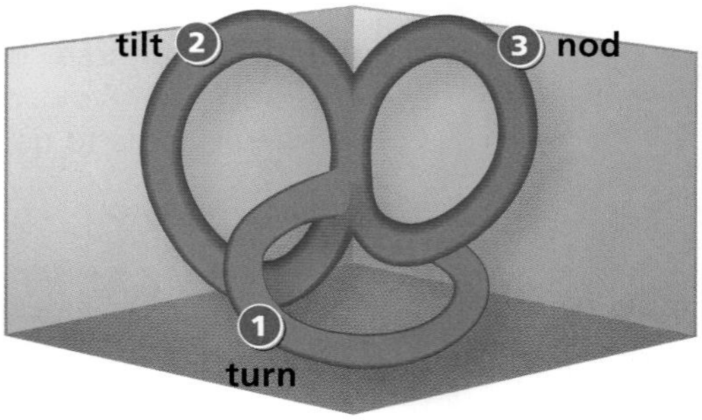

tilt ② ③ nod
① turn

VOCABULARY
mucus p. 403
semicircular canals p. 404

Reviewing Vocabulary

Write a sentence describing the relationship between the terms in each pair.

1. pressure, artery

2. vein, artery

3. artery, capillary

4. circulatory system, vein

5. mucus, fluid

Reviewing Key Concepts

6. Pressure is measured by the amount of force acting on a(n) (7.6)
   a. point   c. area
   b. line   d. volume

7. In what direction(s) does a difference in pressure cause a liquid to move? (7.6)
   a. toward the area of higher pressure
   b. toward the area of lower pressure
   c. into the center of the liquid
   d. outward in all directions

8. When you inhale, air moves into your lungs because (7.6)
   a. outside air at higher pressure pushes into your lungs
   b. your lungs pull the outside air into your body
   c. contractions of your heart cause your lungs to expand
   d. your diaphragm relaxes and compresses your lungs

9. As blood flows away from the heart and back again, in what order does it go through the different types of blood vessels? (7.6.j)
   a. capillaries, veins, arteries
   b. arteries, veins, capillaries
   c. arteries, capillaries, veins
   d. veins, capillaries, arteries

10. Which blood vessels need to withstand the greatest pressure? (7.6.j)
   a. veins near the lungs
   b. capillaries in the head
   c. arteries in the hands
   d. arteries near the heart

11. Which structures are only one cell thick? (7.6.j)
   a. the walls of capillaries
   b. the walls of arteries
   c. the muscles around atria
   d. the muscles around ventricles

12. If you push on liquid, what happens? (7.6)
   a. The pressure increases.
   b. The pressure decreases.
   c. The fluid expands.
   d. The fluid compresses.

13. What function does the fluid in your semicircular canals serve? (7.5.g)
   a. It carries nutrients to and wastes from parts of your eye.
   b. It transmits sound waves to your inner ear.
   c. It helps match the air pressures near your eardrum.
   d. It helps you detect motions of your head.

14. What do eustachian tubes help you do? (7.5.g)
   a. balance air pressure
   b. detect motion of your head
   c. detect sound waves
   d. produce ear wax

15. What condition is called glaucoma? (7.5.b)
   a. too little aqueous humor
   b. too much pressure in the aqueous humor
   c. too little pressure in the tear ducts
   d. excess tears

Short Answer *Write a short answer to each question.*

16. What muscle contracts and helps expand your lungs when you inhale?

17. When the heart muscle contracts, what happens to the blood pressure inside the heart? (7.6.j)

18. What main function does blood serve?

19. Your ear has an outer, a middle, and an inner part. Which of these are filled with fluid? (7.5.g)

20. What structure in your ear helps you maintain balance? (7.5.g)

Thinking Critically

Use the diagram below to help you answer the next two questions.

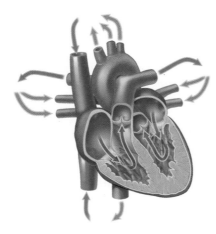

21. COMPARE AND CONTRAST How do the functions of the atria and ventricles of the heart differ? How are they alike? (7.6.j)

22. ANALYZE What is the function of the valves in the heart? (7.6.j)

23. CONCLUDE What makes a fluid different from a solid? (7.6.)

24. INFER To inflate the cuff of a device that measures blood pressure, you squeeze repeatedly on a flexible bulb. The bulb works something like a ventricle: when you squeeze, air is pushed from the bulb into the cuff. When you release the bulb, air from the room moves into the bulb. What can you infer must be at each end of the bulb's inner chamber? (7.6.j)

25. CONNECT How can walking help your blood circulation? To help you answer, think about where most of your blood is at any particular time. (7.6.j)

26. ANALYZE Think about how blood circulates in the pulmonary and systemic circuits. Where is blood pressure especially high? Where do you think blood moves most slowly? (7.6.j)

27. INFER Explain the function of valves in your veins. (7.6.j)

28. COMPARE AND CONTRAST Use a Venn diagram with three circles to show the characteristics of arteries, veins, and capillaries. Remember to put shared characteristics in the overlapping areas. (7.6.j)

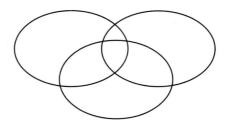

29. INFER Is your blood in an open container or a closed container? Explain your answer. (7.6.j)

30. PROVIDE EXAMPLES Describe three fluids in the body that move materials. What type of material does each move?

Using Math Skills in Science

31. What is the pressure when a force of 10 newtons acts on an area of 0.5 square meters? (7.6)

32. What force will produce a pressure of 100,000 N/m^2 on an area of 1 cm^2? (7.6)

33. A pressure of 16,000 Pa will produce a force of 0.4 N over what area? (7.6)

the BIG idea

34. SYNTHESIZE How do fluids and fluid pressures affect your ears? Use the chart on page 403 to help you answer the question. (7.5.g)

35. APPLY Return to the question about the photograph on page 384. Answer the question again, using what you have learned in the chapter. (7.5.g)

UNIT PROJECTS

Evaluate all the data, results, and information from your project folder. Prepare to present your project.

Interpreting a Passage

7.6.j

Read the following passage. Then answer the questions that follow.

The heart drives the circulatory system by pumping blood. Contractions of the heart exert pressure, which causes blood to flow through the blood vessels. Blood flows from this region of higher pressure to regions of lower pressure.

Physicians measure two types of blood pressure, typically in the arteries of the upper arm. Systolic blood pressure is the maximum pressure exerted when the heart is contracting. Diastolic blood pressure is the pressure when the heart is at rest. The readings are usually written as systolic pressure over diastolic pressure, such as 120/80. The pressures are expressed in units of millimeters of mercury (mm Hg). A value less than 120/80 mm Hg is considered healthy. A systolic reading greater than 140 mm Hg or a diastolic reading greater than 90 mm Hg is considered to be high blood pressure.

1. What happens when the heart contracts?

   a. The heart exerts pressure on the blood.

   b. Blood flows from lower to higher pressure.

   c. The person has unhealthy, high blood pressure.

   d. A physician measures diastolic blood pressure.

2. Which of the following blood pressure readings would be considered healthy?

   a. 145/70 mm Hg   **c.** 115/75 mm Hg

   b. 110/95 mm Hg   **d.** 130/100 mm Hg

3. Physicians normally measure the blood pressure in

   a. veins   **c.** capillaries

   b. arteries   **d.** the heart

4. Your arteries contract when you are in a stressful situation. If that contraction reduced the area across your arteries to half the original size, how would your blood pressure be affected? (Recall that $P = F/A$.)

   a. It would stay the same.   **c.** It would be half as much.

   b. It would double.   **d.** It would quadruple.

5. A typical adult has 4–6 liters of blood. When a person donates blood, the amount taken is usually 400–500 milliliters. What effect would you expect blood donation to have on a person's blood pressure?

   a. no effect   **c.** small increase

   b. large decrease   **d.** small decrease

Extended Response

Answer the two questions in detail. Include some of the terms from the word box in your answers. Underline each term you use.

fluid	pressure	artery
vein	capillary	volume

6. Arteries have thick, strong, elastic walls. Veins have thinner walls and one-way valves. Explain how these structures help the blood vessels function differently. Remember that the blood pressure is much higher in arteries than in veins.

7. Salt can help keep excess fluids in the body, which may increase the volume of blood in the body. What effect do you think that eating too much salt will have on blood pressure, and why?

UNIT 4

Physical Principles in Hearing and Vision

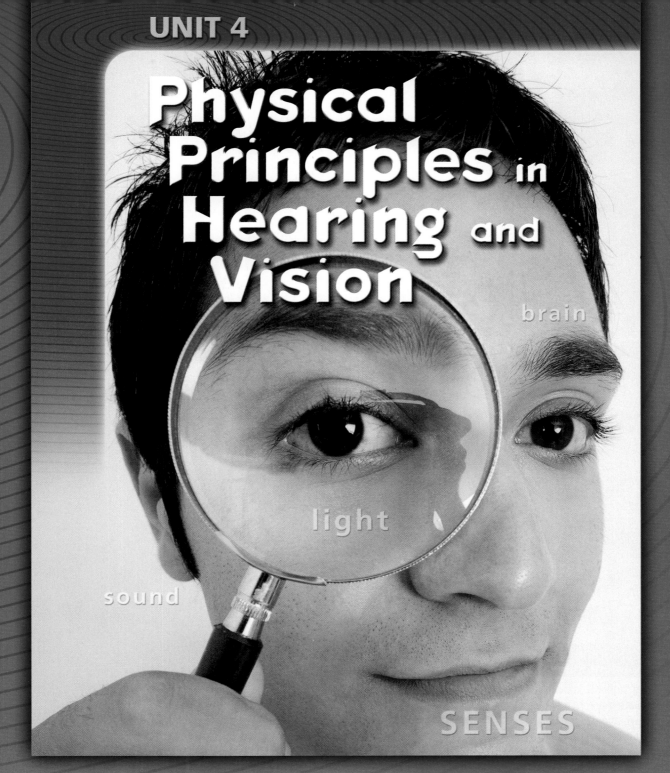

brain

light

sound

SENSES

Contents Overview

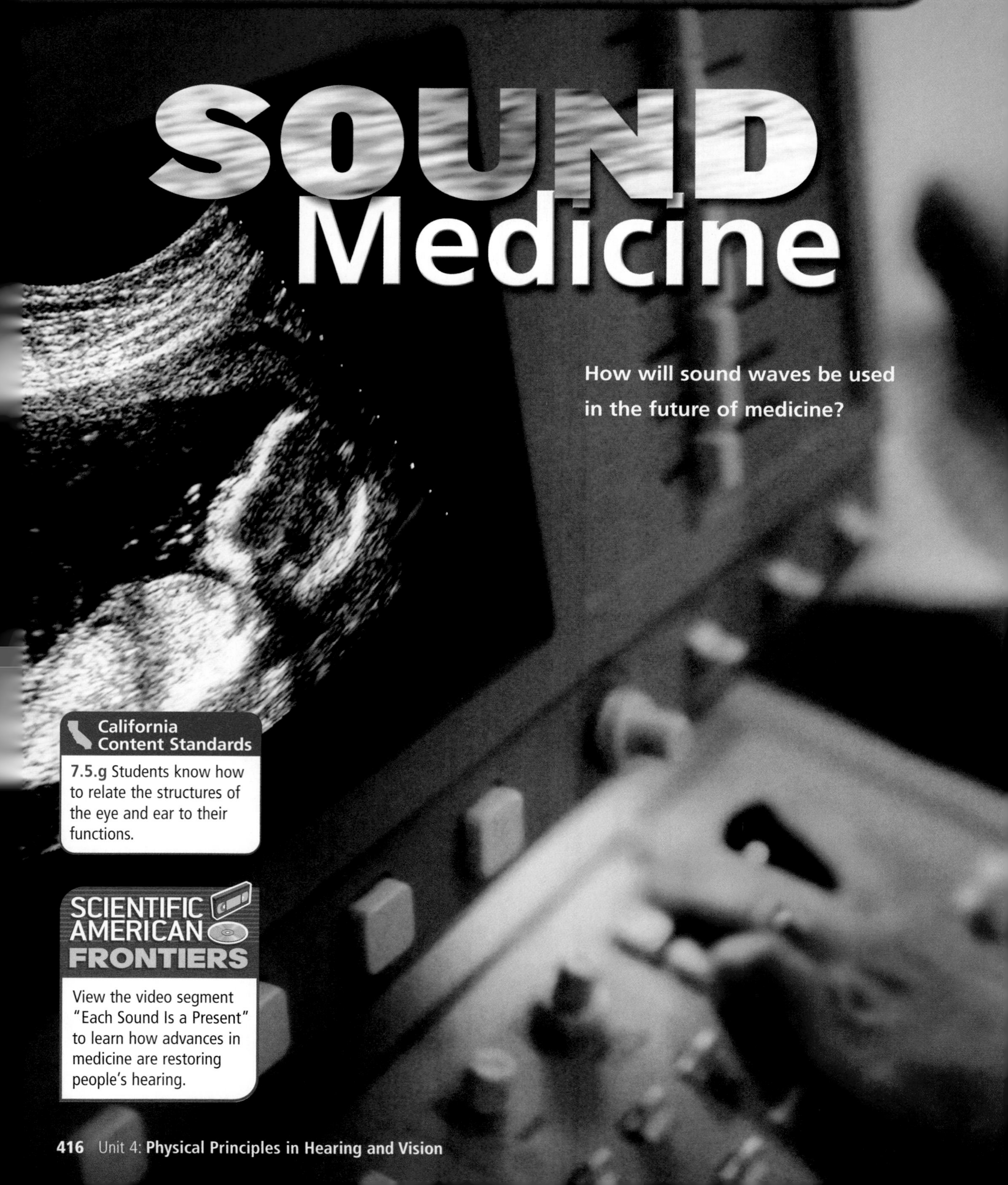

SOUND
Medicine

How will sound waves be used in the future of medicine?

California Content Standards

7.5.g Students know how to relate the structures of the eye and ear to their functions.

SCIENTIFIC AMERICAN FRONTIERS

View the video segment "Each Sound Is a Present" to learn how advances in medicine are restoring people's hearing.

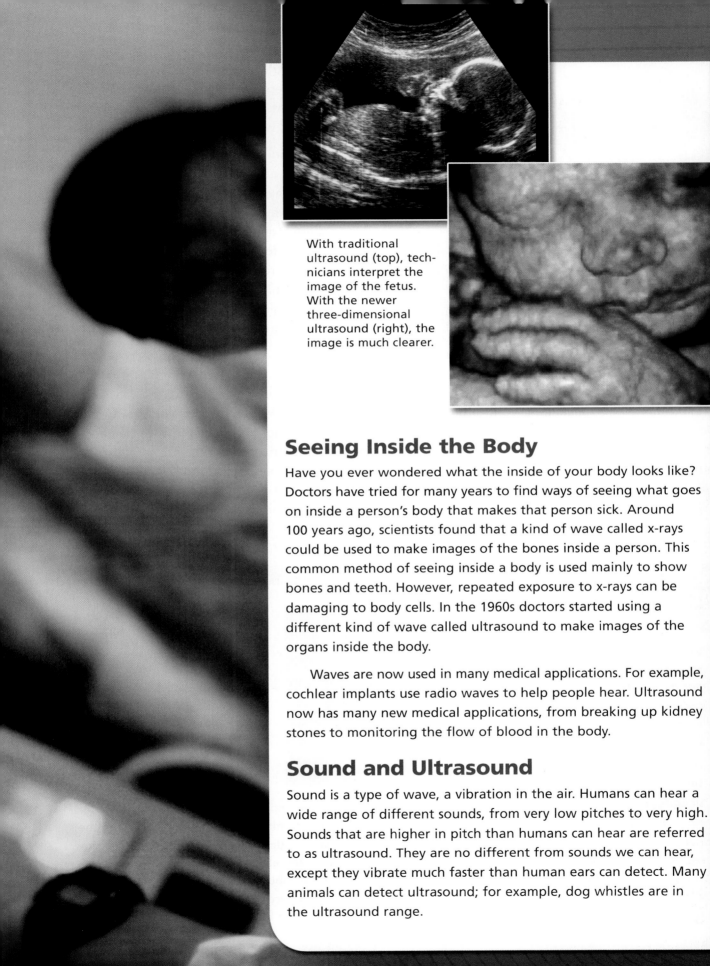

With traditional ultrasound (top), technicians interpret the image of the fetus. With the newer three-dimensional ultrasound (right), the image is much clearer.

Seeing Inside the Body

Have you ever wondered what the inside of your body looks like? Doctors have tried for many years to find ways of seeing what goes on inside a person's body that makes that person sick. Around 100 years ago, scientists found that a kind of wave called x-rays could be used to make images of the bones inside a person. This common method of seeing inside a body is used mainly to show bones and teeth. However, repeated exposure to x-rays can be damaging to body cells. In the 1960s doctors started using a different kind of wave called ultrasound to make images of the organs inside the body.

Waves are now used in many medical applications. For example, cochlear implants use radio waves to help people hear. Ultrasound now has many new medical applications, from breaking up kidney stones to monitoring the flow of blood in the body.

Sound and Ultrasound

Sound is a type of wave, a vibration in the air. Humans can hear a wide range of different sounds, from very low pitches to very high. Sounds that are higher in pitch than humans can hear are referred to as ultrasound. They are no different from sounds we can hear, except they vibrate much faster than human ears can detect. Many animals can detect ultrasound; for example, dog whistles are in the ultrasound range.

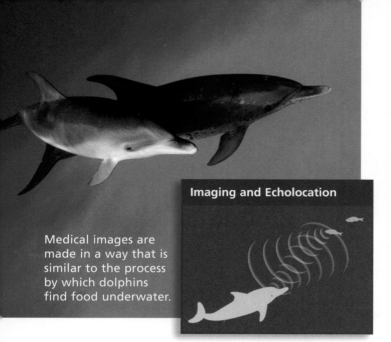

Imaging and Echolocation

Medical images are made in a way that is similar to the process by which dolphins find food underwater.

the sound to travel to the object and return. Echolocation enables bats to capture flying insects at night and dolphins to catch fish in the ocean depths, where light doesn't penetrate.

Similarly, in ultrasound imaging, a machine sends a beam of ultrasound into a person's body and detects any echoes. The waves reflect whenever they strike a boundary between two objects with different densities. A computer measures the time required for the wave to travel to the boundary and reflect back. This information is used to determine the location and shape of the organ. The computer can then generate a live image of the organ inside the body.

The technology of ultrasound in medicine is based upon a process similar to that used by bats and dolphins to find food, a process called echolocation. The animal emits an ultrasound click or chirp and then listens for an echo. The echo indicates that an object has reflected the sound back to the animal. Over time, these animals have evolved the ability to judge how far away the object is by noting the time required for

Ultrasound imaging has been used most often to monitor the development of a fetus inside its mother and to observe the valves of the heart. Blood flow can be color coded with faster flow in one color and slower flow in another color. The colors make it easier to see the location of blockages affecting the rate of flow in the blood vessels. This helps doctors detect blockages and diagnose heart problems.

SCIENTIFIC AMERICAN FRONTIERS

View the "Each Sound Is a Present" segment of your *Scientific American Frontiers* video to learn how a cochlear implant restores hearing to a young girl.

IN THIS SCENE FROM THE VIDEO ▶
A young girl's cochlear implant is turned on for the first time.

HEARING IS A GIFT A recent development in technology is about to give seven-year-old Kelley Flynn something she has always wanted —better hearing. Kelley has been almost completely deaf since she was two years old, and now she is losing the little hearing she does have. The development is a device called

a cochlear implant. Cochlear implants work inside the ear, stimulating the brain when a sound is detected.

Normally, sound travels as vibrations from the outer ear through the middle ear to the inner ear, where thousands of tiny cells—called hair cells— register the quality of the sound and send a signal to the brain. In a cochlear implant, tiny electrical sensors, or electrodes, mimic the hair cells by registering the sound and sending a signal to the brain. The signals get to the electrodes through a system that includes a computer, a microphone, a radio transmitter, and a receiver. Using this system, people with little or no hearing are able to sense sounds.

Recent advances in ultrasound technology include the development of portable devices that display images of the body, such as this hand-held device.

Advances in Ultrasound

Waves, including ultrasound, transfer energy. Physical therapists often use this fact when applying ultrasound to sore joints, heating the muscles and ligaments so they can move more freely. If the ultrasound waves are given stronger intensity and sharper focus, they can transfer enough energy to break up kidney stones in the body. The use of focused sound waves is now being tested for its ability to treat other problems, such as foot injuries.

Other recent advances in medical ultrasound include the development of devices that produce clearer images and use equipment that is smaller in size. In the late 1990s portable ultrasound devices were developed that allow the technology to be brought to the patient.

UNANSWERED Questions

As scientists learn more about the use of sound and other types of waves, new questions will arise.

• Will new methods of imaging the body change the way diseases are diagnosed?

• How closely do sounds heard using a cochlear implant resemble sounds heard by the ear?

UNIT PROJECTS

As you study this unit, work alone or with a group on one of these projects.

Magazine Article (7.6)

Write a magazine article about the medical uses of ultrasound.

• Collect information about medical ultrasound and take notes about applications that interest you.

• If possible, conduct an interview with a medical practitioner who uses ultrasound.

• Read over all your notes and decide what information to include in your article.

Make a Music Video (7.5.g)

Make a music video for a song of your choice, and explain how the video uses sound waves and light waves.

• Plan the sound portion of the video, including how the music will be played and amplified.

• For the lighting, use colored cellophane or gels to mix different colors of light. Explain your choices.

• Rehearse the video. Record the video and present it to the class.

Design a Demonstration (7.6)

Design a hands-on demonstration of echolocation.

• Research the use of echolocation by animals.

• Design a demonstration of echolocation using a tennis ball and an obstacle.

• Present your demonstration to the class.

CAREER CENTER
CLASSZONE.COM

Learn more about careers in audiology.

12 Sound

the **BIG** idea

The ear responds to sound waves.

Key Concepts

SECTION

1 Sound is one type of wave.
Learn that sound is a pressure wave, and learn about wave frequency, speed, and wavelength.

SECTION

2 People produce and detect sound waves.
Learn how sound waves of different frequencies are produced and detected in the body.

SECTION

3 The ear responds to sounds.
Learn how the inner ear detects sound and sends signals to the brain.

 California ClassZone

CLASSZONE.COM

Chapter 12 online resources: Content Review, Simulation, Visualization, three Resource Centers, Math Tutorial, Test Practice

How does the sound of the guitar get to your ears?

EXPLORE (the **BIG** idea)

How Does a Sound Change If You Move Your Head?

 7.5.g Students know how to relate the structures of the eye and ear to their functions.

Tap your finger lightly on a table. Listen with your head turned to one side so your ear is facing down. Tap your finger hard on the table. Repeat with your head turned to the other side. Now, place your head on the table so that one ear is flat against the table. Tap the table again.

Observe and Think
How did the sounds differ each time? When did the tapping sound the loudest?

How Can Energy Be Passed Along?

 7.6 Physical principles underlie biological structures and functions.

Stand several videos up in line. Knock over the first video, and notice the motion of the other videos.

Observe and Think Write down your observations. How far did each video move? What traveled from the beginning to the end of the line? Where did the energy to move the last video come from?

NSTA
scilinks.org

SC*L*INKS

What Is Sound? **Code: MDL028**

Getting Ready to Learn

◀ CONCEPT REVIEW

- Energy can be transferred from one place to another.
- Forces can cause changes in motion.

◀ VOCABULARY REVIEW

force p. 364

pressure p. 388

See Glossary for definitions.

density, energy

CONTENT REVIEW
CLASSZONE.COM

Review concepts and vocabulary.

▶ TAKING NOTES

OUTLINE

As you read, copy the headings on your paper in the form of an outline. Then add notes in your own words that summarize what you have read.

VOCABULARY STRATEGY

Place each vocabulary term at the center of a **description wheel** diagram. Write some words on the spokes describing it.

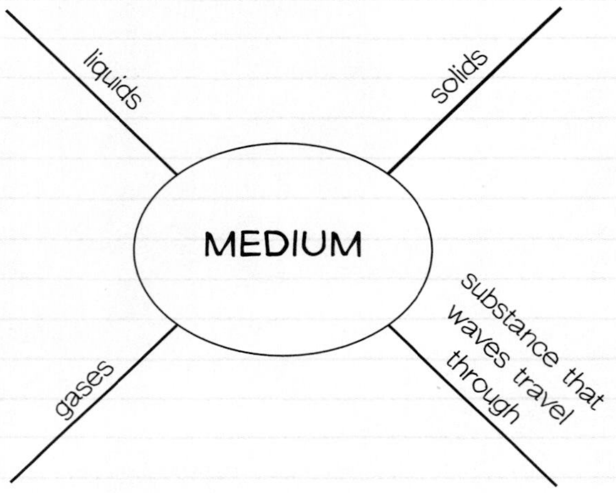

See the Note-Taking Handbook on pages R45–R51.

SCIENCE NOTEBOOK

I. Sound is one type of wave.
  A. Sound is a pressure wave.
  B. Moving air carries sound waves.
    1. longitudinal waves
    2. transverse waves
  C. Sound needs a medium to travel.

Description wheel diagram: center **MEDIUM**; spokes labeled liquids, solids, gases, substance that waves travel through.

Sound is one type of wave.

CALIFORNIA
Content Standard

Background for 7.5.g Students know how to relate the structures of the eye and ear to their functions.

◀ BEFORE, you learned

- Pressure can cause a fluid to move and transfer a force
- Air can be compressed and will expand to fill its container

▶ NOW, you will learn

- How sound waves are produced
- How sound waves transfer energy
- About the characteristics of waves

VOCABULARY

wave p. 423
sound p. 423
medium p. 424
frequency p. 428
hertz p. 428
wavelength p. 428

EXPLORE Sound (7.5.g)

Can you hear if you plug your ears?

PROCEDURE

1. Tie the middle of the string to the spoon handle.

2. Wrap the string ends around your left and right index fingers. Place the tips of these fingers gently in your ears and hold them there.

3. Stand over your desk so that the spoon dangles without touching your body or the desk. Then move a little to make the spoon tap the desk lightly. Listen to the sound.

WHAT DO YOU THINK?

- What did you hear when the spoon tapped the desk?
- How did sound travel from the spoon to your ears?

MATERIALS
- piece of string
- large metal spoon

OUTLINE
Start an outline for this section. Remember to leave room for details.

I. Main idea
  A. Supporting idea
    1. Detail
    2. Detail
  B. Supporting idea

Sound is a pressure wave.

A ringing telephone, a honking horn, and the sound of a friend's voice are all examples of sounds that you might hear today. But what is sound? Where does it come from? Every sound that you hear depends on sound waves. A **wave** is a disturbance that transfers energy from one place to another.

When an object vibrates—moves back and forth rapidly—the pressure in the surrounding air changes. This vibration creates areas of high and low air pressure. The energy from the vibration is transferred through the air as a sound wave. **Sound** is a pressure wave that is produced by a vibrating object and travels through matter.

Moving air carries sound waves.

You are probably familiar with waves in water. Sound waves can travel through air, solid materials, and liquids. A substance that sound and other waves can travel through is called a **medium.** Air is a medium made up of molecules of different gases. How can you picture sound waves moving through air?

For example, think about a drum that has been struck. What happens between the time the drum is struck and when the sound is heard?

- The drum skin vibrates rapidly. It moves in and out again and again. The motion, called a vibration, is very fast. With each movement outward, the drum skin pushes against the air nearby. The particles that make up the air are pushed together, or compressed.

- The movement of the particles transfers the disturbance to the listener. The bunched-up areas are called compressions. The less-dense areas between the compressions are called rarefactions. Together the compressions and rarefactions make up the wave.

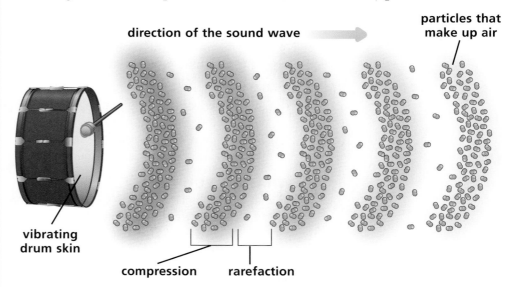

direction of the sound wave

particles that make up air

vibrating drum skin

compression   rarefaction

Notice in the diagram above that the sound wave consists of a repeating pattern of compressions and rarefactions. Air in the compression of the wave is more dense and therefore at a higher pressure than the surrounding air. The particles in the compression bump into each other more often. The bumping compresses the air to the right. This pushes on the surrounding air, which then pushes on the air around that. A less dense area is left behind—a rarefaction. A rarefaction is an area of low pressure. Soon a sound wave has traveled through the air and has transferred energy from one place to another.

SIMULATION
CLASSZONE.COM

Explore how sound travels through air.

CHECK YOUR READING   Summarize how sound travels through air.

Longitudinal Waves

A sound wave moves forward through the air. The particles of air do not all travel forward. Instead they move back and forth. The particles move back and forth due to the change in pressure. Look at the diagram below to see what happens to a single particle as a sound wave travels through the air.

RESOURCE CENTER
CLASSZONE.COM

Learn more about waves.

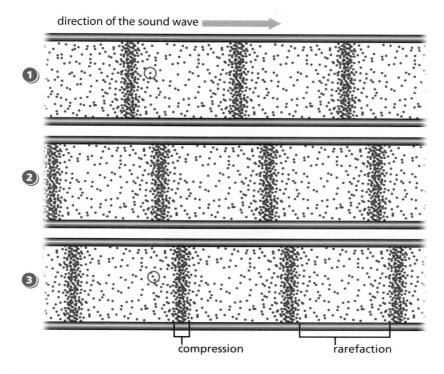

direction of the sound wave

compression   rarefaction

❶ Notice that the circled particle is in an area of low pressure, or rarefaction.

❷ An area of high pressure pushes into the particle's location. The particles in this area are pushed together and compressed as the wave moves.

❸ As the area of high pressure moves on, the particles spread out into the less compressed area, or rarefaction.

Notice that the particle moves back and forth within a small area as the disturbance travels through the air. The particle is not carried with the wave. The wave carries its energy through the medium.

Waves can be classified by how they move. Sound waves are examples of longitudinal (LAHN-jih-TOOD-n-uhl) waves. In a longitudinal wave, the wave travels in the same direction as the disturbance. Any vibrating object can start a longitudinal wave. Longitudinal waves are also sometimes called compressional waves, or pressure waves.

READING TiP

The word *long* can help you remember longitudinal waves. The disturbance moves along the direction of motion of the wave.

Transverse Waves

Some waves transfer an up-and-down or a side-to-side motion, and are known as transverse waves. Suppose one end of a rope is tied to a doorknob. You can apply force to the rope by flicking it upward and downward. This sends a wave through the rope, as shown below. Your hand causes a disturbance in the rope. This wave travels forward along the length of the rope, from your hand toward the doorknob.

Transverse Wave

direction of disturbance   direction of wave

READING TiP

Perpendicular means at a 90° angle.

90°

The wave in the rope is transverse. *Transverse* means "across" or "crosswise." In a transverse wave, the direction of the disturbance is perpendicular, or at right angles, to the direction that the wave travels. The disturbance in the rope is up-and-down, across the rope's length.

Like longitudinal waves, transverse waves transfer energy. Ocean waves are examples of transverse waves. They transfer energy forward but leave the water in place. A big ocean wave can transfer enough energy to knock someone down.

INVESTIGATE Wave Types

How do waves travel?

PROCEDURE

1. Place the spring toy on the floor on its side. Have your partner hold one end of the spring. Hold the other end of the spring and stretch it slightly.

2. Quickly move your end of the spring toward and then away from your partner. Observe the movement in the spring.

3. Hold the spring as in step 1. Quickly move the end of the spring sideways, then back. Remember that a transverse wave travels at right angles to the disturbance.

WHAT DO YOU THINK?

- Compare the two types of waves that you made. How are they alike? How are they different?
- What kind of wave did you make in step 2?

CHALLENGE Can you change the speed at which the wave travels?

SKILL FOCUS
Modeling (7.5.g)

MATERIALS
spring toy

TIME
10 minutes

Sound needs a medium to travel.

Sound can move only through a medium that is made up of matter. Sound waves can travel through air, solid materials, and liquids, such as water, because all of these mediums are made up of particles. Sound waves cannot travel through a vacuum.

READING TiP
A vacuum is a space containing few or no particles of matter.

Different types of waves travel at different speeds. For example, light waves travel through air almost a million times faster than sound waves travel through air. Suppose you are in the stands during an exciting baseball game. A pitch flies from the mound toward home plate. You see the batter draw back, swing, and hit the ball. A split second later you hear the crack of the bat meeting the ball. You notice that the sound of the hit comes later than the sight of it. Why does this happen?

The light waves arrive first. So you see the action of the bat hitting the ball while the sound waves are still on their way. Two main factors affect the speed of sound: the material that makes up the medium—such as air or water—and its temperature. If we know the medium and the temperature we can predict the speed of sound. Sound waves travel faster through a medium at higher temperatures, and slower at lower temperatures.

CHECK YOUR READING What two factors affect the speed of sound?

You have probably heard sounds in more than one medium. Think about the medium in which you most often hear sound—air. You listen to your friend talking. You hear the siren of a fire truck. These sound waves travel through air.

Now think about swimming. You dip below the water's surface and hear strange underwater sounds. Sound travels faster in liquids than it does in gases because liquids are denser than gases. This means that the particles are packed closer together. It takes less time for one water molecule to bump into another.

Sound can also travel through solid materials. In solid materials, atoms are attached more firmly to one another. The atoms are not as free to move. Steel is an example of a material that is very dense. Sound travels very rapidly through steel. Look at the chart on the right. Compare the speed of sound in air with the speed of sound in steel.

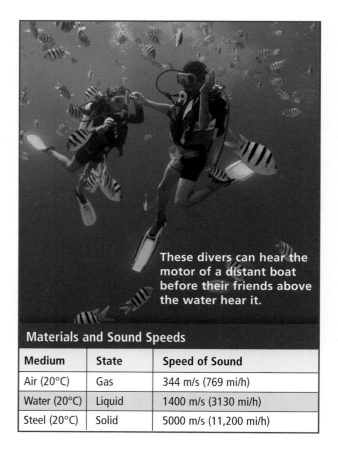

These divers can hear the motor of a distant boat before their friends above the water hear it.

Materials and Sound Speeds

Medium	State	Speed of Sound
Air (20°C)	Gas	344 m/s (769 mi/h)
Water (20°C)	Liquid	1400 m/s (3130 mi/h)
Steel (20°C)	Solid	5000 m/s (11,200 mi/h)

Sound and other waves have measurable properties.

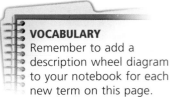
VOCABULARY
Remember to add a description wheel diagram to your notebook for each new term on this page.

You learned that the speed of sound depends on both the medium and its temperature. In addition to speed, there are two other important properties of a wave—frequency and wavelength.

Think again about a transverse wave moving along a rope. Each up-and-down motion of your hand produces a wave with one high point and one low point. This is one cycle. **Frequency** is the number of cycles in a given amount of time. The word *frequent* means "often," so frequency measures how often a cycle occurs. You can determine the frequency of a wave by counting the number of peaks that pass a fixed point in a measured amount of time. The unit for frequency is the hertz. One **hertz** (Hz) is one cycle per second.

Wavelength is the distance from any point of one cycle to the identical point of the next cycle. In the rope, the wavelength can be measured from the high point in one wave to the high point in the next wave. You can measure from any point in the wave, such as the center points or low points. In longitudinal waves, you can measure wavelength from the center of one compression to the center of the next compression.

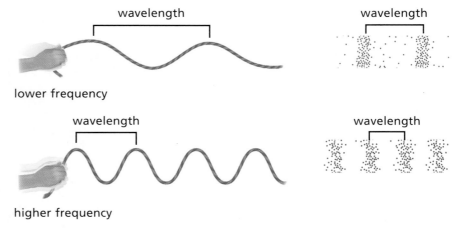

The frequency and wavelength of a wave in a medium are related. When frequency increases, more cycles pass a fixed point each second. This means the wavelength shortens. So, as frequency increases, wavelength decreases. The opposite is also true—as frequency decreases, wavelength increases.

Suppose you are making waves in the rope. If you make one cycle every second, the frequency is one per second (1/s). Now suppose you want to increase the frequency to more than one cycle per second. You flick the rope up and down faster. The tops of the waves are now closer together, meaning the wavelengths are shorter.

Frequency, wavelength, and speed are related.

Think about what happens when you hear a knock at the door. How is the sound made? How does the sound travel to your ear?

1 Your hand strikes the door. The strike produces a set of disturbances, not just one. Each of these disturbances is a sound wave. The diagram on the right shows one of these sound waves.

2 The door vibrates. The sound wave travels through the door. The compressions of the wave in the door are shown in blue stripes. Both surfaces of the door vibrate.

3 Each surface of the door pushes on the surrounding air producing compressions and rarefactions. The resulting sound wave travels through the air. Sound is produced on both sides of the door. It travels back to your ear as well as through the door and through the air on the other side of the door.

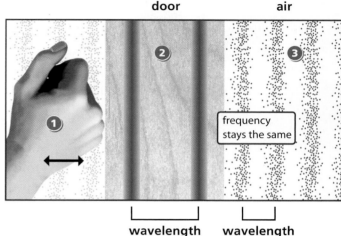

Recall that frequency, wavelength, and speed are all related. Sound travels faster in a solid medium—the door—than in air. The speed of the wave changes as it enters the air but the frequency stays the same. As a result, the wavelength changes. The blue stripes in the door and the dotted stripes in the air show how the wavelength is shorter in air, where the wave moves more slowly.

The relationships among speed, frequency, and wavelength can be expressed in a formula:

$$\textbf{wavelength} = \textbf{Speed/frequency}$$
$$\lambda = S/f$$

Wavelength is measured in meters, frequency in hertz, and speed in meters per second. The formula can be used to find the wavelength of a sound wave if you know the wave's speed and its frequency. For example, the musical note middle C has a frequency of 256 hertz, or 256 cycles per second. Under typical conditions the speed of sound in air is about 340 meters per second (m/s).

$$\lambda = \frac{340 \text{ m/s}}{256 \text{ Hz}} = 1.32 \text{ m}$$

The wavelength of middle C is about 1.3 meters (about 4.4 ft). Compare this length to the length of your outstretched arms.

> **REMINDER**
> The formula can be rearranged to find speed or frequency.
> Speed = wavelength · frequency
> $S = \lambda f$
> frequency = $\frac{\text{Speed}}{\text{wavelength}}$
> $f = \frac{S}{\lambda}$

Most sound comes to you through air. If sounds are all traveling through air at the same speed (340 m/s), then a high-frequency wave has a short wavelength and a low-frequency wave has a long wavelength.

Most sounds that you hear are a combination of different frequencies and wavelengths. So why are some sounds considered noise and other sounds considered music? Noise is random sound; that means it has no intended pattern. Noise is a combination of many different frequencies and wavelengths.

Music is based upon sounds that have repeating cycles and specific frequencies. For example, a tuning fork for the musical note middle A produces regular sound waves with the frequency of 440 hertz. A guitar or flute also produces regular waves of 440 hertz when middle A is played. However, other frequencies are also produced in addition to 440 hertz. These combinations of frequencies give each instrument its own characteristic sound. The particular pattern of frequencies makes a guitar sound different from a flute. They also help you recognize the sounds as music.

 How is noise different from music?

12.1 Review

KEY CONCEPTS

1. Describe how sound waves can be produced.
2. Describe how particles move as energy is transferred by a sound wave through air.
3. What two measurements of a wave do you need to calculate wave speed?

CRITICAL THINKING

4. **Provide Examples** Give examples of transverse waves and longitudinal waves.
5. **Predict** Would the sound from a distant train travel faster through air or through steel train tracks? Explain.

CHALLENGE

6. **Evaluate** A famous riddle asks this question: If a tree falls in the forest and there is no one there to hear it, does it make a sound? What do you think? Give reasons for your answer.

STEREOPHONIC HEARING

Sound in Movies

> **7.5.g** Students know how to relate the structures of the eye and ear to their functions.

Since the early 1900s, Hollywood, California, has been famous for its movie industry. The first movies were silent. Since then, Hollywood filmmakers have found ways to use sound to make the experience seem more realistic.

Think about watching a movie where a plane seems to come from behind you. You hear it while it's behind you, before it passes into view. Then the sound seems to be coming from a moving object overhead. You know the sound is really coming from speakers, but no speaker moves overhead as the plane seems to. Everyone in the movie theater has the same experience. The sound engineers have fooled your ears.

It Takes Two

Several factors help you tell where a sound comes from. One is loudness. A plane is louder when it is closer. The loudness may be different in your two ears. A plane to your left sends sound waves straight to your left ear. Your head blocks the waves to your right ear, and so the sound is softer on your right. Also, each

Your two ears help you tell the direction of a sound, but fixed speakers in a theater can fool your ears.

sound wave from the plane gets to your left ear a tiny bit sooner than it gets to your right ear. Your brain takes in all the information: the loudness, the difference in loudness in your two ears, and the difference in timing. If you turn your head while listening, your brain gets even more information. Then you get a sense of where the sound comes from. When the sound is loud, you may also feel the waves of air pressure with other parts of your body.

It Takes Many

Speakers placed around a movie theater produce the sound. Two speakers would be enough to reproduce the loudness and timing for your two ears. But people in different locations would hear different things. Modern movies and movie theaters use many speakers to reproduce the sound correctly for any location in the theater.

Grauman's Chinese Theater in Hollywood, California

WRITING ABOUT SCIENCE

What would happen if moviegoers wore headphones? Write a few paragraphs in which you compare speakers around the walls of a theater with speakers at each person's ears.

KEY CONCEPT

People produce and detect sound waves.

CALIFORNIA
Content Standard

7.5.g Students know how to relate the structures of the eye and ear to their functions.

◀ BEFORE, you learned

- Sound waves are produced by vibrations
- Frequency is the number of cycles in a given amount of time.

▶ NOW, you will learn

- How the frequency of a wave affects the way it sounds
- About the range of frequencies of sound
- About the structure and functions of the human ear

VOCABULARY

pitch p. 432
outer ear p. 436
eardrum p. 436
middle ear p. 437
inner ear p. 437

EXPLORE Pitch (7.5.g)

Why does the sound change?

PROCEDURE

① Hold the ruler flat on the edge of a desk so that it sticks out about 25 centimeters beyond the edge.

② With your free hand, push the tip of the ruler down and then let it go. As the ruler vibrates, slide it back onto the desk. Listen to the sounds the ruler makes.

WHAT DO YOU THINK?

- What happened to the sound as you slid the ruler back onto the desk?
- Describe the motion of the ruler.

MATERIALS
ruler

Faster vibrations produce higher frequencies.

VOCABULARY
Remember to add a description wheel diagram in your notebook for *pitch*.

When you listen to music, you hear both high and low sounds. The characteristic of highness or lowness of a sound is called **pitch.** The frequency of a sound wave determines the pitch of the sound you hear. Remember that frequency is the number of cycles in a given period of time. A high-frequency wave has a high-pitched sound. Examples include a whistle, a child's scream, and an ambulance siren. A low-frequency wave has a low-pitched sound. Examples include a foghorn, a cat's purr, and notes from a tuba. An object vibrating very fast produces a high-pitched sound, while the same object vibrating more slowly produces a lower-pitched sound.

 How is frequency related to pitch?

So how do people make sounds when they speak? The vocal cords produce sounds. Your vocal cords are located within the voice box, or larynx, in your throat. Gently place your fingers against the front of your throat. Now hum. Do you feel the vibrations?

Your vocal cords relax when you breathe to allow air to pass in and out of your windpipe. Your vocal cords tighten, or tense up, and draw close together when you are about to speak or sing. The illustration below shows how sound waves are produced by human vocal cords.

1 Your muscles push air up from your lungs and through the narrow opening between the vocal cords.

2 The force of the air causes your tense vocal cords to vibrate.

3 Your vibrating vocal cords produce sound waves.

The pitch of your voice depends on two things—the length of your vocal cords and how tense they are. Remember that an object vibrating very fast produces a high-pitched sound. When your vocal cords are tense, you produce higher-pitched sounds.

 CHECK YOUR READING How do human vocal cords produce sound waves?

How Vocal Cords Produce Sound

Sound waves are produced by vibrations.

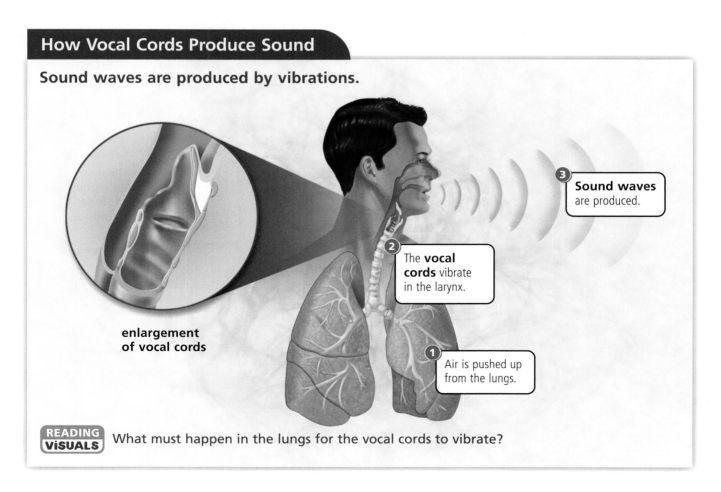

enlargement
of vocal cords

3 **Sound waves** are produced.

2 The **vocal cords** vibrate in the larynx.

1 Air is pushed up from the lungs.

READING VISUALS What must happen in the lungs for the vocal cords to vibrate?

Sound Frequencies Heard by Animals

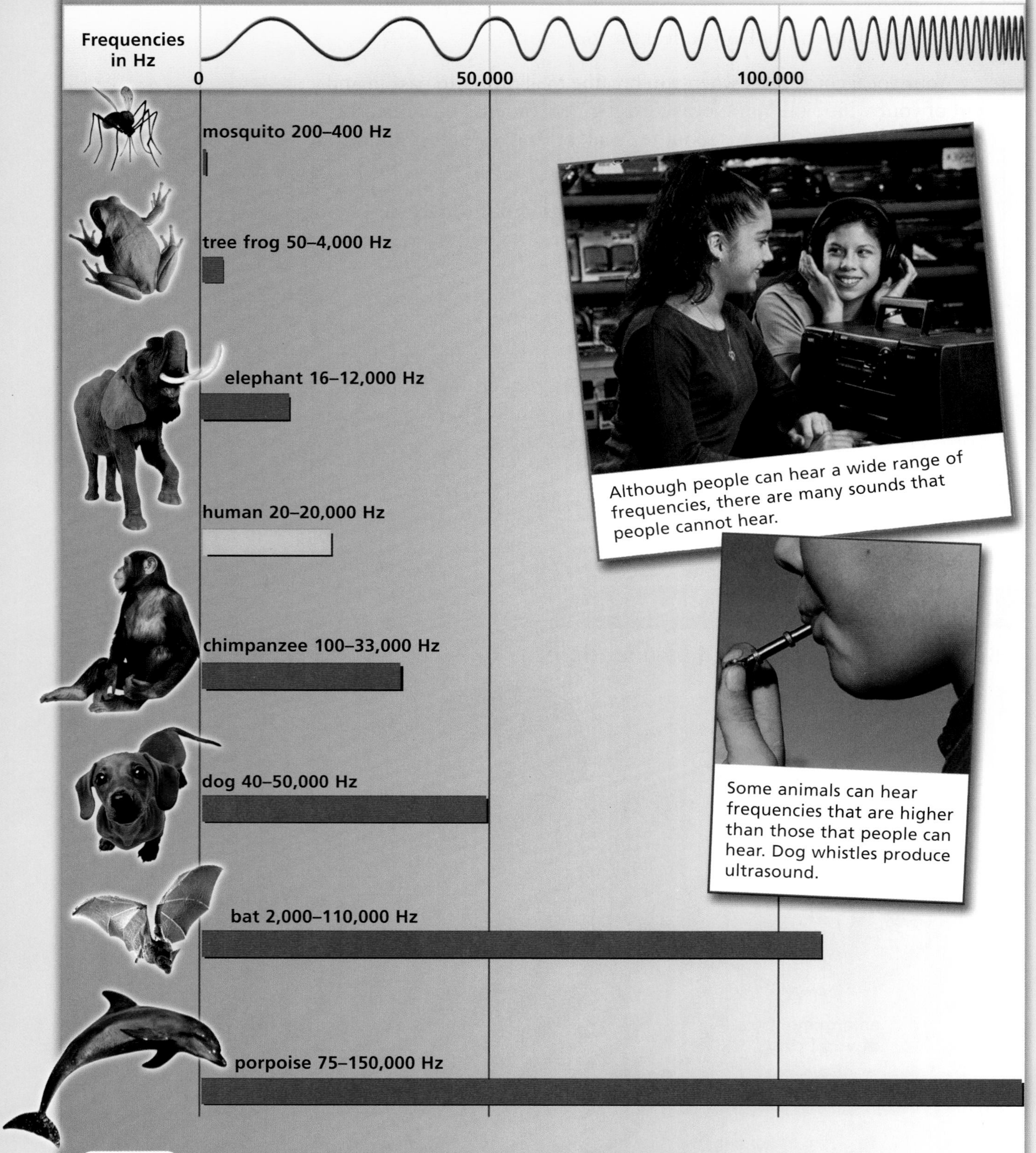

Frequencies in Hz

| 0 | 50,000 | 100,000 |

mosquito 200–400 Hz

tree frog 50–4,000 Hz

elephant 16–12,000 Hz

human 20–20,000 Hz

chimpanzee 100–33,000 Hz

dog 40–50,000 Hz

bat 2,000–110,000 Hz

porpoise 75–150,000 Hz

Although people can hear a wide range of frequencies, there are many sounds that people cannot hear.

Some animals can hear frequencies that are higher than those that people can hear. Dog whistles produce ultrasound.

READING VISUALS Which animals on this chart can hear frequencies above those that humans can hear?

Humans can hear a wide range of frequencies.

In the last section you learned that the unit for measuring frequency and pitch is the hertz. A wave with a frequency of 100 hertz has 100 cycles per second.

Look at the chart of sound frequencies on page 434. Note that humans can hear sounds in the range of 20 hertz to 20,000 hertz. Sound waves below 20 hertz are called infrasound. Humans cannot hear sound in this range. Infrasound waves have very long wavelengths. They can travel great distances without losing much energy. Elephants may use infrasound to communicate over long distances. Some of the waves that elephants use travel through the ground instead of the air, and they may be detected by another elephant up to 32 kilometers (about 20 miles) away.

Sound of frequencies greater than 20,000 hertz are called ultrasound. Although people cannot hear ultrasound, many animals can. Look at the chart on page 434 again. Which animals listed can hear in the ultrasound range?

READING TIP
The prefix *infra-* means "below," and the prefix *ultra-* means "beyond."

 CHECK YOUR READING What is the range of frequencies that humans can hear?

INVESTIGATE The Eardrum

How does sound affect the eardrum?

PROCEDURE

1. Cut off the neck of the balloon with the scissors.

2. Stretch the balloon over the mouth of the jar and pull the sides down past the rim of the jar's mouth. Use a rubber band to make a tight fit.

3. Hold your mouth close to the balloon and talk. Gently touch the surface of the balloon as you continue to speak.

4. Loosen the balloon and repeat step 3. What happens to the balloon's surface now?

WHAT DO YOU THINK?

- What did you hear and feel?
- How do you think sound affects a stretched membrane?
- How did loosening the membrane affect the results?

CHALLENGE Now try humming with your mouth close to the balloon in a high frequency and a low frequency. What happens? Do you detect any differences?

SKILL FOCUS
Observing (7.5.g)

MATERIALS
- small jar
- balloon
- scissors
- rubber band

TIME
10 minutes

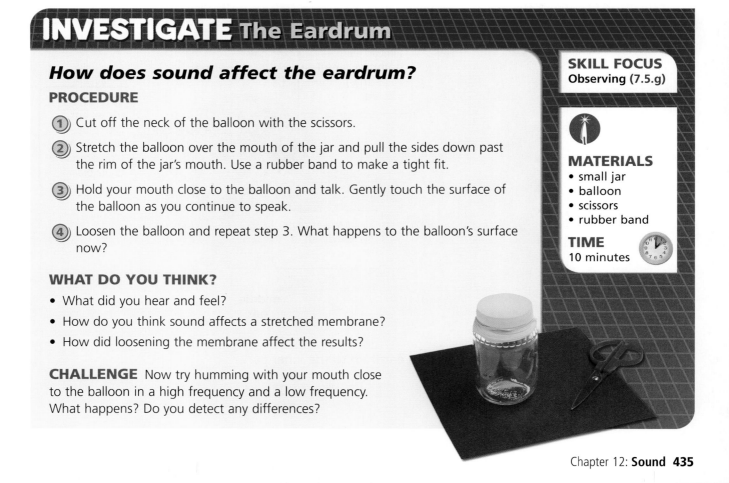

The human ear has three main parts.

The human ear is shaped in a way that helps it collect sound waves. The part of the ear that you can see is only a small part of the ear. The illustration below shows the three main parts of the human ear—the outer ear, middle ear, and inner ear.

Outer Ear Some animals are able to move their ears to face the direction from which a sound is coming. Humans cannot move their ears in this way. The **outer ear** consists of the part of the ear on the outside of your skull and the ear canal. Your outer ear directs sound waves to your eardrum. The **eardrum** is a thin, tightly stretched membrane that separates the outer ear and the middle ear. Remember that sound waves are pressure waves. The waves move through the ear canal and push against the eardrum. They cause the eardrum to move back and forth. The eardrum vibrates at the same frequency as the sound waves that are hitting it.

VISUALIZATION
CLASSZONE.COM

See the process of hearing in action.

CHECK YOUR READING What happens to sound waves in your outer ear?

How the Ear Detects Sound

Sound waves are detected in the human ear, beginning with vibrations of the eardrum.

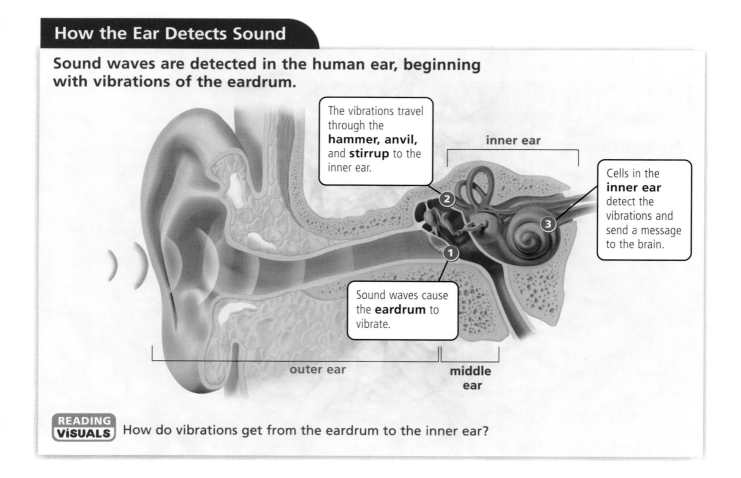

The vibrations travel through the **hammer, anvil, and stirrup** to the inner ear.

Cells in the **inner ear** detect the vibrations and send a message to the brain.

Sound waves cause the **eardrum** to vibrate.

inner ear

outer ear

middle ear

READING VISUALS How do vibrations get from the eardrum to the inner ear?

Middle Ear The **middle ear** is a chamber filled with air. It is connected to the throat by the eustachian tube. The middle ear contains three tiny, connected bones called the hammer, anvil, and stirrup. These bones act as levers. These bones carry the vibrations from the eardrum to another membrane called the oval window. The oval window separates the middle ear from the inner ear. The area of the oval window is smaller than the area of the eardrum. The pressure is greater because the force is concentrated into a smaller area. This pressure moves the oval window back and forth.

Inner Ear The **inner ear** contains the semicircular canals and another fluid-filled structure shaped like a snail. In the inner ear, sensory cells detect the sound waves. The cells send electrical signals along nerves to your brain. Only when the brain receives and processes these signals do you actually perceive a sound. You will learn more about this process in the next section.

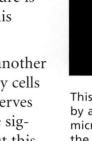

This image produced by a scanning electron microscope (SEM) shows the three bones of the middle ear—hammer, anvil, and stirrup.

 Why is your brain important for hearing?

If you have ever listened to a recording of your voice, you know that it sounds different from the way your speaking voice sounds to you. When you are listening to someone else speak, you hear the sound through air. When you are speaking, the vibrations travel through the air. But vibrations also travel through your body to your eardrums. These internal vibrations are at different frequencies than the sound waves of your voice in air.

12.2 Review

KEY CONCEPTS

1. Describe how a high-pitched sound and a low-pitched sound differ. (7.6)

2. Compare human hearing to that of other animals. List one animal that can hear lower frequencies and one that can hear higher frequencies than humans can hear. (7.5.g)

3. Explain what happens after a sound wave enters your ear. (7.5.g)

CRITICAL THINKING

4. **Apply** When a sound of a 1000 Hz enters your ear, how many times per second do you think your eardrum vibrates?

5. **Analyze** What do you think would happen to your ability to hear if one of the bones in the middle ear were broken?

○ CHALLENGE

6. **Infer** What range of frequencies do you think the human voice can produce? Explain your reasoning.

CHAPTER INVESTIGATION

Modeling the Human Ear

OVERVIEW AND PURPOSE The human ear detects sound waves from the environment and then sends signals to the brain. The part of the ear that we refer to in everyday life is just part of the outer ear. A doctor may examine the rest of your outer ear—the ear canal and eardrum. In this investigation you will

- make models of different structures in the ear
- use the models to learn how the ear functions

▶ Problem

How do the different structures of your ear help you detect sound waves?

▶ Procedure

Part A Modeling the Ear Canal and Eardrum

1. Cover one end of the shorter cardboard tube with plastic wrap. Pull the plastic tight and smooth, and tape it to the tube to represent the eardrum. Draw a diagram of the result.

2. Show how the eardrum can move when acted on by sound waves. Hold the open end of the tube near your mouth and speak quietly. Feel what happens to the plastic wrap as you do this.

3. Record your observations. Remember to record anything you observe with your senses, not just what you see.

MATERIALS
- cardboard tube from bathroom tissue
- plastic wrap
- tape
- plastic drinking straw
- cardboard tube from paper towel roll

  7.5.g, 7.7.d

Content Standard
7.5.g Students know how to relate the structures of the eye and ear to their functions.

Investigation Standard
7.7.d Construct scale models, maps, and appropriately labeled diagrams to commu-nicate scientific knowledge (e.g., motion of Earth's plates and cell structure).

Part B Modeling the Middle Ear

4 Fold the drinking straw into a shape like the letter N.

5 Gently hold one end of the folded straw. Tap the other end of the straw. Record your observations.

Part C Modeling the Cochlea

6 Cover each end of the long tube with plastic wrap. Pull the wrap slightly and tape it in place. The wrap should not be stretched too tightly.

7 Lightly tap the plastic on one end. Observe the other end. Record your observations.

▶ Observe and Analyze

1. **OBSERVE** What happened in Part A?

2. **INFER** In what way does the model eardrum represent a real eardrum?

3. **OBSERVE** What happened in Part B?

4. **COMPARE AND CONTRAST** How is the folded straw similar to the bones in your middle ear? How was it different?

5. **OBSERVE** What happened in Part C?

6. **ANALYZE** Which parts of the model represent the membranes of the oval window and the round window?

▶ Conclude

1. **CONNECT** How might the three models be put together to represent the functions of the ear? Do you think the resulting model would work? Explain your answer.

2. **ANALYZE** What do the movements of the bones of the middle ear affect?

3. **SEQUENCE** Beginning with vibrations in the air, write a sequence that results in a sound being heard.

4. **INTERPRET** Answer the problem question.

5. **IDENTIFY LIMITS** How is each part of the model different from a human ear?

6. **APPLY** How would hearing be affected if the eardrum were not tight and smooth?

▶ INVESTIGATE Further

CHALLENGE How might you make a scale model of your ear? List the pieces of information you would need to design this model. If you have time, build your model.

Modeling the Human Ear

Problem How do the structures of your ear help you detect sound waves?

Observe and Analyze

Table 1. Models and Observations

	Diagram	Observations
Ear canal and eardrum		
Middle ear		
Inner ear		

Conclude

12.3 The ear responds to sounds.

CALIFORNIA
Content Standard

7.5.g Students know how to relate the structures of the eye and ear to their functions.

◄ **BEFORE, you learned**

- Frequency determines the pitch of a sound
- Humans hear sounds of 20–20,000 hertz
- The human ear has three main parts

▶ **NOW, you will learn**

- How the inner ear functions in hearing
- How the ear responds to loud sounds
- How sound can be controlled

VOCABULARY

decibel p. 442

THINK ABOUT

What makes a sound louder?

A drum player has to play softly at some times and loudly at others. Think about what the drummer must do to produce each type of sound. If you could watch the drumsticks in the photograph in action, what would you see? How would they move to make a loud, booming sound? How would they make a very soft sound?

Air pressure moves the eardrum.

OUTLINE
Make an outline for this heading. Remember to include main ideas and details.

I. Main idea
  A. Supporting idea
    1. Detail
    2. Detail
  B. Supporting idea

When a drumstick hits a drum, it causes the drum skin to vibrate. When sound waves hit a solid surface, they can cause the surface to vibrate. Some of the sound's energy is transferred to the solid. Recall that this is how sound waves are transferred to your eardrum.

The sound waves reach your outer ear and move through your ear canal to your eardrum. Your eardrum moves back and forth with each cycle. The louder the sound, the farther the eardrum moves. The vibrations of your eardrum then move through the three bones in your middle ear to your inner ear. Another membrane called the oval window transfers the vibrations to the inner ear.

 CHECK YOUR READING How do sound waves affect your eardrum?

Detecting Sound

Inside the inner ear is the cochlea (KAWK-lee-uh). The cochlea is about the size of a pea and is divided into long coiled chambers. These chambers are filled with fluid. When the stirrup bone vibrates against the oval window, the pressure of the fluid in the cochlea changes. This change in pressure causes the fluid to move. As the fluid moves around the length of the cochlea, another small membrane, called the round window, balloons out. The ballooning action releases some of the pressure in the inner ear.

The moving fluid also disturbs another chamber in the cochlea. The pressure of the fluid bends tiny extensions of the hair cells called cilia. These cilia are special to the hair cells in the inner ear. They line the length of the cochlea. When the cilia move, the hair cells are stimulated and send electrical signals to the brain through the auditory nerve. In the brain the signals are analyzed and interpreted.

You might think that each cycle from a sound wave bends the cilia and starts a new signal to the brain. But this is not the case. Different locations on the cochlea are sensitive to different frequencies. High frequency waves are detected close to the oval window. Lower frequencies are detected farther along the length of the cochlea.

Inside the cochlea, cells are stimulated by sounds and send electrical signals to the brain.

INVESTIGATE Frequency

How is length related to frequency?

PROCEDURE

1. Cut a notch in the middle of each end of the cardboard. Stretch the rubber band around the cardboard so that it fits into the notches as shown.

2. Slide the pencils under the rubber band near each end, near the notches.

3. Pull the part of the rubber band that is between the pencils to one side and let it go. Listen to the sound the rubber band makes.

4. Move the pencils closer together and repeat step 3. Then move them closer and again observe the result. Record your observations.

WHAT DO YOU THINK?

How did the distance between the pencils affect the pitch you heard?

CHALLENGE Repeat the experiment using a thick and a thin rubber band of the same length. How do the sounds made by the two rubber bands compare?

SKILL FOCUS
Observing (7.5.g)

MATERIALS
- piece of cardboard
- scissors
- large rubber band
- 2 pencils
- ruler

TIME
15 minutes

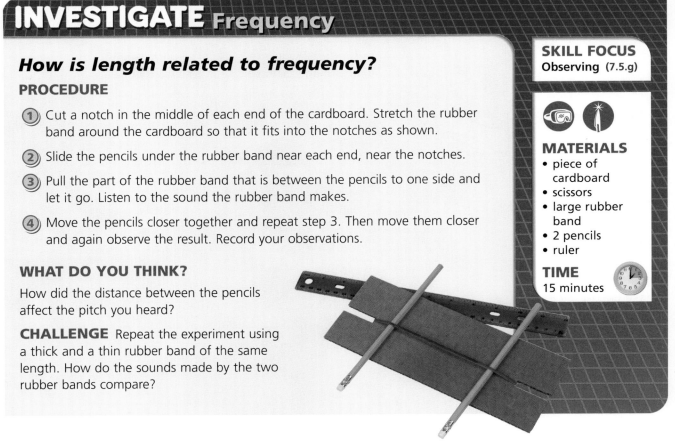

Levels of Sound

less compressed =
softer sound

more compressed =
louder sound

You read earlier that all waves carry energy. When air is more compressed, the pressure and energy are greater. If a sound wave is more compressed it hits your ear with a greater force. It sounds louder. The loudness of a sound is described using a unit called a **decibel (dB).** A sound that is less than 10 decibels can barely be heard. The faint rustling of leaves is about 10 decibels. A sound that is greater than 100 decibels, such as an airplane taking off, is very loud and can hurt your ears.

Sounds gradually fade out over distance. Think about a dog barking. When you are near the dog, the bark is loud. When you are farther away, the bark is softer. Sound waves travel in all directions from their source. As the waves travel farther and farther away from the dog, their energy is spread out over a greater area. The sound reaching your ears is softer. Also, remember that high and low pressure areas—the compressions and rarefactions of the waves—tend to equalize. This also causes the sound to become softer. When sound waves hit a solid surface, they can transfer energy. When objects absorb the energy from sound, the sound becomes softer.

CHECK YOUR READING How is energy related to loudness?

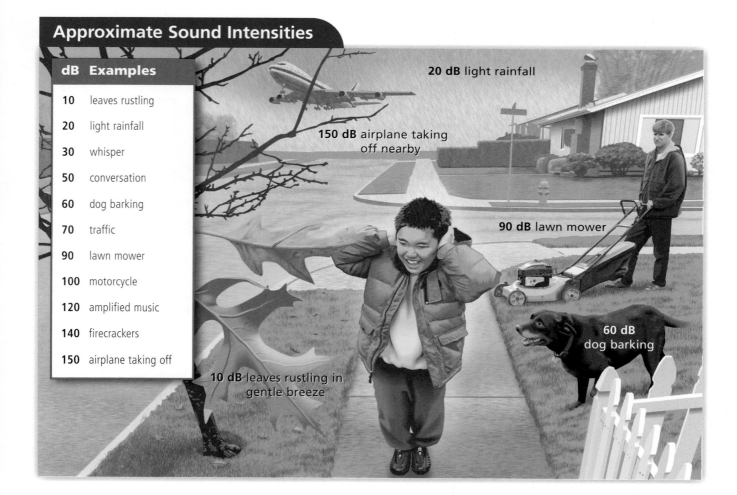

Approximate Sound Intensities

dB	Examples
10	leaves rustling
20	light rainfall
30	whisper
50	conversation
60	dog barking
70	traffic
90	lawn mower
100	motorcycle
120	amplified music
140	firecrackers
150	airplane taking off

20 dB light rainfall

150 dB airplane taking off nearby

90 dB lawn mower

60 dB dog barking

10 dB leaves rustling in gentle breeze

Loudness affects the ear.

When a train screeches to a stop in a subway station, the sound of the squealing brakes echoes, or bounces, off the tunnel walls. Without thinking about it, you cover your ears with your hands. This response helps protect your ears from possible damage.

Response of the Ear

When the ear detects a loud sound, it adjusts. Muscles in the middle ear reduce the effects of sound. One muscle reduces the motion of the stirrup bone. As a result, less energy is transferred to the cochlea. But these muscles can only do so much to protect the ear. A very loud sound can cause damage.

An extremely loud noise can destroy the cilia on the hair cells in the cochlea. Noises above 130 decibels are especially dangerous. Noises above 140 decibels can be painful. It is best to avoid such noises altogether. If you find yourself exposed suddenly to such a noise, covering your ears with your hands may be the best protection. Being exposed to very loud noises, especially for more than a short time, is harmful to hearing. Moderately loud sounds of 90 decibels can also damage or destroy your cilia if you are exposed to these sounds continually.

 CHECK YOUR READING How can sounds damage hearing?

Controlling Sound

Have you ever heard a car with a broken muffler? You were probably surprised at how loud it was. Mufflers on cars and trucks help to reduce engine noise. The burning of fuel in an engine produces hot gases that expand quickly and make a very loud noise. A muffler absorbs some of the energy of the sound waves. As a result, the sound you hear is much softer than it would be without the muffler. There are also many other ways to control the loudness of sounds.

People can use earplugs to reduce the sounds they hear. Earplugs, like mufflers on cars and trucks, help to absorb some of the energy of the sound waves before it gets to the eardrum. Using earplugs can prevent damage from loud sounds. Music at a rock concert can be between 85 and 120 decibels. Damage can also occur from the use of noisy tools or from noisy environments. In some cases, the noise of machines can be reduced or limited to certain areas. In the United States, laws require employers to reduce sounds at work sites to below 90 decibels or to provide workers with ear protection.

healthy cilia

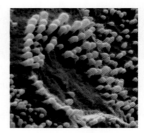
damaged cilia

CALIFORNIA Focus

California's enforcement unit of the Occupational Safety and Health Administration (Cal/OSHA) requires that employers try to avoid subjecting workers to sounds of 90 dB for more than eight hours per day. If the sounds cannot be reduced enough, workers wear protective gear to protect their ears from damaging noise.

RESOURCE CENTER
CLASSZONE.COM
Find out more about sound and protecting your hearing.

The pointed tiles in this sound-testing room are designed to absorb sound waves and prevent any echoes.

The shapes and surfaces in this concert hall direct sound waves to the audience.

Sound can also be controlled in ways that maintain its loudness or change its direction. Acoustics (uh-KOO-stihks) is the scientific study of sound. It involves both how sound is produced and how it is received and heard by humans and animals.

Experts called acoustical engineers help design buildings to control the loudness by designing walls and ceilings with acoustical tiles. The shapes and surfaces of the acoustical tiles are designed to absorb and redirect some of the energy of the sound waves. This can reduce or enhance sounds in a particular space. Acoustical engineers also can design spaces to reduce unwanted echoes. An echo is simply a reflected sound wave.

 CHECK YOUR READING How can loudness be controlled inside buildings?

12.3 Review

KEY CONCEPTS

1. What structures in your ears send signals to your brain? (7.5.g)
2. How do loud sounds cause damage to hearing? (7.5.g)
3. List three ways people control sounds.

CRITICAL THINKING

4. **Apply** Why do road construction workers often need to wear ear protection?
5. **Infer** Think of how your ear responds to a loud sound. How might this response make it difficult to hear a soft sound?

⬤ CHALLENGE

6. **Apply** Which of these acoustical designs would be best for a concert hall? Why?
   a. bare room with hard walls, floor, and ceiling
   b. room padded with sound-absorbing materials such as acoustical tile
   c. room with some hard surfaces and some sound padding

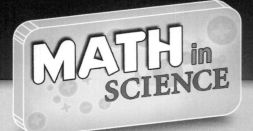

MATH in SCIENCE

MATH TUTORIAL
CLASSZONE.COM
Click on Math Tutorial for more help with interpreting line graphs.

Math 7.AF.3.3

SKILL: INTERPRETING GRAPHS

Measuring Hearing Loss

An audiogram is a graph that can be used to determine if a patient has a hearing loss. The vertical axis shows how loud a sound must be, in decibels, for a patient to hear each frequency tested. Notice that loudness is numbered from top to bottom on an audiogram.

To determine the loudness needed at a given frequency, find the frequency on the horizontal axis. Follow the line straight up until you see the data points, shown as ✖ for the right ear and ● for the left ear. Look to the left to find the loudness in decibels. For example, the loudness needed for both ears to hear the frequency 250 Hz is 10 dB.

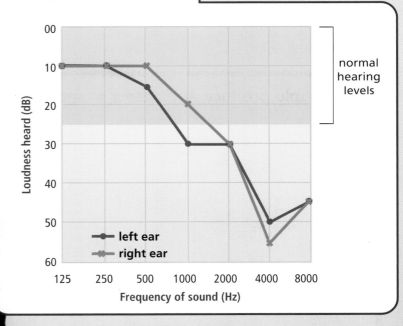

Audiogram for Patient A

normal hearing levels

Loudness heard (dB)

left ear
right ear

Frequency of sound (Hz)

Use the graph to answer the following questions.

1. What is the loudness needed for the patient's left ear at 1000 Hz? the patient's right ear at the same frequency?

2. At which frequencies are the data points for both ears within normal hearing levels?

3. Data points outside the normal hearing levels indicate a hearing loss. At which frequencies are the data points for both ears outside the normal levels?

CHALLENGE A dip in the graph at 3000 to 4000 Hz is a sign that the hearing loss was caused by exposure to loud noises. The patient is referred to a specialist for further testing. Should Patient A get further testing? Why or why not?

This air traffic ground controller wears ear protection to prevent hearing loss.

CONTENT REVIEW
CLASSZONE.COM

the BIG idea

The ear responds to sound waves.

KEY CONCEPTS SUMMARY

1 Sound is one type of wave.

disturbance

wave

Sound is a longitudinal wave that travels through a material medium, such as air.

VOCABULARY
wave p. 423
sound p. 423
medium p. 424
frequency p. 428
hertz p. 428
wavelength p. 428

2 People produce and detect sound waves.

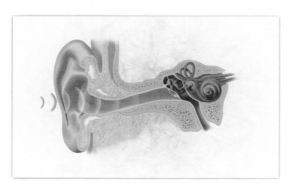

- A sound wave with a lower frequency is perceived to have a lower pitch.

- A sound wave with a higher frequency is perceived to have a higher pitch.

VOCABULARY
pitch p. 432
outer ear p. 436
eardrum p. 436
middle ear p. 437
inner ear p. 437

3 The ear responds to sounds.

- The fluid-filled cochlea transfers sound waves in the inner ear into electrical signals that are then transmitted by nerves to the brain.

- When air is more compressed, the pressure and energy are greater and the sound you hear is loud.

VOCABULARY
decibel p. 442

Reviewing Vocabulary

Draw a diagram of the ear. Label the following parts on your diagram.

1. outer ear
2. eardrum
3. middle ear
4. inner ear
5. cochlea
6. cilia

Describe how the vocabulary terms in each of the following pairs of words are related. Underline each vocabulary term in your answer.

7. wave, medium
8. decibel, sound
9. frequency, hertz
10. pitch, wavelength

Reviewing Key Concepts

Multiple Choice *Choose the letter of the best answer.*

11. Sound waves transfer energy through cycles of changing (7.6)
    a. wavelength
    b. pressure
    c. frequency
    d. speed

12. As a sound wave travels across a room, it causes the air particles to
    a. move across the room
    b. become cooler
    c. move a little back and forth
    d. spread out in all directions

13. The disturbance in both longitudinal and transverse waves
    a. transfers energy in the direction of motion
    b. consists of compressions and rarefactions
    c. is along the wave's direction of motion
    d. is across the wave's direction of motion

14. Which unit is a measure of sound frequency?
    a. hertz
    b. decibel
    c. degree
    d. meter

15. In which of the following materials would sound waves move fastest?
    a. water
    b. cool air
    c. hot air
    d. steel

16. How are the frequencies of the sounds you hear related to their wavelengths?
    a. High frequencies have long wavelengths.
    b. High frequencies have short wavelengths.
    c. High and low frequencies have the same wavelength.
    d. The frequency is not related to the wavelength.

17. A high frequency means that a sound is
    a. loud
    b. soft
    c. high pitched
    d. low pitched

18. The outer ear channels sound waves to the (7.5.g)
    a. cochlea
    b. eardrum
    c. brain
    d. stirrup bone

19. The energy from sound waves moves from the eardrum to what? (7.5.g)
    a. the brain and then the cochlea
    b. the hair cells and then the three small bones
    c. the eustachian tube and then the hair cells
    d. the three small bones and then the cochlea

20. What final event must happen for you to perceive sound? (7.5.g)
    a. Your eardrum vibrates.
    b. Your brain receives signals.
    c. Fluid bends the cilia in your cochlea.
    d. Your stirrup bone pushes on the oval window.

Short Answer *Look at the diagrams of waves below. For the next two items, choose the wave diagram that best fits the description, and explain your choice.*

a.   b.   c.

21. the sound of a basketball coach blowing a whistle during practice

22. the sound of a cow mooing in a pasture

Thinking Critically

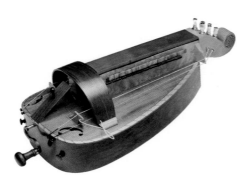

Look at the photograph of an instrument above. Write a short answer to the next two questions.

23. HYPOTHESIZE How might sound waves be produced using the instrument in the photograph?

24. APPLY How might a person playing the instrument in the photograph vary the loudness?

25. COMMUNICATE Two people are singing at the same pitch, yet they sound different. Explain why this could be.

26. SEQUENCE Copy the following sequence chart on your paper. Write the events in the correct sequence on the chart.

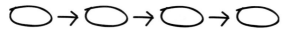

Events

a. Sound waves race out from the wind chime.

b. Forces in air gradually weaken the chime sound.

c. A breeze makes a wind chime vibrate.

d. A person nearby hears the wind chime.

27. ANALYZE When sound waves hit your eardrum, the energy is changed from pressure waves to vibrations of your eardrum. What happens to the energy as it continues from your eardrum to each other part of your ear? (7.5.g)

28. APPLY What would happen if air pressure in your middle ear kept your eardrum from moving? (7.5.g)

Using Math in Science

Read the line graph below showing traffic noise levels at a toll collector's booth. Use the data in the graph to answer the next four questions.

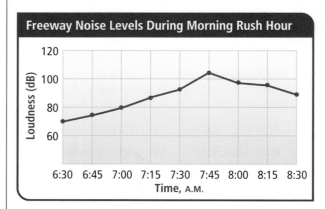

29. Which is the noisiest quarter-hour?

30. Estimate the loudest level of sound that the toll collector is exposed to.

31. If ear protection should be worn for a sound level above 90 dB, should the toll collector wear hearing protection? If so, during which times? (7.5.g)

32. Describe how you could turn the line graph into a bar graph. Would the bar graph be as informative? Explain your answer.

the BIG idea

33. ANALYZE Look back at the photograph on pages 420–421. How are sound waves being produced?

34. SUMMARIZE Write a paragraph summarizing this chapter. Use the Big Idea on page 420 as your topic sentence. Write examples of each key concept listed on page 420. (7.5.g)

UNIT PROJECTS

If you are doing a unit project, make a folder for your project. Include in your folder a list of the resources you will need, the date on which the project is due, and a schedule to keep track of your progress. Begin gathering data.

Analyzing Experiments

7.5.a, 7.5.g

Read the following description of the way scientists study animals' hearing. Then answer the questions below.

Scientists test the hearing ranges of a human by making a sound and asking the person to say whether it was heard. This cannot be done with animals. Scientists use different methods to find animals' hearing ranges. In some experiments, they train animals—by rewarding them with food or water—to behave in specific ways when they hear a sound. Another method is to study an animal's nervous system for electrical reactions to sounds.

Researchers have found that dogs and cats can hear a wide range of sounds. Both dogs and cats can hear much higher frequencies than humans can. Lizards and frogs can hear sounds only in a much narrower range than humans can. Elephants can hear a wider range than lizards and frogs but not as wide a range as dogs and cats. Elephants can hear the lowest frequency sounds of all these animals.

1. What type of behavior would be best for scientists to train animals to make as a signal that they hear a sound?

a. a typical motion that the animal makes frequently

b. a motion that is difficult for the animal to make

c. a motion the animal makes rarely but does make naturally

d. a complicated motion of several steps

2. According to the passage, which animals can hear sounds with the highest frequencies?

a. cats

b. elephants

c. frogs

d. lizards

3. The high-pitched sounds of car brakes are sometimes more bothersome to pet dogs than they are to their owners. Based on the experimental findings, what is the best explanation for that observation?

a. The dogs have not been trained to respond to the high-frequency sounds.

b. The dogs have not been trained to respond to the low-frequency sounds.

c. The dogs hear low-frequency sounds that their owners cannot hear.

d. The dogs hear high-frequency sounds that their owners cannot hear.

4. Which animal hears sounds with the longest wavelengths?

a. cat

b. dog

c. elephant

d. frog

Extended Response

Answer the two questions below in detail.

5. The outermost parts of a grizzly bear's ears are shaped somewhat like funnels. A tortoise has ears that are barely visible from outside. How might these different structures serve different functions?

6. Some animals can turn the outermost parts of their ears in different directions. How might this affect their ability to hear?

Light

the BIG idea

Visible light is a small band of the electromagnetic spectrum.

What forms of electromagnetic radiation are produced by objects in this photograph?

Key Concepts

SECTION

1 Light is an electromagnetic wave.
Learn about visible light and other forms of electromagnetic radiation.

SECTION

2 Light is produced in different ways.
Learn about the ways that matter can give off light.

SECTION

3 Light interacts with materials.
Learn how light and matter affect one another.

SECTION

4 Color comes from light.
Learn how light, materials, and your eyes and brain produce the colors you see.

CALIFORNIA CLASSZONE

CLASSZONE.COM

Chapter 13 online resources: Content Review, Simulation, Visualization, two Resource Centers, Math Tutorial, Test Practice.

Seeing Color

> **7.6.e** Students know that white light is a mixture of many wavelengths (colors) and that retinal cells react differently to different wavelengths.

Find a color photograph or drawing in a magazine or newspaper. Place it on a well-lit, flat surface. Use a hand lens to observe the image. Start with the lens right on top of the image and then slowly move the lens away. You may need to move your head to help you see through the lens. When the view is as large and clear as possible, examine other parts of the image.

Observe and Think
How do the colors appear through the hand lens? How did the colors seem different when enlarged?

Internet Activity: Electromagnetic Waves

> **7.6.a** Students know visible light is a small band within a very broad electromagnetic spectrum.

Go to **ClassZone.com** to explore images of the Sun. See how light of different frequencies shows different layers of the Sun. Pay attention to the ways colors are used to represent different frequencies.

Observe and Think
Why can we see only some of the light coming from the Sun?

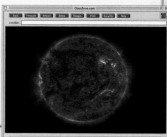

NSTA
scilinks.org

SCLINKS

Light and Color **Code: MDL029**

Getting Ready to Learn

◀ CONCEPT REVIEW

- A wave is a disturbance that transfers energy.
- Sound waves move through a medium.
- Frequency, wavelength, and speed are related.
- Waves react to a change in medium.

◀ VOCABULARY REVIEW

medium p. 424

frequency p. 428

hertz p. 428

wavelength p. 428

field *See Glossary.*

CONTENT REVIEW
CLASSZONE.COM

Review concepts and vocabulary.

▶ TAKING NOTES

SUPPORTING MAIN IDEAS

Make a chart to show main ideas and the information that supports them. Copy each main idea, or blue heading. Then add supporting information, such as reasons, explanations, and examples.

VOCABULARY STRATEGY

Write each new vocabulary term in the center of a **frame game** diagram. Decide what information to frame it with. Use examples, descriptions, parts, sentences that use the term in context, or pictures. You can change the frame to fit each term.

See the Note-Taking Handbook on pages R45–R51.

SCIENCE NOTEBOOK

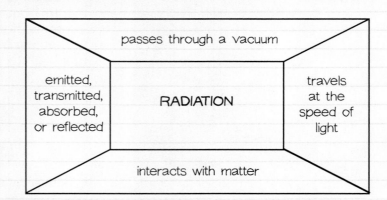

An electromagnetic wave is a disturbance in a field.

→ Visible light is an electromagnetic wave.

→ Electromagnetic waves occur as fields change.

→ Most EM waves are invisible.

| passes through a vacuum |
| emitted, transmitted, absorbed, or reflected | RADIATION | travels at the speed of light |
| interacts with matter |

13.1 Light is an electromagnetic wave.

CALIFORNIA Content Standards

7.6.a Students know visible light is a small band within a very broad electromagnetic spectrum.

7.6.b Students know that for an object to be seen, light emitted by or scattered from it must be detected by the eye.

BEFORE, you learned

• Waves transfer energy
• Sound waves need a medium to travel

NOW, you will learn

• About light and other electromagnetic waves
• About the speed, frequencies, and wavelengths of EM waves
• About the different ranges of EM radiation

VOCABULARY

electromagnetic wave p. 453
radiation p. 455
absorb p. 455
electromagnetic spectrum p. 455

EXPLORE Light (7.6.e)

How can you analyze light?

PROCEDURE

① Hold the disk and paper in sunlight.

② Reflect sunlight from the disk onto the paper. Try holding the disk at different angles and at different distances from the paper.

WHAT DO YOU THINK?

• What did you see on the paper?
• What do you think happened to the sunlight?

MATERIALS
• compact disk (CD)
• white paper

An electromagnetic wave is a disturbance in a field.

When you think about outer space, or even the air around you, it may seem very empty. Much of outer space has very little matter, but it is filled with light and similar waves traveling in all directions. If a baseball whizzes in front of you, you are aware of it even if it doesn't touch you. In contrast, waves of light can pass by without your knowing. You only become aware of light if you interact with it, such as when it enters your eyes or when enough goes into your skin. Then, you might see the light or feel its energy as warmth on your skin.

Visible light is one type of electromagnetic wave. An **electromagnetic wave** (ih-LEHK-troh-mag-NEHT-ihk) is a disturbance in a field. A field, such as a magnetic field, is an area of space that can exert a force. Electromagnetic waves are also called EM waves. Most EM waves are invisible to humans, but some of the invisible waves can still affect your body.

VOCABULARY
Create a frame game diagram for the term *electromagnetic wave.*

EM Waves in a Vacuum

VISUALIZATION
CLASSZONE.COM

Learn more about the nature of EM waves.

Sound waves and water waves travel by making matter move. They can only travel where matter is present. Those waves cannot travel through empty space, but electromagnetic waves can.

Electromagnetic radiation depends on electric fields and magnetic fields. Have you felt clothing stick together with static electricity or felt the pull or push of two magnets? Then you have felt the effects of electric or magnetic fields. Electric and magnetic fields can exist in matter, but they can also exist away from the matter that produces them. They can exist in the vacuum of outer space.

Like other waves, an electromagnetic wave is a disturbance. The disturbance goes through a cycle with a definite frequency, just like a sound or water wave. An EM wave moves with a certain speed and has a certain wavelength, just like a sound or water wave.

READING TiP

To *disturb* means to agitate or unsettle.

 CHECK YOUR READING What two types of fields are disturbed by an EM wave?

Recall how sound travels in air. The disturbance, or the cycles of compression and rarefaction, travels forward through the air. The molecules that make up the air move back and forth but are left behind as the wave passes. Electromagnetic waves are harder to imagine, but the fields change in a cycle that travels forward. A sound wave gets less loud as it travels because the energy spreads out and the air pressure tends to even out. In contrast, EM waves do not need matter and do not usually lose energy as they travel. People have detected EM waves that have been traveling through the universe for billions of years.

Speed of EM Waves

In a vacuum, EM waves all travel at the same speed. They travel very, very fast—about 300,000 kilometers per second, or 186,000 miles per second. This speed is called the speed of light, and it is often represented by the letter c. It takes much less than a second for an EM wave to travel the distance between any two points on Earth. About 8 minutes pass as light and other EM waves travel the 150 million kilometers (93 million mi) between the Sun and Earth. The vast distances of space are often measured in units of light-years—the distance light travels in a year. For example, the galaxy shown in the photograph is 60 million light-years from Earth.

Light, Waves, Rays, and Particles

Scientists use different models to understand EM waves. Waves tend to spread out, or radiate, from a flame or other source. Scientists define electromagnetic **radiation** to mean energy that moves in the form of EM waves. Sometimes, scientists think of light as being made of many narrow beams, as shown in the photograph below. Each beam takes a different path. One possible path of light, called a ray, is represented by a straight line or arrow. You will use this ray model when you learn about lenses and images.

READING TiP

EM waves are also called rays. The words *radiation* and *radiate* come from the Latin word *radius*, which means "ray" or "spoke."

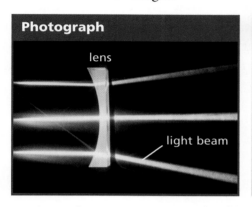

Photograph

lens

light beam

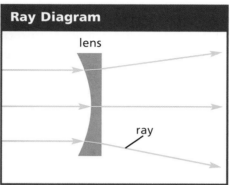

Ray Diagram

lens

ray

Sometimes scientists think of light as being made of particles. EM radiation is produced as tiny bundles of energy called photons. A photon ceases to exist when it gives up its energy to matter. The matter **absorbs,** or takes in, light when it takes up the photon's energy. The energy of a photon depends on its frequency. A photon of higher frequency has greater energy than a photon of lower frequency.

 CHECK YOUR READING   What are two of the ways that scientists think about light?

The Electromagnetic Spectrum

Sometimes scientists use wavelength to describe an EM wave. Sometimes they use frequency. You have already read how the frequency, wavelength, and speed of a wave are related. The speed of EM waves in air is almost the same as it is in a vacuum. Thus, you can use either frequency or wavelength to describe an EM wave.

You have seen a spectrum (SPEHK-truhm) when you have seen a rainbow or the bands of color from a compact disk. You see bands of color because the frequencies are spread out. Scientists also use the idea of a spectrum to describe all the possible frequencies of EM waves, or the **electromagnetic spectrum.** The frequencies are measured in hertz, or cycles per second. Some waves are several thousand hertz while others are many trillions of hertz. Wavelengths can be tens of kilometers or trillionths of a centimeter. To make sense of these huge variations, scientists use different terms to describe different parts of the EM spectrum. Visible light is one small part.

EM waves have a wide range of frequencies.

SUPPORTING MAIN IDEAS
Write details that support the main idea that EM waves have a wide range of frequencies.

The diagram below represents the electromagnetic spectrum, arranged from low frequencies to high frequencies. Ranges of frequencies are given different names. For example, infrared light has frequencies just below those of red light. *Infra-* means "below."

The ranges, or bands, of the electromagnetic spectrum are radio waves, microwaves, infrared light, visible light from red to violet, ultraviolet light, x-rays, and gamma rays. But these ranges overlap. Many are divided into smaller bands. They have different names because different types of EM waves were discovered in different ways. Only later did scientists find out that these different-seeming waves, rays, and particles were different only in frequency and wavelength.

The Electromagnetic Spectrum

Frequency in Hertz (1 Hz = 1 cycle/second)

10^4 10^5 10^6 10^7 10^8 10^9 10^{10} 10^{11} 10^{12} 10^{13}

Radio Waves   **Infrared Light**

Microwaves

This woman is speaking on a radio program. **Radio waves** are used to code and send radio and television signals. They are also used for cordless phones, garage door openers, alarm systems, and baby monitors.

Astronomers use all types of EM radiation. Telescopes like the one above pick up **microwaves** from space. Microwaves are also used for radar, cell phones, ovens, and satellite communications.

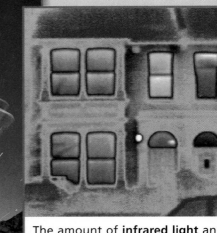

The amount of **infrared light** an object gives off depends on the object's temperature. Above, different colors indicate different amounts of infrared light.

Different types of EM radiation interact with matter in different ways. An interaction depends on the energy of the photon, which depends on its frequency. For example, your skin absorbs photons of infrared and visible light. The energy goes into your skin and makes it warmer. Your skin also absorbs ultraviolet light, but the photons carry enough energy to cause damage, such as sunburn. Higher-energy photons can do even more damage to the tissues that absorb them.

Each type of EM radiation is similar to the types next to it. For example, infrared light is similar to visible light. Yet the range of frequencies in the EM spectrum is huge. The differences between the ways radio waves and gamma rays interact with matter are also huge.

The Sun produces all the different ranges of EM waves. People have developed technologies that use different ranges of EM waves. As you will see, technologies can also produce different EM waves.

RESOURCE CENTER
CLASSZONE.COM

Learn more about the electromagnetic spectrum.

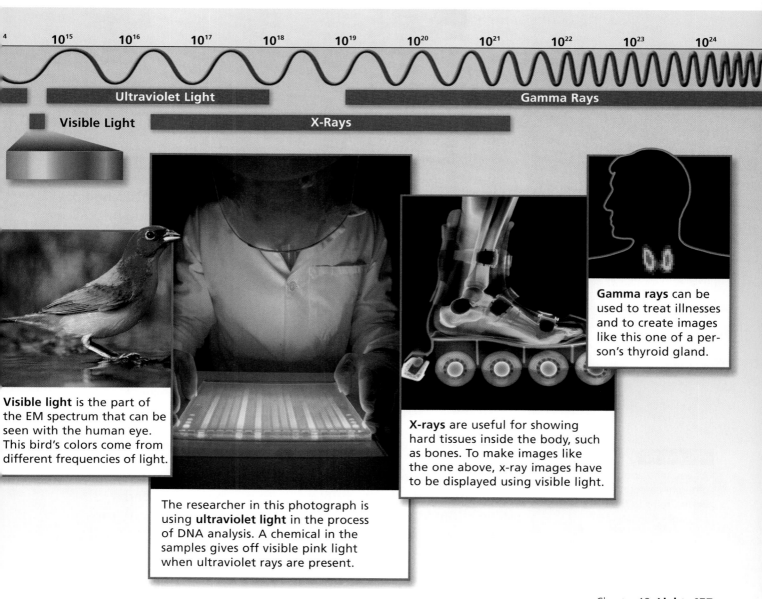

Visible light is the part of the EM spectrum that can be seen with the human eye. This bird's colors come from different frequencies of light.

The researcher in this photograph is using **ultraviolet light** in the process of DNA analysis. A chemical in the samples gives off visible pink light when ultraviolet rays are present.

X-rays are useful for showing hard tissues inside the body, such as bones. To make images like the one above, x-ray images have to be displayed using visible light.

Gamma rays can be used to treat illnesses and to create images like this one of a person's thyroid gland.

Radio Waves

Radio waves can be produced easily by varying an electric current in a wire. They produce electric current in metal, so can they can be detected using a long wire or antenna. Radio waves from distant stars and galaxies have been detected by long wires or strips of metal arranged in fields, valleys, and structures of different shapes such as dishes and horns.

Radio waves and sound waves are very different. Remember that EM waves can travel long distances without losing energy. People developed technologies to convert a pattern of sound waves into a pattern of radio waves. The radio waves carry the information over a long distance. A receiving device uses the pattern to produce sound waves again.

REMINDER

Sound waves involve the motion of air or other matter.

1 Sound waves enter the microphone, which produces electrical impulses.

2 The electrical impulses are used by the transmitter to produce radio waves.

3 The radio waves reach a radio receiver which produces sound waves.

Radio broadcasts use radio waves. The numbers you see on the radio receiver—such as 670 or 99.5—are the radio wave frequencies in kilohertz (1,000 Hz) or megahertz (1,000,000 Hz). One technology varies the strength, or amplitude, of the radio waves' pattern. It is called amplitude modulation—AM. Another technology varies, or modulates, the frequencies—FM. Television images are also encoded into radio waves at "very high frequencies" (VHF on an old television set) or "ultrahigh frequencies" (UHF).

CALIFORNIA Focus

The Hat Creek Observatory, near Mount Lassen, California, is a radio telescope observatory. The radio telescopes there will search for signs of intelligent life outside our solar system.

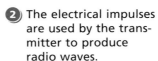

AM Signal

Information is encoded in the signal by varying the radio wave's amplitude.

FM Signal

Information is encoded in the signal by varying the radio wave's frequency.

Microwaves

The radio waves of higher frequencies are also called microwaves. Cell phones and other technologies use microwaves to send information. Microwaves bounce off the surfaces of aircraft, cars, asteroids, raindrops, and other objects. A technology called radar uses microwaves to measure the distances to and speeds of these objects.

READING TiP

As you read about the different categories of EM waves, refer to the diagram on pages 456 and 457.

The term *radar* stands for "radio detection and ranging." Ranging means finding the distance to something. EM waves are sent out, bounce off objects, and return to the sender. The time EM waves take for a round trip is used to determine the distance.

Many molecules can give off or absorb microwaves easily. People developed microwave ovens that use this property. They use microwaves to transfer energy directly to some of the molecules that make up food. The food then becomes hot. Scientists use microwaves to identify molecules in space or in unknown materials. Different types of molecules give off microwaves of certain frequencies. Thus, a spectrum of microwaves can show which molecules are present.

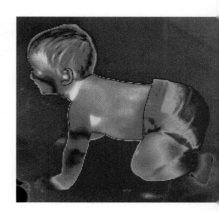

reflecting fan
microwave source
microwaves
absorption

 How are radio waves and microwaves related?

Infrared Radiation

Infrared (IR) waves are easily given off and absorbed by solids, liquids, and some gases. So people often use IR light to heat materials. A heat lamp in a cafeteria gives off mostly infrared light. You cannot see IR light, but you can often feel it as it warms your skin. Some animals, such as pit viper snakes, can see infrared light.

You and most of the objects on Earth are giving off radiation in the low frequencies of the infrared range. These photons can be used to determine temperature. Therefore, the lower-frequency part of the infrared range is called the thermal IR. Ear thermometers, some IR cameras, and weather satellites detect thermal IR. The high frequencies near the visible light range are called near-IR. Night-vision goggles often use the near-IR light reflected by objects. They display the resulting images using different brightnesses or colors of visible light.

In this infrared image, warmer areas appear red and orange, while cooler ones appear blue, green, and purple.

Visible Light

The part of the EM spectrum that human eyes can detect is called visible light. The range is small, but important. Roughly half of the radiation from the Sun that reaches the ground is visible light. Many species have adaptations that use this light. The photosynthesis of plants and the vision of many animals depend on visible light. Humans see the lowest frequencies (longest wavelengths) as red. The highest frequencies (shortest wavelengths) look violet. Two other bands are named for these colors. Frequencies just below red are called infrared. Those just above violet are called ultraviolet.

INVESTIGATE Ultraviolet Light

How can you tell if sunscreen blocks ultraviolet light?

DESIGN — YOUR OWN — EXPERIMENT

PROCEDURE

1. Hold the beads under a bright light. Then hold them in direct sunlight, which includes UV light. Record your observations.

2. Using what you learned, design an experiment to help you estimate how well a sunscreen lotion blocks UV light. Use a control in your procedure.

3. Carry out your experiment. Make adjustments and repeat the experiment if necessary. Record your results.

WHAT DO YOU THINK?

- How well were you able to evaluate the sunscreen?
- How did the trial with sunscreen compare with the control?

CHALLENGE Design an experiment that tests UV light in some other way. For example, you might compare the amount of UV light from different sources or test how well sunglasses or car windshields block UV light.

SKILL FOCUS
Designing Experiments (7.6.a)

MATERIALS
- UV-sensitive beads
- lamp
- plastic bags
- sunscreen
- other materials requested and approved

TIME
20 minutes

Ultraviolet Light

Ultraviolet light (UV) is not visible to humans. Some animals, such as bees, can see UV light. As you can see in the photograph below, bees can see patterns that show where a flower's nectar is located.

Photons of ultraviolet light carry more energy than those of lower frequencies. The energy can break apart molecules. UV light can damage materials, such as those in living cells. UV light can be used to sterilize medical instruments and food by killing bacteria.

Radiation from the Sun includes UV light. This light breaks down molecules of ozone high in Earth's atmosphere. The ozone forms again. Ozone prevents much of the UV part of sunlight from reaching Earth's surface, but there is still enough UV light to damage your skin and eyes. Ultraviolet light can break molecules of DNA and cause cancer. Sunscreen can absorb excess UV light before it enters your skin. The lower frequencies of UV light cause your skin cells to produce vitamin D, which your body needs.

The photograph below shows a flower as it appears in visible light. The photograph to the right shows how different areas appear bright in ultraviolet light.

 CHECK YOUR READING What are two effects of UV light on your body?

X-Rays

Photons of x-rays have even more energy than photons of UV light. X-rays can pass through some matter. X-rays pass through skin, muscle, and other soft tissues of the body. Dense materials such as bone or metal absorb x-rays. When an x-ray lamp shines through a person's body onto photographic film or an electronic detector, bones block the x-rays. X-rays are used to find bone fractures and dense tumors. However, too many x-rays can cause more damage than your body can repair. Even in small doses, repeated exposure to x-rays can cause cancer over time. X-rays of higher frequencies, called hard x-rays, cause more damage than medical x-rays when absorbed.

X-ray photons carry so much energy that they can remove electrons from atoms, or ionize the atoms. A layer high in Earth's atmosphere, called the ionosphere, absorbs the x-rays in sunlight. As a result almost no x-rays from sunlight reach Earth's surface.

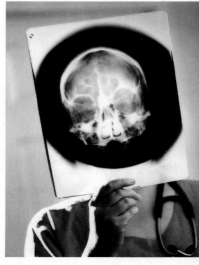

The person is holding a photographic film that is dark where it absorbed x-rays. The shadows of bones appear white.

Gamma Rays

Photons of gamma rays have the highest energies of the EM spectrum. Like x-rays, they pass through many materials. Most gamma rays from sunlight are absorbed by the atmosphere high above Earth's surface.

Gamma rays are often produced when atoms are broken apart. Gamma rays can help scientists detect exploding stars and other high-energy events in space. Gamma rays are also produced by nuclear explosions and radioactive materials. The resulting photons can break apart important materials in cells. Then the cells die. Doctors sometimes use gamma rays to kill cancer cells and fight tumors.

 What are the effects of x-rays and gamma rays on atoms?

13.1 Review

KEY CONCEPTS

1. How are radio waves and visible light similar? (7.6.a)
2. What two properties of EM waves change from one end of the EM spectrum to the other? (7.6.a)
3. List the seven ranges, or bands, of EM radiation and make one statement about each. (7.6.a)

CRITICAL THINKING

4. **Compare and Contrast** Describe some of the sources of EM radiation. How are they similar and different?
5. **Infer** Why do you think remote controls for TVs, DVD players, and sound systems use infrared light rather than ultraviolet light?

▲ CHALLENGE

6. **Apply** There is less energy per photon in microwaves than in visible light. Yet the photons inside a microwave oven can carry more total energy than the photons from a desk lamp carry. How do you think the number of photons inside a microwave oven compares with the number of photons from a desk lamp?

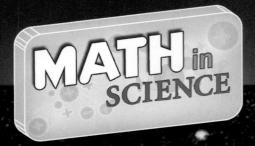

EM Frequencies

The Chandra X-Ray Observatory in the photograph is a space telescope that detects high-frequency EM waves called x-rays. An x-ray might have a frequency of 10 billion billion cycles per second, or hertz. In standard form—using zeros—10 billion billion Hz looks like this:

10,000,000,000,000,000,000 Hz

Because this number is hard to read, scientists use an exponent to write it. Ten billion billion is written using an exponent as **10^{19}**.

Exponents can also represent very small numbers. For example, an x-ray with a frequency of 10^{19} Hz is about one hundredth of one billionth of a meter long. That wavelength can be written in standard form as **0.00000000001 m.** Using exponents, the wavelength can be written more simply as **10^{-11} m.**

Examples

Large Numbers

To write a multiple of 10 in exponential form, count the number of zeros. Then use the total as the exponent.

(1) 10,000 has 4 zeros.

(2) 4 is the exponent.

ANSWER 10^4 is the way to write 10,000 using exponents.

Decimals

To convert a decimal into exponential form, count the number of places to the right of the decimal point, including the first nonzero place. Then, use the total with a negative sign as the exponent.

(1) 0.000001 has 6 places to the right of the decimal point.

(2) Add a negative sign to make the exponent –6.

ANSWER 10^{-6} is the way to write 0.000001 using exponents.

Answer the following questions.

Write each wavelength or frequency using an exponent.

1. 10,000,000 Hz (radio)   **4.** 0.0001 m (IR)

2. 0.00001 m (IR)   **5.** 10,000,000,000 Hz (microwave)

3. 100,000 m (radio)

Write the number in standard form.

6. 10^8 Hz (radio)   **8.** 10^{17} Hz (UV)

7. 10^{-8} m (UV)   **9.** 10^{-15} m (gamma)

CHALLENGE Using exponents, multiply 10^2 m by 10^3 Hz. Explain how you got your result.

MATH TUTORIAL
CLASSZONE.COM

Click on Math Tutorial for more help with positive and negative exponents.

Math 7.NS.1.2
Science 7.6.a

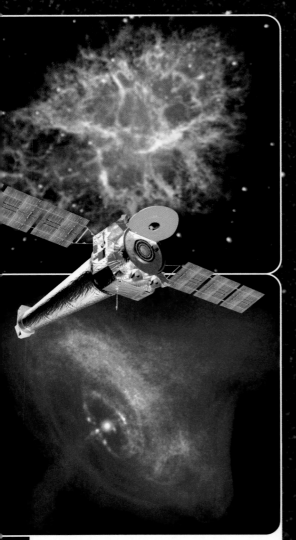

The top photograph shows an image of the Crab Nebula made using three frequencies of visible light. The bottom photograph shows the same nebula as it appears at higher—x-ray—frequencies.

13.2 Light is produced in different ways.

CALIFORNIA
Content Standards

7.6.b Students know that for an object to be seen, light emitted by or scattered from it must be detected by the eye.

Background for

7.6.e Students know that white light is a mixture of many wavelengths (colors) and that retinal cells react differently to different wavelengths.

VOCABULARY

emit p. 463

BEFORE, you learned

- Visible light is part of the EM spectrum
- EM waves can be produced by matter

NOW, you will learn

- How hot matter produces light
- About other sources of light
- About different sources of energy that can make matter produce light

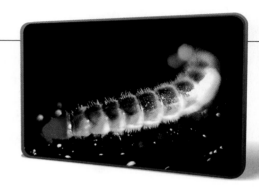

THINK ABOUT

Why is light important?

This railroad worm has green lights on its sides and a red light on its head. The animal probably uses these lights for illumination and discouraging predators. Almost every living organism, including humans, depends on visible light. Think of as many different ways as you can that plants, animals, and people use light. Then, think of all the sources of visible light that you know of. Why is light important to living organisms?

RESOURCE CENTER
CLASSZONE.COM

Learn more about visible light.

Matter can produce light.

It is hard to imagine life without light. People and many other animals see because Earth is lit by the Sun's visible light. Sunlight provides the energy for plants to make sugars through photosynthesis. The energy from sunlight keeps the land and oceans warm enough for life to exist.

You can see objects that glow because they **emit,** or give off, visible light that can then enter your eye. Matter emits light when it converts some other form of energy into electromagnetic radiation. You see a glowing object only when the the light enters your eye and is absorbed. When matter absorbs light, the energy changes form again. In this section, you will learn about the different ways matter can emit light.

 CHECK YOUR READING What is needed to produce light?

Light is produced by hot matter.

Have you ever noticed how a coil on an electric stove cools? When it is very hot, it glows orange-red. As it cools, it becomes more reddish. It also dims, or emits less visible light. Then it darkens and looks just like a room-temperature coil, but it is still hot. You can feel that infrared radiation is coming from the coil. This cooling-off sequence follows the pattern of the electromagnetic spectrum. Orange-red light has higher frequencies—greater energy per photon—than red light. Red light has higher frequencies than infrared light.

The hotter a material is, the more energy it can give off. More of the energy is emitted as photons of greater frequency. The coil emits mostly infrared light when warm, but emits some visible light when hot. This is thermal emission, or emission related to temperature.

Incandescent matter produces visible light because it is hot. The color depends on the temperature. To give off some visible light, matter must be hundreds or thousands of degrees Celsius. Red-hot coals, the glowing wires of an electric heater, and the bright, hot gases of the Sun's surface are incandescent. People who work with very hot metal, molten glass, or hot clay ovens learn to estimate the temperature of the material by its color. Astronomers estimate the temperatures of distant stars by their colors.

You, the objects around you, and Earth's surface are warm enough to emit infrared light. Devices can measure the infrared light coming from the ground and clouds, an engine, or the inside of your ear. These devices can determine the temperature from the infrared light.

VOCABULARY
Don't forget to make a word frame for the term *incandescent*.

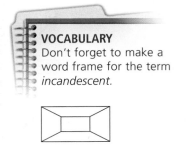

 CHECK YOUR READING When a red-hot object gets hotter, how does its appearance change?

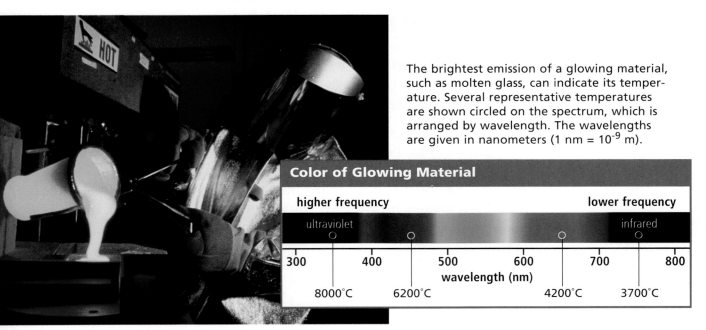

The brightest emission of a glowing material, such as molten glass, can indicate its temperature. Several representative temperatures are shown circled on the spectrum, which is arranged by wavelength. The wavelengths are given in nanometers (1 nm = 10^{-9} m).

Color of Glowing Material

higher frequency   lower frequency

ultraviolet   infrared

300	400	500	600	700	800

wavelength (nm)

8000°C   6200°C   4200°C   3700°C

Incandescent materials give off a range of EM frequencies. The Sun gives off visible light, but also a lot of infrared and ultraviolet light. Red-hot stoves and even light bulbs give off much more infrared light than visible light.

An incandescent light bulb uses thermal emission to produce light. An electric current heats a thin wire, called a filament, until it glows brightly. Most filaments are made of the element tungsten. Tungsten can become very hot—about 3400 degrees Celsius (about 6100°F)—without melting. But if the tungsten filament were heated in air, it would go through chemical reactions with oxygen and would break. Instead, the filament is enclosed in a sealed glass bulb that is filled with a different gas, usually argon.

A halogen bulb is a different type of incandescent bulb. It is designed so that the filament gets hotter than regular incandescent bulbs. The light is brighter and has more blue light and relatively less infrared light. To allow these high temperatures, the gas inside is one or more of a group of gases called halogens. The gas and filament are within a small bulb made of quartz. Quartz is less likely than regular glass to melt at the high temperatures produced.

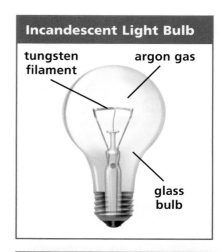

Incandescent Light Bulb

tungsten filament

argon gas

glass bulb

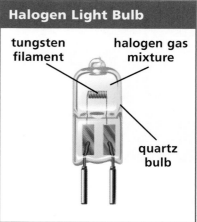

Halogen Light Bulb

tungsten filament

halogen gas mixture

quartz bulb

INVESTIGATE Artificial Lighting

Is all artificial light the same?

Light sources differ in the ways they produce light, the amount of energy they use, the amount of light they produce, and other characteristics.

DESIGN — YOUR OWN — EXPERIMENT

PROCEDURE

1. Design a procedure to find and record differences among different types of artificial lighting. Compare two or more characteristics of the light sources. For example, you might compare the color and brightness of different lights shining on white paper. Remember to control as many variables as you can.

2. Write up your experiment. When your teacher approves, carry it out.

WHAT DO YOU THINK?

- What differences did you discover among bulbs of different types and sizes?

- How would you improve your design if you were to repeat your experiment?

SKILL FOCUS
Designing experiments (7.6.e)

MATERIALS
Artificial lighting with a variety of bulb types and sizes

TIME
30 minutes

Light can be produced from different sources of energy.

READING TIP

The Latin root word *lumen* means "light."

You have just read that light can be produced from the energy of hot matter. Light can also be produced in other ways. Matter that gives off light in one of these other ways—not incandescence—is said to be luminescent. Luminescent objects may be hot or cool to the touch.

Chemical Reactions

A firefly produces light by combining chemicals.

Perhaps you have seen the light of fireflies or other insects. When organisms, such as bacteria, fungi, or animals, give off light, they are said to be bioluminescent. The energy for a firefly's light comes from chemical reactions. Glow sticks—tubes of glowing liquid—also use chemical reactions to produce light. The light is emitted even though the material may remain cool. Most of the energy of the chemical reaction is released as light, so very little of the energy heats the material. However, the glow continues only as long as the chemical reaction continues.

Charged Particles and Radiation

The auroras, or northern and southern lights, occur when the gases of Earth's atmosphere glow. The energy comes from fast-moving charged particles. When a gas emits light, the light often has a distinct color. The nitrogen and oxygen gases of the atmosphere can emit green, red, or blue light. The auroras are typically green. In a similar way, some lamps use fast-moving charged particles—electric currents—to make gases glow. Neon gas can give off a lot of red light. Sodium gives off mostly yellow light. The colors depend on the particular gases.

Some solid materials turn energy from charged particles into light. For example, a television tube aims a beam of charged particles at the front surface of the tube. There, tiny spots of solid material gain energy from the charged particles. Then they give off colored light.

Materials can also get the energy to produce radiation by first absorbing radiation. Fluorescent materials emit photons after absorbing photons of a different, usually higher, frequency. For example, some minerals give off colorful glows when lit by ultraviolet light. If a material emits visible light in this way, it is called a phosphor. White shirts and special paints may have phosphors that look brighter in UV-containing sunlight. Some phosphors keep giving off light for a long time even after they stop absorbing. Glow-in-the-dark materials are made from these types of phosphors.

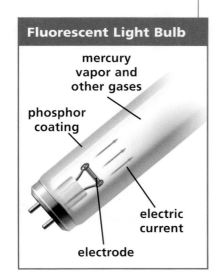

Fluorescent Light Bulb

mercury vapor and other gases

phosphor coating

electric current

electrode

The familiar long tubes of fluorescent lights use phosphors along with glowing gases. Electric current makes the gas inside—often mercury—emit ultraviolet light. A coating inside the tube absorbs the UV light and gains its energy. Then the coating emits visible light. A grid of tiny, colored fluorescent lights makes up a plasma television set. The gas inside these and other fluorescent lights has a great deal of energy and is called a plasma. It usually becomes very hot. Much of the energy supplied to a fluorescent light goes into heating the gas.

 CHECK YOUR READING What are three sources of energy that can make matter give off light? Use the red headers to check your answer.

Other Sources of Energy

Some materials give off light when they are squeezed or broken. For example, tiny crystals within certain candies give off green light when broken.

Semiconductors—the materials used to make computer chips—often produce infrared light when an electric current is applied. These materials can also be designed to produce visible light. The resulting device is called a light-emitting diode, or LED. Many remote controls use infrared LEDs. Visible-light LEDs are used in flashlights, traffic lights, and many other places.

Much of the energy that goes into an LED is given off as radiation. Only a fraction of the energy is wasted heating the materials. Also, an LED does not need time to heat up or cool down. It turns on and off much more quickly than an incandescent light bulb.

LEDs are being used more and more in place of incandescent bulbs.

13.2 Review

KEY CONCEPTS

1. What property of EM radiation can be used to find the temperature of an object without touching it? (7.6.a)

2. Give two examples where the color of light emitted depends on the material of the light source. (7.6.e)

3. List three of the sources of energy that can make matter emit light. (7.6.b)

CRITICAL THINKING

4. **Connect** Which sources of visible light can be cool to the touch?

5. **Infer** A white shirt may look duller in lamplight than in sunlight. What can you infer about the difference between the amount of UV light in sunlight and lamplight?

CHALLENGE

6. **Apply** Weather satellites can detect thermal infrared radiation from the ground and clouds. They also detect visible light. Explain which one is more useful at night.

 13.3 Light interacts with materials.

CALIFORNIA
Content Standards

7.6.c Students know that light travels in straight lines if the medium it travels through does not change.

7.6.f Students know light can be reflected, refracted, transmitted, and absorbed by matter.

BEFORE, you learned

- Light and other electromagnetic radiation can travel through empty space
- Matter can emit light in several different ways
- The color of thermal emission is related to the temperature of the matter

NOW, you will learn

- How light is absorbed
- How light is transmitted and refracted
- How light is reflected

VOCABULARY

reflect p. 468
transmit p. 469
diffuse p. 469
refract p. 471

EXPLORE Reflection (7.6.f)

How does the signal from a remote control travel?

PROCEDURE

① Turn the TV on and off using the remote control.

② Work with a partner to try to turn on the TV by aiming the remote control at the mirror.

WHAT DO YOU THINK?
How did you have to position the remote control and the mirror in order to operate the TV? Why do you think this worked?

MATERIALS
- TV with remote control unit
- mirror with stand

Light can interact with matter.

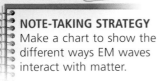
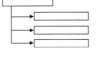

NOTE-TAKING STRATEGY
Make a chart to show the different ways EM waves interact with matter.

You have read about the ways matter can produce light and other EM radiation. The radiation can then travel through empty space. It does not need a material medium. However, EM radiation can travel through a material medium.

Visible light travels through air, water, and other clear materials. We call these materials clear or transparent because visible light can travel straight through them. Many materials, such as this book, are not clear. Light cannot pass through them. Materials that are not clear may absorb light. They may **reflect** light, or cause light to bounce off of them. In different materials, light is reflected, absorbed, and let through in different amounts.

 CHECK YOUR READING What are three things that can happen when light encounters matter?

Matter can absorb or transmit light.

Absorption—the process of absorbing—is the reverse of emission—the process of emitting. Remember that matter absorbs light by taking in the light's energy. Photons of light cease to exist, or disappear. The light's energy usually warms the matter. Sometimes, the energy ends up in other forms. It can even end up as other EM radiation.

READING TiP

When you see the terms *absorption, emission, transmission,* and *refraction,* look for the root words *absorb, emit, transmit,* and *refract.*

Light can be absorbed at the surface of a material, such as the ink on this page. Light can also be absorbed as it moves through a material. For example, light travels into lake water, below the water's surface. But most of the light is absorbed before reaching the lake's deep bottom.

CHECK YOUR READING What are two ways light can be absorbed by matter?

Matter can **transmit** light, or let it pass through. A material can be described by the way it transmits or does not transmit light.

① **Transparent** (trans-PAIR-uhnt) materials allow light to pass straight through them. You can see objects through a transparent material. Air, water, and clear glass are transparent materials.

② **Translucent** (trans-LOO-suhnt) materials allow some light to pass through, but mostly not in straight lines. Translucent materials **diffuse** (dih-FYOOZ) the light, or cause it to spread out in many directions. You cannot see objects clearly through translucent materials, but you can tell that there is light. Frosted glass, many clouds, and thin paper are translucent.

READING TiP

Diffuse is also used as an adjective to describe light that goes in many directions. However, the final letter is pronounced as an *s* instead of as a *z*.

③ **Opaque** (oh-PAYK) materials do not allow light to pass through them. You cannot see objects through an opaque material. Wood, most rocks, and metal are opaque materials. Opaque materials may absorb and reflect light.

Materials can fall in between these categories. The wavy glass in the picture can be called translucent or transparent. Also, materials can be transparent to some frequencies and opaque to others. The clear blue glass is transparent to blue light but opaque to red light.

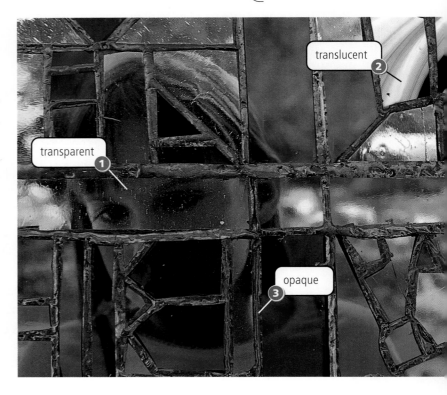

transparent ①

translucent ②

opaque ③

INVESTIGATE Light and Mediums

How can a change in medium affect light?

PROCEDURE

1. Fill the container about three-fourths of the way with water.

2. Shine the flashlight into the container at different angles.

3. Stir 2 spoonfuls of milk into the water. Then repeat step 2.

WHAT DO YOU THINK?

- How were the results of steps 2 and 3 different?
- What do you think happened to the light?

CHALLENGE What happens when you add more milk to the water?

SKILL FOCUS
Designing experiments (7.6.f)

MATERIALS
- clear plastic container
- water
- flashlight
- spoon
- milk

TIME
30 minutes

Scattering

Light usually travels in a straight line. However, when light encounters a change in medium, it may change direction. Some materials cause the light passing through to go in many different directions. This process is called scattering. The resulting light is diffuse. Fog, smoke, or other tiny particles in air will scatter visible light. Dirt or other particles in water and tiny flaws in glass will also scatter light. The air, water, or glass becomes more translucent than transparent.

Think about a foggy day. As light travels through the foggy air, more and more of the light is scattered. The light travels only a short distance before it changes direction. You may see your hand clearly because much of the light can travel straight from your hand to your eye. You might have trouble seeing a street sign because it is farther away, and most of the light is scattered before it can get to your eye. Light from other directions is also scattered toward your eye. You may see a bright haze. If the medium scatters light more, you can't see as far. The distance that you can see through foggy air or other mediums is called the visibility.

Fine particles, such as those in fog, scatter light and reduce visibility.

 CHECK YOUR READING What happens to light that moves through foggy or smoky air?

Refraction

A material can cause light to change direction in an orderly, or regular, way. When light moves from one medium to another, it often changes speed. As a result, it may change direction in a predictable way. Light **refracts** when it changes direction due to a change in its speed. For example, light refracts when it moves from air into water or from water into air.

Refraction can make objects look different. If you put one end of a pencil in a glass of water, the pencil will seem to be broken at the water's surface. The two parts of the pencil may seem to be different sizes. The pencil is not broken, but the path of the light is bent at each surface.

Light usually refracts at the surface of a new medium. However, light can also refract within a medium if the medium is uneven. If you look through the air over a fire or very hot material, the objects beyond may look wavy. The air above the fire is of different densities, so it refracts the light that passes through it. Water may look wavy as it is heated or as sugar or salt are added to it. Uneven air can also cause light from the blue sky to bend toward your eye. The result may look like water on the ground—a mirage.

CHECK YOUR READING — What happens when light enters a new material and changes speed?

Scientists often use a ray model when they work out how an object will refract light. They use lines to represent some of the paths the light will take. The lines are called rays. Rays are straight except where refraction occurs. In the diagrams below, parallel rays represent a straight beam of light.

The bright areas in the shadow of the glass occur because light changes direction as it passes through the glass and water.

This mirage makes the road look wet. Uneven air causes you to see the blue of the sky where you expect to see black road.

Scattered by a Cloud
The rays bend in all directions because the medium scatters the light. The rays bend in different places within the cloud.

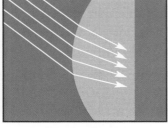

Refracted at a Surface
The rays bend at the surface between two mediums—air and glass. Within a medium, the rays are straight.

Refracted in a Medium
The rays bend in a curve because the density of the air changes gradually. The speed of the light also changes gradually.

Matter can reflect light.

Opaque materials do not allow light to pass through them. They may absorb light. They may also reflect light, or cause the light to bounce off of them. Most materials absorb some light and reflect some light. Some materials also transmit some light.

This photograph shows both regular reflection (the mirror) and diffuse reflection (everything else).

Think about your reflection in a mirror. The light bounces off the mirror in a very predictable, uniform way because the mirror is very smooth. If all the light comes from one direction (parallel rays) then they all bounce off the mirror in exactly the same way. After reflecting, the rays are all still parallel. This is called regular reflection. Very smooth surfaces, such as smooth glass, reflect light in this way. So, even though windows are transparent and transmit most of the light that hits them, they also reflect a small amount. You may be able to see your reflection in a window at night. You will learn more about regular reflection in Chapter 14.

You probably think of reflection as regular reflection. But most of the objects around you reflect light in a different way, called diffuse reflection. Rays coming from one direction bounce off the surface in many new directions. Surfaces that are slightly rough usually produce diffuse reflection. Your skin, this page, and a roughened glass surface will all cause light to be diffuse after reflection. When light bounces off an object in this way and is then detected in your eye, you can see the object.

 How do a mirror and this page reflect light differently?

You can think of a rough surface as being made of many tiny, smooth surfaces joined together. The tiny pieces each produce regular reflection. However, each tiny piece is at a different angle from the pieces nearby. So, one ray bends in one direction, but a nearby ray bends in a very different direction. The result is that light from a rough surface can be seen from all directions, even when the light shines on the surface from just one direction. The light seems to come from the surface, as if the material had emitted the light.

Have you ever seen a fuzzy reflection of yourself in a polished tabletop? You can see both your reflection and the table easily. Some surfaces produce both types of reflection. The surface is rough, but enough smooth pieces are lined up to produce regular reflection.

Regular and Diffuse Reflection

Light seems to come *through* a smooth surface but *from* a rough surface.

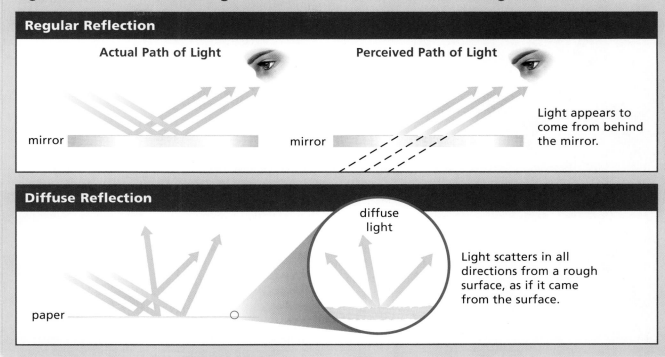

Regular Reflection

Actual Path of Light

Perceived Path of Light

mirror

mirror

Light appears to come from behind the mirror.

Diffuse Reflection

diffuse light

paper

Light scatters in all directions from a rough surface, as if it came from the surface.

Light may be emitted by the Sun, pass through the atmosphere and a window, bounce off your face, bounce off a mirror, and finally enter your eye. You see the light as if it came from your reflection. When your eyes and brain put together the information, you see your reflection as if the light had come through the mirror from behind. In a ray diagram, people often use dashed lines to show where the light appears to be coming from. In Chapter 14, dashed lines will help you see how your image in a mirror is formed.

13.3 Review

KEY CONCEPTS

1. Is light always absorbed at the surface of a new medium? Explain. (7.6.f)

2. What are some things that can happen when light moves into a new medium? (7.6.c)

3. Describe two ways light can bounce off a surface. (7.6.f)

CRITICAL THINKING

4. **Apply** Imagine that you are a firefighter searching a smoke-filled room. Would using a strong light help you see better? Explain your answer.

5. **Compare and Contrast** How is a rough surface like a translucent material? How is it different?

◯ CHALLENGE

6. **Infer** When you look at a window in the daytime, you see objects through the window. But at night, you see the dim reflection of the room. Do you think the window reflects the room during the day? Why or why not?

Smaller Is Better

> **7.6.a** Students know visible light is a small band within a very broad electromagnetic spectrum.

Silicon Valley, a region southeast of San Francisco, is known for its high-technology industries. How did this area get its name? Silicon is an element that makes up much of Earth's crust. Silicon can be treated with certain chemicals to change its properties. Then, electric current can be made to flow through treated silicon more easily or less easily. This fine control makes silicon very useful for making computer chips. Many of the world's computer chips have been designed in Silicon Valley.

Why Use Light?

A computer chip is made of many layers. Each layer has a pattern of metal lines. The lines are the wires of tiny circuits. They are much too thin to draw by hand, or even by using a very good machine. Instead, light shines through a mask onto a piece of silicon called a wafer. Light and shadows form a pattern of thin lines. Where the light shines, a coating of special material changes. The coating is then used to produce the pattern of metal lines. A new pattern of light is used for each layer of the chip.

Shorter Waves, Smaller Patterns

When the patterns of metal lines are made smaller, more circuits fit onto a computer chip. The chip can then do more complicated tasks. However, the size of the thinnest possible line depends on the wavelength of light used to make the pattern. Shorter wavelengths can produce smaller patterns.

Ultraviolet light helps designers make computer chips very small. The next step is to use extreme-ultraviolet (EUV) light, which has shorter wavelengths. However, some of the materials used to transmit longer-wavelength light are opaque to EUV light. A group of researchers in California are developing ways to use EUV light effectively. When EUV technology is developed, Silicon Valley companies will be able to fit more circuits on each computer chip. Then, they can design smaller computers that do complicated tasks faster.

Many computer chips—each with many circuits—are produced on a round wafer of silicon. Then the chips are cut apart.

WRITING ABOUT SCIENCE

Computers are getting smaller and faster every year. Write a paragraph describing what you think computers will look like in 20 years and what new ways people will use them.

Color comes from light.

CALIFORNIA
Content Standards

7.5.g Students know how to relate the structures of the eye and ear to their functions.

7.6.b Students know that for an object to be seen, light emitted by or scattered from it must be detected by the eye.

7.6.e Students know that white light is a mixture of many wavelengths (colors) and that retinal cells react differently to different wavelengths.

VOCABULARY

retina p. 476
rod cell p. 477
cone cell p. 477

BEFORE, you learned

- Matter emits different frequencies of EM radiation
- Matter absorbs, transmits, and reflects light
- You see only when light enters your eye

NOW, you will learn

- How the eye detects light of different frequencies
- How mixtures of frequencies appear as different colors
- About the primary colors of light and how pigments reflect these

THINK ABOUT

What is color?

Have you ever seen an object that looks different indoors and outdoors? Socks that look alike in a drawer might not match when seen in sunlight. You may think of color as being a characteristic of an object. But why might an object's color change? Does an object still have color in the dark? The photograph shows the shadows formed on a wall when several colored lights shine on a person's hands. What color do you think the wall is?

Humans use their eyes and brains to detect and perceive color.

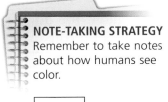

NOTE-TAKING STRATEGY
Remember to take notes about how humans see color.

Light must enter your eye in order for you to see. Special cells inside your eye absorb the light. These cells then produce signals—nerve impulses—that go to your brain. Your brain combines the signals from many cells, and you perceive light, color, shapes, and so on. Your eyes and brain need to work together in order for you to see.

Different types of cells in your eye respond to different frequencies of light. If just one frequency of light enters your eye, you see a single color. However, most of the time objects emit or reflect many different frequencies at once. In this section, you will learn about how the frequencies of light appear as different colors.

CHECK YOUR READING What do you need in order to see color?

Properties of Light

The part of the electromagnetic spectrum called visible light is made up of many different frequencies. When all of these frequencies appear in roughly equal amounts, the light appears white and is called white light. Sunlight is white light. As you will learn, however, light can look white without being an even mixture of all visible frequencies. The frequencies are properties of the light, while the colors you see depend on properties of your eyes.

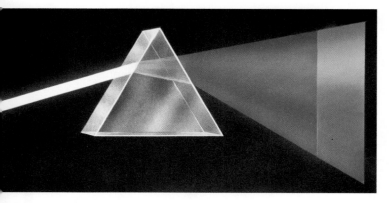

A prism or a diffraction grating can be used to spread light out into a spectrum of different frequencies. A prism refracts light twice at different angles, as shown on the left. Higher frequencies are refracted more. A diffraction grating is a thin sheet of plastic or glass that produces spectrums on both sides of the center. If you take all the light from a spectrum and make it shine on the same spot, it looks white again.

White light is made up of about equal amounts of all frequencies of visible light. A prism can spread these out into a spectrum.

A spectrum of white light could be divided into countless frequencies, each with its own color. However, the frequencies are usually grouped into named colors. Each color shades into the next. From lowest to highest frequency, the most usual everyday names are red, orange, yellow, green, blue, indigo, and violet. When discussing properties of human vision, it works better to group the colors as red, yellow, green, cyan, and blue. Cyan (SY-AN) is a blue-green or green-blue. Scientists often refer to the red end and the blue end of the spectrum. They group violet with blue.

 CHECK YOUR READING   How can you be sure white light is made up of different colors?

Properties of the Eye

Your eye detects light by absorbing it. When your eye absorbs no light from an object, the object looks very dark, like a deep shadow. You do not see it. A small amount of light lets you see the object, but it still looks dark—unlit or black. When your eye absorbs more light, the object looks brighter.

A layer of tissue called the **retina** (REHT-uhn-uh) lines the inside of your eye. The retina has a layer of cells that detect light. As the cells absorb light, they start a signal that goes to the brain. In the retina are two types of light-detecting cells.

VOCABULARY
Remember to make word frames for new terms.

retina

nerve to brain

Rod cells, or rods, are long, thin cells. They let you see in dim light, such as moonlight. The signals they send tell your brain only how bright the light is. You do not see color in dim light. When the light is brighter, your rods absorb too much light and so they do not function well. When the light grows dim, it takes a few minutes for the rods to start working well. It takes more than half an hour for the rods to become fully active, or dark-adapted. Because there are few rod cells in the very center of your retina, you may not see dim light when you look straight at it. If you look slightly to one side, you may see better.

Your **cone cells,** or cones, are wide on one end and narrow on the other. They detect high levels of light and let you see color. Three types of cones absorb three different ranges of frequencies.

- "Red" cones absorb red light best, but also frequencies of yellow and green light.
- "Green" cones absorb well from yellow through cyan. They absorb green light best.
- "Blue" cones absorb the blue end of the spectrum best.

A cone sends the same type of signal when it absorbs light, no matter what the frequency of the light. In other words, your red cones can't tell the difference between red and yellow. You see a yellow frequency as different from red because yellow light is absorbed by two different types of cones at the same time. The red and green cones both absorb about equal amounts of the yellow frequency and send signals to your brain. Then you perceive yellow. Green light is absorbed more by the green cones than the red cones, so you see green as different from yellow.

CHECK YOUR READING What types of cells let you see color?

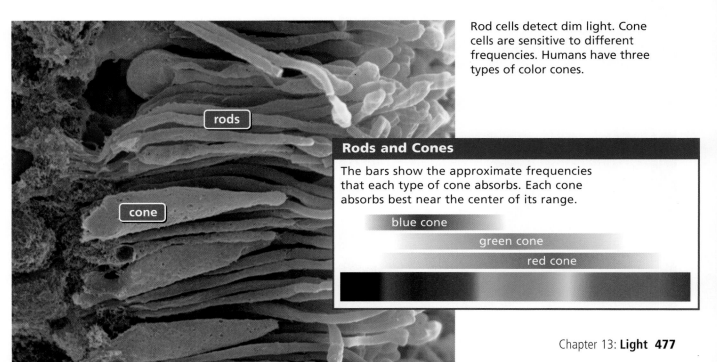

Rod cells detect dim light. Cone cells are sensitive to different frequencies. Humans have three types of color cones.

Rods and Cones

The bars show the approximate frequencies that each type of cone absorbs. Each cone absorbs best near the center of its range.

blue cone

green cone

red cone

Humans see primary colors and mixtures.

You see color when a single frequency of light causes one, two, or all three types of cones to send signals to your brain. These are the colors you see in a spectrum. But most light sources give off many frequencies at once. Most objects reflect many frequencies at once. Thus, most of the colors you perceive are combinations of frequencies.

Primary Colors of Light

Remember that a red, green, or blue frequency is absorbed by just one type of cone, while a yellow frequency is absorbed by two types of cones. However, if you see one frequency of red light and one frequency of green light at the same time, the result also looks yellow. Both red and green cones absorb light equally. The signals to your brain are exactly the same as those produced by a yellow frequency. The red and green light together look exactly the same as yellow light.

In a similar way, green and blue light together will look exactly the same as a single frequency of cyan light. Different combinations of red, green, and blue light can make you think you're seeing any frequency of visible light. A combination of red, green, and blue light can look exactly like white light, even though it is made of only three frequencies. You can use some combination of red, green, and blue light to make your brain see any color. So, red, green, and blue are called primary, or first, colors of light. Sometimes this set of colors is called RGB, the first letter of each color's name.

 CHECK YOUR READING How are the primary colors of light related to your cones?

Primary colors of light from three spotlights combine to make the secondary colors yellow, cyan (light blue), and magenta (dark pink).

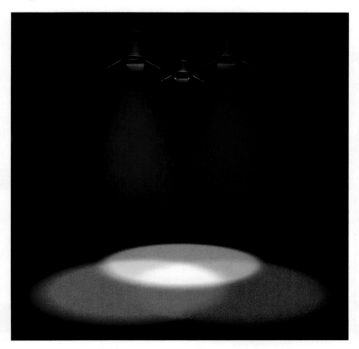

Yellow, cyan, and magenta—a dark pink or purple—are called secondary colors of light. You see a secondary color when two types of cones send signals to your brain. You see yellow when your red and green cones send signals, and cyan when your green and blue cones send signals. If the light causes your red cones and blue cones to send signals to your brain, you see magenta. There is no magenta frequency of light. You see magenta only when your eyes absorb at least two frequencies of light at the same time.

Adding colors together adds light and makes the result brighter. So, the primary and secondary colors of light are called an additive system.

If you examine a color television or computer screen, you will see tiny dots of red, green, and blue. Different combinations of these lights are used to make you see different colors. You can draw colored rays to help you think about what happens to the different frequencies of light. In the diagrams on the left below, the frequencies are sorted into a spectrum even though all the frequencies are really mixed together.

Color Transmission

A material can transmit some frequencies and be opaque to others. The diagram below, at right, shows glass that is opaque to red and blue light. It is transparent to yellow, green, and cyan. These frequencies pass through the glass and you see the result as bright green.

Transparent colored materials are often used to change the color of light. They do not change one frequency into another. They only filter out, or remove, some frequencies. So, they are often called color filters. If a frequency is not present in the light, the filter cannot produce it. If only red light falls on green glass, little or no light passes through it. You see black. The glass filters out the red and nothing is left. The color you see depends on the frequencies of the light that are emitted and on what happens to each frequency before it gets to your eye.

A TV screen uses red, green, and blue dots to reproduce colors.

CHECK YOUR READING What does a filter do?

Seeing Color

The colors your brain perceives depend on the light that enters your eye.

Mixing Color

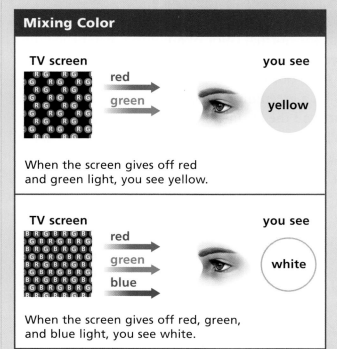

When the screen gives off red and green light, you see yellow.

When the screen gives off red, green, and blue light, you see white.

Filtering Color

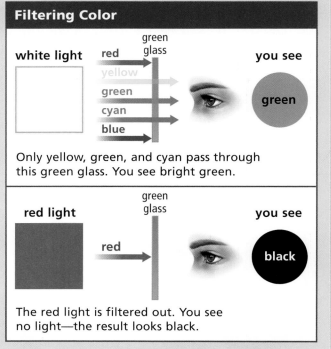

Only yellow, green, and cyan pass through this green glass. You see bright green.

The red light is filtered out. You see no light—the result looks black.

INVESTIGATE Color Mixing

What happens when you mix colors?

PROCEDURE

1. Cover the disk with equal amounts of red, green, and blue paper as shown.

2. Carefully measure and mark 0.5 cm to each side of the disk's center. Use the push pin to make a hole at each mark. Thread the string through the holes and tie the ends together as shown.

3. Hold the ends of the string loop while another student turns the disk 10–20 times. Then pull the ends of the string apart to make the disk spin. Watch the colors. Let the spinning disk twist the string and then pull again.

WHAT DO YOU THINK?

- What color did the spinning disk appear to be?
- What do you think happened to the colors of light?

CHALLENGE What would happen if you mixed just red and green?

SKILL FOCUS
Observing (7.6.e)

MATERIALS
- cardboard disk
- colored paper
- scissors
- glue
- ruler
- push pin
- 1.5 m of thin string

TIME
20 minutes

Color Reflection and Absorption

Objects usually absorb some frequencies of light and reflect others. The frequencies that an object reflects produce the color you see. A green lime absorbs most frequencies, but reflects mostly green light. It may also reflect some yellow and cyan.

When you think of the normal color of an object, you probably think of how the object looks when all visible frequencies—white light—fall on it. The same object can look different when lit by fewer frequencies. In red light, a green lime appears black rather than green. When an object absorbs all the frequencies that fall on it, it appears very dark or black. When an object reflects all the frequencies that fall on it, it appears the same color as the light. This white page reflects all frequencies if white light falls on it. The letters on the page absorb all frequencies and appear black. In red light, the page would appear red and the letters would still appear black.

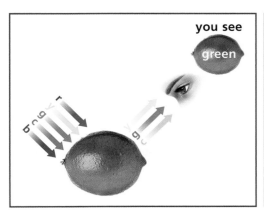

Primary Pigments

When you add one color of light to another, the result is brighter. However, when you add one color of paint to another, the result is darker. The mixed paint absorbs all the frequencies of the first paint plus all the frequencies of the second paint. So, the second color subtracts frequencies from what you see. This type of color mixing is called a subtractive system.

The primary colors in a subtractive system, such as paint, each reflect light that affects two types of cone cells. So, they are the same as the secondary colors of light—cyan, magenta, and yellow (called CMY). The secondary colors in a subtractive system affect just one type of cone cell. So they are the same as the primary colors of light—red, green, and blue. The primary and secondary colors are opposite in additive (light) and subtractive (paint) systems.

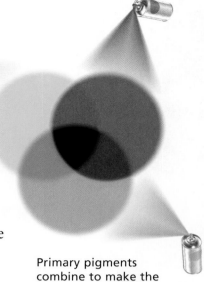

Primary pigments combine to make the secondary pigments red, blue, and green.

 How do subtractive systems and additive systems differ?

Materials that are used to produce colors are called pigments. When you mix pigments the mixture reflects fewer frequencies. The result is darker, so the primary pigments need to be bright.

Sometimes, people place tiny dots of different colors next to each other. The result can be brighter than a mixture of pigments would be. Many printers use tiny patterns of color that look like a single color when seen from a distance.

The image is printed by using tiny, overlapping dots of cyan, magenta, yellow, and black ink.

13.4 Review

KEY CONCEPTS

1. How does the eye detect light of different frequencies? (7.6.b)
2. What is white light? (7.6.e)
3. How are the primary colors of light and of pigment related to cone cells? (7.6.b)

CRITICAL THINKING

4. **Apply** If a person had no green cones, would he or she be able to tell the difference between red and yellow? Explain.
5. **Predict** If you shine a red light, a green light, and a blue light onto the same part of a black curtain, what color will you see?

CHALLENGE

6. **Synthesize** Earth's atmosphere scatters blue light more than it scatters red light. The scattered light goes in all directions. Explain how this appears.

CHAPTER INVESTIGATION

Wavelength and Color

OVERVIEW AND PURPOSE Lighting directors use color filters to change the look of a scene. The color an object appears depends both on the frequencies of light shining on it and on the frequencies of light that it reflects. In this investigation, you will
- make a light box to hold color filters and objects
- study the effect of different colors of light on objects of different colors

▶ Problem

How does the appearance of objects of different colors change in different colors of light?

▶ Procedure

1. Make a data table like the one shown on the sample notebook page to help you compare your predictions and observations of the objects using the different filters.

2. Cut a 10 cm square from each color of acetate. These are your color filters.

3. Make an 8 cm square hole in one end of the box. Light from the lamp will come through this light hole. Filters will cover this hole at times.

4. Make a small hole, about 3 cm across, in the center of the box top. You will look through this viewing hole.

5. Position the light box and lamp so that the light shines through the end hole. Place the white object inside the box and replace the cover. Look through the viewing hole. Adjust the position of the lamp and box if needed.

6. Observe the white object and record your results. Describe the object as bright, medium, or dark. Describe its color. Then observe each of the other objects—black, yellow, and red.

7. Tape the red filter over the viewing hole and observe the white object. Then predict what you will see with this filter for the other objects. Record your predictions.

step 7

MATERIALS
- 3 sheets of acetate (red, blue, and green)
- ruler
- scissors
- shoe box
- masking tape
- light source
- 4 solid-colored objects (white, black, red, and yellow)
- colored pencils

7.6.e, 7.6.f, 7.7.c

Content Standard
7.6.e Students know that white light is a mixture of many wavelengths (colors) and that retinal cells react differently to different wavelengths.

Investigation Standard
7.7.c Students will communicate the logical connection among hypotheses, science concepts, tests conducted, data collected, and conclusions drawn from the scientific evidence.

8 Observe each of the remaining colored objects with the red filter in place.

step 8

9 With each of the two remaining filters, observe the white object, make predictions, and then observe the other objects.

▶ Observe and Analyze

Write It Up

1. **RECORD OBSERVATIONS** Be sure your data table is complete.

2. **COMPARE** Which objects looked darker in blue light? Which looked darker in red light?

3. **ANALYZE** Draw diagrams of colored rays to show which colors of white light—which frequencies—pass through each filter. Then show which colors of white light reflect off each object.

▶ Conclude

Write It Up

1. **INFER** Identify a filter that made an object look darker. How did the filter change the amount of light—the number of different frequencies—reaching the object?

2. **ANALYZE** Using your choice of filter and object from question 1, draw what happens to the different colors of white light as they pass through the filter and then reflect off the object to reach your eye. Do the colors that reach your eye produce the color that you observed?

3. **INFER** Which object looked almost the same in all four observations? Why do you think this was so?

4. **INTERPRET** Answer the problem question.

5. **APPLY** When the Sun is low in the sky, the atmosphere scatters out most of the blue and green light. What colors would a red fire hydrant and a blue house look in this light?

▶ INVESTIGATE Further

CHALLENGE What would happen if you taped the green filter over the red filter on the light box and then observed the objects? Draw colored ray diagrams to predict what you would see. Then test your predictions.

Wavelength and Color

Problem

How does the appearance of objects of different colors change in different colors of light?

Observe and Analyze

Table 1. Predicted and Observed Colors of Objects with Different Colored Filters

Predicted	red filter	blue filter	green filter
black object			
red object			
yellow object			

Observed	no filter	red filter	blue filter	green filter
white object				
black object				

CONTENT REVIEW
CLASSZONE.COM

the **BIG** idea

Visible light is a small band in the electromagnetic spectrum.

◀ KEY CONCEPTS SUMMARY

① Light is an electromagnetic wave.

- Visible light and other electromagnetic (EM) radiation travels at the speed of light in a vacuum.
- The EM spectrum is divided into radio waves, microwaves, infrared light, visible light, ultraviolet light, x-rays, and gamma rays.

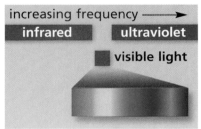
increasing frequency ⟶
infrared   ultraviolet
visible light

VOCABULARY
electromagnetic wave p. 453
radiation p. 455
absorb p. 455
electromagnetic spectrum p. 455

② Light is produced in different ways.

- Incandescent matter emits light of different frequencies according to its temperature.
- Matter can convert different forms of energy into EM radiation. The energy can come from chemical reactions, charged particles (such as in electric currents), radiation, and other sources.

VOCABULARY
emit p. 463

③ Light interacts with materials.

- Light travels in straight lines unless the medium changes.
- Absorption, transmission, and reflection are ways light interacts with matter.
- Opaque objects reflect or absorb light, while translucent materials scatter light.
- Smooth surfaces produce regular reflection, while rough surfaces produce diffuse reflection.

VOCABULARY
reflect p. 468
transmit p. 469
diffuse p. 469
refract p. 471

④ Color comes from light.

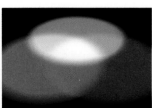

- You see color when your brain combines signals from the red, green, and blue cones in your eyes.
- Most colors are combinations of frequencies.
- Materials can emit, transmit, reflect, and absorb different frequencies in different amounts.

VOCABULARY
retina p. 476
rod cell p. 477
cone cell p. 477

Reviewing Vocabulary

Make a four-square diagram for each of the listed terms. Write the term in the center. Define the term in one square. Write characteristics, examples, and nonexamples in other squares. A sample is shown below.

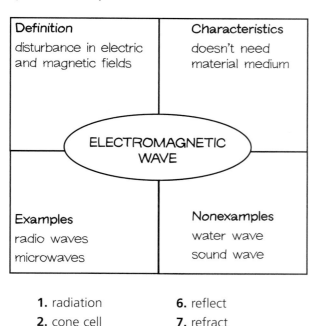

Definition	Characteristics
disturbance in electric and magnetic fields	doesn't need material medium

ELECTROMAGNETIC WAVE

Examples	Nonexamples
radio waves microwaves	water wave sound wave

1. radiation
2. cone cell
3. absorb
4. emit
5. transmit

6. reflect
7. refract
8. diffuse
9. incandescent
10. luminescent

Reviewing Key Concepts

Multiple Choice *Choose the letter of the best answer.*

11. What is the same for all EM waves in a vacuum? (7.6.f)
 a. their speed
 b. their frequency
 c. their wavelength
 d. their energy

12. An electromagnetic wave can travel without a material medium because to travel, it needs only
 a. the Sun
 b. water
 c. fields
 d. air pressure

13. The Sun and a tungsten filament are both (7.6.b)
 a. bioluminescent
 b. incandescent
 c. luminescent
 d. fluorescent

14. Which of the following has higher frequencies than visible light? (7.6.a)
 a. radio waves
 b. microwaves
 c. infrared
 d. ultraviolet

15. What produces refraction? (7.6.c)
 a. a change in the speed of light
 b. a change in the frequency of light
 c. the surface of an opaque material
 d. a surface that is rough

16. Which of these let(s) you see in low levels of light? (7.6.e)
 a. rod cells
 b. cone cells
 c. luminescence
 d. diffuse light

17. How do white paint and black paint affect visible light? (7.6.e)
 a. White paint absorbs all frequencies, while black paint reflects all frequencies.
 b. White paint reflects all frequencies, while black paint absorbs all frequencies.
 c. White paint reflects red, green, and blue, while black paint reflects cyan, magenta, and yellow.
 d. White paint reflects cyan, magenta, and yellow, while black paint reflects red, green, and blue.

Short Answer *Write a short answer to each question.*

18. How does visible light differ from other EM waves? How is it similar? (7.6.a)

19. List all the things necessary for you to see a piece of paper. (7.6.f)

20. What does an object look like if the light emitted by it or reflected by it does not enter your eye? (7.6.b)

Thinking Critically

Use the photograph below to answer the next three questions.

21. **IDENTIFY CAUSE** Why does the lower part of the pencil look different from the upper part? (7.6.c)

22. **COMPARE AND CONTRAST** What is different about the way light interacts with the pencil and with the water? (7.6.f)

23. **ANALYZE** Look at the two ends of the pencil. Describe the medium(s) that light from each end passes through. (7.6.c)

24. **CONNECT** What causes different frequencies of light to be spread out by a prism? (7.6.e)

25. **ANALYZE** Why is EM radiation of higher frequency more likely to damage a material that absorbs it?

26. **PROVIDE EXAMPLES** Give two examples of EM radiation that you can't see but that can affect your body. What is an effect of each? (7.6.a)

27. **CLASSIFY** What are the different things that can happen when light encounters a new material? Group similar items. *Hint:* Transmission and reflection should each include other items. (7.6.f)

28. **PREDICT** If you raise the temperature of a red-hot material, how does its color change?

29. **COMPARE** A computer screen gives off red, green, and blue light. A very hot coil of tungsten gives off all the visible frequencies about equally. How are the effects similar? (7.6.e)

30. **PREDICT** What color will a white object appear if you look at it through a blue filter? (7.6.f)

31. **APPLY** A glass bottle filled with oil sometimes seems to be one solid object—there is no refraction to let you see the inside surface of the glass. What must be true about the speeds of light in the glass and the oil? (7.6.c)

The diagram below shows how far different frequencies of visible light penetrate into ocean water. Use information from this diagram to answer the next three questions.

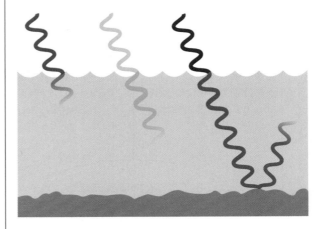

32. **OBSERVE** What keeps some light waves from reaching the ocean floor? (7.6.f)

33. **PREDICT** How would violet light behave in the same water? Think of where violet is on the color spectrum. (7.6.f)

34. **SYNTHESIZE** If you were near the ocean floor, how would the colors you see be affected by the interactions shown in the diagram? (7.6.e)

the BIG idea

35. **SYNTHESIZE** Look again at the large photograph on pages 450–451. Use what you have learned in the chapter to answer the question again. (7.6.a)

36. **ANALYZE** Suppose you look through a window and see a tree in the sunlight. Draw a diagram to show the complete path of the light from the Sun's emission to your eye's absorption. (7.6.f)

UNIT PROJECTS

Check your schedule for your unit project. How are you doing? Be sure that you've placed data or notes from your research in your project folder.

Standards-Based Assessment

Interpreting Diagrams

7.6.a, 7.6.f

The diagram below shows part of the electromagnetic (EM) spectrum. The lower band shows frequency in hertz (Hz). The upper band shows different technologies and the part of the EM spectrum that each uses.

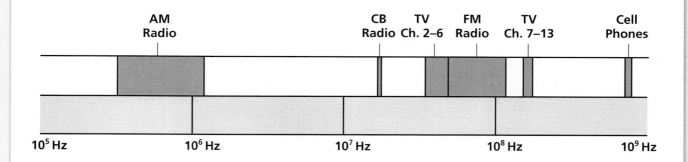

Use the diagram to answer the following questions.

1. Which of the technologies listed below uses the highest frequencies?

a. AM radio

b. CB radio

c. FM radio

d. TV channels 2–6

2. If you were receiving a signal at a frequency of nearly 10^9 Hz, what would you be using?

a. a CB radio

b. an AM radio

c. an FM radio

d. a cell phone

3. All of the technologies in the diagram use radio waves. High-frequency radio waves, starting about halfway between 10^8 Hz and 10^9 Hz, are also called microwaves. Which of these technologies uses microwaves?

a. cell phone

b. AM radio

c. FM radio

d. television

4. Signals with similar frequencies sometimes interfere with each other. Which of the following might you expect to interfere with one another?

a. lower television channels and cell phones

b. upper television channels and FM radio

c. lower television channels and FM radio

d. upper television channels and cell phones

Extended Response

Answer the two questions below in detail. Include some of the terms from the word box. In your answer, underline each term you use.

absorb	frequency	refract
diffuse	medium	retina
emit	reflect	transmit

5. Name at least three types of EM radiation. Explain how they are similar and how they are different.

6. What are the ways that EM radiation interacts with matter? Describe each.

TIMELINES in Science

THE STORY OF LIGHT

Light has fascinated people since ancient times. The earliest ideas about light were closely associated with beliefs and observations about vision. But over the centuries, philosophers and scientists developed an increasingly better understanding of light as a physical reality that obeyed the laws of physics.

With this increased understanding of the nature and behavior of light has come the ability to use light as a tool. Many applications of light technology have led to improvements in human visual abilities. People can now make images of a wide range of objects that were invisible to earlier generations. The study of light has also led to technologies that do not involve sight at all.

This timeline shows just a few of the many steps on the road to understanding light. The boxes below the timeline show how these discoveries have been applied and developed into new technologies.

400 B.C.
Light Travels in a Straight Line
Observing the behavior of shadows, the Chinese philosopher Mo-Ti finds that light travels in a straight line. His discovery helps explain why light passing through a small opening forms an upside-down image.

300 B.C.
Reflection Obeys Law
The Greek mathematician Euclid discovers that light striking a mirror obeys the law of reflection. The angle at which light reflects off a mirror is equal to the angle at which it strikes the mirror.

EVENTS

| 450 B.C. | 425 B.C. | 400 B.C. | 375 B.C. | 350 B.C. | 325 B.C. | 300 B.C. |

APPLICATIONS AND TECHNOLOGY

APPLICATION

Camera Obscura

The principle described by Mo-Ti in 400 B.C. led to the development of the camera obscura. When light from an object shines through a small hole into a dark room, an image of the object appears on the far wall. The darkened room is called, in Latin, camera obscura. Because light travels in a straight line, the highest points on the object appear at the lowest points on the image; thus, the image appears upside down. Room-sized versions of the camera obscura like the one shown here were a popular attraction in the late 1800s.

1666

White Light Is Made of Colors

The British scientist Isaac Newton makes a remarkable discovery. After studying the effects of a prism on white light, Newton realizes that white light is actually made up of different colors. This contradicts the long-held belief that white light is pure light and that colored light gets its color from the impurities of different materials.

A.D. 1000

Eyes Do Not Shoot Rays

The Egyptian mathematician and astronomer Ali Alhazen publishes his *Book of Optics*. A diagram of the eye from Alhazen's book is shown below. Alhazen proves that light travels from objects to the eyes, not the other way around. The previously accepted theory, put forth by the Greek philosopher Plato centuries before, claimed that light traveled from the eyes to objects.

1676

Light Speeds into Distance

Looking through a telescope, the Danish astronomer Olaus Roemer observes one of Jupiter's moons "setting" earlier and earlier as Earth approaches the planet—and later and later as Earth moves farther away. Roemer infers that distance affects the time it takes light to travel from Jupiter to Earth. He estimates the speed of light as 230,000 kilometers per second.

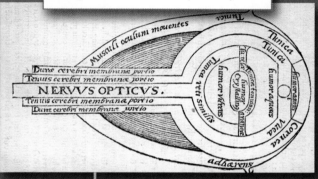

A.D. 1000	1025		1625	1650	1675

TECHNOLOGY

Reflecting Telescopes

Early astronomers, such as Galileo, used refracting telescopes. These telescopes used a lens to concentrate light. They were difficult to focus because of the uneven refraction of different wavelengths. Isaac Newton built the first reflecting telescope, which overcame this difficulty by using a mirror to concentrate and focus light. All major astronomical telescopes, including the Hubble Space Telescope, now use mirrors.

1821
Light Waves Move Like Ripples in a Pond

The French physicist Augustin-Jean Fresnel confirms the idea that light waves are transverse waves. Like water waves, light waves are at right angles to the direction of their travel. This idea helps to explain many observed behaviors of light, including diffraction fringes such as those surrounding this mountain climber.

1801
Light Makes Waves

The British scientist Thomas Young finds that beams of light can interact to produce an interference pattern. He aims light through two slits and observes alternating light and dark bands on a screen. Young concludes that light acts as if it were made up of waves, which contradicts the theory developed by Newton and others that light is made up of particles.

1887
No Material Needed

The U.S. scientists Albert Michelson and Edward Morley carry out an experiment to measure how light is affected by motion through ether. Ether is thought to be the medium of light, as water is the medium of water waves. The men find no effect, which leads many to conclude that no ether exists and therefore that light waves need no material medium.

1750	1775	1800	1825	1850	1875	1900

APPLICATION

Holograms

Holograms are used today to produce images for art, communications, and research. A hologram can be made by an interference pattern between the two halves of a split laser beam. One half shines on film, and the other half shines on the object. The object reflects this second beam onto the film, where it makes an interference pattern with the first beam. The film can then be used to make a three-dimensional image of the object, as in this hologram of a shark.

TECHNOLOGY

Gravitational Lenses

As part of his theory of relativity, Albert Einstein predicted that light would bend in a gravitational field. His prediction was tested and confirmed in 1919. During a solar eclipse, scientists witnessed the bending of light from distant stars as their light passed near the Sun. Astronomers take advantage of this effect to get a better look at objects deep in space. Sometimes light from a distant object passes through a closer object's gravitational field on its way to Earth. By analyzing images of the object, scientists can learn more about it.

1960
Light Beams Line Up
The U.S. inventor Theodore Harold Maiman builds a working laser by stimulating emission of light in a cylinder of ruby crystal. Laser light waves all have the same wavelength, and their peaks occur together.

2001
Light Is Completely Stopped
After slowing light to the speed of a bicycle, the Danish physicist Lene Vestergaard Hau brings it to a complete halt in a super-cold medium. Controlling the speed of light could revolutionize computers, communications, and other electronic technology.

 RESOURCE CENTER
CLASSZONE.COM

Learn more about current research involving light.

1925   1950   1975   2000

APPLICATION

Lasers in Eye Surgery
For centuries, people have used corrective lenses to help their eyes focus images more clearly. Today, with the help of lasers, doctors can correct the eye itself. Using an ultraviolet laser, doctors remove microscopic amounts of a patient's cornea to change the amount it refracts light. As a result, the eye focuses images exactly on the retina. For many near-sighted people, the surgery results in 20/20 vision or better.

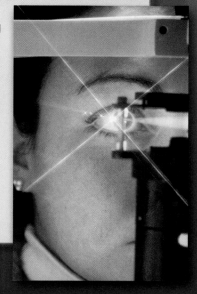

SPOTLIGHT on
PERCY JULIAN

The chemist Percy Julian (1899–1975) synthesized the drug used to treat glaucoma, a disease in which fluid builds up slowly in the eye. This fluid can damage the optic nerve, leading to partial or total blindness. The drug, physostigmine, lowers pressure inside the eye. It also helps improve memory in Alzheimer's patients and can be used as an antidote to nerve gas.

Julian was interested in medicinal plants and believed in using natural products whenever possible. For example, he synthesized physostigmine from the Calabar bean. He used a soy protein to develop AeroFoam, a substance for putting out gasoline and oil fires. Julian also made an inexpensive substitute for cortisone, used for treating arthritis. He was awarded over 100 patents for his inventions and honored on a stamp issued by the U.S. Postal Service.

ACTIVITIES

Make a Camera Obscura
Take a small box and paint the interior black. On one side, make a pinhole. On a side next to that one, make a hole about 5 cm in diameter.

On a bright, sunny day, hold the box so that sunlight enters the box through the pinhole. Fit your eye snugly against the larger hole and look inside.

Writing About Science
Lasers are currently used in entertainment, medicine, communication, supermarkets, and so on. Write a prediction about a specific use of lasers in the future. You might describe a new invention.

Optics

Images are produced
by light in many ways.

Key Concepts

SECTION

1 **Light tends to travel in straight lines.**
Learn about reflection, mirrors, and images.

SECTION

2 **Lenses form images by refracting light.**
Learn how two types of lenses produce images.

SECTION

3 **Optical tools use reflection and refraction.**
Learn about tools that help people use light.

SECTION

4 **The eye is a natural optical tool.**
Learn how your eyes focus light.

California ClassZone

CLASSZONE.COM

Chapter 14 online resources:
Content Review, Simulation,
Visualization, two Resource
Centers, Math Tutorial,
Test Practice

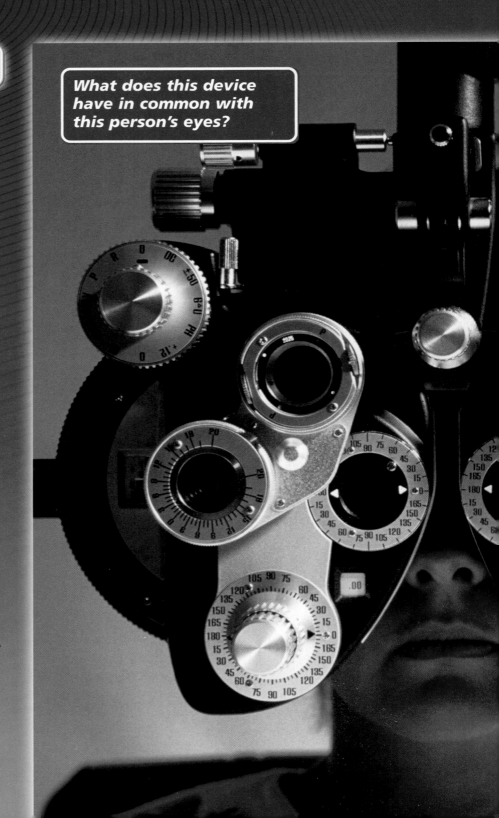

What does this device have in common with this person's eyes?

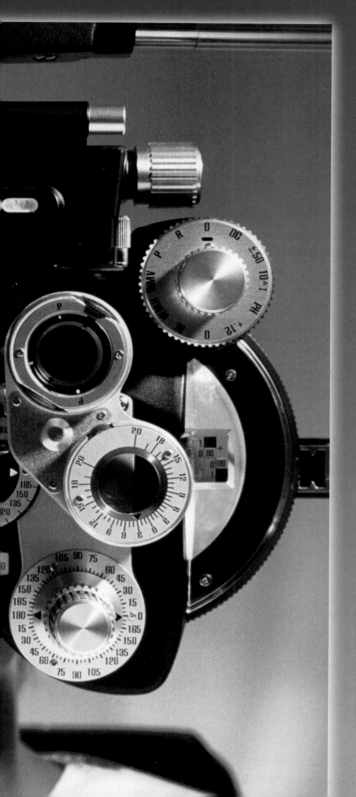

EXPLORE (the **BIG** idea)

How Does a Spoon Reflect Your Face?

> **7.6.f** Students know light can be reflected, refracted, transmitted, and absorbed by matter.

Look at the reflection of your face in the bowl of a shiny metal spoon. How does your face look? Is it different from what you would expect? Does moving the spoon closer or farther away make a difference? Now turn the spoon over and look at your face in the round side. How does your face look this time?

Observe and Think Why do the two sides of the spoon affect the appearance of your face in these ways?

Internet Activity: Optics

> **7.6.d** Students know how simple lenses are used in a magnifying glass, the eye, a camera, a telescope, and a microscope.

Go to **ClassZone.com** to learn more about optics. Find out how different types of telescopes and microscopes work. Notice how rays are used to show possible paths of light.

Observe and Think Why do you think telescopes and microscopes need more than one lens or mirror to work well?

NSTA
scilinks.org
SCI LINKS

Lenses **Code: MDL030**

CHAPTER 14
Getting Ready to Learn

◀ CONCEPT REVIEW

- You see an object when light emitted by or reflected from it enters your eye.
- The speed of light is affected by a material medium.
- Reflection and refraction are two ways that light interacts with materials.

◀ VOCABULARY REVIEW

reflect p. 468
diffuse p. 469
transmit p. 469
refract p. 471
retina p. 476

CONTENT REVIEW
CLASSZONE.COM

Review concepts and vocabulary.

▶ TAKING NOTES

COMBINATION NOTES

To take notes about a new concept, first make an informal outline of the information. Then make a sketch of the concept and label it so you can study it later.

CHOOSE YOUR OWN STRATEGY

Take notes about new vocabulary terms, using one or more of the strategies from earlier chapters—**description wheel** or **frame game**. Feel free to mix and match the strategies, or to use an entirely different vocabulary strategy.

SCIENCE NOTEBOOK

NOTES
The angle of incidence (x) equals the angle of reflection (y).

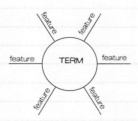

DESCRIPTION WHEEL

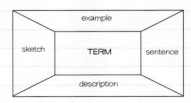

FRAME GAME

See the Note-Taking Handbook on pages R45–R51.

14.1

Light tends to travel in straight lines.

CALIFORNIA
Content Standards

7.6.c Students know light travels in straight lines if the medium it travels through does not change.

7.6.f Students know light can be reflected, refracted, transmitted, and absorbed by matter.

7.6.g Students know the angle of reflection of a light beam is equal to the angle of incidence.

BEFORE, you learned

- Objects can emit, absorb, reflect, or transmit light
- Reflected light can be regular or diffuse
- Rays represent possible paths of light

NOW, you will learn

- About the science of optics
- How light is reflected
- How mirrors form images

VOCABULARY

optics p. 495
angle of incidence p. 496
angle of reflection p. 496
image p. 497
diverge p. 497
converge p. 498
focal point p. 498

EXPLORE Reflection (7.6.b)

How does surface affect reflection?

PROCEDURE

1. Tear off a square sheet of foil. Look at your reflection in the shiny side of the foil.

2. Turn the foil over and look at your reflection in the dull side.

3. Crumple the foil, then smooth it out again. Again, look at your reflection in the shiny side.

WHAT DO YOU THINK?

- How did the three reflections differ from one another?
- What might explain these differences?

MATERIALS
aluminum foil

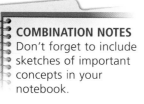
COMBINATION NOTES
Don't forget to include sketches of important concepts in your notebook.

Optics is the science of light and vision.

Light interacts with matter in different ways. You are able to see because of the ways different materials in your eyes transmit and absorb light. **Optics** (AHP-tihks) is the science of light and vision. Optics is also the application of knowledge about visible light to develop tools. Optical tools include eyeglasses, mirrors, magnifying lenses, binoculars, cameras, and telescopes.

Inventors have designed these optical tools based on their understanding of the ways light interacts with materials. Light travels in straight lines through empty space. Light usually travels in straight lines through materials that transmit light—transparent materials. However, the path of light can change when the material changes. At the boundary between two materials, light may be refracted or reflected.

CHECK YOUR READING What can materials do to the direction of light?

Mirrors reflect light in a predictable way.

You have read that scientists use rays to represent the path of light as it interacts with different materials. A flashlight produces a wide, spreading beam of light. However, in the ray diagrams below, only one ray is shown for each diagram. The ray represents the center of the flashlight beam. Other rays could be drawn to show the edges of the beam, but the lines would cross, making the diagram hard to understand. Scientists often draw just one or two rays on a diagram. Ray diagrams help people design new optical tools. Computer programs can produce very complicated ray diagrams. Such programs have many uses, from designing new instruments to making computer graphics, or CG, look very real.

 What does a ray diagram show?

Light bounces off a mirror or other smooth surface in a simple way, much like a ball bouncing off a flat wall. If the light comes in at a low angle, it bounces and leaves at a low angle. If it hits a smooth surface at a right angle, it reflects back to where it came from. Instead of measuring angles from the surface, scientists measure these angles from the normal, an imaginary line perpendicular to the surface. The angle from the normal at which light comes in is the **angle of incidence.** The angle from the normal of the light after bouncing is the **angle of reflection.** In the diagrams below, a short curve from the normal to the ray indicates each angle. In the diagram on the left, both the angle of incidence and the angle of reflection are 60 degrees. In the diagram on the right, both angles are 40 degrees. The angle of incidence always equals the angle of reflection for mirrors and other regular reflectors. This relationship is called the law of reflection.

VISUALIZATION
CLASSZONE.COM
See reflection in action.

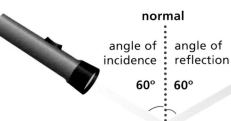

normal

angle of incidence | angle of reflection

60° : 60°

40° : 40°

The angle of reflection equals the angle of incidence.

You can think of a rough surface as many tiny pieces, each with a smooth surface. Each piece of surface has a normal. Light obeys the law of reflection for each tiny piece. However, the normals point in different directions, so incoming light reflects in many different directions. The result is the diffuse reflection of walls and most objects around you.

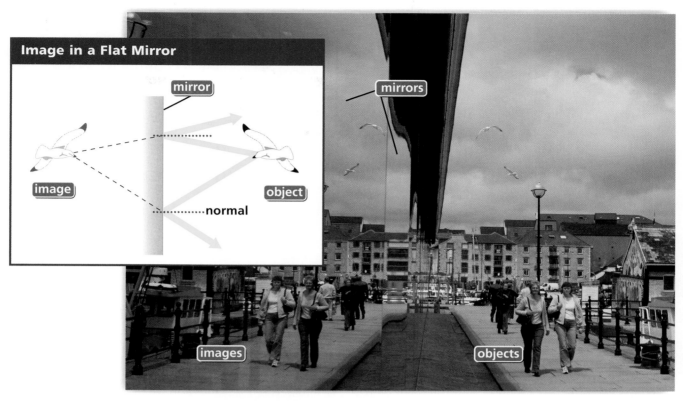

Image in a Flat Mirror

mirror

image

normal

object

mirrors

images

objects

Shape determines how mirrors form images.

When you look at most objects, the light seems to come from the surface of the object. But when you look in a mirror, the light does not seem to come from the mirror. The light seems to come through the mirror from objects behind it. These real-looking objects are called images. In optics, an **image** is a picture of an object that is formed by light. Your reflection in a mirror is an image. Mirrors of different shapes can produce images with different properties.

Flat Mirrors

An image forms as light reflects off an object, and then off the mirror. Light rays **diverge,** or move apart, from any location on the object. Two diverging rays from a gull are shown in the diagram above. Dashed lines show where the rays seem to come from. The image of the gull is located where the dashed lines meet.

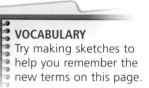

VOCABULARY
Try making sketches to help you remember the new terms on this page.

In a similar way, your image in a flat mirror is on the far side of the mirror. Your image is exactly as far from the mirror as you are. The nose of your reflection is closer to the mirror than the ears are. Your image is right side up—the top of your head appears at the top of your image. You look to your left to see the image of your left arm. However, you see the image as a person facing you, so your left arm looks like your image's right arm.

 CHECK YOUR READING How is your reflection in a flat mirror similar to yourself?

INVESTIGATE The Law of Reflection

How can two mirrors change your view?

PROCEDURE

1. To make a periscope, cut two flaps on opposite sides of the carton, one from the top and one from the bottom, as shown in the illustration.

2. Fold each flap inward until it is at a 45-degree angle to the side cuts. Tape it into place.

3. Attach a mirror to the outside of each flap.

4. Hold the periscope straight up and look through one of the openings.

WHAT DO YOU THINK?

- Where are the objects you see when you look through the periscope?
- What path does light take through the periscope?

CHALLENGE What would happen if the mirrors were set at 30 degrees instead of 45 degrees? Try it.

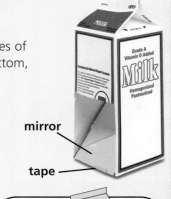

mirror

tape

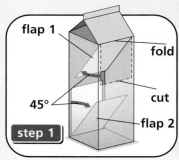

flap 1

fold

45°

cut

flap 2

step 1

SKILL FOCUS
Analyzing (7.6.g)

MATERIALS
- paper milk or juice carton
- scissors
- protractor
- tape
- 2 mirrors slightly smaller than the bottom of the carton

TIME
30 minutes

Curved Mirrors

Think about the law of reflection. If parallel rays hit a flat mirror, they all hit at the same angle of incidence. As a result, they all reflect at the same angle. If the mirror is curved, parallel rays reflect in different directions. The law of reflection applies to every ray. However, the normal is different for different locations on the surface. The rays hit at different angles of incidence, so they reflect at different angles.

A mirror can curve inward or outward. A concave mirror is curved inward toward the center, like the inside of a spoon. A concave mirror reflects parallel rays toward each other. The rays **converge,** or come together, cross, and diverge. The place where these rays cross is called the **focal point** of the mirror. In contrast, a convex mirror is curved outward, like the bottom of a spoon. A convex mirror reflects parallel rays so that they diverge. The rays appear to be diverging from a focal point behind the mirror.

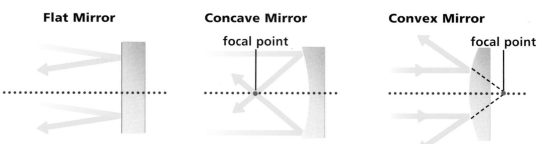

Flat Mirror

Concave Mirror

focal point

Convex Mirror

focal point

Convex Mirror
Your **virtual image** in a convex mirror is smaller than you.

Concave Mirror, Far Away
If you are standing far away, your **real image** in a concave mirror is upside down and smaller than you.

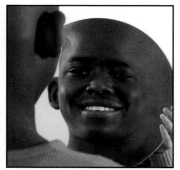

Concave Mirror, Up Close
If you are standing inside the focal point, your **virtual image** in a concave mirror is right-side up and larger.

Properties of Images

Images have different properties. Recall that an image in a flat mirror appears at a location behind the mirror. The light does not actually pass through the image, so the image is called a virtual image. Another type of image, called a real image, forms where light rays converge. You cannot feel a real image, but you can put your finger in the light at the image. If you put a movie screen—or a piece of paper—at the location of a real image, the image will appear to be on the screen. You will learn more about real and virtual images in Section 2.

Images have two other important properties. If you look in a concave mirror, your image may be upside down, or inverted. In a flat mirror, the orientation of your image is right-side up. Another property to notice about an image is the size. Some images are the same size as the original object. Other images are smaller or larger than the original object. These three properties—size, orientation, and location—are used to describe images.

Describe your image in a flat mirror. What three properties did you use?

14.1 Review

KEY CONCEPTS

1. Explain the term *optics* in your own words. (7.6.c)
2. If light hits a surface straight on—at zero degrees from the normal—in what direction is it reflected? (7.6.g)
3. Describe how light rays form an image of your smile when you look into a flat mirror. (7.6.f)

CRITICAL THINKING

4. **Analyze** What type of mirror would be best for examining your eye? for seeing a room behind you? Use the photographs and information above to help you.
5. **Synthesize** How would the letter *R* appear if you held it up to a flat mirror? a convex mirror? Use a spoon to try it.

CHALLENGE

6. **Apply** Flashlights and spotlights usually have a mirror behind the light bulb to help form a beam with nearly parallel edges. What type of mirror would work best? Where would you put the light bulb?

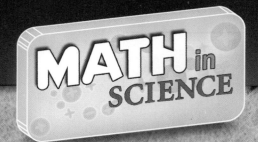

 MATH TUTORIAL
CLASSZONE.COM

Click on Math Tutorial
for more help with
measuring angles.

 Math 7.MG.3.1
Science 7.6.g

Send Help!

Survival kits often contain a small mirror that can be used to signal for help. If you were lost in the desert and saw a search plane overhead, you could use the mirror to reflect sunlight toward the plane and catch the pilot's attention. To aim your signal, you would use the law of reflection. The angle at which a ray of light bounces off a mirror—the angle of reflection—is always equal to the angle at which the ray strikes the mirror—the angle of incidence.

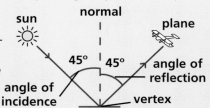

Example

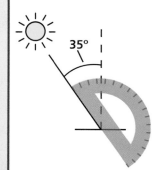

Measure the angle of incidence using a protractor as follows:

(1) Place the center mark of the protractor over the vertex of the angle formed by the incoming ray and the normal.

(2) Place the left 0° mark of the protractor on the incident ray.

(3) Read the number where the normal crosses the scale (35°).

(4) The angle of incidence is 35°.

ANSWER Therefore, the angle of reflection will be 35°.

Trace each of the following angles of incidence, extend its sides, and use a protractor to measure it.

   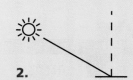

1.   2.   3.   4.

CHALLENGE Trace the drawing below. Use a protractor to find the angle of reflection necessary to signal the plane from point A.

• A

A mirror can be used to signal for help.

14.2 Lenses form images by refracting light.

CALIFORNIA
Content Standards

7.6.c Students know light travels in straight lines if the medium it travels through does not change.

7.6.d Students know how simple lenses are used in a magnifying glass, the eye, a camera, a telescope, and a microscope.

7.6.f Students know light can be reflected, refracted, transmitted, and absorbed by matter.

VOCABULARY

lens p. 503
focal length p. 504

BEFORE, you learned

- Light can refract when it moves into a new material
- The angle of incidence is measured from the normal

NOW, you will learn

- How a material medium can refract light
- How lenses control refraction
- How lenses produce images

EXPLORE Refraction (7.6.c)

How do materials bend light?

PROCEDURE

MATERIALS
- clear plastic cup
- pencil
- water
- mineral oil

(1) Place the pencil in the cup, as shown in the photograph. Look at the cup from the side so that you see part of the pencil through the cup.

(2) Fill the cup one-third full with water and repeat your observations.

(3) Gently add oil until the cup is two-thirds full. After the oil settles into a separate layer, observe.

WHAT DO YOU THINK?

- How did the appearance of the pencil change when you added the water? the oil?
- What might explain these changes?

A change of medium can refract light.

When sunlight strikes a window, most of the light continues through the glass, but its direction changes slightly. Remember that this slight change in direction is called refraction. Refraction occurs because the speed of light changes when the medium changes. Light travels slower in glass than in air. If the light hits the glass straight on—parallel to the normal—then it continues, more slowly, in the same direction. However, if light hits the glass at any other angle, the change in speed produces a change in direction. In this section, you will learn how curved surfaces can refract light in ways that produce images.

 CHECK YOUR READING What causes refraction? What is the effect of refraction?

Refraction of Light

COMBINATION NOTES
Sketch the ways light is refracted when it moves into a denser medium and into a thinner medium.

The change in the direction of light depends on whether the light slows down or speeds up as it moves into a new medium. Remember that the angle of incidence is measured from the normal, an imaginary line that is perpendicular to a surface. The normal extends into both the old and the new medium. If the light slows, it will turn toward the normal. If the light speeds up, it will turn away from the normal. The ray in the diagram below shows this pattern. The angle between the ray and the normal is smaller in glass than in air.

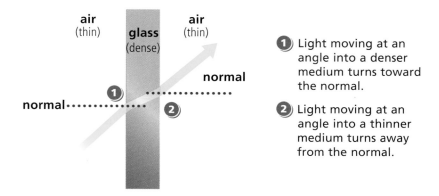

air (thin)   glass (dense)   air (thin)

normal

normal

1. Light moving at an angle into a denser medium turns toward the normal.

2. Light moving at an angle into a thinner medium turns away from the normal.

READING TiP

A dense medium has more mass in a given volume than a thin medium.

The amount of refraction depends on the change in speed. Light moves fastest in a vacuum. It is slower in air, and slower yet in water or glass. Usually, light moves more slowly through denser materials. However, there are exceptions. Scientists measure the speed of light in different materials and calculate a property called optical density. Optical density is a way to compare the speed of light in a material to the speed of light in a vacuum. Scientists use optical densities to predict how much light will refract when it moves from one material into another. This knowledge lets people design technologies that control refraction, such as lenses.

light

water droplet

color spectrum

Light passing through a droplet of water is refracted twice, forming a color spectrum.

Refraction and Rainbows

Different frequencies—colors—of light may travel in a medium at slightly different speeds. As a result, they refract at slightly different angles. A prism uses this property to spread white light into a spectrum of colors. You've seen rainbows in the sky after a rainstorm or in the spray of a sprinkler. The drops of water both refract and reflect light. Each water drop separates the frequencies of sunlight to produce a spectrum. Only one color reaches your eye from each drop. Red appears at the top of a rainbow because it is coming from higher drops, while violet comes from lower drops.

Shape determines how lenses form images.

When you look at yourself in a flat mirror, you see your image clearly, without distortions. Similarly, when you look through a plain glass window, you can see what is on the other side clearly. Just as curved mirrors distort images, certain transparent mediums called lenses alter what you see through them. A **lens** is a clear optical tool that refracts light. Different lenses refract light in different ways. They form images that are useful for a variety of purposes.

READING TiP

Distort means to change the shape of something by twisting or moving the parts around.

Parallel Rays and Focal Points

Like mirrors, lenses can be convex or concave. A convex lens is curved outward; a concave lens is curved inward. A lens typically has two sides that are curved, as shown in the illustrations below.

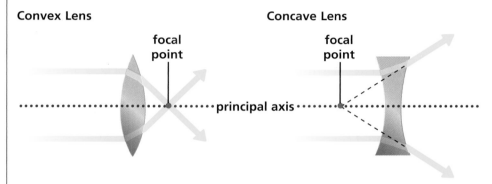

Convex Lens

focal point

principal axis

A convex lens causes parallel light rays to meet at a focal point.

Concave Lens

focal point

A concave lens causes parallel light rays to spread out.

Convex Parallel light rays passing through a convex lens are refracted inward. They converge at a focal point on the other side of the lens. The rays are actually refracted twice—once upon entering the lens and once upon leaving it. This is because both times they are entering a new medium at an angle other than 90 degrees. Rays closest to the edges of the lens are refracted most. Rays passing through the center of the lens—along the principal axis, which connects the centers of the two curved surfaces—are not bent at all. They pass through to the same focal point as all rays parallel to them.

Concave Parallel light rays that pass through a concave lens are refracted outward—they diverge. As with a convex lens, the rays are refracted twice. Rays closest to the edges of the lens are refracted most. Rays along the principal axis pass straight through. The focal point is where the diverging rays appear to have come from.

CHECK YOUR READING Compare what happens to parallel light rays striking a convex lens and a concave lens.

Convex Lenses and Real Images

A convex lens causes rays parallel to the principal axis to converge at the focal point. A convex lens can also cause diverging rays to converge. Therefore, a convex lens is sometimes called a converging lens.

1 In the first diagram on page 505, the principal axis—the center line—has been marked in several places. Each mark shows a **focal length,** which is the distance from the center of the lens to the lens's focal point. Notice that a ray parallel to the principal axis is refracted through the focal point.

2 Remember that the light reflects off most objects in all directions. Rays reflecting off an object—the penguin—diverge. Two such rays from the penguin's head are shown in the second diagram. The lens refracts the diverging rays. It causes the rays to converge and form an image. The image of the penguin's head is located where the rays cross.

3 Rays reflected by the penguin's feet that pass through the lens also converge. They form the image of the penguin's feet. Rays from each point on the penguin meet to form the matching point of the penguin's image.

Recall that an image is called a real image if the rays pass through it. If you put a piece of film in the image, the light will produce an image on the film. Notice that the image is upside down. It is also reduced, or smaller than the object. The lens of a camera and the film are arranged so that the image is small enough to fit on the film.

A convex lens can also form an image that is enlarged, or larger than the object. The size of the image depends on the distance of the object from the lens. If the object is more than two focal lengths from the center of the lens, the image will be smaller than the object. If the object is closer—between one and two focal lengths from the lens— then the image will be larger than the object. Overhead projectors form this type of image, which is then turned right-side up by a mirror and projected onto a screen for viewing.

CHECK YOUR READING What type of image does a convex lens form when the object is far from the lens?

You can estimate the focal length of a convex lens by forming an image of a distant object. Hold the lens on a desktop and then lift it until a sharp image of an overhead light appears on the desktop. Because the light from the ceiling is nearly parallel, the image is nearly at the focal point. The distance from the lens to the desk is approximately one focal length. You can form an image of the view out a window to check your result. Light from a more distant object is more nearly parallel, and so it allows a better estimate of the focal length.

Determining Focal Length
To estimate the focal length of a magnifier or converging lens, lift the lens from a table until you see a sharp image of a ceiling light. The focal length is approximately the distance between the table and the lens.

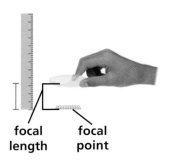

focal   focal
length   point

How a Convex Lens Forms an Image

A convex lens forms an image by refracting light rays. Light rays that diverge from an object are made to converge and form an image.

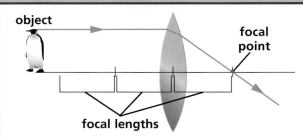

object

focal point

focal lengths

① Light reflects off the penguin in all directions, and some passes through the lens. A ray from the top of the penguin enters the lens and is refracted downward.

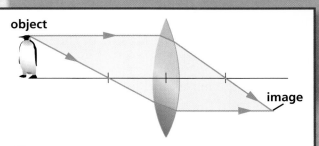

object

image

② Rays from the top of the penguin pass through the lens and are refracted. All of the rays from the top of the penguin converge at the image.

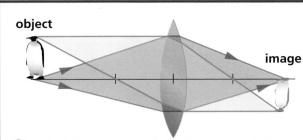

object

image

③ All of the light rays from the penguin's feet converge to form the feet of the image. Light rays from each part of the penguin converge to form the matching point of the image.

READING VISUALS Where do light rays reflected from the middle of the penguin meet?

Convex Lenses and Virtual Images

A convex lens is sometimes called a magnifier because it can be used to make objects look larger. To use a convex lens as a magnifier, the lens must be less than one focal length from the object. When the lens and the object are very close, the light does not form a real image. The light rays do not cross, so there is no place that you can put a screen or a piece of paper to see the image. Instead, you must look through the lens to see a virtual image, just as you must look into a flat mirror to see a virtual image.

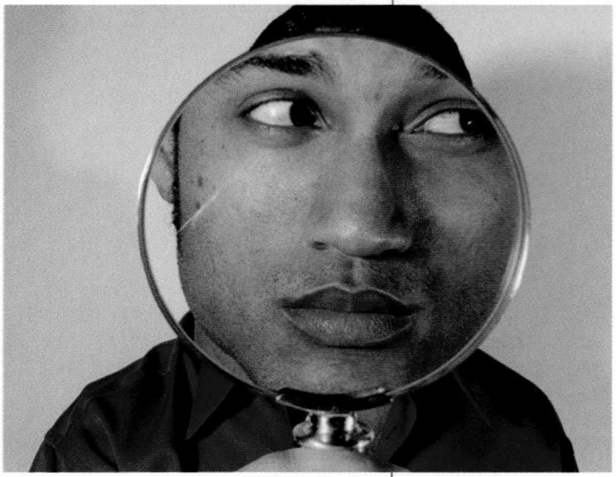

In the photograph at left, you see a face enlarged by a magnifying lens. The object is the man's actual face. The image is right-side up and larger than the object. The virtual image is on the far side of the lens, but not in the same place as the object.

A convex lens can produce a virtual image that is larger than the object and right-side up.

In the table below, diagrams show the lenses and images. A dot indicates a focal point. Rays diverge from the object. The image is located where two or more lines cross.

CHECK YOUR READING What type of image is formed when an object is very close to a convex lens?

Characteristics of Lenses and Images

Lens Type	Distance of Object	Ray Diagram	Image Type	Image Orientation	Image Size
converging (convex)	more than 2 focal lengths	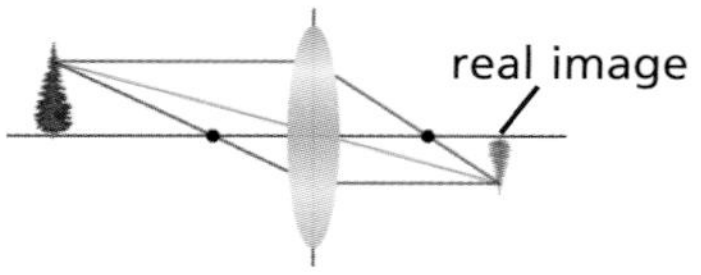 real image	real	upside down	reduced
	1–2 focal lengths	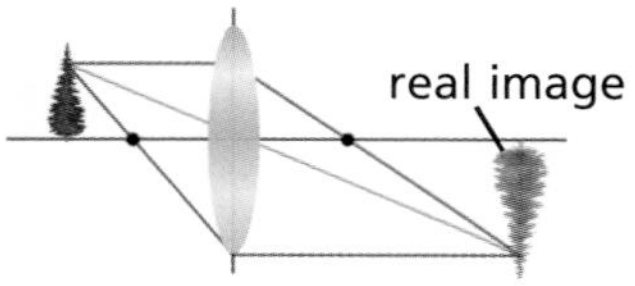 real image	real	upside down	enlarged
	less than 1 focal length	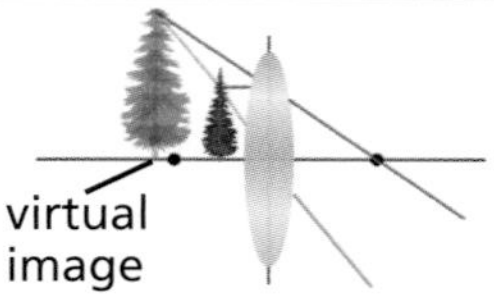 virtual image	virtual	right-side up	enlarged
diverging (concave)	any	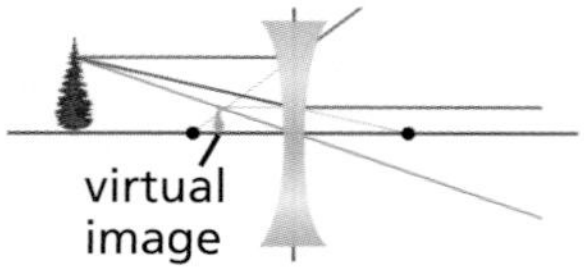 virtual image	virtual	right-side up	reduced

Concave Lenses

A concave lens causes parallel light to diverge. Therefore, a concave lens is sometimes called a diverging lens. The light that diverges from an object will diverge more if it passes through a concave lens. Because the light rays do not cross, a concave lens does not form a real image. You must look through the lens to see a virtual image. The image is right-side up and smaller than the object, no matter how far the object is from the lens. In the photograph at right, you see a face through a diverging lens. The image is smaller than the man's actual face. The last diagram in the table on page 506 shows how a concave lens forms a virtual image.

A concave lens produces a virtual image that is smaller than the object and right-side up.

Other Shapes

Some lenses are curved on one side and flat on the other side. Other lenses have one convex side and one concave side. Eyeglasses, for example, are usually concave on the side nearest the eye. Yet they can be converging or diverging lenses. If a lens is thicker in the center than at the edges, it is a converging lens. It forms images in the same way as a convex lens. If a lens is thinnest in the center, it is a diverging lens. It forms images in the same way as a concave lens. The table on page 506 summarizes the properties of lenses. In the next section, you will see how the characteristics of the images formed by lenses play a role in complex optical tools.

SIMULATION
CLASSZONE.COM

Work with convex and concave lenses to form images.

 CHECK YOUR READING What type of lens is thickest in the center?

14.2 Review

KEY CONCEPTS

1. What quality of a material affects how much it refracts light? (7.6.f)
2. How does the curve in a lens cause it to refract light differently from a flat piece of glass? (7.6.f)
3. How does a convex lens form an image? (7.6.d)

CRITICAL THINKING

4. **Infer** You use a lens and see an image of a building upside down. What type of lens are you using?
5. **Make a Model** Draw the path of a light ray moving at an angle from air into water. Write a caption to explain the process.

⬤ CHALLENGE

6. Study the diagram on page 504. Describe the light rays that would pass through the labeled focal point. Where are they coming from, and how are they related to each other?

CHAPTER INVESTIGATION

Looking at Lenses

OVERVIEW AND PURPOSE Optical tools such as microscopes, telescopes, and eyeglasses use lenses to produce images of objects. In this lab, you will use what you have learned about light and lenses to

- produce images of objects with a convex lens
- determine how to produce different types of images

▶ Procedure

PART A

1. Make a data table like the one shown on the sample notebook page.

2. Draw a stick figure on one index card. Assemble the cards, clay, and lens as shown in the photograph.

3. Position the convex lens so that you can see an enlarged, right-side up image of the stick figure. Measure the distances between the lens and the card, and between the lens and your eye. Record the distances in your data table.

4. Position the lens so that you can see an enlarged, upside-down image of the stick figure. Measure the distances between the lens and the object, and between the lens and your eye. Record the distances in your data table.

5. Position the lens so that you can see a reduced, upside-down image of the stick figure. Measure the distances between the lens and the object, and between the lens and your eye. Record the distances in your data table.

MATERIALS
- index cards
- marker
- modeling clay
- convex lens
- books
- meter stick
- flashlight
- masking tape
- white poster board

7.6.d, 7.7.e

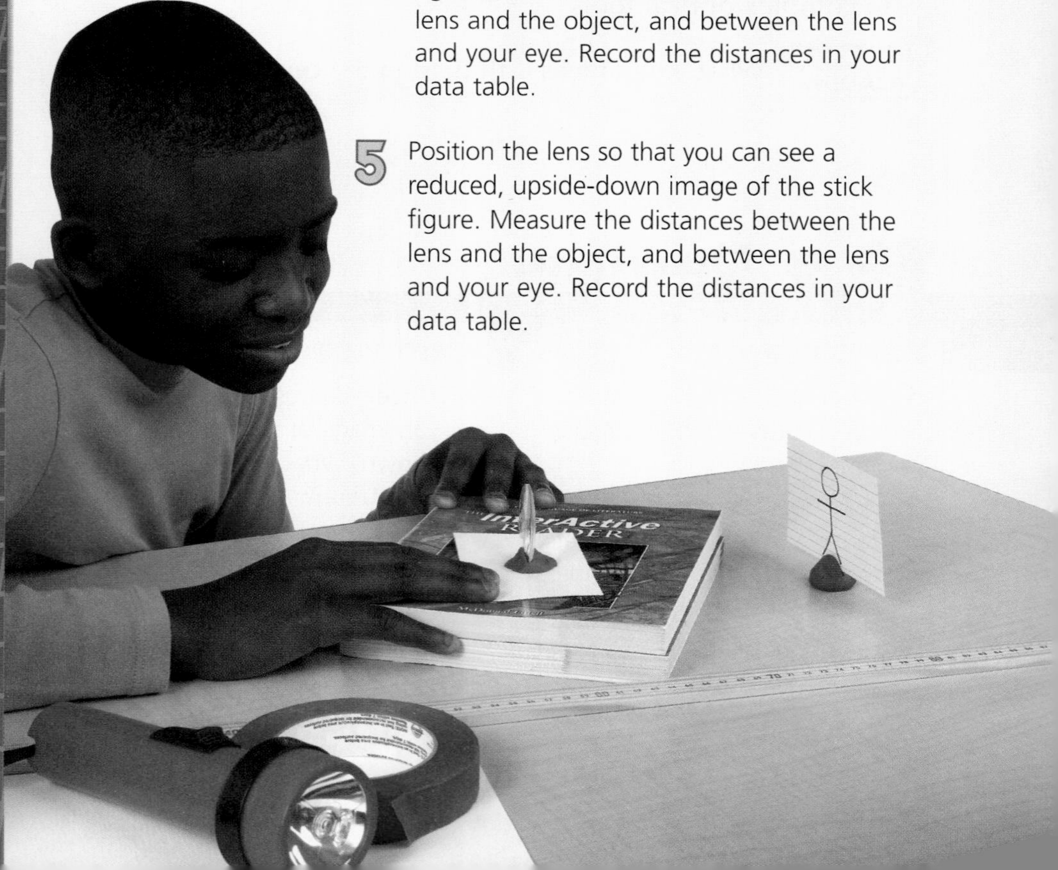

Content Standard
7.6.d Students know how simple lenses are used in a magnifying glass, the eye, a camera, a telescope, and a microscope.

Investigation Standard
7.7.e Communicate the steps and results from an investigation in written reports and oral presentations.

PART B

6 Put an arrow made of tape on the lens of the flashlight as shown.

step 6

7 Assemble poster board and clay to make a screen. Arrange the flashlight, lens, and screen as shown below right.

8 Shine the beam from the flashlight through the lens to form an enlarged, upside-down image on the screen. Measure the distances between the lens and the tape arrow and between the lens and the screen.

9 Repeat step 8, but produce a reduced, upside-down image. Record the distances.

10 Use your results to estimate the lens's focal length. Then estimate the focal length by focusing light from a distant object on the screen.

Observe and Analyze
Write It Up

1. **RECORD OBSERVATIONS** Draw pictures of each setup in steps 3–9 to show what happened. Complete your data table.

2. **ANALYZE** What was the distance from the lens to the object in step 3? Answer this question for each of the other steps. How do the distances compare?

3. **INFER** What would happen if you tried to form an enlarged, right-side up image on the screen?

Conclude
Write It Up

1. **ANALYZE** How were the distances you measured related to the types of image that you observed? **Hint:** Compare the distances to the focal length.

2. **IDENTIFY LIMITS** How did your estimates of the focal length compare? Were they similar?

3. **APPLY** What type of lenses are magnifying glasses? When a magnifying glass produces a sharp, clear image, where is the object located in relation to the lens?

step 7

INVESTIGATE Further

CHALLENGE If you were to attempt steps 8 and 9 with a concave lens, you would not be able to produce an image on the screen. Why not? Experiment or do research to find a way to determine the image distance.

Looking at Lenses
Observe and Analyze
Table 1. Distances from Lens

Image	Object (cm)	Eye (cm)
Enlarged and right-side up		
Enlarged and upside-down		
Reduced and upside-down		
	Flashlight (cm)	Screen (cm)
Enlarged and upside-down		
Reduced and upside-down		

Conclude

14.3 Optical tools use reflection and refraction.

CALIFORNIA
Content Standards

7.6.d Students know how simple lenses are used in a magnifying glass, the eye, a camera, a telescope, and a microscope.

7.6.f Students know light can be reflected, refracted, transmitted, and absorbed by matter.

7.6.g Students know the angle of reflection of a light beam is equal to the angle of incidence.

VOCABULARY

aperture p. 514
fiber optics p. 516

BEFORE, you learned

- Mirrors are optical tools that use reflection
- Lenses are optical tools that use refraction
- Lenses and mirrors can form images with different characteristics

NOW, you will learn

- How mirrors and lenses can be combined to make complex optical tools
- How telescopes and microscopes work
- How cameras work

THINK ABOUT

How can you see the back of your head?

You can look into a mirror to see your reflection. You can see objects behind yourself too. If you turn your head, you may be able to see the side of your face. But you do not see the back of your head when you look into a mirror. To see the back of a new haircut, you can use one mirror to reflect your image from another mirror. Where would you place the two mirrors to see the back of your head?

Mirrors and lenses can be combined to make more effective optical tools.

COMBINATION NOTES
As you read this section, make a list of optical tools. Add sketches to help you remember important concepts.

When you use a mirror to see the back of a new haircut, you see what someone behind you would see. The mirrors help you change the direction from which you see, or your point of view. A periscope uses two mirrors to help people see around corners or above water from below.

Two or more lenses can also be combined. As you will learn, two lenses in a microscope can help you see very small objects. Two lenses in a telescope or four lenses in binoculars can help you see distant objects. Mirrors can also be combined with lenses to make a telescope or other optical tool. The tools let you see objects that you could not see with your eyes alone.

 CHECK YOUR READING What can make up complex optical tools?

Combining Two Optical Tools

A mirror or lens produces an image. When you add a second optical tool, the image from the first tool becomes the object for the second tool. Suppose you first look at your face in a large mirror. Your image is behind the mirror. Now suppose you turn around and look in a second, smaller mirror. You can hold the small mirror so that you see your reflection from the large mirror. The light from the back of your head is reflected twice. In other words, your image from the large mirror is the object for the small mirror.

When you use two flat mirrors, the resulting image is far away. With one mirror, the image is the same distance away as the total distance from the object to the mirror to your eye. With two mirrors, you would have to measure from the object to the first mirror, then to the second mirror, and then to your eye. If you use a curved mirror or add a lens, you can make the image closer or farther, larger or smaller.

In the diagram at right, two lenses are used together. The first lens makes the light from the object converge into a real image. A screen shows the image. The screen is translucent, so you can see the image from either side of the screen. Then a second lens is used to focus the light from the screen. If the screen were removed, the two lenses would still work together in the same way.

One lens can be used to look at the image from another lens. These two lenses would form a telescope if the screen were removed.

INVESTIGATE Combining Lenses

How can lenses be combined?

PROCEDURE

1. Use an overhead light to estimate the focal length of each lens as described on page 504.
2. Assemble the lenses, clay, and index cards as shown in the photograph.
3. Line the lenses up so that you have a straight line of sight through them.
4. Find an arrangement that allows you to see a clear image of an object through both lenses. Try changing the distances between
   - the lenses
   - the far lens and the object
   - the near lens and your eye

WHAT DO YOU THINK?

- What type of image did you see? What arrangement or arrangements worked best to produce this image?
- How do you think the lenses are working together to produce the image?

CHALLENGE How would you arrange the lenses to project the image onto a screen?

SKILL FOCUS
Observing (7.6.d)

MATERIALS
- 2 convex lenses
- modeling clay
- 4 index cards
- meter stick

TIME
15 minutes

RESOURCE CENTER
CLASSZONE.COM

Find out more
about microscopes
and telescopes.

Microscopes

Microscopes are used to see objects that are too small to see well with the naked eye. An ordinary microscope works by combining convex lenses. The lens closer to the object is called the objective. The object is between one and two focal lengths from this lens, so the lens produces a real, enlarged image of the object. The image is inside the microscope.

The microscope lens that you look through is called the eyepiece. You use this lens to look at the image formed by the objective. Like a magnifying glass, the eyepiece lens forms a virtual, enlarged image of the first image. Both lenses help to enlarge what you see. Tiny objects do not reflect much light. Most microscopes use a lamp or a mirror to shine more light onto or through the object.

 CHECK YOUR READING Which types of images do the lenses in a microscope form?

Telescopes

CALIFORNIA Focus

The University of California's Lick Observatory is located on Mt. Hamilton, east of San Jose. The largest of the nine research telescopes used at the observatory is the Shane 3-meter Reflector Telescope.

Telescopes are used to see objects that are too far away to see well with the naked eye. One type of telescope, called a refracting telescope, is made by combining lenses. Another type of telescope, called a reflecting telescope, is made by combining lenses and mirrors.

Refracting telescopes combine convex lenses, just as microscopes do. However, the objects are far away from the objective lens instead of near to it. The object is more than two focal lengths from the objective lens, so the lens produces a real, reduced image of the object inside the telescope. The eyepiece of a telescope then forms a virtual, enlarged image of the first image, just as a microscope does. Notice that the objective lens concentrates the light. Only the eyepiece enlarges what you see. Binoculars work in a similar way.

Reflecting telescopes have the same function as refracting telescopes. However, there is no objective lens where light enters the telescope. Instead, a concave mirror at the opposite end produces the first image of the object. A small flat mirror redirects the light through the side of the telescope. With this arrangement, the eyepiece does not interfere with light on its way to the concave mirror. The eyepiece then forms a virtual, enlarged image of the first image.

Both refracting and reflecting telescopes must make the best use of the small amount of light from distant objects. More light can be gathered and concentrated into the image by increasing the diameter of the objective lens or mirror. Large mirrors are easier and less expensive to make than large lenses. So reflecting telescopes can produce brighter images more cheaply than refracting telescopes.

 CHECK YOUR READING How is a reflecting telescope different from a refracting telescope?

Microscopes and Telescopes

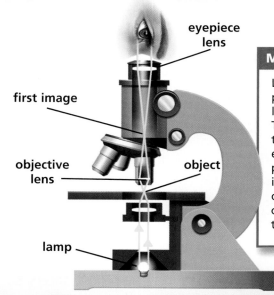

eyepiece lens

first image

objective lens

object

lamp

Microscope

Light from an object passes through a convex lens called an objective. The objective lens focuses the light to form an enlarged image. The eyepiece lens enlarges the image even more. The one-celled algae at right, called diatoms, appear 400 times their normal size.

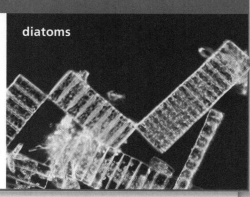

diatoms

Refracting Telescope

surface of the Moon

The objective lens concentrates and focuses light from a distant object to form an image of the object. The eyepiece enlarges the image. The telescope image of the Moon at left shows fine details of the lunar surface.

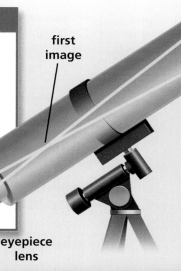

objective lens

light

first image

eyepiece lens

Reflecting Telescope

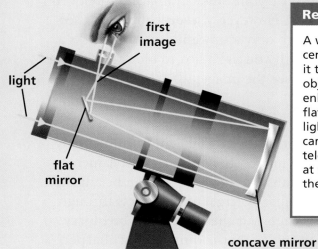

first image

light

flat mirror

concave mirror

A wide concave mirror concentrates light and focuses it to form an image of the object. The eyepiece lens enlarges the image. The flat mirror redirects the light so that the eyepiece can be out of the way. The telescope image of Saturn at right shows details of the planet's rings.

the planet Saturn

READING VISUALS Which type of telescope is similar in construction to a microscope?

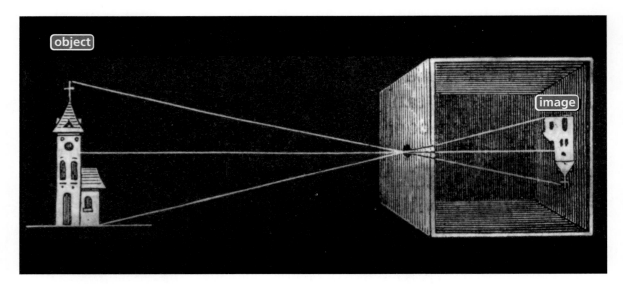

A box with a pinhole can be used as a camera. The image is real, inverted, and usually smaller than the object.

Optical tools control light in different ways.

Lenses and mirrors can be combined with other parts. Some parts limit the amount or directions of light. Other parts record light. Yet other parts change the path of light.

Cameras

The simplest camera produces an image by using an **aperture,** or opening. An aperture does not cause light to converge. Instead, it limits the amount of light from each part of an object. A tiny aperture is called a pinhole. The tiniest pinhole lets through just one ray from each part of an object to form an image. As you can see in the diagram above, the result is similar to an image from a converging lens.

You can use a pushpin to make a pinhole in a piece of foil or heavy paper. If you hold the aperture above your desk, an image of the over-head lights will form on your desk. However, you probably won't see the image. The pinhole lets through only a tiny amount of light. As a result, the image is too dim to see. If you use a box to block light from other sources, you may be able to see the image.

 CHECK YOUR READING   What does an aperture do?

Think about telescopes and microscopes. The light is limited only by the rim of the objective lens or mirror. In contrast, most cameras use a device called an iris to form an aperture. The iris can be adjusted to make the aperture larger or smaller. A larger aperture lets through more light to form a brighter image, but the image may be blurry. A smaller aperture produces an image that is dimmer but sharper. As you will learn in Section 4, your eyes have natural irises.

How Cameras Work

A camera focuses and records an image.

film camera

light · lens · iris · aperture · film

READING VISUALS What part of a camera corresponds to the retina of an eye?

Eye and Camera

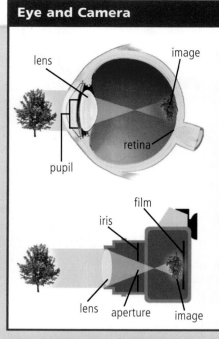

lens · image · pupil · retina

film · iris · lens · aperture · image

Digital Camera

A **digital camera** records images digitally, that is, using a computer.

In most cameras, the iris works together with a lens. The diagram above shows how rays from the top and bottom of a distant object enter a camera. The rays are refracted by a lens and pass through an aperture. They form a small image at the back of the camera. Most cameras use a convex lens to focus light. The object must be more than two focal lengths from the camera's lens to form a reduced, upside-down image. In many cameras, the lens can be moved back and forth to help form the image at the right place. The aperture can also be adjusted.

The image is recorded at the back of the camera. A film camera uses photographic film, which undergoes chemical changes when it absorbs light. The film is removed and treated to bring out the image. A digital camera records the image as a pattern of electrical charges. The pattern is read and stored as a series of numbers in a small computer inside the camera. The computer can reconstruct the image immediately or later on the camera's display screen.

READING TiP

The term *digital* is often used to describe technology involving computers. Computers process information digitally, that is, using numbers.

CHECK YOUR READING What are two ways a camera can record an image?

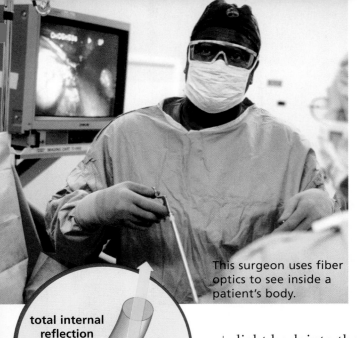

This surgeon uses fiber optics to see inside a patient's body.

total internal reflection

light wave

Fiber Optics

When light changes mediums, part of the light may be reflected and part refracted. When the change in optical density—the change in light's speed—is great, light bends more. When the angle of incidence is great, light bends more. The amount of light reflected also depends on the difference in optical density of the two mediums and the angle of incidence. For example, you can look through the side of an aquarium. But if you try to look through the surface of the water from below, you see the inside of the aquarium instead of seeing through the surface. The surface between the water and air acts as a mirror. It reflects the light back into the water. This behavior of light is called total internal reflection because all of the light is reflected back into the medium.

Thin strings of transparent material, called optical fibers, use total internal reflection. Light passes into one end of a fiber, then reflects off the inside of the fiber again and again until it passes out of the other end of the fiber. The fiber can be bent to transmit light around corners. **Fiber optics** is the use of transparent fibers to transmit images or other information.

Suppose you use one fiber to transmit a ray from each part of an object. A bundle of fibers together can transmit all the parts of an image. A tiny, flexible bundle of fibers can let a surgeon see inside a person's body. Fiber optics can also be used to transmit information very efficiently. Optical fibers and light can carry more signals than a corresponding amount of wire cable and electric current.

CHECK YOUR READING Does fiber optics use reflection or refraction? Explain your answer.

14.3 Review

KEY CONCEPTS

1. How do refracting and reflecting telescopes use lenses and mirrors? (7.6.d)

2. What type of image is formed inside a telescope or microscope? (7.6.d)

3. Where does the image formed by a camera's lens fall? (7.6.d)

CRITICAL THINKING

4. **Connect** Why is it useful for a telescope mirror or a camera lens to be large?

5. **Apply** Think of a way that fiber optics might be useful in your home. Where would the ends of the fiber bundle be located?

CHALLENGE

6. **Compare** Color film uses three layers that absorb red, green, and blue light. Black-and-white film is more sensitive to dim light. How are the types of film like types of cells in your eye's retina?

PHOTOGRAPHER

Photography

7.6.f Students know light can be reflected, refracted, transmitted, and absorbed by matter.

Photographers use the science of optics to help them make the best photographs possible. For example, a portrait photographer chooses the right equipment and lighting to make each person look his or her best. A photographer needs to understand how light reflects, refracts, and diffuses to achieve just the right effect.

Using Reflection

A gold-colored reflector reflects mostly yellow and red frequencies of light onto the subject. Photographers use these to fill in shadows and add warmth.

without gold reflector

with gold reflector

Using Diffusion

When light is directed toward a curved reflective surface, the light scatters in many directions. This diffused light produces a softer appearance than direct light.

direct light

diffused light

Using Refraction

Lenses refract light in different ways. A long lens makes the subject appear closer. A wide-angle lens includes more space around the subject.

long lens

wide-angle lens

EXPLORE

1. **COMPARE** Find photos of people and compare them to the photos above. Which would have been improved by the use of a gold reflector? a long lens? diffused light?

2. **CHALLENGE** Using a disposable camera and a desk lamp, experiment with photography yourself. Try using a piece of paper as a reflector and observe its effects on the photograph. What happens if you use more than one reflector? What happens if you use a different color of paper?

14.4
The eye is a natural optical tool.

CALIFORNIA
Content Standards

7.5.g Students know how to relate the structures of the eye and ear to their functions.

7.6.b Students know that for an object to be seen, light emitted by or scattered from it must be detected by the eye.

7.6.d Students know how simple lenses are used in a magnifying glass, the eye, a camera, a telescope, and a microscope.

BEFORE, you learned

- Mirrors and lenses focus light to form images
- Optical tools can be combined in useful ways
- An iris controls the size of an aperture

NOW, you will learn

- How the eye depends on natural lenses
- How artificial lenses can be used to correct vision problems
- How the eye and the brain work together to produce vision

VOCABULARY

cornea p. 518
pupil p. 519

EXPLORE Focusing Vision (7.6.b)

How does the eye focus an image?

PROCEDURE

① Position yourself so you can see an object about 6 meters (20 feet) away.

② Close one eye. Hold up your index finger and bring it as close to your open eye as you can while keeping the finger clearly in focus.

③ Keeping your finger in place, look just to the side at the more distant object and focus your eye on it.

④ Without looking away from the more distant object, observe your finger.

WHAT DO YOU THINK?

- How does the nearby object look when you are focusing on something distant?
- What might be happening in your eye to cause this change in the nearby object?

The eye uses natural lenses to focus light.

The human eye is similar to a camera in several ways. Both have lenses and irises. Both refract light to produce a reduced, inverted image on a light-sensitive material. Use the diagram on page 519 to see how light travels through the different parts of the eye.

① Light enters the eye through the **cornea** (KAWR-nee-uh), a transparent membrane that covers the front of the eye. The cornea acts as a converging lens. Most of the eye's refracting of light is done at the front surface of the cornea. The light then passes through the fluid behind the cornea, the aqueous humor.

② Light passes through an aperture called the **pupil,** a circular opening that controls how much light enters the eye. The pupil is formed by the iris, which is the colored part of the eye. Muscle tissue causes the iris to open the pupil wide in dim light and to close it down to a pinhole in bright light.

③ Next the light passes through the part of the eye called the lens. The lens is convex on both sides. It refracts light to make fine adjustments for near and far objects. Around the lens are tiny muscles. When the muscles contract, they pull the lens outward and flatten it. The focal length of the lens changes slightly. As a result, the location of the image changes.

④ Light passes through a clear gel that fills the center of the eye. The image forms on the retina, which sends signals through the optic nerve to the brain.

READING TiP

The word *lens* can refer both to an artificial optical tool and to a specific part of the eye.

⬭ **CHECK YOUR READING** What parts of the eye does light pass through?

How the Human Eye Forms an Image

The cornea and lens together focus a reduced, inverted image on the retina.

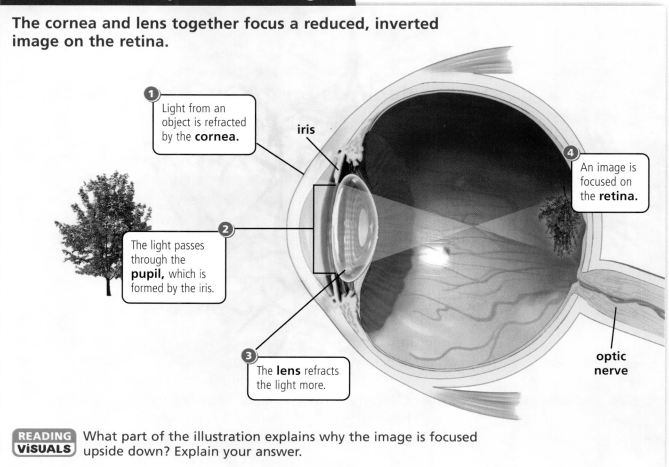

① Light from an object is refracted by the **cornea.**

iris

② The light passes through the **pupil,** which is formed by the iris.

③ The **lens** refracts the light more.

④ An image is focused on the **retina.**

optic nerve

READING ViSUALS What part of the illustration explains why the image is focused upside down? Explain your answer.

INVESTIGATE The Eye

How does the eye work?

PROCEDURE

① Fill the bowl most of the way with water.

② Hold the black construction paper on one side of the bowl so that the hole is next to the center of the bowl. Hold the white poster board on the other side of the bowl.

③ Have another student shine light from the lamp through the hole in the black paper.

④ Shift the poster board from side to side and at different angles until the image of the lamp appears on it.

WHAT DO YOU THINK?

• What type of image appeared? Why did it appear that way?

• How is this model similar to the way the eye works?

CHALLENGE How can you see images right-side up when only inverted images are produced on the retina?

SKILL FOCUS
Modeling
(7.5.g, 7.6.d)

MATERIALS
• round glass bowl
• water
• black construction paper with hole in center
• white poster board
• lamp

TIME

20 minutes

Vision depends on the eye and the brain.

COMBINATION NOTES
Make a chart showing how light interacts with different parts of the eye.

For you to see an object clearly, your eye must focus an image of the object on your retina. Remember that your retina has cone cells that let you see color and rod cells that let you detect dim light. Your retina absorbs the light and produces electrical impulses. The impulses pass through the optic nerve to your brain. Your brain interprets these signals. The image on your retina is upside down. However, your brain interprets the signals so that you see the world as right-side up. Together, your eyes and brain let you see bright and dark, color, shapes, motion, and other patterns.

CHECK YOUR READING What two organs are necessary for vision?

Your two eyes give you slightly different views of the world. These two views help you tell how near or far away objects are. Hold your hand close to your face and look at it with just one eye open. Then look with just the other eye open. Notice that you see different parts of your hand with each eye. When you use both eyes together, your brain interprets the different views as an object that is close to your eyes. Now look at a distant object with each eye in turn. When your two eyes see nearly the same view, the object seems farther away.

Corrective lenses can improve vision.

What happens when the image formed in the eye does not fall exactly on the retina? The result is that the image appears blurry. This can occur either because of the shape of the eye or because of how the lens works. Artificial lenses can be used to correct blurry vision.

Corrective Lenses

Objects are clearer to a nearsighted person when the objects are near. Nearsightedness occurs when the lens of the eye produces the image in front of the retina. The farther away the object is, the farther in front of the retina the image forms. This problem can be corrected with glasses made with concave lenses. The concave lenses cause the light to diverge more, as if the object were closer. The image then falls on the retina.

READING **TiP**

Nearsighted people can see objects near to them best. *Farsighted* people can see objects better when the objects are farther away.

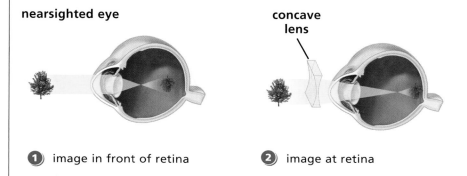

nearsighted eye　　　　**concave lens**

1 image in front of retina　　**2** image at retina

Objects are clearer to a farsighted person when the objects are farther away. Farsightedness occurs when the lens of the eye produces an image behind the retina. This condition can result from aging, which may make the lens less flexible. The closer the object is, the farther behind the retina the image forms. Farsightedness can be corrected with glasses made from convex lenses. The convex lenses bend the light rays inward before they enter the eye. The image then falls on the retina.

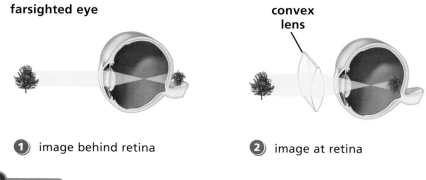

farsighted eye　　　　**convex lens**

1 image behind retina　　**2** image at retina

CHECK YOUR READING　What type of lens is used for correcting nearsightedness?

Surgery and Contact Lenses

Wearing eyeglasses is one effective way to improve poor vision. The lenses bend the light so that the eye's cornea and lens can form an image on the retina. It is also possible to change the shape of the cornea to make the eye form an image on the retina. The front surface of the cornea produces most of the refraction that takes place in the eye. As you know, the eye's lens changes shape to focus light, but the shape of the cornea does not ordinarily change.

However, doctors can change the shape of the cornea. They can use surgical technology to change the way light converges in the eye so that the image falls on the retina. To correct for nearsightedness, a surgeon can remove tissue from the center of the cornea. This flattens the cornea and makes light converge farther back in the eye. To correct for farsightedness, a surgeon can remove tissue from around the edge of the cornea. This increases the cornea's curvature and makes light converge closer to the lens. Surgery changes the shape of the cornea permanently.

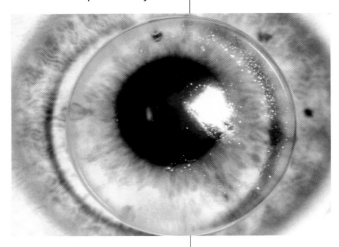

Contact lenses fit directly onto the cornea, changing the way light is refracted as it enters a person's eye.

Contact lenses also correct vision by changing the way the front surface of the eye refracts light. Contact lenses are converging or diverging lenses that fit directly onto the cornea. The lenses actually float on a thin layer of tears. The contact lens, the fluid, and the cornea all function together. The lens of the eye then finishes focusing the light. The change due to contact lenses is temporary. So contact lenses, like eyeglasses, can be changed easily to adjust to changes in the eye.

CHECK YOUR READING What are two ways of changing the way light is refracted as it enters a person's eye?

14.4 Review

KEY CONCEPTS

1. Where do images fall in an eye that is working well? (7.5.g)
2. What causes people with nearsightedness to see blurry images of distant objects? (7.5.g)
3. What happens after the retina absorbs the light of an image? (7.5.g)

CRITICAL THINKING

4. **Make a Model** Draw a diagram to answer the following question: How does a convex lens affect the way a far-sighted eye focuses an image?
5. **Analyze** How are the structures at the front and back of the eye related to their functions?

⬤ CHALLENGE

6. **Compare and Contrast** How are an eye and a camera similar? How are they different?

Bigger Is Better

7.6.b Students know that for an object to be seen, light emitted by or scattered from it must be detected by the eye.

The Hale Telescope, on top of Mount Palomar in southern California, is a giant among telescopes. The dome of Palomar Observatory, where the Hale is housed, is as tall as a ten-story building. The diameter of the light-collecting mirror is 200 inches (5 meters). Until 1993 it was the largest telescope in the world. It is still used for research.

5 meters

The mirror of the Hale Telescope is five meters across. Light from a star that falls on all parts of the mirror converges into a tiny dot of bright light.

A long-exposure photograph shows the Hale Telescope inside its observatory dome on a dark night. The bright streaks near the bottom were made as people walked past carrying flashlights.

Hale and the Human Eye

A telescope is similar to a human eye. Both take in and focus light. But while the Hale Telescope has a 5-meter diameter, the pupil of the human eye is only 4 to 8 millimeters (0.16–0.31 inches) in diameter. The amount of light taken in depends on the area. A telescope or a pupil with a larger area takes in more light. The Hale Telescope can take in about 500,000 times more light than the human eye can. Faint objects can only be seen if a lot of light is taken in and concentrated. Using the Hale Telescope, humans can see stars that are much too faint to see with the eye alone.

Making Images

The eye focuses light onto the retina. The retina responds to the light by sending signals to the brain. The brain is continuously processing the images that form on the retina. In a telescope, the light is focused onto a detector. The detector can be photographic material or a light-detecting computer chip similar to those found in digital cameras. Either type of detector can collect light over a long period of time before the image is processed. Think about taking a long exposure on a photograph such as the one at left. By collecting light over a longer period of time, fainter objects are more likely to show up. If you had been looking at the observatory when the photograph was taken, you would have seen very little detail.

WRITING ABOUT SCIENCE

Nocturnal animals sleep during the day and are active at night. Some of these animals see well at night, when much less light is present. In what ways might their eyes be different from human eyes? Research nocturnal animals and write a paragraph comparing their eyes to human eyes.

14 Chapter Review

the BIG idea

Images are produced by light in many ways.

KEY CONCEPTS SUMMARY

1 Light tends to travel in straight lines.

- Light rays obey the law of reflection.
- Mirrors work by regular reflection.
- Curved mirrors can form images that are distorted in useful ways.

VOCABULARY
optics p. 495
angle of incidence p. 496
angle of reflection p. 496
image p. 497
diverge p. 497
converge p. 498
focal point p. 498

2 Lenses form images by refracting light.

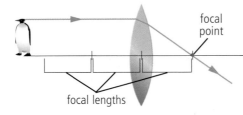

- Lenses have curved surfaces that refract parallel light rays in different amounts.
- Convex lenses bend light inward toward a focal point.
- Concave lenses spread light out.
- Lenses form a variety of useful images.

VOCABULARY
lens p. 503
focal length p. 504

3 Optical tools use reflection and refraction.

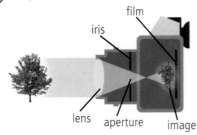

- Many optical tools are made by combining mirrors, lenses, or both.
- Examples of optical tools include telescopes, microscopes, and cameras.

VOCABULARY
aperture p. 514
fiber optics p. 516

4 The eye is a natural optical tool.

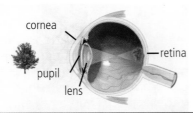

- The eyes of humans and many animals use lenses to focus images on the retina.
- The retina detects images and sends information about them to the brain.

VOCABULARY
cornea p. 518
pupil p. 519

Reviewing Vocabulary

For each item below, fill in the blank. If the right column is blank, give a brief description or definition. If the left column is blank, give the correct term.

Term	Description
1.	to move together
2. diverge	
3.	science of light, vision, and related technology
4.	picture of object formed by light rays
5. focal point	
6.	controls the amount of light entering the eye
7.	distance between mirror or lens and the focal point
8. fiber optics	
9. cornea	
10.	optical tool that refracts light to form an image
11. aperture	

Reviewing Key Concepts

Multiple Choice *Choose the letter of the best answer.*

12. What shape is a mirror that reflects parallel light rays toward a focal point? (7.6.f)

  a. convex   **c.** concave

  b. flat   **d.** regular

13. A light ray that strikes a flat mirror (7.6.g)

  a. continues moving through the mirror in the same direction

  b. moves into the mirror at a slightly different angle

  c. bounces off the mirror toward the direction it came from

  d. bounces off the mirror at the same angle it hits

14. Reflecting telescopes focus light using (7.6.d)

  a. several mirrors

  b. several lenses

  c. both mirrors and lenses

  d. either a mirror or a lens, but not both

15. In the eye, light refracts the most as it enters the (7.5.g)

  a. lens   **c.** pupil

  b. cornea   **d.** retina

16. Nearsighted vision is corrected when lenses (7.6.d)

  a. reflect light away from the eye

  b. allow light rays to focus on the retina

  c. allow light to focus slightly past the retina

  d. help light rays reflect regularly

17. Fiber optics can transmit an image around a bend by using (7.6.f)

  a. convex surfaces

  b. concave surfaces

  c. a bundle of fibers

  d. a single fiber

Short Answer *Write a short answer to each question.*

18. Which optical tool would you use to observe stars? birds in flight? a ladybug? cells? (7.6.d)

19. How are the images that are produced by a convex lens different from those produced by a concave lens? (7.6.d)

20. Describe what typically happens to a ray of light from the time it enters the eye until it strikes the retina. (7.5.g)

21. How do lenses correct nearsightedness and farsightedness? (7.6.d)

22. What does a refracting telescope have in common with a simple microscope? (7.6.d)

23. Describe two ways the distance of an object from a lens can affect the characteristics of the image. (7.6.d)

24. What is different about how light passes through a flat window pane and how it passes through a lens? (7.6.c)

Thinking Critically

INTERPRET *In the four diagrams below, light rays are shown interacting with a material medium. For the next four questions, choose the letter of the diagram that best answers the question.*

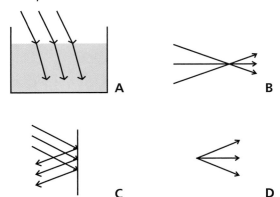

A   B

C   D

25. Which diagram shows reflection by a flat mirror? (7.6.f)

26. Which diagram shows rays diverging? (7.6.f)

27. Which diagram shows refraction? (7.6.f)

28. Which diagram shows light rays converging at a focal point? (7.6.f)

COMPARE AND CONTRAST *Copy the chart below. For each pair of terms, write down one way they are alike (compare) and one way they are different (contrast).* (7.6.d)

Terms	Compare	Contrast
29. flat mirror, curved mirror		
30. convex lens, concave lens		
31. focal point, focal length		
32. nearsighted, farsighted		
33. simple microscope, refracting telescope		
34. refraction, total internal reflection		

35. **INFER** What is the approximate focal length of the eye's cornea and lens combined? How do you know? (7.5.g)

36. **SYNTHESIZE** Suppose you wanted to see the back of your head. You could use a small, flat mirror to view your reflection from a larger mirror. Instead, you use a concave mirror to produce a real, final image that is closer to you. Draw a diagram to show the positions of the mirrors, the object, the first image, and the final image. (7.6.d)

37. **COMPARE AND CONTRAST** How are your eye and a digital camera similar? How are they different? (7.5.g)

38. **APPLY** In order to increase the magnification of a magnifying glass, would you need to make the convex surfaces of the lens more or less curved? (7.6.d)

39. **EVALUATE** Where does vision take place? Justify your choice. (7.5.g)

the BIG idea

40. **SYNTHESIZE** Using what you have learned in this chapter, describe two possible uses of an optical tool like the one shown on pages 492–493. Explain what behaviors of light would be involved in these uses. Then explain how these uses could benefit the person in the photo. (7.6.d)

41. **APPLY** Make a sketch of an optical tool that would use three mirrors to make a beam of light return to its source. Your sketch should include: (7.6.d)

- the path of light waves through the tool
- labels indicating the names of parts and how they affect the light
- several sentences describing one possible use of the tool

UNIT PROJECTS

Evaluate all the data, results, and information from your project folder. Prepare to present your project.

Interpreting Diagrams

7.6.d, 7.6.f, 7.6.g

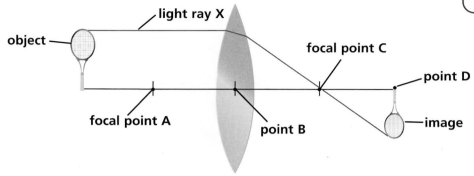

Study the diagram above and then answer the questions that follow.

1. What type of lens is shown in the diagram?
   a. concave   **c.** flat
   b. convex   **d.** prism

2. What happens to parallel light rays passing through this type of lens?
   a. They become polarized.
   b. They form a rainbow.
   c. They bend inward.
   d. They bend outward.

3. All light rays parallel to light ray X will pass through what point?
   a. point A
   b. point B
   c. point C
   d. point D

4. How far is the object in the diagram from the lens?
   a. less than one focal length
   b. one focal length
   c. about two focal lengths
   d. more than three focal lengths

5. Where would you position a screen in order to see the image in focus on the screen?
   a. at point A
   b. at point B
   c. at point C
   d. at point D

Extended Response

Answer the two questions below in detail. Include some of the terms from the word box. In your answer, underline each term you use.

converge	focal point	real image
diverge	refraction	virtual image
flat mirror	reflection	magnifying lens

6. What type of mirror would you use to see what is happening over a broad area? Why?

7. Choose one of the following optical tools and explain how it uses mirrors and/or lenses to form an image: camera, telescope, periscope, binoculars, microscope.

Student Resource Handbooks

Scientific Thinking Handbook

Making Observations

An **observation** is an act of noting and recording an event, character-istic, behavior, or anything else detected with an instrument or with the senses.

Observations allow you to make informed hypotheses and to gather data for experiments. Careful observations often lead to ideas for new experiments. There are two categories of observations:

- **Quantitative observations** can be expressed in numbers and include records of time, temperature, mass, distance, and volume.

- **Qualitative observations** include descriptions of sights, sounds, smells, and textures.

EXAMPLE

A student dissolved 30 grams of Epsom salts in water, poured the solution into a dish, and let the dish sit out uncovered overnight. The next day, she made the following observations of the Epsom salt crystals that grew in the dish.

Table 1. Observations of Epsom Salt Crystals

To determine the mass, the student found the mass of the dish before and after growing the crystals and then used subtraction to find the difference.

The student measured several crystals and calculated the mean length. (To learn how to calculate the mean of a data set, see page R36.)

Quantitative Observations	Qualitative Observations
• mass = 30 g	• Crystals are clear.
• mean crystal length = 0.5 cm	• Crystals are long, thin, and rectangular.
• longest crystal length = 2 cm	• White crust has formed around edge of dish.

Photographs or sketches are useful for recording qualitative observations.

Epsom salt crystals

MORE ABOUT OBSERVING

- Make quantitative observations whenever possible. That way, others will know exactly what you observed and be able to compare their results with yours.

- It is always a good idea to make qualitative observations too. You never know when you might observe something unexpected.

Predicting and Hypothesizing

A **prediction** is an expectation of what will be observed or what will happen. A **hypothesis** is a tentative explanation for an observation or scientific problem that can be tested by further investigation.

EXAMPLE

Suppose you have made two paper airplanes and you wonder why one of them tends to glide farther than the other one.

1. Start by asking a question.

2. Make an educated guess. After examination, you notice that the wings of the airplane that flies farther are slightly larger than the wings of the other airplane.

3. Write a prediction based upon your educated guess, in the form of an "If . . . , then . . ." statement. Write the independent variable after the word *if*, and the dependent variable after the word *then*.

4. To make a hypothesis, explain why you think what you predicted will occur. Write the explanation after the word *because*.

1. Why does one of the paper airplanes glide farther than the other?

2. The size of an airplane's wings may affect how far the airplane will glide.

3. Prediction: If I make a paper airplane with larger wings, then the airplane will glide farther.

To read about independent and dependent variables, see page R30.

4. Hypothesis: If I make a paper airplane with larger wings, then the airplane will glide farther, because the additional surface area of the wing will produce more lift.

Notice that the part of the hypothesis after *because* adds an explanation of why the airplane will glide farther.

MORE ABOUT HYPOTHESES

- The results of an experiment cannot prove that a hypothesis is correct. Rather, the results either support or do not support the hypothesis.

- Valuable information is gained even when your hypothesis is not supported by your results. For example, it would be an important discovery to find that wing size is not related to how far an airplane glides.

- In science, a hypothesis is supported only after many scientists have conducted many experiments and produced consistent results.

Inferring

An **inference** is a logical conclusion drawn from the available evidence and prior knowledge. Inferences are often made from observations.

EXAMPLE

A student observing a set of acorns noticed something unexpected about one of them. He noticed a white, soft-bodied insect eating its way out of the acorn.

The student recorded these observations.

Observations

- There is a hole in the acorn, about 0.5 cm in diameter, where the insect crawled out.
- There is a second hole, which is about the size of a pinhole, on the other side of the acorn.
- The inside of the acorn is hollow.

Here are some inferences that can be made on the basis of the observations.

Inferences

- The insect formed from the material inside the acorn, grew to its present size, and ate its way out of the acorn.
- The insect crawled through the smaller hole, ate the inside of the acorn, grew to its present size, and ate its way out of the acorn.
- An egg was laid in the acorn through the smaller hole. The egg hatched into a larva that ate the inside of the acorn, grew to its present size, and ate its way out of the acorn.

When you make inferences, be sure to look at all of the evidence available and combine it with what you already know.

MORE ABOUT INFERENCES

Inferences depend both on observations and on the knowledge of the people making the inferences. Ancient people who did not know that organisms are produced only by similar organisms might have made an inference like the first one. A student today might look at the same observations and make the second inference. A third student might have knowledge about this particular insect and know that it is never small enough to fit through the smaller hole, leading her to the third inference.

Identifying Cause and Effect

In a **cause-and-effect relationship,** one event or characteristic is the result of another. Usually an effect follows its cause in time.

There are many examples of cause-and-effect relationships in everyday life.

Cause	Effect
Turn off a light.	Room gets dark.
Drop a glass.	Glass breaks.
Blow a whistle.	Sound is heard.

Scientists must be careful not to infer a cause-and-effect relationship just because one event happens after another event. When one event occurs after another, you cannot infer a cause-and-effect relationship on the basis of that information alone. You also cannot conclude that one event caused another if there are alternative ways to explain the second event. A scientist must demonstrate through experimentation or continued observation that an event was truly caused by another event.

EXAMPLE

Make an Observation

Suppose you have a few plants growing outside. When the weather starts getting colder, you bring one of the plants indoors. You notice that the plant you brought indoors is growing faster than the others are growing. You cannot conclude from your observation that the change in temperature was the cause of the increased plant growth, because there are alternative explanations for the observation. Some possible explanations are given below.

- The humidity indoors caused the plant to grow faster.

- The level of sunlight indoors caused the plant to grow faster.

- The indoor plant's being noticed more often and watered more often than the outdoor plants caused it to grow faster.

- The plant that was brought indoors was healthier than the other plants to begin with.

To determine which of these factors, if any, caused the indoor plant to grow faster than the outdoor plants, you would need to design and conduct an experiment.

See pages R28–R35 for information about designing experiments.

Recognizing Bias

Television, newspapers, and the Internet are full of experts claiming to have scientific evidence to back up their claims. How do you know whether the claims are really backed up by good science?

Bias is a slanted point of view, or personal prejudice. The goal of scientists is to be as objective as possible and to base their findings on facts instead of opinions. However, bias often affects the conclusions of researchers, and it is important to learn to recognize bias.

When scientific results are reported, you should consider the source of the information as well as the information itself. It is important to critically analyze the information that you see and read.

SOURCES OF BIAS

There are several ways in which a report of scientific information may be biased. Here are some questions that you can ask yourself:

1. **Who is sponsoring the research?**

   Sometimes, the results of an investigation are biased because an organization paying for the research is looking for a specific answer. This type of bias can affect how data are gathered and interpreted.

2. **Is the research sample large enough?**

   Sometimes research does not include enough data. The larger the sample size, the more likely that the results are accurate, assuming a truly random sample.

3. **In a survey, who is answering the questions?**

   The results of a survey or poll can be biased. The people taking part in the survey may have been specifically chosen because of how they would answer. They may have the same ideas or lifestyles. A survey or poll should make use of a random sample of people.

4. **Are the people who take part in a survey biased?**

   People who take part in surveys sometimes try to answer the questions the way they think the researcher wants them to answer. Also, in surveys or polls that ask for personal information, people may be unwilling to answer questions truthfully.

SCIENTIFIC BIAS

It is also important to realize that scientists have their own biases because of the types of research they do and because of their scientific viewpoints. Two scientists may look at the same set of data and come to completely different conclusions because of these biases. However, such disagreements are not necessarily bad. In fact, a critical analysis of disagreements is often responsible for moving science forward.

Identifying Faulty Reasoning

Faulty reasoning is wrong or incorrect thinking. It leads to mistakes and to wrong conclusions. Scientists are careful not to draw unreasonable conclusions from experimental data. Without such caution, the results of scientific investigations may be misleading.

EXAMPLE

Scientists try to make generalizations based on their data to explain as much about nature as possible. If only a small sample of data is looked at, however, a conclusion may be faulty. Suppose a scientist has studied the effects of the El Niño and La Niña weather patterns on flood damage in California from 1989 to 1995. The scientist organized the data in the bar graph below.

The scientist drew the following conclusions:

1. The La Niña weather pattern has no effect on flooding in California.
2. When neither weather pattern occurs, there is almost no flood damage.
3. A weak or moderate El Niño produces a small or moderate amount of flooding.
4. A strong El Niño produces a lot of flooding.

Flood and Storm Damage in California

Estimated damage (millions of dollars) — Weak–moderate El Niño, Strong El Niño — Starting year of season (July 1–June 30)

SOURCE: *Governor's Office of Emergency Services, California*

For the six-year period of the scientist's investigation, these conclusions may seem to be reasonable. However, a six-year study of weather patterns may be too small of a sample for the conclusions to be supported. Consider the following graph, which shows information that was gathered from 1949 to 1997.

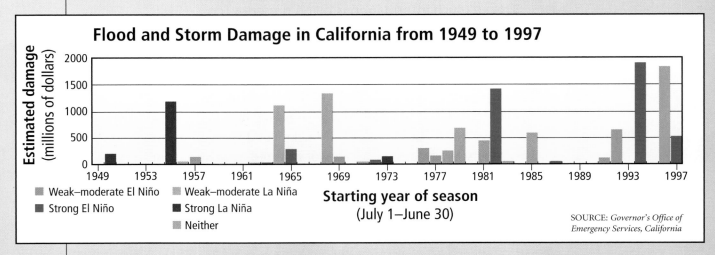

Flood and Storm Damage in California from 1949 to 1997

Estimated damage (millions of dollars)

Weak–moderate El Niño Weak–moderate La Niña
Strong El Niño Strong La Niña
Neither

Starting year of season (July 1–June 30)

SOURCE: *Governor's Office of Emergency Services, California*

The only one of the conclusions that all of this information supports is number 3: a weak or moderate El Niño produces a small or moderate amount of flooding. By collecting more data, scientists can be more certain of their conclusions and can avoid faulty reasoning.

Analyzing Statements

To **analyze** a statement is to examine its parts carefully. Scientific findings are often reported through media such as television or the Internet. A report that is made public often focuses on only a small part of research. As a result, it is important to question the sources of information.

Evaluate Media Claims

To **evaluate** a statement is to judge it on the basis of criteria you've established. Sometimes evaluating means deciding whether a statement is true.

Reports of scientific research and findings in the media may be misleading or incomplete. When you are exposed to this information, you should ask yourself some questions so that you can make informed judgments about the information.

1. **Does the information come from a credible source?**

   Suppose you learn about a new product and it is stated that scientific evidence proves that the product works. A report from a respected news source may be more believable than an advertisement paid for by the product's manufacturer.

2. **How much evidence supports the claim?**

   Often, it may seem that there is new evidence every day of something in the world that either causes or cures an illness. However, information that is the result of several years of work by several different scientists is more credible than an advertisement that does not even cite the subjects of the experiment.

3. **How much information is being presented?**

   Science cannot solve all questions, and scientific experiments often have flaws. A report that discusses problems in a scientific study may be more believable than a report that addresses only positive experimental findings.

4. **Is scientific evidence being presented by a specific source?**

   Sometimes scientific findings are reported by people who are called experts or leaders in a scientific field. But if their names are not given or their scientific credentials are not reported, their statements may be less credible than those of recognized experts.

Differentiate Between Fact and Opinion

Sometimes information is presented as a fact when it may be an opinion. When scientific conclusions are reported, it is important to recognize whether they are based on solid evidence. Again, you may find it helpful to ask yourself some questions.

1. **What is the difference between a fact and an opinion?**

   A **fact** is a piece of information that can be strictly defined and proved true. An **opinion** is a statement that expresses a belief, value, or feeling. An opinion cannot be proved true or false. For example, a person's age is a fact, but if someone is asked how old they feel, it is impossible to prove the person's answer to be true or false.

2. **Can opinions be measured?**

   Yes, opinions can be measured. In fact, surveys often ask for people's opinions on a topic. But there is no way to know whether or not an opinion is the truth.

HOW TO DIFFERENTIATE FACT FROM OPINION

Human Activities and the Environment

Unfortunately, human use of fossil fuels is one of the most significant developments of the past few centuries. Humans rely on fossil fuels, a non-renewable energy resource, for more than 90 percent of their energy needs.

This careless misuse of our planet's resources has resulted in pollution, global warming, and the destruction of fragile ecosystems. For example, oil pipelines carry more than one million barrels of oil each day across tundra regions. Transporting oil across such areas can only result in oil spills that poison the land for decades.

Opinions

Notice words or phrases that express beliefs or feelings. The words *unfortunately* and *careless* show that opinions are being expressed.

Opinion

Look for statements that speculate about events. These statements are opinions, because they cannot be proved.

Facts

Statements that contain statistics tend to be facts. Writers often use facts to support their opinions.

Lab Handbook

Safety Rules

Before you work in the laboratory, read these safety rules twice. Ask your teacher to explain any rules that you do not completely understand. Refer to these rules later on if you have questions about safety in the science classroom.

Directions

- Read all directions and make sure that you understand them before starting an investigation or lab activity. If you do not understand how to do a procedure or how to use a piece of equipment, ask your teacher.
- Do not begin any investigation or touch any equipment until your teacher has told you to start.
- Never experiment on your own. If you want to try a procedure that the directions do not call for, ask your teacher for permission first.
- If you are hurt or injured in any way, tell your teacher immediately.

Dress Code

goggles

apron

gloves

- Wear goggles when
  — using glassware, sharp objects, or chemicals
  — heating an object
  — working with anything that can easily fly up into the air and hurt someone's eye
- Tie back long hair or hair that hangs in front of your eyes.
- Remove any article of clothing—such as a loose sweater or a scarf—that hangs down and may touch a flame, chemical, or piece of equipment.
- Observe all safety icons calling for the wearing of eye protection, gloves, and aprons.

Heating and Fire Safety

fire safety

heating safety

- Keep your work area neat, clean, and free of extra materials.
- Never reach over a flame or heat source.
- Point objects being heated away from you and others.
- Never heat a substance or an object in a closed container.
- Never touch an object that has been heated. If you are unsure whether something is hot, treat it as though it is. Use oven mitts, clamps, tongs, or a test-tube holder.
- Know where the fire extinguisher and fire blanket are kept in your classroom.
- Do not throw hot substances into the trash. Wait for them to cool or use the container your teacher puts out for disposal.

Electrical Safety

electrical safety

- Never use lamps or other electrical equipment with frayed cords.
- Make sure no cord is lying on the floor where someone can trip over it.
- Do not let a cord hang over the side of a counter or table so that the equipment can easily be pulled or knocked to the floor.
- Never let cords hang into sinks or other places where water can be found.
- Never try to fix electrical problems. Inform your teacher of any problems immediately.
- Unplug an electrical cord by pulling on the plug, not the cord.

Chemical Safety

chemical safety

poison

fumes

- If you spill a chemical or get one on your skin or in your eyes, tell your teacher right away.
- Never touch, taste, or sniff any chemicals in the lab. If you need to determine odor, waft. Wafting consists of holding the chemical in its container 15 centimeters (6 in.) away from your nose, and using your fingers to bring fumes from the container to your nose.
- Keep lids on all chemicals you are not using.
- Never put unused chemicals back into the original containers. Throw away extra chemicals where your teacher tells you to.
- Pour chemicals over a sink or your work area, not over the floor.
- If you get a chemical in your eye, use the eyewash right away.
- Always wash your hands after handling chemicals, plants, or soil.

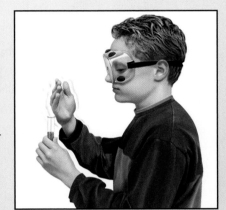

Wafting

Glassware and Sharp-Object Safety

sharp objects

- If you break glassware, tell your teacher right away.
- Do not use broken or chipped glassware. Give these to your teacher.
- Use knives and other cutting instruments carefully. Always wear eye protection and cut away from you.

Animal Safety

- Never hurt an animal.
- Touch animals only when necessary. Follow your teacher's instructions for handling animals.
- Always wash your hands after working with animals.

Cleanup

disposal

- Follow your teacher's instructions for throwing away or putting away supplies.
- Clean your work area and pick up anything that has dropped to the floor.
- Wash your hands.

Using Lab Equipment

Different experiments require different types of equipment. But even though experiments differ, the ways in which the equipment is used are the same.

LAB HANDBOOK

Beakers

- Use beakers for holding and pouring liquids.
- Do not use a beaker to measure the volume of a liquid. Use a graduated cylinder instead. (See page R16.)
- Use a beaker that holds about twice as much liquid as you need. For example, if you need 100 milliliters of water, you should use a 200- or 250-milliliter beaker.

Test Tubes

- Use test tubes to hold small amounts of substances.
- Do not use a test tube to measure the volume of a liquid.
- Use a test tube when heating a substance over a flame. Aim the mouth of the tube away from yourself and other people.
- Liquids easily spill or splash from test tubes, so it is important to use only small amounts of liquids.

Test-Tube Holder

- Use a test-tube holder when heating a substance in a test tube.
- Use a test-tube holder if the substance in a test tube is dangerous to touch.
- Make sure the test-tube holder tightly grips the test tube so that the test tube will not slide out of the holder.
- Make sure that the test-tube holder is above the surface of the substance in the test tube so that you can observe the substance.

Test-Tube Rack

- Use a test-tube rack to organize test tubes before, during, and after an experiment.

- Use a test-tube rack to keep test tubes upright so that they do not fall over and spill their contents.

- Use a test-tube rack that is the correct size for the test tubes that you are using. If the rack is too small, a test tube may become stuck. If the rack is too large, a test tube may lean over, and some of its contents may spill or splash.

Forceps

- Use forceps when you need to pick up or hold a very small object that should not be touched with your hands.

- Do not use forceps to hold anything over a flame, because forceps are not long enough to keep your hand safely away from the flame. Plastic forceps will melt, and metal forceps will conduct heat and burn your hand.

Hot Plate

- Use a hot plate when a substance needs to be kept warmer than room temperature for a long period of time.

- Use a hot plate instead of a Bunsen burner or a candle when you need to carefully control temperature.

- Do not use a hot plate when a substance needs to be burned in an experiment.

- Always use "hot hands" safety mitts or oven mitts when handling anything that has been heated on a hot plate.

Microscope

Scientists use microscopes to see very small objects that cannot easily be seen with the eye alone. A microscope magnifies the image of an object so that small details may be observed. A microscope that you may use can magnify an object 400 times—the object will appear 400 times larger than its actual size.

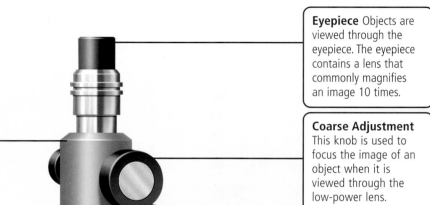

Eyepiece Objects are viewed through the eyepiece. The eyepiece contains a lens that commonly magnifies an image 10 times.

Coarse Adjustment This knob is used to focus the image of an object when it is viewed through the low-power lens.

Fine Adjustment This knob is used to focus the image of an object when it is viewed through the high-power lens.

Low-Power Objective Lens This is the smallest lens on the nosepiece. It magnifies an image approximately 10 times.

Arm The arm supports the body above the stage. Always carry a microscope by the arm and base.

Stage Clip The stage clip holds a slide in place on the stage.

Base The base supports the microscope.

Body The body separates the lens in the eyepiece from the objective lenses below.

Nosepiece The nosepiece holds the objective lenses above the stage and rotates so that all lenses may be used.

High-Power Objective Lens This is the largest lens on the nosepiece. It magnifies an image approximately 40 times.

Stage The stage supports the object being viewed.

Diaphragm The diaphragm is used to adjust the amount of light passing through the slide and into an objective lens.

Mirror or Light Source Some microscopes use light that is reflected through the stage by a mirror. Other microscopes have their own light sources.

VIEWING AN OBJECT

1. Use the coarse adjustment knob to raise the body tube.

2. Adjust the diaphragm so that you can see a bright circle of light through the eyepiece.

3. Place the object or slide on the stage. Be sure that it is centered over the hole in the stage.

4. Turn the nosepiece to click the low-power lens into place.

5. Using the coarse adjustment knob, slowly lower the lens and focus on the specimen being viewed. Be sure not to touch the slide or object with the lens.

6. When switching from the low-power lens to the high-power lens, first raise the body tube with the coarse adjustment knob so that the high-power lens will not hit the slide.

7. Turn the nosepiece to click the high-power lens into place.

8. Use the fine adjustment knob to focus on the specimen being viewed. Again, be sure not to touch the slide or object with the lens.

MAKING A SLIDE, OR WET MOUNT

① Place the specimen in the center of a clean slide.

② Place a drop of water on the specimen.

③ Place a cover slip on the slide. Put one edge of the cover slip into the drop of water and slowly lower it over the specimen.

④ Remove any air bubbles from under the cover slip by gently tapping the cover slip.

⑤ Dry any excess water before placing the slide on the microscope stage for viewing.

Spring Scale (Force Meter)

- Use a spring scale to measure a force pulling on the scale.
- Use a spring scale to measure the force of gravity exerted on an object by Earth.
- To measure a force accurately, a spring scale must be zeroed before it is used. The scale is zeroed when no weight is attached and the indicator is positioned at zero.
- Do not attach a weight that is either too heavy or too light to a spring scale. A weight that is too heavy could break the scale or exert too great a force for the scale to measure. A weight that is too light may not exert enough force to be measured accurately.

Graduated Cylinder

- Use a graduated cylinder to measure the volume of a liquid.
- Be sure that the graduated cylinder is on a flat surface so that your measurement will be accurate.
- When reading the scale on a graduated cylinder, be sure to have your eyes at the level of the surface of the liquid.
- The surface of the liquid will be curved in the graduated cylinder. Read the volume of the liquid at the bottom of the curve, or meniscus (muh-NIHS-kuhs).
- You can use a graduated cylinder to find the volume of a solid object by measuring the increase in a liquid's level after you add the object to the cylinder.

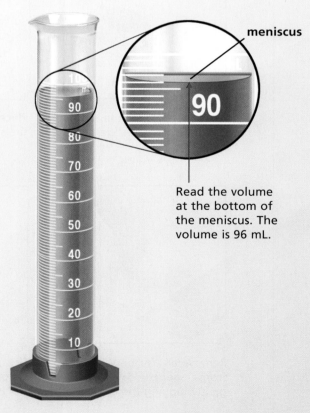

meniscus

Read the volume at the bottom of the meniscus. The volume is 96 mL.

Metric Rulers

- Use metric rulers or meter sticks to measure objects' lengths.

- Do not measure an object from the end of a metric ruler or meter stick, because the end is often imperfect. Instead, measure from the 1-centimeter mark, but remember to subtract a centimeter from the apparent measurement.

- Estimate any lengths that extend between marked units. For example, if a meter stick shows centimeters but not millimeters, you can estimate the length that an object extends between centimeter marks to measure it to the nearest millimeter.

- **Controlling Variables** If you are taking repeated measurements, always measure from the same point each time. For example, if you're measuring how high two different balls bounce when dropped from the same height, measure both bounces at the same point on the balls—either the top or the bottom. Do not measure at the top of one ball and the bottom of the other.

EXAMPLE

How to Measure a Leaf

1. Lay a ruler flat on top of the leaf so that the 1-centimeter mark lines up with one end. Make sure the ruler and the leaf do not move between the time you line them up and the time you take the measurement.

2. Look straight down on the ruler so that you can see exactly how the marks line up with the other end of the leaf.

3. Estimate the length by which the leaf extends beyond a marking. For example, the leaf below extends about halfway between the 4.2-centimeter and 4.3-centimeter marks, so the apparent measurement is about 4.25 centimeters.

4. Remember to subtract 1 centimeter from your apparent measurement, since you started at the 1-centimeter mark on the ruler and not at the end. The leaf is about 3.25 centimeters long (4.25 cm – 1 cm = 3.25 cm).

Triple-Beam Balance

This balance has a pan and three beams with sliding masses, called riders. At one end of the beams is a pointer that indicates whether the mass on the pan is equal to the masses shown on the beams.

1. Make sure the balance is zeroed before measuring the mass of an object. The balance is zeroed if the pointer is at zero when nothing is on the pan and the riders are at their zero points. Use the adjustment knob at the base of the balance to zero it.

2. Place the object to be measured on the pan.

3. Move the riders one notch at a time away from the pan. Begin with the largest rider. If moving the largest rider one notch brings the pointer below zero, begin measuring the mass of the object with the next smaller rider.

4. Change the positions of the riders until they balance the mass on the pan and the pointer is at zero. Then add the readings from the three beams to determine the mass of the object.

300 g	position of largest rider
90 g	position of middle rider
+ 3 g	position of smallest rider
393 g	mass of beaker

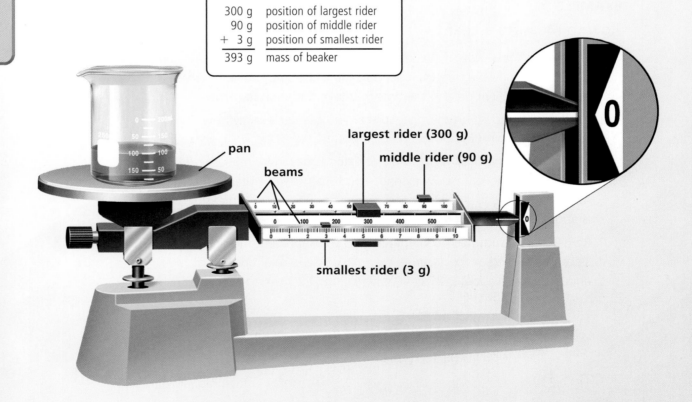

Double-Pan Balance

This type of balance has two pans. Between the pans is a pointer that indicates whether the masses on the pans are equal.

1. Make sure the balance is zeroed before measuring the mass of an object. The balance is zeroed if the pointer is at zero when there is nothing on either of the pans. Many double-pan balances have sliding knobs that can be used to zero them.

2. Place the object to be measured on one of the pans.

3. Begin adding standard masses to the other pan. Begin with the largest standard mass. If this adds too much mass to the balance, begin measuring the mass of the object with the next smaller standard mass.

4. Add standard masses until the masses on both pans are balanced and the pointer is at zero. Then add the standard masses together to determine the mass of the object being measured.

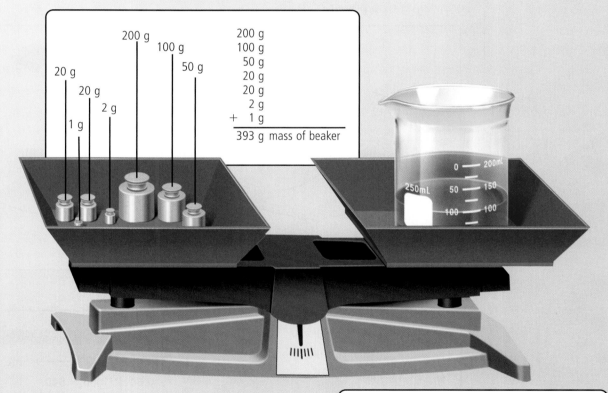

	200 g
	100 g
	50 g
	20 g
	20 g
	2 g
+	1 g

393 g mass of beaker

Never place chemicals or liquids directly on a pan. Instead, use the following procedure:

1 Determine the mass of an empty container, such as a beaker.

2 Pour the substance into the container, and measure the total mass of the substance and the container.

3 Subtract the mass of the empty container from the total mass to find the mass of the substance.

The Metric System and SI Units

Scientists use International System (SI) units for measurements of distance, volume, mass, and temperature. The International System is based on multiples of ten and the metric system of measurement.

Basic SI Units		
Property	**Name**	**Symbol**
length	meter	m
volume	liter	L
mass	kilogram	kg
temperature	kelvin	K

SI Prefixes		
Prefix	**Symbol**	**Multiple of 10**
kilo-	k	1000
hecto-	h	100
deca-	da	10
deci-	d	$0.1 \left(\frac{1}{10}\right)$
centi-	c	$0.01 \left(\frac{1}{100}\right)$
milli-	m	$0.001 \left(\frac{1}{1000}\right)$

Changing Metric Units

You can change from one unit to another in the metric system by multiplying or dividing by a power of 10.

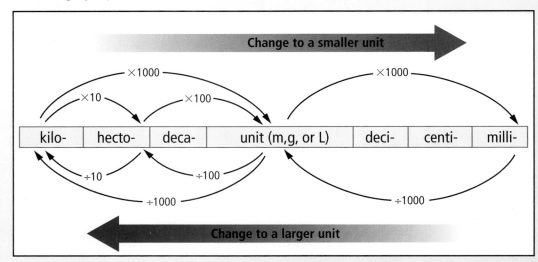

Example

Change 0.64 liters to milliliters.

(1) Decide whether to multiply or divide.

(2) Select the power of 10.

ANSWER 0.64 L = 640 mL

Change to a smaller unit by multiplying.

L $\longrightarrow \times\ 1000 \longrightarrow$ mL

$0.64 \times 1000 = 640.$

Example

Change 23.6 grams to kilograms.

(1) Decide whether to multiply or divide.

(2) Select the power of 10.

ANSWER 23.6 g = 0.0236 kg

Change to a larger unit by dividing.

kg $\longleftarrow \div\ 1000 \longrightarrow$ g

$23.6 \div 1000 = 0.0236$

Temperature Conversions

Even though the kelvin is the SI base unit of temperature, the degree Celsius will be the unit you use most often in your science studies. The formulas below show the relationships between temperatures in degrees Fahrenheit (°F), degrees Celsius (°C), and kelvins (K).

$$°C = \frac{5}{9}(°F - 32)$$

$$°F = \frac{9}{5}°C + 32$$

$$K = °C + 273$$

See page R42 for help with using formulas.

Examples of Temperature Conversions

Condition	Degrees Celsius	Degrees Fahrenheit
Freezing point of water	0	32
Cool day	10	50
Mild day	20	68
Warm day	30	86
Normal body temperature	37	98.6
Very hot day	40	104
Boiling point of water	100	212

Converting Between SI and U.S. Customary Units

Use the chart below when you need to convert between SI units and U.S. customary units.

SI Unit	From SI to U.S. Customary			From U.S. Customary to SI		
Length	When you know	multiply by	to find	When you know	multiply by	to find
kilometer (km) = 1000 m	kilometers	0.62	miles	miles	1.61	kilometers
meter (m) = 100 cm	meters	3.28	feet	feet	0.3048	meters
centimeter (cm) = 10 mm	centimeters	0.39	inches	inches	2.54	centimeters
millimeter (mm) = 0.1 cm	millimeters	0.04	inches	inches	25.4	millimeters
Area	When you know	multiply by	to find	When you know	multiply by	to find
square kilometer (km^2)	square kilometers	0.39	square miles	square miles	2.59	square kilometers
square meter (m^2)	square meters	1.2	square yards	square yards	0.84	square meters
square centimeter (cm^2)	square centimeters	0.155	square inches	square inches	6.45	square centimeters
Volume	When you know	multiply by	to find	When you know	multiply by	to find
liter (L) = 1000 mL	liters	1.06	quarts	quarts	0.95	liters
	liters	0.26	gallons	gallons	3.79	liters
	liters	4.23	cups	cups	0.24	liters
	liters	2.12	pints	pints	0.47	liters
milliliter (mL) = 0.001 L	milliliters	0.20	teaspoons	teaspoons	4.93	milliliters
	milliliters	0.07	tablespoons	tablespoons	14.79	milliliters
	milliliters	0.03	fluid ounces	fluid ounces	29.57	milliliters
Mass	When you know	multiply by	to find	When you know	multiply by	to find
kilogram (kg) = 1000 g	kilograms	2.2	pounds	pounds	0.45	kilograms
gram (g) = 1000 mg	grams	0.035	ounces	ounces	28.35	grams

Precision and Accuracy

When you do an experiment, it is important that your methods, observations, and data be both precise and accurate.

low precision

precision, but not accuracy

precision and accuracy

Precision

In science, **precision** is the exactness and consistency of measurements. For example, measurements made with a ruler that has both centimeter and millimeter markings would be more precise than measurements made with a ruler that has only centimeter markings. Another indicator of precision is the care taken to make sure that methods and observations are as exact and consistent as possible. Every time a particular experiment is done, the same procedure should be used. Precision is necessary because experiments are repeated several times and if the procedure changes, the results will change.

EXAMPLE

Suppose you are measuring temperatures over a two-week period. Your precision will be greater if you measure each temperature at the same place, at the same time of day, and with the same thermometer than if you change any of these factors from one day to the next.

Accuracy

In science, it is possible to be precise but not accurate. **Accuracy** depends on the difference between a measurement and an actual value. The smaller the difference, the more accurate the measurement.

EXAMPLE

Suppose you look at a stream and estimate that it is about 1 meter wide at a particular place. You decide to check your estimate by measuring the stream with a meter stick, and you determine that the stream is 1.32 meters wide. However, because it is hard to measure the width of a stream with a meter stick, it turns out that you didn't do a very good job. The stream is actually 1.14 meters wide. Therefore, even though your estimate was less precise than your measurement, your estimate was actually more accurate.

Making Data Tables and Graphs

Data tables and graphs are useful tools for both recording and communicating scientific data.

Making Data Tables

You can use a **data table** to organize and record the measurements that you make. Some examples of information that might be recorded in data tables are frequencies, times, and amounts.

EXAMPLE

Suppose you are investigating photosynthesis in two elodea plants. One sits in direct sunlight, and the other sits in a dimly lit room. You measure the rate of photosynthesis by counting the number of bubbles in the jar every ten minutes.

1. Title and number your data table.
2. Decide how you will organize the table into columns and rows.
3. Any units, such as seconds or degrees, should be included in column headings, not in the individual cells.

Table 1. Number of Bubbles from Elodea

Time (min)	Sunlight	Dim Light
0	0	0
10	15	5
20	25	8
30	32	7
40	41	10
50	47	9
60	42	9

◄ Always number and title data tables.

The data in the table above could also be organized in a different way.

Table 1. Number of Bubbles from Elodea

Light Condition	Time (min)						
	0	10	20	30	40	50	60
Sunlight	0	15	25	32	41	47	42
Dim light	0	5	8	7	10	9	9

◄ Put units in column heading.

Making Line Graphs

You can use a **line graph** to show a relationship between variables. Line graphs are particularly useful for showing changes in variables over time.

EXAMPLE

Suppose you are interested in graphing temperature data that you collected over the course of a day.

Table 1. Outside Temperature During the Day on March 7

	Time of Day						
	7:00 A.M.	9:00 A.M.	11:00 A.M.	1:00 P.M.	3:00 P.M.	5:00 P.M.	7:00 P.M.
Temp (°C)	8	9	11	14	12	10	6

1. Use the vertical axis of your line graph for the variable that you are measuring—temperature.

2. Choose scales for both the horizontal axis and the vertical axis of the graph. You should have two points more than you need on the vertical axis, and the horizontal axis should be long enough for all of the data points to fit.

3. Draw and label each axis.

4. Graph each value. First find the appropriate point on the scale of the horizontal axis. Imagine a line that rises vertically from that place on the scale. Then find the corresponding value on the vertical axis, and imagine a line that moves horizontally from that value. The point where these two imaginary lines intersect is where the value should be plotted.

5. Connect the points with straight lines.

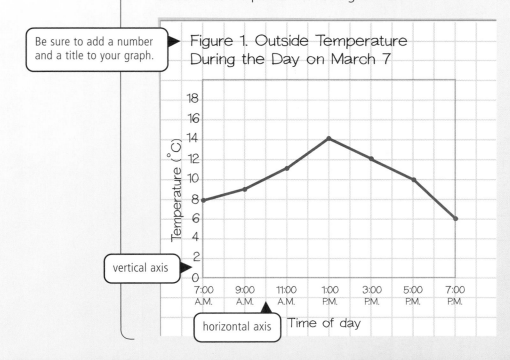

Be sure to add a number and a title to your graph.

Figure 1. Outside Temperature During the Day on March 7

vertical axis

horizontal axis

Making Circle Graphs

You can use a **circle graph,** sometimes called a pie chart, to represent data as parts of a circle. Circle graphs are used only when the data can be expressed as percentages of a whole. The entire circle shown in a circle graph is equal to 100 percent of the data.

EXAMPLE

Suppose you identified the species of each mature tree growing in a small wooded area. You organized your data in a table, but you also want to show the data in a circle graph.

1. To begin, find the total number of mature trees.

    $$56 + 34 + 22 + 10 + 28 = 150$$

2. To find the degree measure for each sector of the circle, write a fraction comparing the number of each tree species with the total number of trees. Then multiply the fraction by 360°.

    Oak: $\frac{56}{150} \times 360° = 134.4°$

3. Draw a circle. Use a protractor to draw the angle for each sector of the graph.

4. Color and label each sector of the graph.

5. Give the graph a number and title.

Table 1. Tree Species in Wooded Area

Species	Number of Specimens
Oak	56
Maple	34
Birch	22
Willow	10
Pine	28

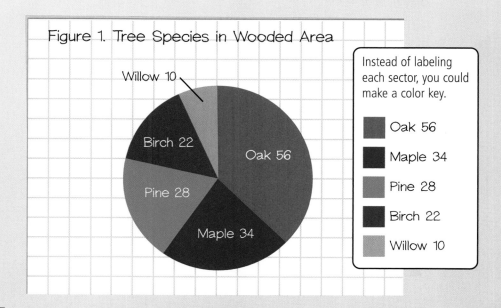

Figure 1. Tree Species in Wooded Area

Instead of labeling each sector, you could make a color key.

- Oak 56
- Maple 34
- Pine 28
- Birch 22
- Willow 10

Bar Graph

A **bar graph** is a type of graph in which the lengths of the bars are used to represent and compare data. A numerical scale is used to determine the lengths of the bars.

EXAMPLE

To determine the effect of water on seed sprouting, three cups were filled with sand, and ten seeds were planted in each. Different amounts of water were added to each cup over a three-day period.

Table 1. Effect of Water on Seed Sprouting

Daily Amount of Water (mL)	Number of Seeds That Sprouted After 3 Days in Sand
0	1
10	4
20	8

1. Choose a numerical scale. The greatest value is 8, so the end of the scale should have a value greater than 8, such as 10. Use equal increments along the scale, such as increments of 2.

2. Draw and label the axes. Mark intervals on the vertical axis according to the scale you chose.

3. Draw a bar for each data value. Use the scale to decide how long to make each bar.

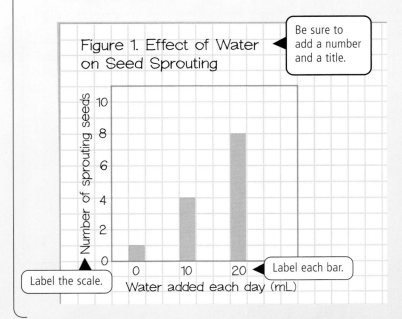

Figure 1. Effect of Water on Seed Sprouting

Be sure to add a number and a title.

Label the scale.

Label each bar.

Double Bar Graph

A **double bar graph** is a bar graph that shows two sets of data. The two bars for each measurement are drawn next to each other.

EXAMPLE

The seed-sprouting experiment was done using both sand and potting soil. The data for sand and potting soil can be plotted on one graph.

1. Draw one set of bars, using the data for sand, as shown below.
2. Draw bars for the potting-soil data next to the bars for the sand data. Shade them a different color. Add a key.

Table 2. Effect of Water and Soil on Seed Sprouting

Daily Amount of Water (mL)	Number of Seeds That Sprouted After 3 Days in Sand	Number of Seeds That Sprouted After 3 Days in Potting Soil
0	1	2
10	4	5
20	8	9

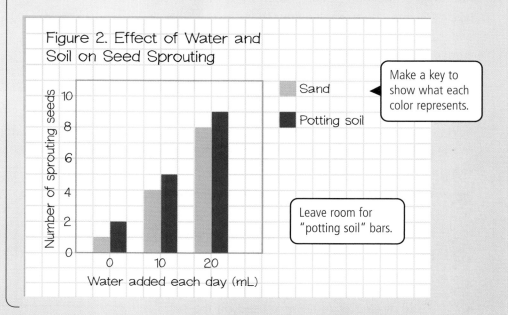

Figure 2. Effect of Water and Soil on Seed Sprouting

Make a key to show what each color represents.

Leave room for "potting soil" bars.

Designing an Experiment

Use this section when designing or conducting an experiment.

Determining a Purpose

You can find a purpose for an experiment by doing research, by examining the results of a previous experiment, or by observing the world around you. An **experiment** is an organized procedure to study something under controlled conditions.

Don't forget to learn as much as possible about your topic before you begin.

1. Write the purpose of your experiment as a question or problem that you want to investigate.

2. Write down research questions and begin searching for information that will help you design an experiment. Consult the library, the Internet, and other people as you conduct your research.

EXAMPLE

Middle school students observed an odor near the lake by their school. They also noticed that the water on the side of the lake near the school was greener than the water on the other side of the lake. The students did some research to learn more about their observations. They discovered that the odor and green color in the lake  came from algae. They also discovered that a new fertilizer was being used on a field nearby. The students inferred that the use of the fertilizer might be related to the presence of the algae and designed a controlled experiment to find out whether they were right.

Problem
How does fertilizer affect the presence of algae in a lake?

Research Questions
- Have other experiments been done on this problem? If so, what did those experiments show?
- What kind of fertilizer is used on the field? How much?
- How do algae grow?
- How do people measure algae?
- Can fertilizer and algae be used safely in a lab? How?

Research
As you research, you may find a topic that is more interesting to you than your original topic, or learn that a procedure you wanted to use is not practical or safe. It is OK to change your purpose as you research.

Writing a Hypothesis

A **hypothesis** is a tentative explanation for an observation or scientific problem that can be tested by further investigation. You can write your hypothesis in the form of an "If . . . , then . . . , because . . ." statement.

Hypothesis

If the amount of fertilizer in lake water is increased, then the amount of algae will also increase, because fertilizers provide nutrients that algae need to grow.

◄ **Hypotheses**
For help with hypotheses, refer to page R3.

Determining Materials

Make a list of all the materials you will need to do your experiment. Be specific, especially if someone else is helping you obtain the materials. Try to think of everything you will need.

Materials

- 1 large jar or container
- 4 identical smaller containers
- rubber gloves that also cover the arms
- sample of fertilizer-and-water solution
- eyedropper
- clear plastic wrap
- scissors
- masking tape
- marker
- ruler

Determining Variables and Constants

EXPERIMENTAL GROUP AND CONTROL GROUP

An experiment to determine how two factors are related always has two groups—a control group and an experimental group.

1. Design an experimental group. Include as many trials as possible in the experimental group in order to obtain reliable results.

2. Design a control group that is the same as the experimental group in every way possible, except for the factor you wish to test.

> **Experimental Group:** two containers of lake water with one drop of fertilizer solution added to each
>
> **Control Group:** two containers of lake water with no fertilizer solution added

> Go back to your materials list and make sure you have enough items listed to cover both your experimental group and your control group.

VARIABLES AND CONSTANTS

Identify the variables and constants in your experiment. In a controlled experiment, a **variable** is any factor that can change. **Constants,** or controlled parameters, are all of the factors that are the same in both the experimental group and the control group.

> **Hypothesis**
> If the amount of fertilizer in lake water is increased, then the amount of algae will also increase, because fertilizers provide nutrients that algae need to grow.

1. Read your hypothesis. The **independent variable** is the factor that you wish to test and that is manipulated or changed so that it can be tested. The independent variable is expressed in your hypothesis after the word *if*. Identify the independent variable in your laboratory report.

2. The **dependent variable** is the factor that you measure to gather results. It is expressed in your hypothesis after the word *then*. Identify the dependent variable in your laboratory report.

Table 1. Variables and Constants in Algae Experiment

Independent Variable	Dependent Variable	Constants
Amount of fertilizer in lake water	Amount of algae that grow	• Where the lake water is obtained • Type of container used • Light and temperature conditions where water will be stored

> Set up your experiment so that you will test only one variable.

LAB HANDBOOK

MEASURING THE DEPENDENT VARIABLE

Before starting your experiment, you need to define how you will measure the dependent variable. An **operational definition** is a description of the one particular way in which you will measure the dependent variable.

Your operational definition is important for several reasons. First, in any experiment there are several ways in which a dependent variable can be measured. Second, the procedure of the experiment depends on how you decide to measure the dependent variable. Third, your operational definition makes it possible for other people to evaluate and build on your experiment.

EXAMPLE 1

An operational definition of a dependent variable can be qualitative. That is, your measurement of the dependent variable can simply be an observation of whether a change occurs as a result of a change in the independent variable. This type of operational definition can be thought of as a "yes or no" measurement.

Table 2. Qualitative Operational Definition of Algae Growth

Independent Variable	Dependent Variable	Operational Definition
Amount of fertilizer in lake water	Amount of algae that grow	Algae grow in lake water

A qualitative measurement of a dependent variable is often easy to make and record. However, this type of information does not provide a great deal of detail in your experimental results.

EXAMPLE 2

An operational definition of a dependent variable can be quantitative. That is, your measurement of the dependent variable can be a number that shows how much change occurs as a result of a change in the independent variable.

Table 3. Quantitative Operational Definition of Algae Growth

Independent Variable	Dependent Variable	Operational Definition
Amount of fertilizer in lake water	Amount of algae that grow	Diameter of largest algal growth (in mm)

A quantitative measurement of a dependent variable can be more diffic[ult] to make and analyze than a qualitative measurement. However, this ty[pe of] data provides much more information about your experiment and is [much] more useful.

Writing a Procedure

Write each step of your procedure. Start each step with a verb, or action word, and keep the steps short. Your procedure should be clear enough for someone else to use as instructions for repeating your experiment.

> If necessary, go back to your materials list and add any materials that you left out.

> **Controlling Variables**
> The same amount of fertilizer solution must be added to two of the four containers.

Procedure

1. Put on your gloves. Use the large container to obtain a sample of lake water.

2. Divide the sample of lake water equally among the four smaller containers.

3. Use the eyedropper to add one drop of fertilizer solution to two of the containers.

4. Use the masking tape and the marker to label the containers with your initials, the date, and the identifiers "Jar 1 with Fertilizer," "Jar 2 with Fertilizer," "Jar 1 without Fertilizer," and "Jar 2 without Fertilizer."

5. Cover the containers with clear plastic wrap. Use the scissors to punch ten holes in each of the covers.

6. Place all four containers on a window ledge. Make sure that they all receive the same amount of light.

7. ...rve the containers every day for one week.

8. ...to measure the diameter of the largest clump of ...ntainer, and record your measurements daily.

Recording Observations

Once you have obtained all of your materials and your procedure has been approved, you can begin making experimental observations. Gather both quantitative and qualitative data. If something goes wrong during your procedure, make sure you record that too.

Observations
For help with making qualitative and quantitative observations, refer to page R2.

For more examples of data tables, see page R23.

Table 4. Fertilizer and Algae Growth

	Experimental Group		Control Group		
Date and Time	Jar 1 with Fertilizer (diameter of algae in mm)	Jar 2 with Fertilizer (diameter of algae in mm)	Jar 1 without Fertilizer (diameter of algae in mm)	Jar 2 without Fertilizer (diameter of algae in mm)	Observations
5/3 4:00 P.M.	0	0	0	0	condensation in all containers
5/4 4:00 P.M.	0	3	0	0	tiny green blobs in jar 2 with fertilizer
5/5 4:15 P.M.	4	5	0	3	green blobs in jars 1 and 2 with fertilizer and jar 2 without fertilizer
5/6 4:00 P.M.	5	6	0	4	water light green in jar 2 with fertilizer
5/7 4:00 P.M.	8	10	0	6	water light green in jars 1 and 2 with fertilizer and in jar 2 without fertilizer
5/8 3:30 P.M.	10	18	0	6	cover off jar 2 with fertilizer
5/9 3:30 P.M.	14	23	0	8	drew sketches of each container

Notice that on the sixth day, the observer found that the cover was off one of the containers. It is important to record observations of unintended factors because they might affect the results of the experiment.

Use technology, such as a microscope, to help you make observations when possible.

Drawings of Samples Viewed Under Microscope on 5/9 at 100x

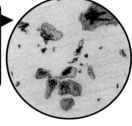
Jar 1 with Fertilizer

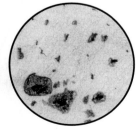
Jar 2 with Fertilizer

Jar 1 without Fertilizer

Jar 2 without Fertilizer

LAB HANDBOOK

Summarizing Results

To summarize your data, look at all of your observations together. Look for meaningful ways to present your observations. For example, you might average your data or make a graph to look for patterns. When possible, use spreadsheet software to help you analyze and present your data. The two graphs below show the same data.

EXAMPLE 1

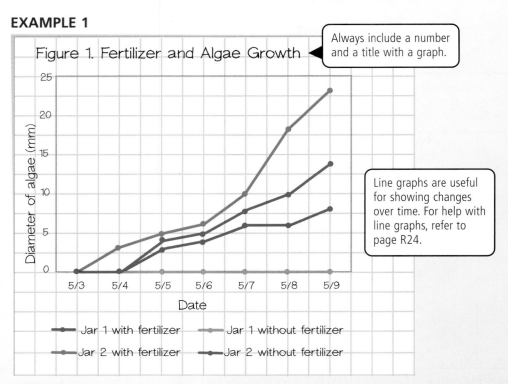

Figure 1. Fertilizer and Algae Growth

Always include a number and a title with a graph.

Line graphs are useful for showing changes over time. For help with line graphs, refer to page R24.

EXAMPLE 2

Bar graphs are useful for comparing different data sets. This bar graph has four bars for each day. Another way to present the data would be to calculate averages for the tests and the controls, and to show one test bar and one control bar for each day.

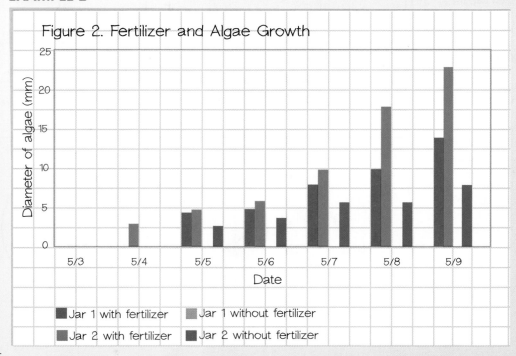

Figure 2. Fertilizer and Algae Growth

Drawing Conclusions

RESULTS AND INFERENCES

To draw conclusions from your experiment, first write your results. Then compare your results with your hypothesis. Do your results support your hypothesis? Be careful not to make inferences about factors that you did not test.

> For help with making inferences, see page R4.

Results and Inferences

The results of my experiment show that more algae grew in lake water to which fertilizer had been added than in lake water to which no fertilizer had been added. My hypothesis was supported. I infer that it is possible that the growth of algae in the lake was caused by the fertilizer used on the field.

> Notice that you cannot conclude from this experiment that the presence of algae in the lake was due only to the fertilizer.

QUESTIONS FOR FURTHER RESEARCH

Write a list of questions for further research and investigation. Your ideas may lead you to new experiments and discoveries.

Questions for Further Research

- What is the connection between the amount of fertilizer and algae growth?
- How do different brands of fertilizer affect algae growth?
- How would algae growth in the lake be affected if no fertilizer were used on the field?
- How do algae affect the lake and the other life in and around it?
- How does fertilizer affect the lake and the life in and around it?
- If fertilizer is getting into the lake, how is it getting there?

Math Handbook

Describing a Set of Data

Means, medians, modes, and ranges are important math tools for describing data sets such as the following widths of fossilized clamshells.

13 mm   25 mm   14 mm   21 mm   16 mm   23 mm   14 mm

Mean

The **mean** of a data set is the sum of the values divided by the number of values.

> **Example**
>
> To find the mean of the clamshell data, add the values and then divide the sum by the number of values.
>
> $$\frac{13 \text{ mm} + 25 \text{ mm} + 14 \text{ mm} + 21 \text{ mm} + 16 \text{ mm} + 23 \text{ mm} + 14 \text{ mm}}{7} = \frac{126 \text{ mm}}{7} = 18 \text{ mm}$$
>
> **ANSWER** The mean is 18 mm.

Median

The **median** of a data set is the middle value when the values are written in numerical order. If a data set has an even number of values, the median is the mean of the two middle values.

> **Example**
>
> To find the median of the clamshell data, arrange the values in order from least to greatest. The median is the middle value.
>
> 13 mm   14 mm   14 mm   16 mm   21 mm   23 mm   25 mm
>
> **ANSWER** The median is 16 mm.

Mode

The **mode** of a data set is the value that occurs most often.

Example

To find the mode of the clamshell data, arrange the values in order from least to greatest and determine the value that occurs most often.

13 mm   14 mm   14 mm   16 mm   21 mm   23 mm   25 mm

ANSWER The mode is 14 mm.

A data set can have more than one mode or no mode. For example, the following data set has modes of 2 mm and 4 mm:

2 mm   2 mm   3 mm   4 mm   4 mm

The data set below has no mode, because no value occurs more often than any other.

2 mm   3 mm   4 mm   5 mm

Range

The **range** of a data set is the difference between the greatest value and the least value.

Example

To find the range of the clamshell data, arrange the values in order from least to greatest.

13 mm   14 mm   14 mm   16 mm   21 mm   23 mm   25 mm

Subtract the least value from the greatest value.

13 mm is the least value.
25 mm is the greatest value.

25 mm − 13 mm = 12 mm

ANSWER The range is 12 mm.

Using Ratios, Rates, and Proportions

You can use ratios and rates to compare values in data sets. You can use proportions to find unknown values.

Ratios

A **ratio** uses division to compare two values. The ratio of a value a to a nonzero value b can be written as $\frac{a}{b}$.

Example

The height of one plant is 8 centimeters. The height of another plant is 6 centimeters. To find the ratio of the height of the first plant to the height of the second plant, write a fraction and simplify it.

$$\frac{8 \text{ cm}}{6 \text{ cm}} = \frac{4 \times \overset{1}{\cancel{2}}}{3 \times \underset{1}{\cancel{2}}} = \frac{4}{3}$$

ANSWER The ratio of the plant heights is $\frac{4}{3}$.

You can also write the ratio $\frac{a}{b}$ as "a to b" or as $a : b$. For example, you can write the ratio of the plant heights as "4 to 3" or as $4 : 3$.

Rates

A **rate** is a ratio of two values expressed in different units. A unit rate is a rate with a denominator of 1 unit.

Example

A plant grew 6 centimeters in 2 days. The plant's rate of growth was $\frac{6 \text{ cm}}{2 \text{ days}}$. To describe the plant's growth in centimeters per day, write a unit rate.

Divide numerator and denominator by 2: $\quad \frac{6 \text{ cm}}{2 \text{ days}} = \frac{6 \text{ cm} \div 2}{2 \text{ days} \div 2}$

You divide 2 days by 2 to get 1 day, so divide 6 cm by 2 also.

Simplify: $\quad = \frac{3 \text{ cm}}{1 \text{ day}}$

ANSWER The plant's rate of growth is 3 centimeters per day.

Proportions

A **proportion** is an equation stating that two ratios are equivalent. To solve for an unknown value in a proportion, you can use cross products.

Example

If a plant grew 6 centimeters in 2 days, how many centimeters would it grow in 3 days (if its rate of growth is constant)?

$$\textit{Write a proportion:} \quad \frac{6 \text{ cm}}{2 \text{ days}} = \frac{x}{3 \text{ days}}$$

$$\textit{Set cross products:} \quad 6 \text{ cm} \cdot 3 = 2x$$

$$\textit{Multiply 6 and 3:} \quad 18 \text{ cm} = 2x$$

$$\textit{Divide each side by 2:} \quad \frac{18 \text{ cm}}{2} = \frac{2x}{2}$$

$$\textit{Simplify:} \quad 9 \text{ cm} = x$$

ANSWER The plant would grow 9 centimeters in 3 days.

Using Decimals, Fractions, and Percents

Decimals, fractions, and percentages are all ways of recording and representing data.

Decimals

A **decimal** is a number that is written in the base-ten place value system, in which a decimal point separates the ones and tenths digits. The values of each place is ten times that of the place to its right.

Example

A caterpillar traveled from point A to point C along the path shown.

A   **36.9 cm**   **B**   **52.4 cm**   C

ADDING DECIMALS To find the total distance traveled by the caterpillar, add the distance from A to B and the distance from B to C. Begin by lining up the decimal points. Then add the figures as you would whole numbers and bring down the decimal point.

$$
\begin{array}{r}
36.9 \text{ cm} \\
+ \; 52.4 \text{ cm} \\
\hline
89.3 \text{ cm}
\end{array}
$$

ANSWER The caterpillar traveled a total distance of 89.3 centimeters.

Example continued

SUBTRACTING DECIMALS To find how much farther the caterpillar traveled on the second leg of the journey, subtract the distance from *A* to *B* from the distance from *B* to *C*.

$$\begin{array}{r} 52.4 \text{ cm} \\ -\ 36.9 \text{ cm} \\ \hline 15.5 \text{ cm} \end{array}$$

ANSWER The caterpillar traveled 15.5 centimeters farther on the second leg of the journey.

Example

A caterpillar is traveling from point *D* to point *F* along the path shown. The caterpillar travels at a speed of 9.6 centimeters per minute.

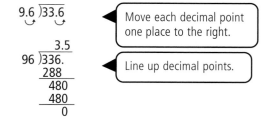

D   **E**   **33.6 cm**   **F**

MULTIPLYING DECIMALS You can multiply decimals as you would whole numbers. The number of decimal places in the product is equal to the sum of the number of decimal places in the factors.

For instance, suppose it takes the caterpillar 1.5 minutes to go from *D* to *E*. To find the distance from *D* to *E*, multiply the caterpillar's speed by the time it took.

Align as shown.

$$\begin{array}{rl} 9.6 & \quad 1 \quad \text{decimal place} \\ \times\ 1.5 & \quad +\ 1 \quad \text{decimal place} \\ \hline 480 & \\ 96 & \\ \hline 14.40 & \quad 2 \quad \text{decimal places} \end{array}$$

ANSWER The distance from *D* to *E* is 14.4 centimeters.

DIVIDING DECIMALS When you divide by a decimal, move the decimal points the same number of places in the divisor and the dividend to make the divisor a whole number.

For instance, to find the time it will take the caterpillar to travel from *E* to *F*, divide the distance from *E* to *F* by the caterpillar's speed.

$$9.6\,\overline{)33.6}$$ Move each decimal point one place to the right.

$$\begin{array}{r} 3.5 \\ 96\,\overline{)336.} \\ \underline{288} \\ 480 \\ \underline{480} \\ 0 \end{array}$$ Line up decimal points.

ANSWER The caterpillar will travel from *E* to *F* in 3.5 minutes.

Fractions

A **fraction** is a number in the form $\frac{a}{b}$, where b is not equal to 0. A fraction is in **simplest form** if its numerator and denominator have a greatest common factor (GCF) of 1. To simplify a fraction, divide its numerator and denominator by their GCF.

Example

A caterpillar is 40 millimeters long. The head of the caterpillar is 6 millimeters long. To compare the length of the caterpillar's head with the caterpillar's total length, you can write and simplify a fraction that expresses the ratio of the two lengths.

Write the ratio of the two lengths: $\dfrac{\text{Length of head}}{\text{Total length}} = \dfrac{6 \text{ mm}}{40 \text{ mm}}$

Write numerator and denominator as products of numbers and the GCF: $= \dfrac{3 \times 2}{20 \times 2}$

Divide numerator and denominator by the GCF: $= \dfrac{3 \times \overset{1}{\cancel{2}}}{20 \times \underset{1}{\cancel{2}}}$

Simplify: $= \dfrac{3}{20}$

ANSWER In simplest form, the ratio of the lengths is $\frac{3}{20}$.

Percents

A **percent** is a ratio that compares a number to 100. The word *percent* means "per hundred" or "out of 100." The symbol for *percent* is %.

For instance, suppose 43 out of 100 caterpillars are female. You can represent this ratio as a percent, a decimal, or a fraction.

Percent	Decimal	Fraction
43%	0.43	$\frac{43}{100}$

Example

In the preceding example, the ratio of the length of the caterpillar's head to the caterpillar's total length is $\frac{3}{20}$. To write this ratio as a percent, write an equivalent fraction that has a denominator of 100.

Multiply numerator and denominator by 5: $\dfrac{3}{20} = \dfrac{3 \times 5}{20 \times 5}$

$= \dfrac{15}{100}$

Write as a percent: $= 15\%$

ANSWER The caterpillar's head represents 15 percent of its total length.

Using Formulas

A **formula** is an equation that shows the general relationship between two or more quantities.

The term *variable* is also used in science to refer to a factor that can change during an experiment.

In science, a formula often has a word form and a symbolic form. The formula below expresses Ohm's law.

Word Form

$$\text{Current} = \frac{\text{voltage}}{\text{resistance}}$$

Symbolic Form

$$I = \frac{V}{R}$$

In this formula, I, V, and R are variables. A mathematical **variable** is a symbol or letter that is used to represent one or more numbers.

Example

Suppose that you measure a voltage of 1.5 volts and a resistance of 15 ohms. You can use the formula for Ohm's law to find the current in amperes.

Write the formula for Ohm's law: $\quad I = \dfrac{V}{R}$

Substitute 1.5 volts for V and 15 ohms for R: $\quad I = \dfrac{1.5 \text{ volts}}{15 \text{ ohms}}$

Simplify: $\quad I = 0.1 \text{ amp}$

ANSWER The current is 0.1 ampere.

If you know the values of all variables but one in a formula, you can solve for the value of the unknown variable. For instance, Ohm's law can be used to find a voltage if you know the current and the resistance.

Example

Suppose that you know that a current is 0.2 amperes and the resistance is 18 ohms. Use the formula for Ohm's law to find the voltage in volts.

Write the formula for Ohm's law: $\quad I = \dfrac{V}{R}$

Substitute 0.2 amp for I and 18 ohms for R: $\quad 0.2 \text{ amp} = \dfrac{V}{18 \text{ ohms}}$

Multiply both sides by 18 ohms: $\quad 0.2 \text{ amp} \cdot 18 \text{ ohms} = V$

Simplify: $\quad 3.6 \text{ volts} = V$

ANSWER The voltage is 3.6 volts.

Finding Areas

The area of a figure is the amount of surface the figure covers.

Area is measured in square units, such as square meters (m^2) or square centimeters (cm^2). Formulas for the areas of three common geometric figures are shown below.

Area = (side length)²
$A = s^2$

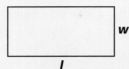

Area = length × width
$A = lw$

Area = $\frac{1}{2}$ × base × height
$A = \frac{1}{2} bh$

Example

Each face of a halite crystal is a square like the one shown. You can find the area of the square by using the steps below.

3 mm
3 mm

Write the formula for the area of a square: $A = s^2$

Substitute 3 mm for s: $= (3 \text{ mm})^2$

Simplify: $= 9 \text{ mm}^2$

ANSWER The area of the square is 9 square millimeters.

Finding Volumes

The volume of a solid is the amount of space contained by the solid.

Volume is measured in cubic units, such as cubic meters (m^3) or cubic centimeters (cm^3). The volume of a rectangular prism is given by the formula shown below.

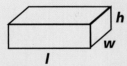

Volume = length × width × height
$V = lwh$

Example

A topaz crystal is a rectangular prism like the one shown. You can find the volume of the prism by using the steps below.

10 mm
12 mm
20 mm

Write the formula for the volume of a rectangular prism: $V = lwh$

Substitute dimensions: $= 20 \text{ mm} \times 12 \text{ mm} \times 10 \text{ mm}$

Simplify: $= 2400 \text{ mm}^3$

ANSWER The volume of the rectangular prism is 2400 cubic millimeters.

Using Significant Figures

The **significant figures** in a decimal are the digits that are warranted by the accuracy of a measuring device.

When you perform a calculation with measurements, the number of significant figures to include in the result depends in part on the number of significant figures in the measurements. When you multiply or divide measurements, your answer should have only as many significant figures as the measurement with the fewest significant figures.

Example

Using a balance and a graduated cylinder filled with water, you determined that a marble has a mass of 8.0 grams and a volume of 3.5 cubic centimeters. To calculate the density of the marble, divide the mass by the volume.

Write the formula for density: $\quad$ Density $= \dfrac{\text{mass}}{\text{Volume}}$

Substitute measurements: $\qquad\qquad = \dfrac{8.0\text{ g}}{3.5\text{ cm}^3}$

Use a calculator to divide: $\qquad\quad \approx 2.285714286 \text{ g/cm}^3$

ANSWER Because the mass and the volume have two significant figures each, give the density to two significant figures. The marble has a density of 2.3 grams per cubic centimeter.

Using Scientific Notation

Scientific notation is a shorthand way to write very large or very small numbers. For example, 73,500,000,000,000,000,000,000 kg is the mass of the Moon. In scientific notation, it is 7.35×10^{22} kg.

Example

You can convert from standard form to scientific notation.

Standard Form	Scientific Notation
720,000	7.2×10^5
5 decimal places left	Exponent is 5.
0.000291	2.91×10^{-4}
4 decimal places right	Exponent is −4.

You can convert from scientific notation to standard form.

Scientific Notation	Standard Form
4.63×10^7	46,300,000
Exponent is 7.	7 decimal places right
1.08×10^{-6}	0.00000108
Exponent is −6.	6 decimal places left

MATH HANDBOOK

Note-Taking Handbook

Note-Taking Strategies

Taking notes as you read helps you understand the information. The notes you take can also be used as a study guide for later review. This handbook presents several ways to organize your notes.

Content Frame

1. Make a chart in which each column represents a category.
2. Give each column a heading.
3. Write details under the headings.

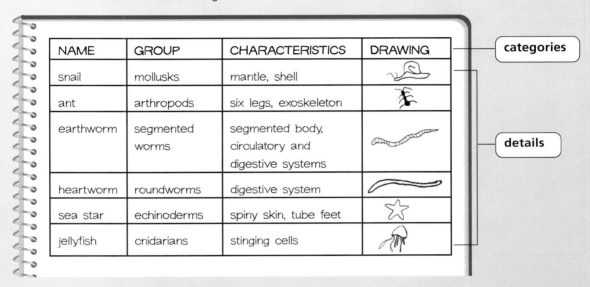

NAME	GROUP	CHARACTERISTICS	DRAWING
snail	mollusks	mantle, shell	
ant	arthropods	six legs, exoskeleton	
earthworm	segmented worms	segmented body, circulatory and digestive systems	
heartworm	roundworms	digestive system	
sea star	echinoderms	spiny skin, tube feet	
jellyfish	cnidarians	stinging cells	

categories

details

Combination Notes

1. For each new idea or concept, write an informal outline of the information.
2. Make a sketch to illustrate the concept, and label it.

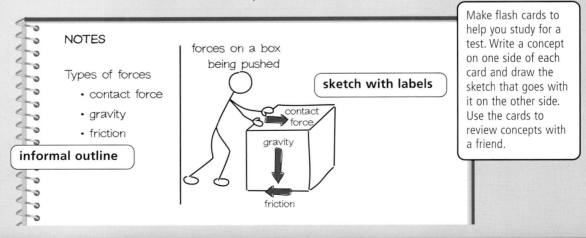

NOTES

Types of forces
- contact force
- gravity
- friction

informal outline

forces on a box being pushed

contact force

gravity

friction

sketch with labels

Make flash cards to help you study for a test. Write a concept on one side of each card and draw the sketch that goes with it on the other side. Use the cards to review concepts with a friend.

Main Idea and Detail Notes

1. In the left-hand column of a two-column chart, list main ideas. The blue headings express main ideas throughout this textbook.

2. In the right-hand column, write details that expand on each main idea.

You can shorten the headings in your chart. Be sure to use the most important words.

When studying for tests, cover up the detail notes column with a sheet of paper. Then use each main idea to form a question—such as "How does latitude affect climate?" Answer the question, and then uncover the detail notes column to check your answer.

MAIN IDEAS	DETAIL NOTES
1. Latitude affects climate.	1. Places close to the equator are usually warmer than places close to the poles.
	1. Latitude has the same effect in both hemispheres.
2. Altitude affects climate.	2. Temperature decreases with altitude.
	2. Altitude can overcome the effect of latitude on temperature.

main idea 1

main idea 2

details about main idea 1

details about main idea 2

Main Idea Web

1. Write a main idea in a box.

2. Add boxes around it with related vocabulary terms and important details.

You can find definitions near highlighted terms.

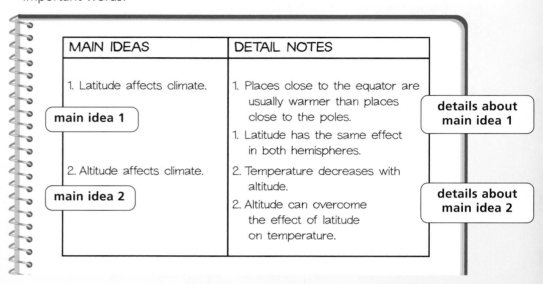

definition of *work*

Work is the use of force to move an object.

formula

Work = force · distance

main idea

Force is necessary to do work.

The joule is the unit used to measure work.

definition of *joule*

Work depends on the size of a force.

important detail

NOTE-TAKING HANDBOOK

Mind Map

1. Write a main idea in the center.
2. Add details that relate to one another and to the main idea.

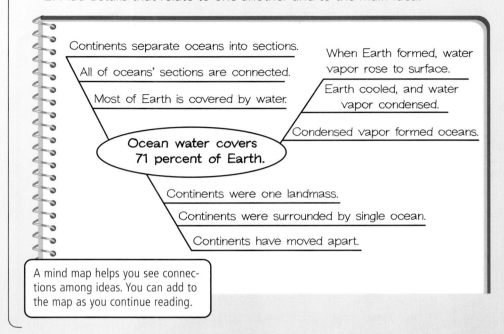

Continents separate oceans into sections.

All of oceans' sections are connected.

Most of Earth is covered by water.

When Earth formed, water vapor rose to surface.

Earth cooled, and water vapor condensed.

Condensed vapor formed oceans.

Ocean water covers 71 percent of Earth.

Continents were one landmass.

Continents were surrounded by single ocean.

Continents have moved apart.

A mind map helps you see connections among ideas. You can add to the map as you continue reading.

Supporting Main Ideas

1. Write a main idea in a box.
2. Add boxes underneath with information—such as reasons, explanations, and examples—that supports the main idea.

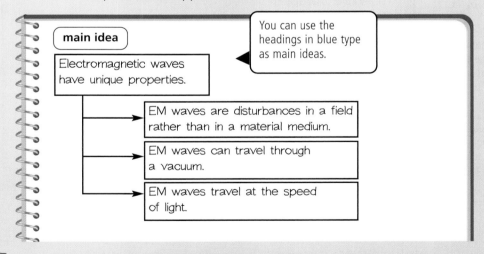

main idea

Electromagnetic waves have unique properties.

You can use the headings in blue type as main ideas.

EM waves are disturbances in a field rather than in a material medium.

EM waves can travel through a vacuum.

EM waves travel at the speed of light.

Outline

1. Copy the chapter title and headings from the book in the form of an outline.

2. Add notes that summarize in your own words what you read.

Cell Processes

1st key idea

I. Cells capture and release energy.

1st subpoint of I

   A. All cells need energy.

2nd subpoint of I

   B. Some cells capture light energy.

1st detail about B

      1. Process of photosynthesis

2nd detail about B

      2. Chloroplasts (site of photosynthesis)
      3. Carbon dioxide and water as raw materials
      4. Glucose and oxygen as products

   C. All cells release energy.
      1. Process of cellular respiration
      2. Fermentation of sugar to carbon dioxide
      3. Bacteria that carry out fermentation

II. Cells transport materials through membranes.

   A. Some materials move by diffusion.
      1. Particle movement from higher to lower concentrations
      2. Movement of water through membrane (osmosis)

   B. Some transport requires energy.
      1. Active transport
      2. Examples of active transport

Correct Outline Form
Include a title.

Arrange key ideas, subpoints, and details as shown.

Indent the divisions of the outline as shown.

Use the same grammatical form for items of the same rank. For example, if A is a sentence, B must also be a sentence.

You must have at least two main ideas or subpoints. That is, every A must be followed by a B, and every 1 must be followed by a 2.

Concept Map

1. Write an important concept in a large oval.
2. Add details related to the concept in smaller ovals.
3. Write linking words on arrows that connect the ovals.

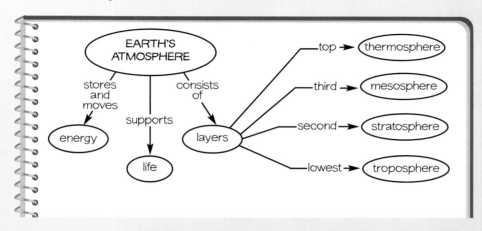

> The main ideas or concepts can often be found in the blue headings. An example is "The atmosphere stores and moves energy." Use nouns from these concepts in the ovals, and use the verb or verbs on the lines.

Venn Diagram

1. Draw two overlapping circles, one for each item that you are comparing.
2. In the overlapping section, list the characteristics that are shared by both items.
3. In the outer sections, list the characteristics that are peculiar to each item.
4. Write a summary that describes the information in the Venn diagram.

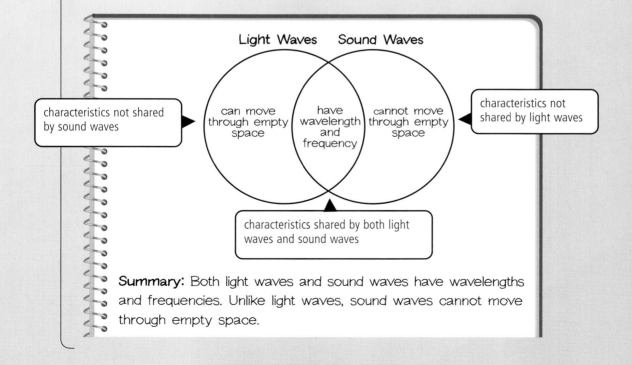

Summary: Both light waves and sound waves have wavelengths and frequencies. Unlike light waves, sound waves cannot move through empty space.

Vocabulary Strategies

Important terms are highlighted in this book. A definition of each term can be found in the sentence or paragraph where the term appears. You can also find definitions in the Glossary. Taking notes about vocabulary terms helps you understand and remember what you read.

Description Wheel

1. Write a term inside a circle.
2. Write words that describe the term on "spokes" attached to the circle.

When studying for a test with a friend, read the phrases on the spokes one at a time until your friend identifies the correct term.

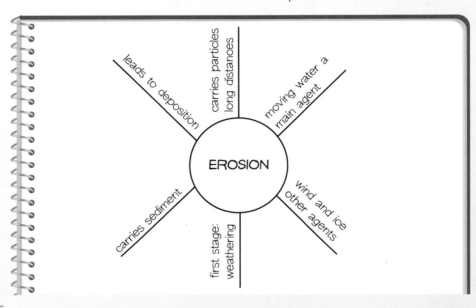

Four Square

1. Write a term in the center.
2. Write details in the four areas around the term.

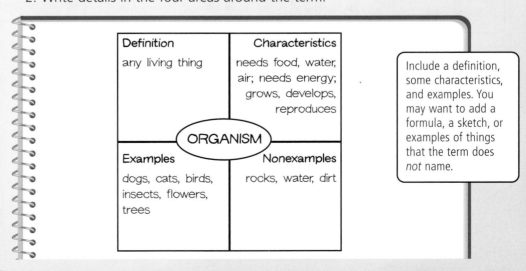

Include a definition, some characteristics, and examples. You may want to add a formula, a sketch, or examples of things that the term does *not* name.

Frame Game

1. Write a term in the center.
2. Frame the term with details.

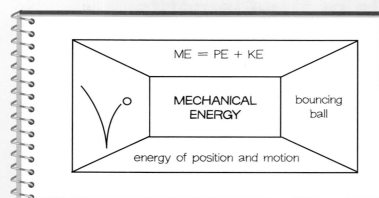

Include examples, descriptions, sketches, or sentences that use the term in context. Change the frame to fit each new term.

Magnet Word

1. Write a term on the magnet.
2. On the lines, add details related to the term.

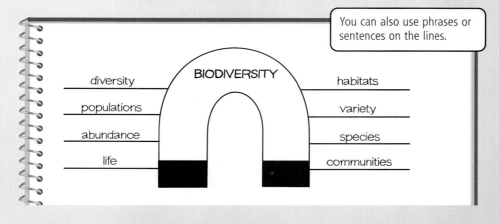

You can also use phrases or sentences on the lines.

Word Triangle

1. Write a term and its definition in the bottom section.
2. In the middle section, write a sentence in which the term is used correctly.
3. In the top section, draw a small picture to illustrate the term.

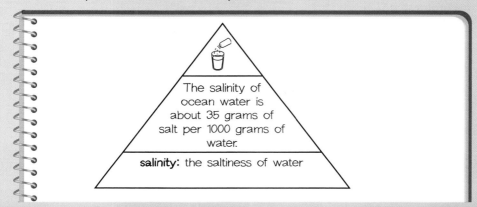

Appendix

The Periodic Table of the Elements

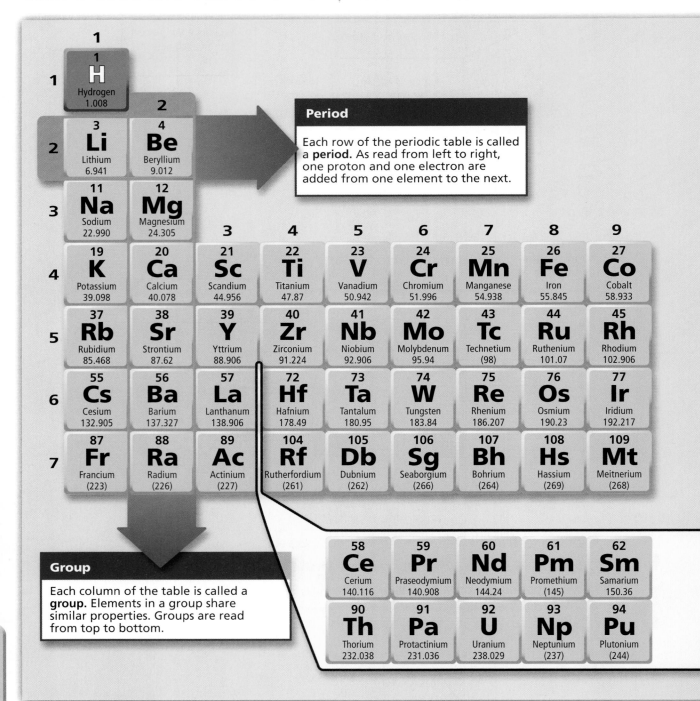

Period

Each row of the periodic table is called a **period.** As read from left to right, one proton and one electron are added from one element to the next.

Group

Each column of the table is called a **group.** Elements in a group share similar properties. Groups are read from top to bottom.

1 — 1 H Hydrogen 1.008		
2 — 3 Li Lithium 6.941 / 4 Be Beryllium 9.012		
3 — 11 Na Sodium 22.990 / 12 Mg Magnesium 24.305		

Group 3: 21 Sc Scandium 44.956 — 39 Y Yttrium 88.906 — 57 La Lanthanum 138.906 — 89 Ac Actinium (227)

Group 4: 22 Ti Titanium 47.87 — 40 Zr Zirconium 91.224 — 72 Hf Hafnium 178.49 — 104 Rf Rutherfordium (261)

Group 5: 23 V Vanadium 50.942 — 41 Nb Niobium 92.906 — 73 Ta Tantalum 180.95 — 105 Db Dubnium (262)

Group 6: 24 Cr Chromium 51.996 — 42 Mo Molybdenum 95.94 — 74 W Tungsten 183.84 — 106 Sg Seaborgium (266)

Group 7: 25 Mn Manganese 54.938 — 43 Tc Technetium (98) — 75 Re Rhenium 186.207 — 107 Bh Bohrium (264)

Group 8: 26 Fe Iron 55.845 — 44 Ru Ruthenium 101.07 — 76 Os Osmium 190.23 — 108 Hs Hassium (269)

Group 9: 27 Co Cobalt 58.933 — 45 Rh Rhodium 102.906 — 77 Ir Iridium 192.217 — 109 Mt Meitnerium (268)

Period 4: 19 K Potassium 39.098 — 20 Ca Calcium 40.078

Period 5: 37 Rb Rubidium 85.468 — 38 Sr Strontium 87.62

Period 6: 55 Cs Cesium 132.905 — 56 Ba Barium 137.327

Period 7: 87 Fr Francium (223) — 88 Ra Radium (226)

58 Ce Cerium 140.116 — 59 Pr Praseodymium 140.908 — 60 Nd Neodymium 144.24 — 61 Pm Promethium (145) — 62 Sm Samarium 150.36

90 Th Thorium 232.038 — 91 Pa Protactinium 231.036 — 92 U Uranium 238.029 — 93 Np Neptunium (237) — 94 Pu Plutonium (244)

 Metal   **Metalloid**   **Nonmetal**   Solid   Liquid   Gas

APPENDIX

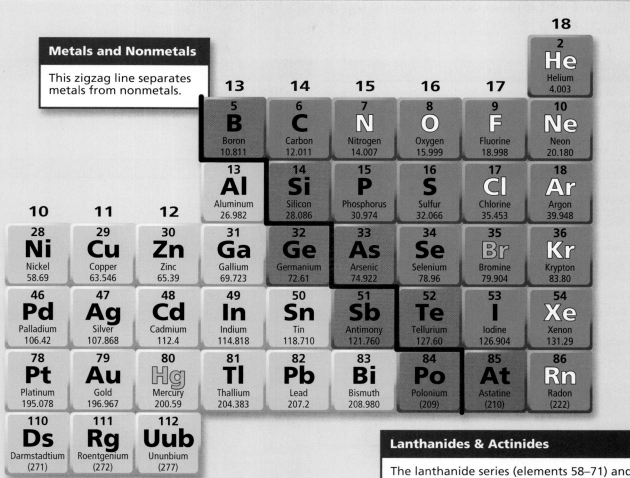

Metals and Nonmetals

This zigzag line separates metals from nonmetals.

18

| 2 | He | Helium | 4.003 |

| 13 | 14 | 15 | 16 | 17 |

| 5 B Boron 10.811 | 6 C Carbon 12.011 | 7 N Nitrogen 14.007 | 8 O Oxygen 15.999 | 9 F Fluorine 18.998 | 10 Ne Neon 20.180 |

| 13 Al Aluminum 26.982 | 14 Si Silicon 28.086 | 15 P Phosphorus 30.974 | 16 S Sulfur 32.066 | 17 Cl Chlorine 35.453 | 18 Ar Argon 39.948 |

| 10 | 11 | 12 |

| 28 Ni Nickel 58.69 | 29 Cu Copper 63.546 | 30 Zn Zinc 65.39 | 31 Ga Gallium 69.723 | 32 Ge Germanium 72.61 | 33 As Arsenic 74.922 | 34 Se Selenium 78.96 | 35 Br Bromine 79.904 | 36 Kr Krypton 83.80 |

| 46 Pd Palladium 106.42 | 47 Ag Silver 107.868 | 48 Cd Cadmium 112.4 | 49 In Indium 114.818 | 50 Sn Tin 118.710 | 51 Sb Antimony 121.760 | 52 Te Tellurium 127.60 | 53 I Iodine 126.904 | 54 Xe Xenon 131.29 |

| 78 Pt Platinum 195.078 | 79 Au Gold 196.967 | 80 Hg Mercury 200.59 | 81 Tl Thallium 204.383 | 82 Pb Lead 207.2 | 83 Bi Bismuth 208.980 | 84 Po Polonium (209) | 85 At Astatine (210) | 86 Rn Radon (222) |

| 110 Ds Darmstadtium (271) | 111 Rg Roentgenium (272) | 112 Uub Ununbium (277) |

Lanthanides & Actinides

The lanthanide series (elements 58–71) and actinide series (elements 90–103) are usually set apart from the rest of the periodic table.

| 63 Eu Europium 151.964 | 64 Gd Gadolinium 157.25 | 65 Tb Terbium 158.925 | 66 Dy Dysprosium 162.50 | 67 Ho Holmium 164.930 | 68 Er Erbium 167.26 | 69 Tm Thulium 168.934 | 70 Yb Ytterbium 173.04 | 71 Lu Lutetium 174.967 |

| 95 Am Americium (243) | 96 Cm Curium (247) | 97 Bk Berkelium (247) | 98 Cf Californium (251) | 99 Es Einsteinium (252) | 100 Fm Fermium (257) | 101 Md Mendelevium (258) | 102 No Nobelium (259) | 103 Lr Lawrencium (262) |

Atomic Number
number of protons in the nucleus of the element

1

H

Hydrogen
1.008

Name

Symbol
Each element has a symbol.
The symbol's color represents the element's state at room temperature.

Atomic Mass
average mass of isotopes of this element

Plant and Animal Cells

Plants and animals are eukaryotes, that is, their cells contain a nucleus and other membrane-bound structures called organelles. The diagrams on page R55 show the different structures that can be found in plant and animal cells. The table below lists the functions of the structures.

Cell Structures and Their Functions	Plant Cell	Animal Cell
Nucleus	✔	✔
stores genetic material that enables a cell to function and divide		
Cell Membrane	✔	✔
controls what comes into and goes out of a cell		
Cell Wall	✔	
controls what comes into and goes out of a cell		
Central Vacuole	✔	
holds water and other materials and may provide support		
Ribosome	✔	✔
uses genetic material to assemble materials needed to make proteins		
Endoplasmic reticulum	✔	✔
manufactures proteins and other materials a cell needs to function		
Golgi apparatus	✔	✔
finishes processing proteins and transports them		
Vesicle	✔	✔
stores and transports materials and wastes		
Mitochondrion	✔	✔
releases chemical energy stored in sugars		
Chloroplast	✔	
uses energy from sunlight to make sugars		
Lysosome		✔
breaks down food particles and wastes		

Plant Cell

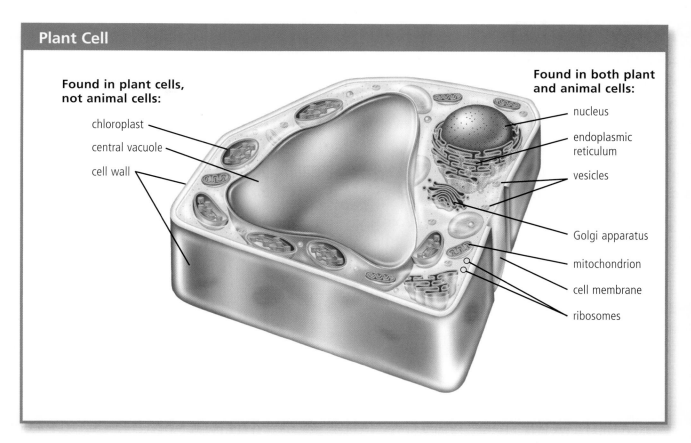

Found in plant cells, not animal cells:

chloroplast

central vacuole

cell wall

Found in both plant and animal cells:

nucleus

endoplasmic reticulum

vesicles

Golgi apparatus

mitochondrion

cell membrane

ribosomes

Animal Cell

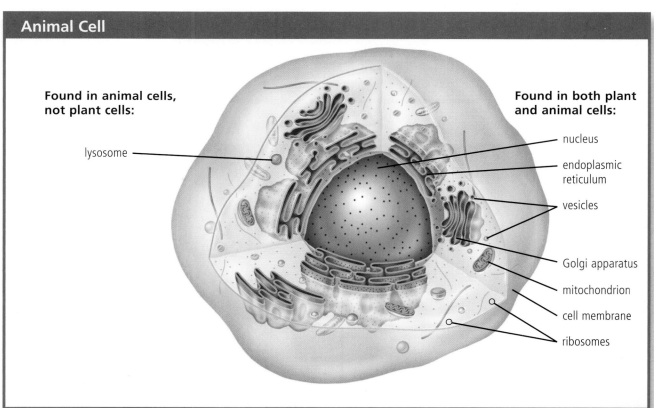

Found in animal cells, not plant cells:

lysosome

Found in both plant and animal cells:

nucleus

endoplasmic reticulum

vesicles

Golgi apparatus

mitochondrion

cell membrane

ribosomes

Divisions of Geologic Time

The geologic time scale is divided into eons, eras, periods, epochs (ehp-uhks), and ages. Unlike divisions of time such as days or minutes, the divisions of the geologic time scale have no exact fixed lengths. Instead, they are based on changes or events recorded in rocks and fossils.

Eon The largest unit of time is an eon. Earth's 4.6-billion-year history is divided into four eons.

The Hadean, Archean, and Proterozoic eons together are called Precambrian time and make up almost 90 percent of Earth's history.

Geologic Time Scale

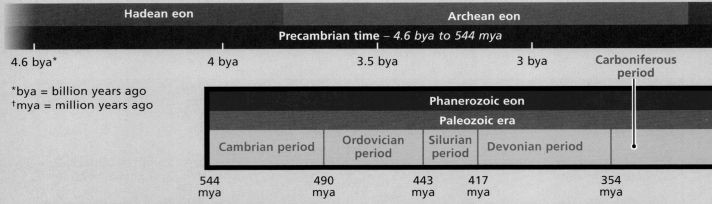

Hadean eon | Archean eon

Precambrian time – 4.6 bya to 544 mya

4.6 bya*   4 bya   3.5 bya   3 bya   Carboniferous period

*bya = billion years ago
†mya = million years ago

Phanerozoic eon
Paleozoic era

| Cambrian period | Ordovician period | Silurian period | Devonian period | |

544 mya   490 mya   443 mya   417 mya   354 mya

Precambrian Time at 3.6 Billion Years Ago

For nearly 4 billion years, during most of Precambrian time, no plants or animals existed.

Paleozoic Era at 544 Million Years Ago

At the beginning of the Paleozoic era, all life lived in the oceans.

The fossil record for Precambrian time consists mostly of tiny organisms that cannot be seen without a microscope. Other early forms of life had soft bodies that rarely formed into fossils.

The Phanerozoic eon stretches from the end of Precambrian time to the present. Because so many more changes are recorded in the fossil record of this eon, it is further divided into smaller units of time called eras, periods, epochs, and ages.

The Phanerozoic eon is divided into three eras: the Paleozoic, the Mesozoic, and the Cenozoic. Each era is subdivided into a number of periods. The periods of the Cenozoic, the most recent era, are further divided into epochs, which are in turn further divided into ages. The smaller time divisions relate to how long certain conditions and life forms on Earth lasted and how quickly they changed or became extinct.

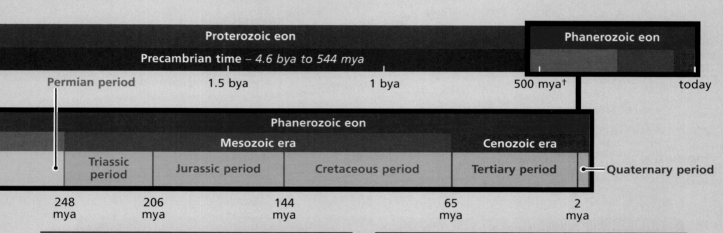

Proterozoic eon	Phanerozoic eon
Precambrian time – 4.6 bya to 544 mya	

Permian period   1.5 bya   1 bya   500 mya†   today

Phanerozoic eon					
Mesozoic era				Cenozoic era	
Triassic period	Jurassic period	Cretaceous period		Tertiary period	Quaternary period

248 mya   206 mya   144 mya   65 mya   2 mya

Mesozoic Era at 195 to 65 Million Years Ago

During the Mesozoic era, dinosaurs lived along with the first mammals, birds, and flowering plants.

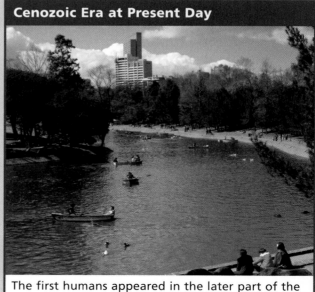

Cenozoic Era at Present Day

The first humans appeared in the later part of the Cenozoic era, which continues today.

Half-Life

Over time, a radioactive element breaks down at a constant rate into another form.

The rate of change of a radioactive element is measured in half-lives. A half-life is the length of time it takes for half of the atoms in a sample of a radioactive element to change from an unstable form into another form. Different elements have different half-lives, ranging from fractions of a second to billions of years.

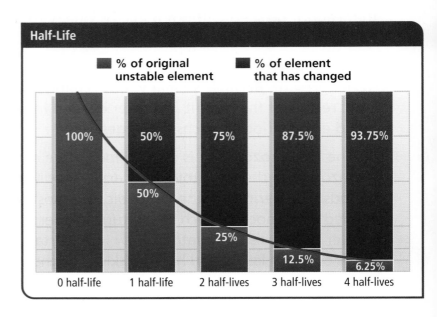

Half-Life

■ % of original unstable element   ■ % of element that has changed

0 half-life	1 half-life	2 half-lives	3 half-lives	4 half-lives
100%	50% / 50%	75% / 25%	87.5% / 12.5%	93.75% / 6.25%

Radiometric Dating

Radiometric dating works best with igneous rocks. Sedimentary rocks are formed from material that came from other rocks. For this reason, any measurements would show when the original rocks were formed, not when the sedimentary rock itself formed.

Elements with half-lives of millions to billions of years are used to date rocks.

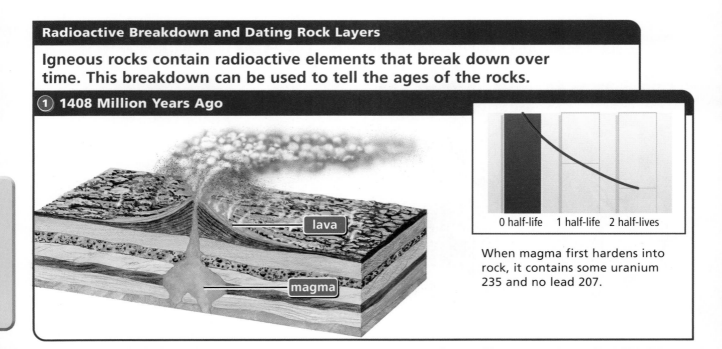

Radioactive Breakdown and Dating Rock Layers

Igneous rocks contain radioactive elements that break down over time. This breakdown can be used to tell the ages of the rocks.

① 1408 Million Years Ago

lava

magma

0 half-life   1 half-life   2 half-lives

When magma first hardens into rock, it contains some uranium 235 and no lead 207.

APPENDIX

Uranium 235, an unstable element found in some igneous rocks, has a half-life of 704 million years. Over time, uranium 235 breaks down into lead 207.

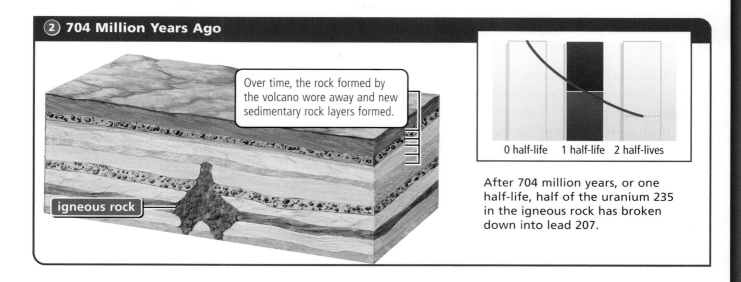

② 704 Million Years Ago

Over time, the rock formed by the volcano wore away and new sedimentary rock layers formed.

igneous rock

0 half-life   1 half-life   2 half-lives

After 704 million years, or one half-life, half of the uranium 235 in the igneous rock has broken down into lead 207.

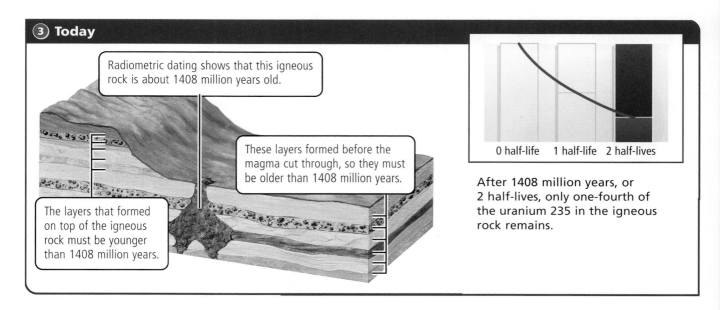

③ Today

Radiometric dating shows that this igneous rock is about 1408 million years old.

These layers formed before the magma cut through, so they must be older than 1408 million years.

The layers that formed on top of the igneous rock must be younger than 1408 million years.

0 half-life   1 half-life   2 half-lives

After 1408 million years, or 2 half-lives, only one-fourth of the uranium 235 in the igneous rock remains.

Just as uranium 235 can be used to date igneous rocks, carbon 14 can be used to find the ages of the remains of some things that were once alive. Carbon 14 is an unstable form of carbon, an element found in all living things. Carbon 14 has a half-life of 5730 years. It is useful for dating objects between about 100 and 70,000 years old, such as the wood from an ancient tool or the remains of an animal from the Ice Age.

Fossils in Rocks

If an organism is covered by or buried in sediment, it may become a fossil as the sediments become rock. Many rock fossils are actual body parts, such as bones or teeth, that were buried in sediment and then replaced by minerals and turned to stone. Fossils in rock include molds and casts, petrified wood, carbon films, and trace fossils.

① **Molds and Casts** Some fossils that form in sedimentary rock are mold fossils. A mold is a visible shape that was left after an animal or plant was buried in sediment and then decayed away. In some cases, a hollow mold later becomes filled with minerals, producing a cast fossil. The cast fossil is a solid model in the shape of the organism. If you think of the mold as a shoeprint, the cast would be what would result if sand filled the print and hardened into stone.

Fossils in Rocks

Rock fossils show shapes and traces of past life.

① Molds and Casts

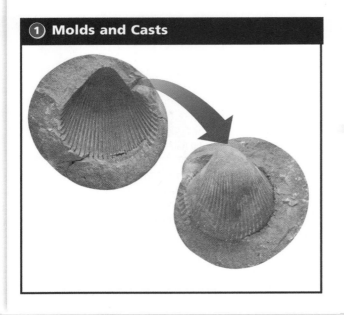

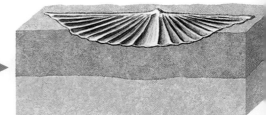

An organism dies and falls into soft sediment.

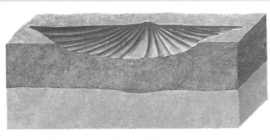

Over time, the sediment becomes rock and the organism decays, leaving a mold.

Minerals fill the mold and make a cast of the organism.

2 Petrified Wood The stone fossil of a tree is called petrified wood. In certain conditions, a fallen tree can become covered with sediments. Over time, water passes through the sediments and into the tree's cells. Minerals that are carried in the water take the place of the cells, producing a stone likeness of the tree.

In this close-up, you can see the minerals that replaced the wood, forming petrified wood.

3 Carbon Films Carbon is an element that is found in every living thing. Sometimes when a dead plant or animal decays, its carbon is left behind as a visible layer. This image is called a carbon film. Carbon films can show details of soft parts of animals and plants that are rarely seen in other fossils.

This carbon film of a moth is about 10 million years old. Carbon films are especially useful because they can show details of the soft parts of organisms.

4 Trace Fossils Do you want to know how fast a dinosaur could run? Trace fossils might be able to tell you. These are not parts of an animal or impressions of it, but rather evidence of an animal's presence in a given location. Trace fossils include preserved footprints, trails, animal holes, and even feces. By comparing these clues with what is known about modern animals, scientists can learn how prehistoric animals may have lived, what they ate, and how they behaved.

A trace fossil, such as this footprint of a dinosaur in rock, can provide important information about where an animal lived and how it walked and ran.

Diversity of Living Things

Six Kingdoms of Life

Scientists arrange the variety of living things, also called **organisms,** into groups. Organisms with similar features are grouped together.

CHARACTERISTICS OF LIVING THINGS

Living things appear to differ in many ways, but they all share certain characteristics. Living things

- are organized into cells
- grow and develop
- reproduce
- respond to their environment

Living things need energy, materials, and living space if they are to grow and develop. They reproduce, or make more of their own kind, by copying the genetic material in their cells and passing it on to their offspring. Finally, living things must be able to respond to changes in their surroundings if they are to survive.

VIRUSES

Most scientists consider viruses to be nonliving. Viruses are not made of cells and cannot grow or develop. Although viruses contain genetic material and can reproduce, they cannot do so outside of living cells.

CELL TYPE

There are two basic types of cells. In **prokaryotic** cells, genetic material is found free in the cytoplasm. Cells with genetic material enclosed in a nucleus are called **eukaryotic** cells.

All living things are classified into three large groups, called domains. These are: Archaea, Bacteria, and Eukarya. Organisms in the domains Archaea and Bacteria have prokaryotic cells. They are separated into two different domains because their cell chemistry is different. Organisms classified in the domain Eukarya have eukaryotic cells. Domains are further divided into kingdoms, kingdoms into phyla, and phyla into even smaller groups.

Kingdom Archaea

Domain Archaea includes one kingdom, which is also called Archaea. **Archaea** are prokaryotes, or single-celled organisms that do not have nuclei. Instead, the cell's genetic material floats in the cytoplasm. Archaea can survive in a large range of environments. Some of these environments are very extreme. They may be very hot, very cold, or contain so much of a substance such as salt that other organisms would be poisoned. Scientists once thought that archaea could live only in extreme environments. Recently, however, many marine archaea have been found living in the oceans among other organisms in more moderate conditions. Archaea are often grouped according to where they live.

Methanogens This group of archaea is named for the methane, or natural gas, that the organisms produce. Methanogens are simple organisms that get energy by converting carbon dioxide and hydrogen gases to methane. Methanogens die if they are exposed to oxygen. They can live only in oxygen-free habitats, such as in the mud of swamps and marshes and in the guts of cows and termites. Cows depend on the archaea that live in their stomachs to break down the tough cell walls of the grass that the cows eat.

Halophiles Halophiles live in very salty lakes and ponds, such as the Dead Sea, the Great Salt Lake, and Mono Lake. Some halophiles die if their watery habitat is not salty enough. When a salty pond dries up, the halophiles living there also dry up. They survive the drying and begin to divide and grow when water returns to the pond.

Thermophiles Thermophiles are archaea that live in extreme heat. They have been found in the hot, acidic sulfur springs and geysers of Yellowstone National Park and near hot vents deep under the ocean. Scientists believe that modern thermophiles are similar to some of the first organisms that appeared on Earth 3.8 billion years ago. Modern thermophiles live in habitats that resemble Earth's early environment of boiling springs and toxic gases.

Kingdom Bacteria

Domain Bacteria includes one kingdom, which is also called Bacteria. Like Archaea, **Bacteria** are prokaryotes, or single-celled organisms that do not have nuclei. Bacteria live almost everywhere on Earth, including inside the human body. Bacteria share many characteristics with archaea, although these two groups differ chemically. Like archaea, bacteria contain a loop of DNA that floats freely in their cytoplasm. Most are protected by a cell wall that lies outside the cell membrane. Both archaea and bacteria reproduce by binary fission, a process similar to mitosis and cytokinesis. In binary fission, one cell divides into two cells after its DNA has been duplicated.

TYPES OF BACTERIA

Bacteria can be grouped in three different groups according to their shape.

- Round-shaped bacteria may occur singly or in pairs, chains, or grape-like clusters.
- Rod-shaped bacteria may occur singly or in chains.
- Spiral-shaped bacteria occur in single strands.

Bacteria get energy in different ways. Some bacteria, called cyanobacteria, contain chlorophyll and trap energy from sunlight. These bacteria are **producers.** Producers are a major food source for organisms that cannot make their own food. They also provide much of the oxygen that animals breathe.

Many bacteria are decomposers. **Decomposers** get energy by breaking down materials in dead or decaying organisms. When once-living materials are broken down, the nutrients they contain can be used by other organisms. Decomposers also break down waste materials from other organisms. Cities use these bacteria to break down sewage so it can be released safely into the environment. Without decomposers, Earth's surface would be covered with dead matter and wastes.

RELATIONSHIPS WITH OTHER ORGANISMS

Bacteria may live either inside or on the surface of other organisms, called hosts. Some bacteria help their host organisms or host cells. For example, certain bacteria live inside the roots of some plants. These bacteria convert the nitrogen gas in air to nitrogen compounds that the plants use to make proteins.

Other bacteria, called **pathogens,** harm their hosts by causing diseases. For example, strep throat, tuberculosis, and cholera are all diseases of humans that are caused by bacteria. Bacteria also cause diseases in other animals and in plants. Bacteria cause disease in three ways. They can invade parts of the body, multiplying in tissues and dissolving cells. They can poison the body with chemicals they produce or with chemicals that are part of the bacteria themselves. Many bacterial diseases can be prevented with vaccinations or fought with antibiotics.

Bacteria

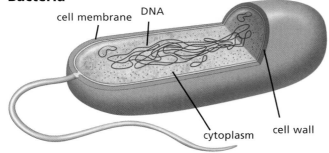

cell membrane   DNA

cytoplasm   cell wall

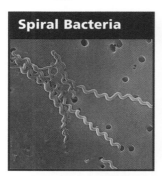

Spiral Bacteria

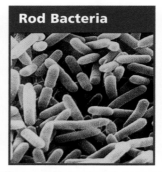

Rod Bacteria

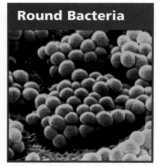

Round Bacteria

Kingdom Protista

Domain Eukarya consists of eukaryotes. These are organisms made of a single or many cells; their cells have a nucleus. The kingdom protista is the first of four kingdoms of eukaryotes.

THE FIRST EUKARYOTES

Scientists hypothesize that about two billion years ago, some small prokaryotic cells began to live inside larger prokaryotic host cells. Some of the small cells contained chlorophyll and could make their own food. Over time, these small cells lost the ability to live alone and became chloroplasts. Other small cells that needed to take in food for energy also became dependent on their host cells. These evolved into mitochondria. Chloroplasts and mitochondria still have the same kind of DNA as in the cells from which they arose. A nucleus may have evolved when part of a cell membrane folded into a cell and enclosed the cell's DNA.

DIVERSITY OF PROTISTS

Most protists are tiny, single-celled organisms. Larger multicellular protists, such as seaweeds, have simple structures. Protists get energy in three ways.

Algae Plantlike protists that contain chlorophyll are called algae. They get energy from sunlight during photosynthesis, as plants do. In photosynthesis, carbon dioxide and water are taken in, and oxygen is released. Many algae exist as **plankton,** organisms that drift on ocean and lake surfaces. Algae produce much of the oxygen that animals breathe.

Algae are very diverse, but all have a nucleus and chloroplasts and live in moist environments.

- *Euglena,* in phylum Euglenophyta, is a tiny, single-celled alga that moves with a long flagellum.

Euglena

magnified 2800 ×

- *Volvox,* in phylum Chlorophyta, is a colonial protist. Volvox cells live closely together, forming a ball of single-celled organisms that work together.
- Large seaweeds, such as kelp, belong to the phylum Phaeophyta.

Protozoa Protozoa are single-celled, animal-like protists that get energy by eating other organisms. Because they cannot use sunlight for energy, protozoa must move around to find food. Protozoa can be grouped according to how they move.

- *Paramecium,* in phylum Ciliophora, swims rapidly using thousands of short, hairlike cilia.

Paramecium

40 ×

- Protozoa, classified in phylum Sarcomastigophora, move with one or two long, whiplike flagella.
- Amoebas, grouped in phylum Rhizopoda, move by extending part of their flexible cells outward and oozing along surfaces.
- Some protists, in phylum Apicomplexa, mostly lack structures for moving around. They are parasites.

Decomposers The decomposers are fungus-like protists that get energy from dead or decaying material in their environments. These protists look like molds—which are members of the kingdom fungi—but the protists have simpler structures.

- Water molds, in phylum Oomycota, form fuzzy growth on live or decaying plants and animals.
- Slime molds live on decaying plants on the forest floor.
- Cellular slime molds, grouped in phylum Acrasiomycota, are single-celled organisms that eat bacteria and move by oozing. When food is scarce, the cells come together to form a multicellular colony.
- Plasmodial slime molds, in phylum Myxomycota, form a single giant cell that oozes across rotting logs and other surfaces.

Kingdom Fungi

Many fungi are decomposers. They decompose large molecules in dead plants and animals and in animal wastes. Fungi get energy by absorbing nutrients from materials they decompose.

Some fungi live together with single-celled algae in a network called a **lichen.** The fungus holds the alga in place and provides structure for the lichen. The algae provide sugar and other nutrients the fungus needs. Lichens can survive in areas where neither the fungus nor the algae could live as individuals.

FUNGI

Fungi are simple organisms. A cell of a fungus has one or more nuclei. A thick cell wall provides support. All fungi, except for yeasts, are multicellular. However, fungi do not have tissues and organs like plants and animals. Most fungi are made up of a network of threadlike structures called **hyphae.** A mass of hyphae forms a **mycelium.**

NUTRITION

Hyphae are only one cell thick, so the cells in the mycelium are close to whatever the fungus is living on. The cells release chemicals that digest the materials around them. Then the cells absorb and get energy from the nutrients that form. The parts of the cell walls that connect the cells have holes in them, so nutrients can flow from cell to cell.

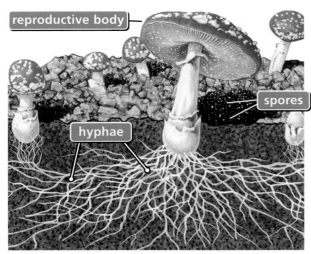

Fungi

REPRODUCTION

Fungi reproduce by using spores. A **spore** is a single reproductive cell that can grow into a new organism. Spores can be produced either sexually or asexually. They are released into the air and spread by wind. Fungi can also reproduce asexually if hyphae break off and form a new mycelium. Yeasts reproduce asexually by pinching off a small bud from the parent cell.

Fungi are grouped according to their sexual reproductive structures.

Phylum Zygomycota The fuzzy material that sometimes grows on food consists of the hyphae and spore-producing structures of the fungi commonly called molds. Mold hyphae grow into the food source, such as bread, and digest it.

Phylum Ascomycota This group contains yeasts, morels and truffles, and fungi that cause plant diseases such as Dutch elm disease. Yeasts are single-celled fungi that grow in moist environments. If they grow too rapidly, they can cause disease. Yeasts break down sugars to form alcohol and carbon dioxide. This process makes them useful in making bread, beer, and wine.

Phylum Basidiomycota This phylum contains most of the species that form mushrooms. Mushrooms are spore-forming structures that have a cap and a stalk. Spores are produced in the cap; the stalk holds up the cap. Hyphae fill both the cap and the stalk. A single mycelium can produce many mushrooms, which are all part of the same organism.

Other Fungi Scientists are still learning how to classify fungi. For some species, no sexual structure has yet been identified. Many fungi are important to humans. They produce penicillin, cheeses, and soy sauce. Others cause skin diseases, such as athlete's foot.

Kingdom Plantae

The kingdom Plantae is made up of multicellular, eukaryotic organisms that produce sugars using the Sun's energy. Their cells have thick cell walls made of cellulose. Tough cell walls support a plant so it can grow very large. Plants grow throughout their lifetimes. Their life cycles have two parts.

PLANT STRUCTURES

Plants have structures that work together to supply the materials needed for the plant's functions. Leaves and stems make up the shoot system of a plant. The leaves take in carbon dioxide from the air and release oxygen. Stems transport materials and hold the leaves up toward the Sun. The root system takes in water and nutrients from the soil and anchors the plant.

TRANSPORT

In most plants, water, nutrients, and sugars move from one part of the plant to another through a **vascular system.** This vascular system consists of long, hollow, tubelike cells arranged in bundles. Xylem is vascular tissue that carries water and dissolved nutrients up from the roots. Phloem tissue transports sugars down from the leaves.

Vascular System

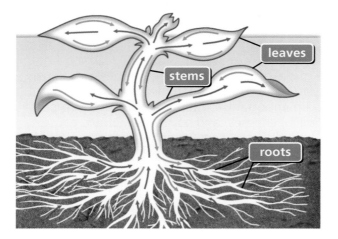

PHOTOSYNTHESIS

Plants are **autotrophs.** They do not need food from other organisms. Plants capture energy from sunlight and convert it to chemical energy through the process of **photosynthesis.** In photosynthesis, carbon dioxide and water are combined to form energy-rich sugars and oxygen. The sugars are used for energy and as materials for growth.

Leaves are specialized for photosynthesis. This process takes place in chloroplasts, cell organelles that contain chlorophyll. Chlorophyll absorbs the energy in sunlight. Most chloroplasts are found in cells in the upper surface of leaves, the part of the leaf that is turned toward the Sun. Vascular tissue in the leaf brings water and nutrients to the cells and carries away sugars.

GAS EXCHANGE

The lower surface of leaves contains thousands of tiny openings, called stomata. When the stomata are open, carbon dioxide from the air enters the leaf and oxygen exits. This process is called gas exchange. Stomata also allow water to evaporate. The movement of water vapor out of a plant is called transpiration. Plants must regulate the opening and closing of their stomata so that the leaves get carbon dioxide for photosynthesis, but do not lose too much water vapor. They do this by closing the stomata in hot, dry weather and opening them at night, when it is cool.

APPENDIX

SEEDLESS NONVASCULAR PLANTS

The first living things probably lived in watery environments such as warm shallow seas. Fossil evidence suggests that plants were among the first organisms to appear on land.

Mosses, liverworts, and hornworts are members of phyla Bryophyta, Hepaticophyta, and Anthocerotophyta. All are small, simple plants that lack vascular tissue and reproduce with spores rather than seeds. They probably arose from an alga-like ancestor that lived in water. Although members of these phyla live on land, they must live in moist environments because they need water to reproduce. Spores are produced in a spore capsule at the tip of a stalk. This is the first part of the plant's life cycle. When the spores are released, they grow into small leafy plants. The plants produce sperm and egg in the second part of the life cycle. The sperm swim through water to fertilize the egg, which then grows into the stalk and spore capsule. The cycle is repeated.

Because these plants have no vascular tissue, water and nutrients must move through the plant body from cell to cell. This is possible because their simple root-, stem-, and leaf-like structures are only one or two cells thick. Some mosses, such as the peat moss that is used in gardening, can absorb large amounts of water.

Liverwort

SEEDLESS VASCULAR PLANTS

Ferns, whisk ferns, horsetails, and club mosses are plants that have vascular tissue and reproduce with spores rather than seeds. Having a vascular system allows a plant to grow large because water and nutrients move quickly through the plant. Vascular tissue also supports a larger plant.

Ferns (Phylum Pterophyta) Ferns have true leaves, called fronds. Clusters of spores form on the underside of the fronds. When a spore is released and begins to grow in a moist location, it forms a tiny structure that produces sperm and eggs. This is the first part of the life cycle. The sperm swim through water to the egg and fertilize it. A plant with roots, stems, and fronds grows from the tiny structure. This is the second part of the life cycle. Ferns range in size from very small to the size of a large tree.

Whisk Ferns (Phylum Psilophyta) Whisk ferns have many features in common with ferns, but they are simpler than ferns. A typical whisk fern has a branched stem, but no roots or leaves.

Horsetails (Phylum Sphenophyta) Horsetails, also called scouring rushes, consist of a hollow stem with whorls of leaves at intervals on the stem. The stem is filled with a glass-like substance that made the plant useful to early Americans for cleaning pots.

Club Mosses (Lycophyta) Club mosses look like large mosses, but they contain vascular tissue.

spores

Fern

spore cluster

SEED PLANT ADAPTATIONS

In all plants, fertilization produces an **embryo,** the immature form of an organism that has the potential to grow and develop. A **seed** consists of an embryo and its food supply wrapped in a protective coating. The ability to form seeds was an important adaptation in plants. Seeds protect the embryo from drying out and allow it to survive until conditions are favorable for growth. The embryo can remain inside the seed for a long time without growing. When temperature and moisture are favorable, the seed will germinate. **Germination** is the beginning of growth of a new plant from a spore or seed. A spore is a single cell; a seed is a multicellular structure.

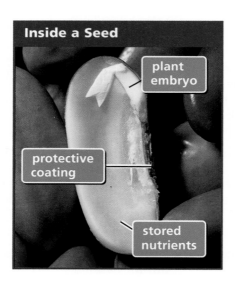

Inside a Seed

- plant embryo
- protective coating
- stored nutrients

Seedless plants need water for a sperm to swim to an egg; plants with seeds do not. Instead, seed plants produce pollen. A **pollen** grain is a small dry structure that holds a sperm cell. Its hard covering prevents the sperm from drying out. The process of pollination ends when a pollen grain attaches to the part of the plant that contains the egg and releases the sperm.

NONFLOWERING SEED PLANTS

A pine tree is a typical nonflowering seed plant. The reproductive structures of pines are called cones. Sperm and egg cells are produced in cones. This is the first part of the pine life cycle.

In male cones, sperm cells form in pollen grains, which are released into the air. Female cones produce egg cells in compartments within the scales of the cone. When a pollen grain lands on a female cone, a pollen tube grows to the egg. The sperm passes through this tube and fertilizes the egg. The fertilized egg then develops into an embryo enclosed in a seed. Eventually, the cone opens, and the seeds are released. They are carried long distances by the wind. When they land on soil, they may germinate to form a new pine tree. The seed and the tree that grows from the seed represent the second part of the life cycle.

GYMNOSPERMS

Plants that produce seeds that are not enclosed in fruit are called **gymnosperms.** There are four phyla of gymnosperms.

Conifers (Phylum Coniferophyta) Conifers, such as pine, spruce, fir, and redwood trees, produce seeds in cones. Many conifers are adapted for living in cold, dry climates by having leaves that are shaped like needles. A thick waxy covering makes the needles waterproof and prevents water loss through transpiration. Most conifers keep their needles all year long.

Seed cones

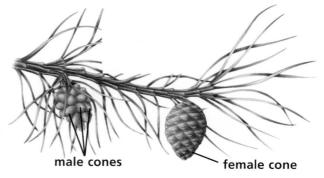

male cones   female cone

Cycads (Phylum Cycadophyta) Cycads are palmlike plants that are found in tropical regions. They produce seeds in cones.

Ginkgoes (Phylum Ginkgophyta) These plants shed leaves in winter. They form fleshy seeds that hang from branches rather than within cones.

Gnetophytes (Phylum Gnetophyta) Many of these woody plants grow in the tropics. They produce seeds in cones.

FLOWERING SEED PLANTS

Angiosperms are seed plants that produce flowers and fruit. Most plants now living are angiosperms. They are classified in phylum Anthophyta.

Angiosperms and gymnosperms are similar in many ways. Both live their entire life cycle within a single plant. Both have separate male and female reproductive parts. Sperm are protected in a pollen grain and do not need an outside source of water to reach the eggs. The eggs develop into embryos that are enclosed within seeds.

While gymnosperm sperm and eggs are produced in cones, the sperm and eggs of angiosperms are contained in flowers. A **flower** is the reproductive structure of an angiosperm.

- The male part of the flower is the stamen. It consists of an anther and a stalk called a filament. The anther produces sperm cells, which are enclosed within pollen grains.
- The female flower part is the pistil. The top of the pistil, the stigma, is where the pollen grains land. At the base of the pistil is the ovary, where eggs develop. Each egg cell lies inside a structure called an ovule. This will later form the seed's covering.
- Sepals are leafy flower parts that enclose the flower before it opens. After it opens, the sepals form the base of the flower.
- Petals are colorful structures arranged around the pistil. Petals help to attract animals that pollinate the flower.

In many species, the male and female structures are on the same flower. In other species, there are separate male and female plants.

Pollen grains are released by the anther and carried to the pistil of the same flower or a different flower by insects, animals, or wind. Once a pollen grain attaches to a stigma, a pollen tube starts to grow toward the egg. Sperm travels through the tube to reach the egg cell. After an egg is fertilized and a seed forms, the ovule wall thickens to form the seed coat. The ovary itself becomes a fruit surrounding the seed. A **fruit** is a ripened ovary. It may fall to the ground or be eaten by an animal. If the seed within lands in a place where it can germinate, it will grow into a new plant.

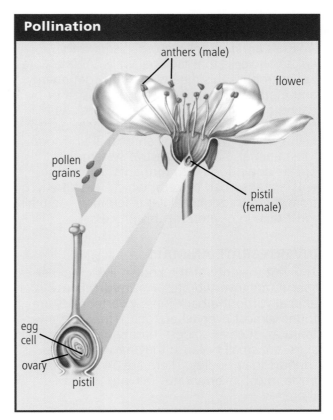

Pollination

anthers (male)

flower

pollen grains

pistil (female)

egg cell

ovary

pistil

Some fruits, such as cherries and peaches, have one seed. Others, such as apples and oranges, have more than one seed. These fleshy fruits are juicy. Most nuts are dry fruits. They have a shell to protect the seed.

ASEXUAL REPRODUCTION

Many plants can also reproduce by asexual methods. For example, strawberries send out shoots called runners that form new plants. Moss and other plants may break off a small piece that grows into a new plant. Asexual reproduction allows plants to spread when conditions are not right for germination of seeds.

Animals spread both seeds and pollen. Plants are a food source for many animals. Animals eat fruit, and they deposit the seeds on the ground along with their own wastes. Bees and other insects transfer pollen from one flower to another when they collect the sweet nectar that they eat. An animal that pollinates a flower is called a pollinator.

Kingdom Animalia

Animals are multicellular organisms with eukaryotic cells that lack cell walls. Animals are heterotrophs. This means that they get energy and materials by eating other organisms or by eating food made by other organisms. All animals can move, although some appear not to. Being able to move helps an animal find food. Most animals have a digestive system that breaks down food into nutrients. These nutrients are absorbed by cells, which release energy from them through cellular respiration. Animals must take in oxygen for this process.

INVERTEBRATE ANIMALS

The vast majority of the known living animal species are invertebrates. An **invertebrate** is an animal without a backbone. Invertebrates are found almost everywhere on Earth. Most invertebrates, such as spiders, earthworms, and sea stars, are small because they have no bones to support their bodies. There are 14 invertebrate phyla; most invertebrates fall into eight of them.

SPONGES (PHYLUM PORIFERA)

The simplest invertebrates are **sponges.** Adult sponges are **sessile,** which means they do not move from place to place. They live in water, usually fastened to the ocean or lake floor.

Specialized Cells Sponges have no tissues or organs, but several kinds of specialized cells perform all of its life functions. A typical sponge is unsymmetrical. This means that one side of its body doesn't match the other side. The sponge has a tubelike body that may be branched. Its body wall has many holes, or pores. The inside of the wall is lined with specialized cells that have flagella. Beating flagella cause water to flow into the sponge through the pores. Cells remove oxygen from the water and filter out and digest tiny plankton. The filtered water then passes out of the sponge through a hole at the top.

Most sponges have stiff, hard spines called spicules within their walls. Spicules help to support the sponge and give it its shape.

Reproduction Sponges can reproduce asexually by breaking into pieces. Each piece grows into a new animal. Sponges also reproduce sexually. Sperm are released into the water. When water enters a sponge through its pores, sperm are carried to the eggs. A fertilized egg becomes a **larva,** an immature form. Sponge larvae can swim. They swim away from the parent, attach to the ocean floor, and develop into new sponges.

Sponge

CNIDARIANS (PHYLUM CNIDARIA)

Jellyfish, corals, sea anemones, and hydras are **cnidarians.** They live in water and trap small plankton, fish, and clams for food. Cnidarians that are sessile for most of their lives have special adaptations for capturing food. Fingerlike body extensions, called **tentacles,** surround a mouth-like opening. Specialized stinging cells on the tentacles contain nematocysts, capsules that hold a coiled, barbed filament. When prey organisms touch a stinging cell, the harpoon-like filament is triggered. It stabs the prey and releases a substance that paralyzes them. The tentacles then stuff the prey into the cnidarian's mouth. Cnidarians have a radial body plan. This means that a cnidarian's body is arranged around a central point. This allows it to find food in all directions.

Body Tissues Cnidarian bodies are arranged into layers of tissue, but not into organs. Digestion takes place in a central cavity, and wastes leave the body through the mouth. Nerve and muscle cells allow the animal to sense and respond to its environment. Muscles allow the animal to bend and to move its tentacles, even during the part of the life cycle when the animal is sessile.

Reproduction Cnidarians reproduce much like sponges do. Water carries sperm to eggs. The fertilized eggs develop into free-swimming larvae, which become adults. Jellyfish have a two-part life cycle. When a jellyfish larva settles on the ocean floor, it grows into a sessile form called a polyp. The polyp produces a stack of disc-shaped buds. When the buds are released, they are called medusas. A medusa is an adult jellyfish. It is **motile,** meaning it can move from place to place.

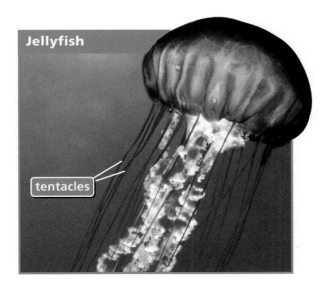

Jellyfish
tentacles

FLATWORMS (PHYLUM PLATYHELMINTHES)

Flatworms have flat, ribbonlike bodies with bilateral symmetry. This is a body plan in which the body is divided into two mirror-image halves. Animals with bilateral symmetry have a head at the front end. Flatworms take in oxygen, dissolved in water, through their skin. This is why they must live in moist environments, such as water or moist soil. Some flatworms are so small that they move with cilia rather than with muscles. Most flatworms, such as tapeworms, are parasites that feed off host organisms. Such parasites do not need a digestive system because they absorb digested nutrients directly from their hosts. Flatworms that are not parasitic, such as planaria, have a simple digestive system with one opening. Wastes leave the body through the mouth.

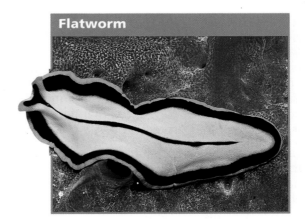

Flatworm

ROUNDWORMS (PHYLUM NEMATODA)

Nematodes, called roundworms, are found in almost all moist environments. Their cylinder-shaped bodies are more complex than flatworm bodies. They have strong muscles, a nervous system, and a digestive system. Food is sucked into the mouth and is processed as it moves through the organs of the digestive system. Wastes exit at the other end. Having a digestive system with two openings allows the worm to feed, digest food, and eliminate wastes at the same time. Some roundworms are parasites. For example, *Trichinella* is a roundworm that lives in pigs. If humans eat undercooked pork, they may get the disease trichinosis.

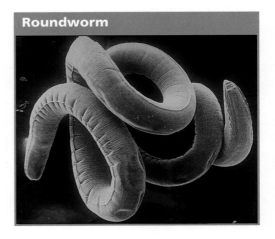

Roundworm

MOLLUSKS (PHYLUM MOLLUSCA)

Mollusks are soft-bodied animals. Most live in water, while others live on land. Most mollusks have complex organ systems. Male and female reproductive structures are usually in separate organisms. Two structural features identify a mollusk: a muscular foot and a mantle, a layer of folded skin that protects the internal organs.

Gastropods Snails and slugs are land gastropods. They breathe with **lungs,** organs that absorb oxygen from the air. Conches and whelks are gastropods that live in water. They breathe with **gills,** organs that filter oxygen out of water. Most gastropods have a shell. The animal can hide in its shell for protection. A gastropod's head is attached to its foot. The head has two tentacles with eyes at the ends. The mouth contains a radula, a structure that shreds food. Most gastropods eat plants or algae.

Bivalves Clams, oysters, mussels, and scallops are bivalves. They have two hard shells that are hinged together. When the shells close, the body is completely hidden. All bivalves live in water or buried in sand near water. Bivalves have no head, but they do have a mouth and sensory organs. The foot is adapted in different species for creeping, digging, or burrowing in sand. Bivalves are filter feeders. They filter food from the surrounding water. Oxygen is removed as the water passes over a pair of gills. Blood picks up the oxygen from the gills and carries it throughout the body.

Cephalopods Octopuses, squids, and nautiluses live in the ocean. They have well-developed bodies, large brains, and eyes. Gills take in oxygen, which circulates through the body in the blood. The foot, which surrounds the mouth, is divided into tentacles that are adapted for catching prey. The mantle is adapted for taking in water and pushing it out the rear of the body. This produces a jet of water that shoots the animal forward. Octopuses and squid have no shells, but nautiluses do.

SEGMENTED WORMS (PHYLUM ANNELIDA)

Segmented worms include earthworms and leeches. Their bodies are divided into segments, allowing different segments to have different organs and functions.

Digestion Earthworms eat decayed matter in soil. They suck soil into the mouth. As soil moves through the digestive organs, nutrients are removed. Wastes leave the body at the other end. A circulatory system with blood and several hearts sends nutrients to all parts of the worm.

Gas Exchange Oxygen enters the worm through its moist skin. Blood carries it to the cells. Carbon dioxide leaves the body in the reverse direction.

Movement Earthworms have several layers of muscles for movement. Hairlike bristles on the worm's underside anchor it in the soil as it moves.

Reproduction Each earthworm has both male and female parts. Two worms exchange sperm, which fertilize the eggs in their bodies. The eggs are laid and hatch into larvae.

Clam

foot

Segmented Worm

APPENDIX

ARTHROPODS (PHYLUM ARTHROPODA)

Arthropods are invertebrates with a segmented body, jointed appendages, and an exoskeleton. An **exoskeleton** is a hard outer covering made of chitin. Flexible joints allow the animal to move. An exoskeleton does not grow and must be shed as the body grows, a process called **molting.** An arthropod body usually has three sections: a head, thorax, and abdomen. Legs and other appendages are jointed. Arthropods have well-developed body systems and senses. Blood flows through the body between organs rather than through blood vessels.

Molting Cicada

Insects Grasshoppers, butterflies, beetles, and bees are examples of insects. **Insects** are arthropods with three body sections, two antennae, and six legs attached to the thorax. Many insects fly, using one or two pairs of wings. They have keen sensory organs, such as large compound eyes and antennae. Oxygen enters the body through openings in the exoskeleton called spiracles. Many species have mouthparts that are adapted for eating specific foods. During their life cycle, insects undergo a process called **metamorphosis** in which their appearance and body systems change. Complete metamorphosis has three stages: larva, pupa, and adult. Some insects, such as grasshoppers, have a simple metamorphosis in which they grow and molt several times before becoming adults.

Crustaceans Crabs, lobsters, and shrimp are crustaceans. Most live in water, although pill bugs live on land. Crustaceans have three or more pairs of legs and two pairs of antennae. Many have gills. Some crustaceans are an important food source for other ocean animals such as fish and whales.

Arachnids Spiders, mites, ticks, and scorpions are arachnids. All arachnids have eight legs, only two body sections, and no antennae. Some get oxygen through spiracles, but many spiders have leaf-like plates called book lungs. Some spiders trap prey by spinning silk into netlike webs. Others wrap their prey in silk. Still others poison their prey.

Millipedes and Centipedes Both centipedes and millipedes have long, segmented bodies and many legs. Millipedes have two pairs of legs on each segment. They move slowly and eat decaying plants. Centipedes have one pair of legs per segment. They move quickly and eat insects.

ECHINODERMS (PHYLUM ECHINODERMATA)

Sea stars, sea urchins, sea cucumbers, and sand dollars are **echinoderms.** They live in the ocean and feed off the ocean floor as they move. Some species filter tiny organisms from water. Others are predators that eat mollusks. Echinoderms have radial symmetry with a central mouth. There is no head or brain. A simple, spiny skeleton under the skin is composed of non-bony, hard plates. Sharp spines may stick out of the animal.

Echinoderms are identified by a water vascular system. Five water-filled tubes radiate out from the center of the body. At the base of the tubes are many tube feet that stick out through the skin. Water enters the system through a plate on the animal's surface and moves into the tube feet. When muscles in the tube feet contract and relax, suction is produced and released. Suction from tube feet is used for movement and feeding.

sea urchin

VERTEBRATE ANIMALS

Phylum Chordata contains the **vertebrates,** animals that have backbones. A backbone is part of an **endoskeleton,** an internal support system that grows with the animal. An animal with an endoskeleton can move easily because its muscles work with its skeleton. Vertebrates have heads and well-developed body systems. Fish, amphibians, reptiles, birds, and mammals are subgroups of phylum Chordata.

FISH

Fish make up the largest group of vertebrates. When a fish swims, it takes in water through its mouth and pushes the water over its gills. Gills remove oxygen from water and exchange it for carbon dioxide in the fish's blood. The water is forced out of the fish's body through openings called gill slits. Fins help a fish move by pushing its streamlined body through the water. Most fish have eyes that are adapted for seeing under water.

Most fish reproduce sexually. Males produce sperm, and females produce eggs. Both are released into the water, where the eggs are fertilized. Fish eggs are surrounded by a soft egg case that water and dissolved oxygen can pass through. The egg contains a food source, called a yolk, for the developing fish.

Jawless Fish

Fish can be classified into three groups depending on their body features.

Jawless Fish Lampreys and hagfish are jawless fish. They have simple tube-shaped bodies and a digestive system with no stomach. Although they have teeth, they cannot chew because they have no jaw bones. Most jawless fish attach onto another animal's body and suck out flesh and fluids.

Cartilaginous Fish Sharks and rays are cartilaginous fish. Their skeletons are made of flexible cartilage rather than hard bone. Many sharks feed on mollusks and crustaceans, but others are filter feeders. Rays are flat-bodied fish that live most of their lives on the ocean floor. Their mouths are on the underside of their bodies; they eat by pulling small animals out of the sand.

Cartilaginous Fish

Bony Fish Most fish living today are bony fish. Tuna, goldfish, trout, and eels are examples. They have skeletons made of hard bone. Bony fish have many adaptations for living in water. An organ called a swim bladder allows a fish to control the depth at which it floats. The lateral line, a sensory organ, allows a fish to sense vibrations of objects that are nearby. Most bony fish are covered with overlapping bony structures called **scales.** Bony fish have jaws, teeth, and several pairs of fins. They have a wide range of body shapes, colors, and behaviors that adapt them for life in varied watery environments such as in coral reefs or among seaweeds.

AMPHIBIANS

Amphibians—frogs, toads, and salamanders—were the first vertebrates to live on land. They have four legs, obtain oxygen mainly through their smooth moist skin, and have sensory organs adapted for sensing on land. Most amphibians live in damp places so they can get oxygen from water. They also must lay their eggs in water. Many live underground or under wet leaves. Others are active at night when the ground is wet with dew.

Reproduction Most amphibians reproduce in water the way fish do, but their life cycle is different from that of fish. Amphibian eggs laid in water hatch into larvae called tadpoles, which look and behave like fish. They breathe with gills, eat algae, and swim using their tail. As it grows, the tadpole's body begins to change to adapt to life on land. Lungs and legs develop, and the tail shrinks. The animal begins to breathe through its skin and with lungs as the gills stop functioning. It moves onto land and eats insects. The tadpole is now an adult frog.

wood frog

REPTILES

Turtles, snakes, lizards, and crocodiles are **reptiles.** Whereas amphibians need water for part of their life cycles, reptiles are true land animals. Reptiles have four legs and are protected by tough dry skin covered with scales. Sensory organs are adapted for sensing on land, and lungs take in oxygen from air.

Reproduction Reptiles reproduce only on land. Reproduction is sexual, and fertilization takes place within the female's body. A shell then forms around each fertilized egg. The reptile egg is an important adaptation for life on land. It contains the embryo, sources of water and nutrients, a system for gas exchange, and a place to store wastes. Membranes separate the different parts of the egg, which is covered by a tough leathery shell that prevents the egg from drying out. The female lays the eggs on land, in a nest or buried in the ground. When young reptiles hatch from the eggs, they look like small adults.

Body Temperature Amphibians and reptiles are **ectotherms,** animals whose body temperature changes with environmental conditions. For example, a snake's body temperature is lower on a cold day than on a hot day. Ectotherms usually move and respond more slowly when cold. Their life processes slow down. When very cold, they are not likely to reproduce and they may die. Ectotherms keep their bodies from getting too hot or too cold through their behavior. Turtles and snakes warm themselves in cold weather by basking in the sun. Others curl up to prevent heat loss. In hot weather, many ectotherms find shade to avoid overheating. Others cool off by spending time in water. Some desert reptiles, such as lizards, burrow into sand during the hot day and are more active at night when air temperatures are cooler.

lizard

BIRDS

Birds are closely related to reptiles, but several adaptations allow birds to fly and to live in many habitats. Birds have feathers, a beak, two scaly legs and two wings, and eggs with hard shells. The shape of a bird's beak is adapted for the kind of food it eats.

Body Temperature Birds are **endotherms,** animals that can maintain a constant body temperature. This adaptation allows birds to live in places where amphibians and reptiles cannot survive. Birds can stay active in cold weather by eating large amounts of food. Food is the source of the energy that produces body heat. Birds have soft feathers, called down, that keep warm air close to their bodies. They also shiver when they are cold. This muscle movement generates heat.

Birds have adaptations for keeping cool in hot weather. Like some reptiles, they rest in the shade during the hottest part of the day. They also fluff out their feathers to release body heat.

Reproduction The reproductive process of birds is similar to that of reptiles, except that the shells of bird eggs are hard and rigid rather than flexible. Many birds have distinctive ways of attracting mates. The female usually chooses a mate, rather than vice versa. Females lay their eggs in a nest. They use their body heat to keep the eggs warm, a process called **incubation.** When the eggs hatch, the parent birds must provide food, warmth, and protection until the young can fly and find food.

Both parents feed the 3- to 8-day old tanagers.

Flight Most birds can fly. Flight allows a bird to find food in large areas or in areas that other animals cannot reach. Flight also allows birds to escape danger on the ground and to migrate. **Migration** is the movement of animals to a different region in response to seasonal changes in the environment. A bird may migrate to a warmer climate if its food source is no longer available in its summer home when the weather gets cold. For example, hummingbirds that feed on flower nectar will no longer have food when flowering plants die back in winter, so they fly south in winter.

Many adaptations made birds capable of flight.

- Some of the bones in a bird's skeleton are fused together. This makes the skeleton light and strong, but less flexible.
- Feathers form a strong surface for pushing against air. Contour feathers make the bird water-resistant. Flight feathers along the wing help in gliding and lifting.
- The respiratory system of birds is specialized for taking in large amounts of oxygen. This oxygen is needed to produce energy for flying.
- Many of a bird's bones are hollow with internal braces, which make the bones strong, but lightweight.

hollow bone

- Birds have highly developed senses of sight and hearing, which are important in flight.

APPENDIX

MAMMALS

Mammals are a diverse group of animals that have hair during some part of their lives and teeth that are specialized for a particular kind of food. Mammals produce milk that they feed to their young. Some mammals, such as whales, live in water. Squirrels, dogs, and humans live on land, and bats can fly.

Body Temperature Mammals, like birds, are endotherms. They can stay active in cold weather because they use some of the food they consume to generate body heat. They also have adaptations for controlling their body temperature.

Mammal bodies are covered with hair. Soft, fluffy underhairs keep an animal's body warm in cold weather in the same way that down feathers keep birds warm. Guard hairs, like contour feathers in birds, keep an animal dry. Some mammals have specialized hairs as well. For example, a cat's whiskers are sensitive to touch, and a porcupine's quills function in self-defense.

Porcupine

quills

Mammals that live in water have a layer of fat, called blubber, which keeps them warm. The fat cells in blubber also store energy that the animal can use when it hibernates or when food is not available. Ground squirrels are mammals that hibernate during cold winters when there is no food.

Reproduction A mammal must find a mate when it is ready to reproduce. Many mammals have certain behaviors that attract mates. Fertilization takes place within the female's body. In most mammals, an organ called a **placenta** grows in the female. It transports nutrients, water, disease-fighting substances, and oxygen from the mother's blood to the developing embryo. It also removes wastes from the embryo to the mother's blood.

Gestation is the length of time a mammal develops inside its mother. Gestation varies among mammal species, from about three weeks in mice to more than 80 weeks in elephants. When the young are born, the mother feeds them milk. This energy-rich liquid food is produced in the female's mammary glands. Males have mammary glands, too, but they do not function. The young of different mammal species are born at varying stages of development, so they require different amounts of care until they can survive on their own. For example, giraffes can walk almost as soon as they are born. Newborn mice are helpless and blind and must be cared for by their parents. The young of marsupials—kangaroos and opossums—are born when tiny and undeveloped. They crawl into a pouch on the outside of the mother's body to finish developing. Humans probably care for their young for the longest time among all mammals.

Dog feeding puppies with milk.

Human Systems

The Body's Organization

The human body has five levels of organization: cell, tissue, organ, organ system, and organism.

CELLS AND TISSUES

The basic level of organization in the body is the cell. All organisms are made of cells. Some organisms, such as bacteria, consist of only one cell. The single cell must perform all the functions the organism needs to survive. Plants and animals have many cells. Each kind of cell in these organisms is specialized to perform a specific job.

A **tissue** is a group of cells that work together to perform a particular function. Tissues are grouped according to their function.

- Epithelial tissue—functions as coverings or boundaries of the inner and outer surfaces of the body. Example: a layer of skin
- Nerve tissue—carries electrical impulses to and from the brain in response to changing conditions. Example: spinal cord
- Muscle tissue—contracts and relaxes to cause movement of different body parts. Example: biceps
- Connective tissue—holds body parts together to provide support, strength, insulation, and protection. Example: fat

ORGANS AND ORGAN SYSTEMS

An **organ** is a structure that carries out a particular function in the body. Each organ is made up of two or more kinds of tissues that work together. For example, the stomach contains muscle, connective, and epithelial tissue layers.

A group of organs make up an **organ system.** The organs in an organ system work together to perform a life process, such as digestion, which helps an organism survive. The digestive system includes the stomach, small intestine, and large intestine, for example.

ORGANISMS

Organ systems interact to keep internal conditions constant in the whole organism. The ability of the body to maintain internal conditions is called **homeostasis.** For example, cells break down sugar during cellular respiration to release energy. The amount of sugar in the blood must be kept constant so cells have a ready supply. After you eat, sugar passes from your digestive system into the blood in your circulatory system. The level of sugar in the blood increases. This signals the pancreas, part of the endocrine system, to release the hormone insulin. Insulin causes cells in the liver and muscles to store excess sugar, and blood levels of sugar fall to normal. Another hormone signals the cells to release the stored sugar when blood levels decrease, such as when you skip a meal.

The Skeletal System

The **skeletal system** is made of bone, cartilage, tendons, and ligaments—all connective tissues. It provides support, protects internal organs, and serves as an anchor for body movement.

The **axial skeleton** consists of the skull, spinal column, and ribs. It protects the brain, the spinal cord, and soft internal organs such as the heart and lungs. The remaining bones make up the **appendicular skeleton,** which supports the body and allows movement.

BONE TISSUE

A bone is made of living tissues including,

- **compact bone,** a dense, hard, outer layer that forms a bony web containing calcium.
- **spongy bone,** the strong, lightweight inner part of a bone that is filled with spaces.
- **marrow,** the inner part of a bone that produces blood cells. Marrow fills the spaces in spongy bone.
- **blood vessels,** which run through the bone. Blood carries nutrients to bone cells and carries away wastes.

JOINTS

Bones meet at joints and are held together by ligaments. There are three MAIN types of joints.

Immovable Joints Immovable joints lock together like puzzle pieces. Example: joints of the cranium

Slightly Movable Joints Slightly movable joints bend a little. Example: ribs attached to sternum

Freely Movable Joints These joints allow the body to bend and move. Movable joints are classified by the movement they produce.

Kind of Joint	Movement	Example
Hinge	Back-and-forth	Knee
Pivot	Bones rotate around each other	Elbow
Ball-and-socket	Rotational	Hip, shoulder
Gliding	Bones slide past each other	Bones in wrist

DEVELOPMENT

Because bones are living tissue, they change as the body develops and ages.

Infancy The bones of a newborn's skull have spaces between them. As the brain grows, the skull grows. The spaces between the bones close.

Childhood Bone growth occurs at areas called growth plates. Growth plates are made of cartilage, a flexible connective tissue. The long bones of the arms and legs grow at their ends surrounding the growth plates.

Adolescence At the end of adolescence, bones stop growing and become hard. The growth plates are the last part to harden. New growth cannot take place after growth plates harden.

Adulthood Although bones no longer grow in adulthood, old bone breaks down and new bone forms. As people age, more bone breaks down than is formed. This leads to a decrease in bone density. Less-dense bones can break easily. Bone loss can be prevented or slowed by exercise and supplements such as calcium.

The Muscular System

Every movement in your body is caused by muscles. Muscles also help keep your body temperature constant and maintain your posture. The muscles that move bones make up the muscular system.

MOVEMENT

The **muscular system** works with the skeletal system to allow body movement. Each end of a muscle is attached to a bone by a tendon. Tendons are made of connective tissue. Muscles are made of muscle cells called fibers, which contract and relax. When a muscle contracts, it shortens. The shortened muscle exerts a force on the tendon by pulling it. The tendon then pulls on the bone, and the bone moves. Muscles can pull, but they cannot push. For the bone to move in the opposite direction, another muscle must contract. Thus, muscles usually work in pairs. When one muscle in a pair contracts, the other one relaxes.

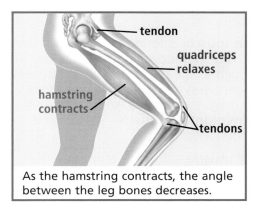

As the hamstring contracts, the angle between the leg bones decreases.

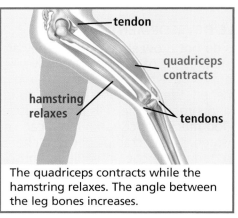

The quadriceps contracts while the hamstring relaxes. The angle between the leg bones increases.

MAINTAINING BODY TEMPERATURE AND POSTURE

Muscles help to regulate body temperature. When your body is cold, you shiver. Shivering is caused by rapid muscle contractions. Muscles release heat when they contract. The heat warms your body. Shivering is a way to maintain homeostasis.

Most muscles in the body are always slightly contracted. This slight contraction is called muscle tone. Muscle tone causes you to stand up straight

TYPES OF MUSCLE TISSUE

There are three types of muscle. Each type has a different function.

Skeletal muscle is attached to bones. It causes movements that you control, such as running or doing push-ups. Because these movements are voluntary, skeletal muscles are sometimes called voluntary muscles. Skeletal muscles that allow slow movements are called slow-twitch muscles. Muscles that allow quick movement are fast-twitch muscles.

Smooth muscle is found inside your internal organs. It causes movements that are automatic, such as the passage of food through your digestive system. Because you cannot control these movements, smooth muscle is called **involuntary muscle.** Smooth muscle contracts slowly.

Cardiac muscle is found only in the heart. The muscle cells are connected together like a web, which allows the heart to beat. Cardiac muscle is involuntary and contracts slowly.

MUSCLE DEVELOPMENT

Muscles do not grow strong unless they are used. The muscles of a newborn are weak because they have not yet developed and strengthened. Exercise causes muscles to get bigger and stronger. The cells in the muscle get bigger. Too much exercise, however, can cause muscle soreness and cramps because chemicals build up during exercise. In addition, muscle fibers can be torn and overstretched by hard exercise. This kind of damage takes time to heal.

The Respiratory System

The main function of the **respiratory system** is to take in oxygen from the air and remove carbon dioxide and other waste products from the body.

GAS EXCHANGE

Oxygen is needed for the chemical reactions that release energy in your cells. Without oxygen, cells would die. Air is about 20 percent oxygen and less than 1 percent carbon dioxide. When you inhale, you take air into your lungs. Some oxygen is removed from the air and transported to body cells by red blood cells. At the cells, oxygen is released, and carbon dioxide and other gas wastes are picked up. The blood carries the wastes to the lungs. The waste gases leave the body when you exhale. Therefore, exhaled air contains less oxygen and more carbon dioxide than inhaled air.

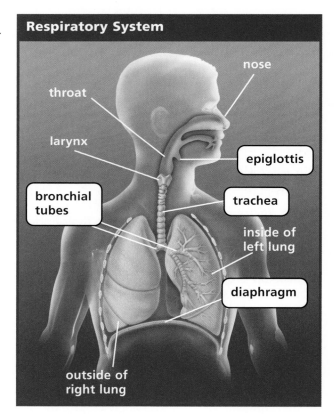

Respiratory System

nose

throat

larynx

epiglottis

bronchial tubes

trachea

inside of left lung

diaphragm

outside of right lung

APPENDIX

STRUCTURES IN THE RESPIRATORY SYSTEM

The structures of the respiratory system work together so you can breathe.

Nose, Throat, and Trachea When you inhale, air enters your body through the nose or mouth. Tiny hairs in the nose filter out dirt. Mucus traps particles such as pollen and dust. The air is warmed and moistened before it passes down your throat and through the windpipe, or trachea. A structure called the epiglottis prevents the food from entering the trachea.

Lungs The trachea divides to form two bronchial tubes. Each bronchial tube enters a lung and branches into smaller and smaller tubes. At the end of the smallest tubes in the lungs, the air passes into tiny air sacs called alveoli. Because the walls of the alveoli are only one cell thick, oxygen readily passes through them and diffuses into the blood. At the same time, carbon dioxide in the blood passes into the alveoli.

Diaphragm and Ribs A large muscle called the diaphragm stretches across the bottom of your chest, or thoracic cavity. When your diaphragm contracts, it pulls downward, making the thoracic cavity larger. Your ribs move outward to make room for the lungs to expand and fill with air. The decreased air pressure in your expanded lungs causes air to rush into your body. Inhalation is complete. When you exhale, the process reverses. The diaphragm relaxes and moves upward, making the thoracic cavity smaller. The lungs get smaller, and air is pushed out. Thus, breathing is caused by mechanical movements of the diaphragm. The nervous system regulates the rate at which you breathe, so oxygen and carbon dioxide in the blood remain constant. This is a way your body maintains homeostasis.

OTHER FUNCTIONS

In addition to providing oxygen and removing carbon dioxide, the respiratory system has other functions.

Speech The larynx, or voice box, is a small organ located at the top of the trachea. The larynx contains folds of tissue called vocal cords. When air from the lungs is forced over the vocal cords, they begin to vibrate. Sound waves are generated. Muscles in your throat, mouth, cheeks, and lips shape the sound waves into words.

Other Respiratory Movements Some movements of the respiratory system allow you to clear particles out of your nose and throat or to express emotions. Sighing and yawning both involve taking deep breaths. Laughing and crying also involve respiratory movements. A hiccup is a sudden inhalation. As air rushes into your throat, your diaphragm contracts. The air passageway between the vocal cords closes, producing the sound of a hiccup. Hiccups are caused by eating too fast, sudden temperature changes, and stress.

Water Removal The air you exhale contains water vapor as well as carbon dioxide. Water vapor is a waste product of cellular respiration. When you hiccup, cough, yawn, speak, or breathe, water vapor is released into the environment.

The Digestive System

The digestive system provides energy and materials. Your body needs energy to fuel its functions. It also needs raw materials to build new body parts. Energy and raw materials come from nutrients in food. **Nutrients** are substances that enable the body to grow, move, and maintain homeostasis. Carbohydrates, proteins, fats, and water are nutrients that your body needs.

- Carbohydrates are the main source of energy for the body.
- Proteins are used by the body for growth and repair of cells and tissues.
- Fats store energy for future use.
- Water makes up two-thirds of the body. Almost all processes take place in water.

Before your body can use these nutrients, they must be broken down into smaller substances. **Digestion** is the process of breaking down food into smaller substances that your body can use.

DIGESTION

The **digestive system** breaks down food. Food moves through the organs of the digestive system by wavelike contractions of smooth muscles. These muscular movements are called **peristalsis.** As the food is pushed along, it is moistened by mucus that is produced throughout the system. Food is digested in two ways: physically and chemically. **Mechanical digestion** is the physical processing of food. You chew food with your teeth to break it into smaller pieces. Your stomach also grinds up food mechanically with its muscular contractions. **Chemical digestion** changes the food into different substances. For example, saliva changes starches to sugars in the mouth. Acids in the stomach change proteins to smaller substances so they can be digested further.

ORGANS IN THE DIGESTIVE SYSTEM

Food travels through the mouth, esophagus, stomach, small intestine, and large intestine as it is processed. The liver, gall bladder, and pancreas also take part in digestion, although food does not pass through these organs.

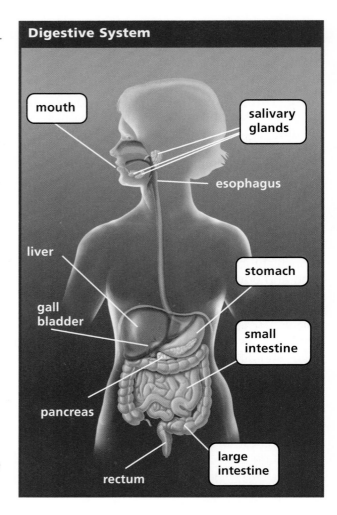

Digestive System

mouth · salivary glands · esophagus · liver · stomach · gall bladder · small intestine · pancreas · large intestine · rectum

Mouth Both mechanical and chemical digestion take place in the mouth. Your lips and tongue move the food so the teeth can grind it up. Salivary glands produce saliva that changes starches to sugars. The tongue pushes the food down into your throat when you swallow.

Esophagus The muscles in your esophagus contract and relax, pushing the partially digested food through the esophagus to the stomach.

Stomach Powerful muscles in your stomach physically mash up the food particles. Strong acids chemically break down proteins in the food. The inside of the stomach is coated with mucus, which prevents the acids from damaging the lining of the stomach.

APPENDIX

Small Intestine Most chemical digestion takes place here. Chemicals released by the pancreas, liver, and gall bladder mix with chemicals made in the small intestine to complete the breakdown of food. Nutrients that are formed are absorbed by folded structures, called villi, that line the walls of the small intestine. The nutrients pass into the blood and are transported throughout the body. Recall that blood is part of the circulatory system.

Large Intestine No more digestion takes place in the large intestine. Water is removed from the remaining material, which is mostly waste. The solid waste exits the body through the rectum.

OTHER ORGANS

The liver, gall bladder, and pancreas also are part of the digestive system. They produce chemicals that are necessary for digestion.

Liver Your liver produces bile, a liquid that physically breaks down particles of fat. The liver also breaks down medicines in the body, produces chemicals that help blood to clot if you cut yourself, filters and cleans the blood, and stores unneeded nutrients for later use.

Gall Bladder The gall bladder is a sac that concentrates and stores the bile produced by the liver. Bile flows from the gall bladder into the small intestine, where it breaks down fats.

Pancreas When food leaves the stomach, it is very acidic. The pancreas produces chemicals that decrease the acidity. Other chemicals made in the pancreas break down proteins, fats, and carbohydrates. Without the pancreas, your body could not absorb, process, and use the food to release energy.

The Circulatory System

The **circulatory system** works with the digestive and respiratory systems to carry oxygen and nutrients to body cells and remove wastes. Oxygen-poor blood comes from the body cells and enters the right atrium. From there, it flows to the right ventricle. The right ventricle pumps the blood out of the heart and sends it to the lungs. In the lungs, the blood absorbs oxygen and releases carbon dioxide. The oxygen-rich blood returns to the heart, where it enters the left atrium. It flows to the left ventricle and is pumped to the rest of the body.

BLOOD

Oxygen, nutrients, and wastes are carried in the blood. **Blood** is a tissue that is made up of

- **plasma,** a fluid that contains proteins, glucose, other nutrients, hormones, and gases dissolved in water.
- **red blood cells,** cells that pick up oxygen in the lungs and deliver it to body cells.
- **white blood cells,** cells that help your body fight infection by attacking disease-causing organisms.
- **platelets,** large cell fragments that help form blood clots when a blood vessel is injured. Platelets stick to the injured area and release chemicals that result in a clot.

THE HEART

The heart is an organ that acts like a pump. It pushes blood through a network of blood vessels to all parts of the body. The right side of the heart pumps carbon dioxide-rich blood to the lungs, where the carbon dioxide is dropped off and oxygen is picked up. The left side of the heart pumps oxygen-rich blood to the rest of the body.

Each side of the heart is divided into two chambers. The upper chamber—the atrium—receives blood. The lower chamber—the ventricle—pumps the blood out of the heart. Blood moves from an atrium to a ventricle. A valve prevents blood from flowing backwards.

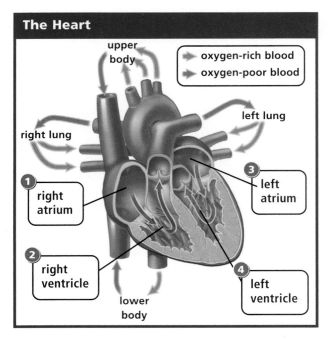

The Heart

oxygen-rich blood
oxygen-poor blood

upper body

left lung

right lung

1 right atrium

3 left atrium

2 right ventricle

4 left ventricle

lower body

BLOOD VESSELS

Blood moves through a system of tubes called blood vessels. Arteries and veins branch off to form very narrow capillaries.

- **Arteries** carry blood away from the heart. They have strong, thick, elastic walls that withstand the pressure produced when the heart beats.
- **Veins** carry blood back to the heart. Vein walls are thinner than artery walls. Valves in the veins prevent blood from flowing backwards.
- **Capillaries** connect arteries to veins. Oxygen and nutrients pass from blood in the arteries to body cells through the thin walls of capillaries. Carbon dioxide and other wastes pass through capillary walls from body cells into the blood in veins.

Most arteries carry oxygen-rich blood, and most veins carry oxygen-poor blood. However, the pulmonary blood vessels are exceptions. The two pulmonary arteries carry oxygen-poor blood to the lungs. The two pulmonary veins carry oxygen-rich blood from the lungs to the heart.

Blood exerts pressure on blood vessels. The force produced when the heart beats travels through the blood, putting pressure on the blood vessels. This force is called blood pressure. Healthy blood pressure must be maintained for the circulatory system to function properly. If blood pressure is too low, some cells will not get materials they need. If blood pressure is too high, the heart must pump harder to push blood through the blood vessels. Blood pressure is expressed with two numbers. The first number is the pressure in the arteries when the heart contracts. The second number is the pressure in the arteries when the heart relaxes between beats.

BLOOD TYPES

Red blood cells have substances on their surfaces called antigens. Two of these antigens, called A and B, determine blood type.

- type A—blood cells have the A antigen
- type B—blood cells have the B antigen
- type AB—blood cells have both A and B antigens
- type O—blood cells have neither antigen

Blood Transfusions Blood type is important when a person receives a blood transfusion. If the donated blood is not compatible with the receiver's blood, his or her immune system will identify the donated blood as foreign and attack it. Donated blood of the same type or certain other types is compatible; it is not destroyed by the immune system.

Blood Type Compatibility The table shows which blood types are compatible. Because type O blood lacks the A and B antigens, the immune system of someone with A, B, or AB blood will not attack donated O blood cells. However, a person with type O blood cannot receive any blood except type O because his or her immune system would attack A or B antigens.

Blood Type Compatibility		
Blood Type	**Can Donate Blood To**	**Can Receive Blood From**
A	A, AB	A, O
B	B, AB	B, O
AB	AB	A, B, AB, O
O	A, B, AB, O	O

The Urinary System

Many life processes produce waste materials. Digestion produces solid waste, which is removed from the body through the rectum. Cellular respiration produces carbon dioxide and water vapor wastes that leave the body through the lungs. The skin releases wastes in the form of sweat. **The urinary system** removes liquid waste products from the blood.

STRUCTURES OF THE URINARY SYSTEM

The structures of the urinary system work together to remove wastes from the body.

Kidneys Two kidneys are the major organs of the urinary system. Blood travels through the kidneys, where it is filtered. Chemical wastes are removed, and needed materials are returned to the blood.

Ureters, Bladder, and Urethra After the wastes are filtered out of the blood, they pass through two tubes called ureters. The ureters bring the wastes to the bladder, a muscular storage sac. When the muscles of the bladder contract, the liquid wastes—called **urine**—pass out of the body through a tube called the urethra.

HOW THE KIDNEYS FILTER BLOOD

The kidneys filter all the blood in your body many times a day. Inside each kidney are about one million nephrons. Each nephron has a cuplike part called a glomerulus and a twisted tube part. The tubes are surrounded by blood vessels. Wastes, nutrients, and salts are filtered out of the blood in the glomerulus. These substances, which are dissolved in liquid, then pass into the nephron's tube system. As the filtered liquid passes through the tubes, nutrients, water, and salts are absorbed back into the blood vessels surrounding the tube. The filtered blood returns to the circulatory system. The liquid wastes pass into a collecting duct. The wastes are now called urine. The urine passes from the kidney to the ureters, and then into the bladder. When the bladder is full, it contracts and removes the wastes from the body.

WATER BALANCE

The kidneys regulate the amount of water in the body by adjusting the amount of water in urine. If your body has too much water in it, the kidneys produce more-watery urine. If there is too little water in the body, more water is absorbed back before the urine is made.

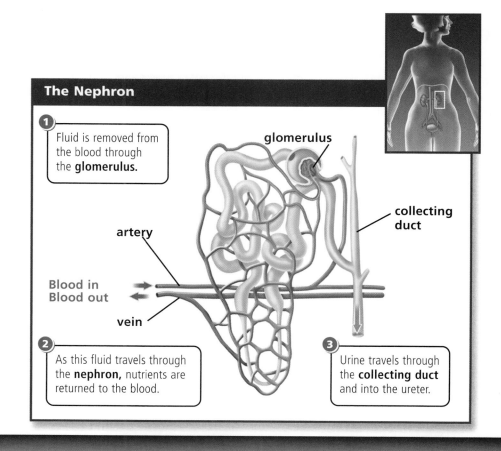

The Nephron

1. Fluid is removed from the blood through the **glomerulus.**

glomerulus

collecting duct

artery

Blood in
Blood out

vein

2. As this fluid travels through the **nephron,** nutrients are returned to the blood.

3. Urine travels through the **collecting duct** and into the ureter.

The Immune System

Disease-causing agents, called **pathogens,** harm your body. They enter through the skin, the air you breathe, and the foods and liquids you eat and drink. Three systems form the first line of defense against pathogens and other harmful materials.

Integumentary System Your skin forms a barrier between you and the outside world, but pathogens can enter the body if the skin is cut. The circulatory system contains blood cells that attack pathogens. Growth of pathogens on your eyes is slowed by substances in tears.

Respiratory System Sneezing and coughing expel pathogens from the body. Hairlike cilia and thick, slippery mucus in the nose and lungs also protect the body by trapping dirt and dust particles in the air.

Digestive System Pathogens that enter your digestive system are destroyed by saliva in your mouth, mucus that coats the digestive organs, enzymes from the liver and pancreas, and acids in the stomach.

If pathogens get past the first line of defense, the **immune system** responds by producing large numbers of white blood cells, specialized cells that destroy foreign organisms.

WHITE BLOOD CELLS

Tissues in the bone marrow, spleen, thymus gland, and lymph nodes produce white blood cells. Some white blood cells produce a non-specific response to injury or infection. Others may engulf the invader. Still other white blood cells produce proteins called **antibodies** that respond to specific invaders. White blood cells travel through the blood to injured or infected areas. They leave the blood vessels and move to the damaged areas, where the immune response takes place.

THE LYMPHATIC SYSTEM

White blood cells also travel through vessels in the lymphatic system. This system of tubes carries lymph rather than blood. Lymph is fluid that is left in tissues by the circulatory system. Lymph collects and moves in lymph vessels. As it moves, it passes through lymph nodes, organs that filter out pathogens and store white blood cells and antibodies. The lymph nodes become swollen during an infection because they are making so many white blood cells.

IMMUNE RESPONSE

The immune system responds to foreign materials in the body in two ways. The white blood cells that first respond to an injury or infection attack foreign materials in nonspecific ways. Other white blood cells produce antibodies that are specific to each kind of pathogen.

NONSPECIFIC RESPONSE

When tissue is damaged, it releases large amounts of histamine. Histamine causes inflammation—heat, redness, and swelling. It increases blood flow to the tissue, bringing more white blood cells and antibodies to the damaged area. When foreign material affects more than one area of the body, many tissues produce histamine. A series of responses causes the whole body's temperature to rise. Any temperature above the human average of 37°C (98.6°F) is called a fever. High fevers can damage tissues.

SPECIFIC RESPONSE

Antigens are chemical markers on a cell's surface that indicate whether the cell is from your body or is foreign material. When the body detects a foreign antigen, a specific immune response occurs. A specific immune response also provides protection if you are exposed in the future to the same antigen. Different types of white blood cells, including T cells and B cells, are part of a specific immune response.

Specific Immune Response

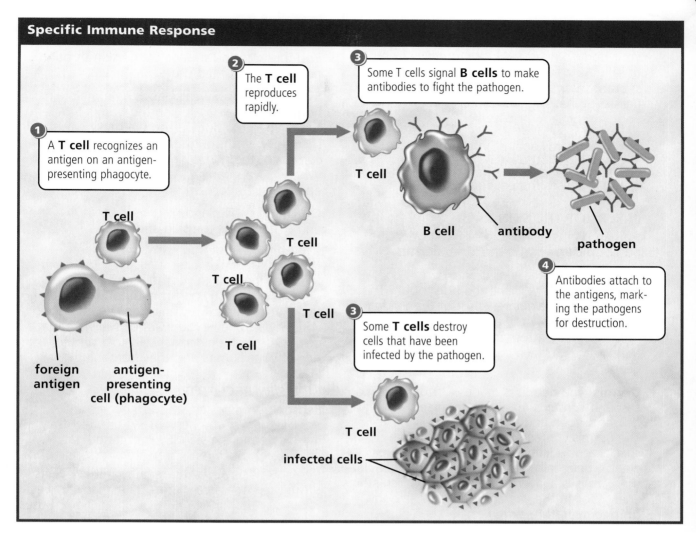

1 A **T cell** recognizes an antigen on an antigen-presenting phagocyte.

2 The **T cell** reproduces rapidly.

3 Some T cells signal **B cells** to make antibodies to fight the pathogen.

3 Some **T cells** destroy cells that have been infected by the pathogen.

4 Antibodies attach to the antigens, marking the pathogens for destruction.

T cell

foreign antigen

antigen-presenting cell (phagocyte)

B cell

antibody

pathogen

infected cells

Phagocytes and T Cells Phagocytes ingest and break down pathogens. Small pieces of the pathogen, containing foreign antigens, fuse with the phagocyte's cell membrane. T cells detect these foreign antigens and begin to divide rapidly, forming two kinds of T cells. One kind of T cell attacks and kills cells that have been infected by the pathogen.

B Cells The second kind of T cell signals B cells that recognize the same foreign antigen to produce antibodies against the pathogen. The antibodies attach to the foreign antigens, allowing other cells of the immune system to destroy the pathogen.

DEVELOPMENT OF IMMUNITY

Some B cells do not make antibodies, but remain in the body as an immune system memory. If the same kind of pathogen enters the body in the future, the immune system can respond immediately.

This resistance to a disease is called **immunity.** There are two kinds of immunity: passive and active.

- Passive immunity occurs when antibodies are transferred to your body.
- Active immunity occurs when your body makes its own antibodies.

Vaccines Another way to develop immunity is to receive a **vaccine.** Vaccines contain small amounts of weak or dead pathogens that stimulate an immune response but do not cause disease.

Disease Treatment Some treatments of disease attack pathogens directly. **Antibiotics** are medicines that block the growth and reproduction of bacteria. Other treatments reduce the symptoms while the immune system fights the pathogens.

The Integumentary System

Your body is wrapped in a protective layer of skin. Skin is part of the **integumentary system,** which also includes your hair and nails. Skin has four functions.

- Skin repels water.
- Skin guards against infection.
- Skin helps to maintain homeostasis.
- Skin senses the environment.

LAYERS OF THE SKIN

Human skin is composed of two layers: the outer **epidermis** and the inner **dermis.**

Epidermis The cells of the epidermis contain protein fibers that make the skin tough. These cells form in the deepest part of the epidermis. They move slowly toward the surface as new cells form beneath them and old cells rub off the surface. Surface cells in the epidermis are dead.

Dermis The dermis is made of strong, elastic tissue. It contains many blood vessels that deliver oxygen and nutrients to its living cells. The dermis contains structures that have specialized functions, such as sweat and oil glands, hair, nails, and sensory receptors. Below the dermis is a layer of fatty tissue, which stores energy for future use and protects the body from temperature extremes.

SWEAT AND OIL GLANDS

Sweat and oil glands are found in the dermis. Both open to the surface of the skin through tiny openings called pores.

Sweat Glands Sweat glands help maintain homeostasis by controlling the body's temperature. When the body is too warm, sweat glands secrete sweat through the pores and onto the surface of the skin. Sweat is 99 percent water. When it evaporates, heat is released. The skin and the body cool off.

Oil Glands Oil glands secrete oil that moistens and waterproofs the skin and hair.

HAIR AND NAILS

Many of the cells in your hair and nails are dead, but they still perform important functions. In cold weather, hair traps heat close to your body to keep you warmer. Nails are made of thick, tough epidermal cells that protect the tips of your fingers and toes from injury.

SENSORY RECEPTORS

Sensory receptors attached to nerves are actually part of the nervous system, but they are located in the skin. By detecting heat, cold, pain, touch, and pressure and sending messages to the brain, they help protect your body.

Skin Structure

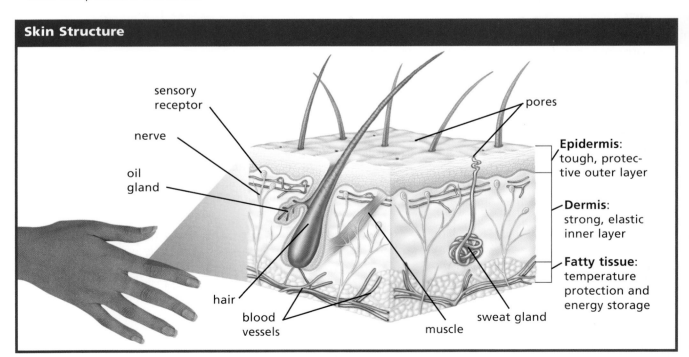

sensory receptor

nerve

oil gland

hair

blood vessels

muscle

pores

sweat gland

Epidermis: tough, protective outer layer

Dermis: strong, elastic inner layer

Fatty tissue: temperature protection and energy storage

GROWTH AND HEALING

Most of the growth of the skin occurs at the base of the epidermis, just above the dermis. New cells constantly replace older cells that die and are rubbed off the surface. If the skin is injured, it can usually repair itself. In first-degree burns, the skin becomes red, and the burn soon heals. In second-degree and third-degree burns, however, the body loses fluids, and death can result from fluid loss or infection. Too much exposure to sunlight also burns and blisters the skin. Specialized cells in the skin produce melanin, a pigment that absorbs the Sun's ultraviolet rays and helps prevent tissue damage. To take good care of your skin, you should keep your skin clean, eat a balanced diet, drink plenty of water, use sun block in summer, and protect your skin from cold in winter.

The Nervous System

To maintain homeostasis and to survive, the body must constantly monitor its environment. It does this through the sense organs, which see, hear, smell, touch, and taste. Receptors in the sense organs detect changes in the environment and send messages to the brain through the nerves. The brain interprets the messages and signals your muscles or other organs to respond to the changes. Any change in the environment that you react to is called a **stimulus.**

SIGHT

Light is a stimulus. You detect light because your eyes, the sense organs for sight, focus images and turn them into signals that are processed by the brain. Light rays enter the eye through the cornea, which bends and focuses them. The light then passes through the pupil. Muscles that vary the size of the pupil regulate the amount of light that enters the eye.

The light passes through the lens, where it is further bent and focused. At the back of the eye, the light rays strike the retina, where they form an inverted image. Receptors in the retina, called rods and cones, detect changes in brightness and color. Finally, a nerve sends the information to the brain, where the stimulus is processed and interpreted.

HEARING

Sound, like light, is a stimulus. Sound waves are produced by vibrations and can travel through air. Your ears, the sense organs for hearing, detect the sound waves that enter the ear. At the end of the auditory canal is a membrane called the eardrum. Sound waves pass the vibrations to the eardrum, which transmits them to tiny bones called the hammer, anvil, and stirrup. Pressure from the vibrations of the bones causes fluid in the cochlea of the inner ear to move. This movement causes receptors to send signals that the brain interprets as sound.

TOUCH

There are many sensory receptors in the skin. Nerves near the top of the dermis sense textures, such as rough and smooth. Nerves deeper in the dermis sense pressure. Other receptors in the dermis sense temperature changes, which protects you from being burned. Each receptor transmits signals to the brain to be interpreted.

SMELL AND TASTE

Receptors for smell and taste detect chemical information rather than physical information such as light and sound. Scent receptors found in hairlike fibers at the back of your nose sense chemicals in the air. The scent molecules enter your nose, stick to mucus coating the fibers, and bind to the receptors in the fibers. The receptors send a signal to your brain, and you recognize a scent. Taste receptors, called taste buds, are found on your tongue, throat, and the roof of your mouth. Each taste bud has a cluster of sensory cells that are specialized to detect sweet, sour, bitter, and salty tastes. Taste depends on sense organs in your nose, too. Thus, taste and smell are related.

CENTRAL NERVOUS SYSTEM

The **central nervous system** consists of the brain and the spinal cord. It communicates with the rest of the nervous system through electrical impulses sent through nerve cells, called **neurons.**

Brain The brain directly controls voluntary behavior such as walking and thinking. It also controls most involuntary responses such as heartbeat and breathing. Each area of the brain has a specific function, although some functions involve more than one area. Your skull protects your brain.

Spinal Cord The spinal cord, which connects the brain with the nerves throughout the body, is the main pathway for information. Nerve fibers form the cord's outside layer, and nerve cell bodies form the inner layer. Along the cord's length are 31 pairs of nerves. The spine protects and supports the spinal cord.

PERIPHERAL NERVOUS SYSTEM

The nerves found throughout your body are referred to as the **peripheral nervous system.** This nerve network contains both sensory and motor neurons. Sensory neurons receive information from the environment and pass it to the spinal cord, which sends it to the brain. Motor neurons receive signals from the brain and spinal cord and send them to the muscles and glands. The peripheral nervous system has two parts: the voluntary nervous system and the autonomic nervous system.

VOLUNTARY NERVOUS SYSTEM

The **voluntary nervous system** controls skeletal muscles that cause movements and functions such as walking and talking. These movements and functions are voluntary; you control them by thinking about them.

AUTONOMIC NERVOUS SYSTEM

The **autonomic nervous system** regulates the smooth and cardiac muscles that cause automatic responses such as breathing and digestion. These functions are involuntary; you cannot control them. The autonomic nervous system has two divisions. Both control the same internal organs, but they have opposite effects on them. One division works under normal conditions to control heartbeat, respiration, and balance in a way that conserves energy. The other division works when your body is under stress, causing a "fight or flight" response. Your heartbeat, respiration, and other functions speed up so your body can react to the danger.

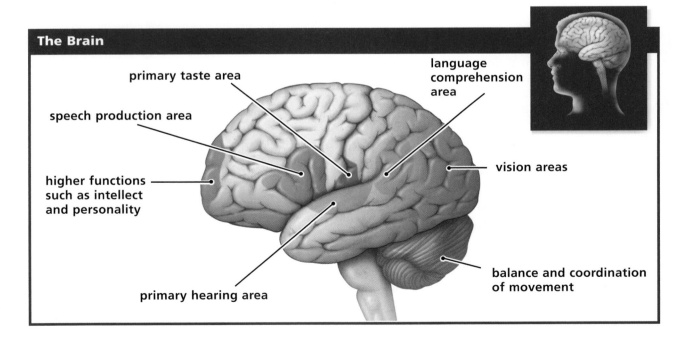

The Brain

primary taste area

speech production area

language comprehension area

higher functions such as intellect and personality

vision areas

primary hearing area

balance and coordination of movement

APPENDIX

The Endocrine System

The **endocrine system** controls the conditions in your body by making and releasing chemicals that are transported throughout the body. Most endocrine system responses are controlled by the autonomic nervous system. They work automatically without your conscious control.

HORMONES

Hormones are chemicals that are made in one organ, travel through the blood, and produce an effect in target cells that are often located in organs far from where the hormone was produced. This is why they are often called chemical messengers. Some hormones cause responses in only one organ; other hormones affect the entire body. In order to function, a hormone must first bind to a receptor on or inside a target cell. After it binds to the receptor, the hormone begins the chemical changes that cause the target cell to function in a specific way. The target cell may make another hormone, regulate the balance of chemicals such as glucose in the blood, or produce responses to changes in the environment.

GLANDS

The main structures of the endocrine system are groups of specialized cells called **glands.** Many glands produce hormones and release them into the circulatory system, which carries the hormones to the target cells.

FEEDBACK MECHANISMS

Hormones maintain homeostasis and regulate body conditions. Because hormones are powerful chemicals capable of producing dramatic changes, their levels in the body must be carefully regulated. The endocrine system has several control methods. Most glands are regulated by the pituitary gland, which in turn is controlled by the hypothalamus, part of the brain. The endocrine system helps to maintain homeostasis through the action of negative feedback mechanisms.

NEGATIVE FEEDBACK

Most feedback mechanisms in the body are called negative mechanisms because the final effect of the response is to turn off the response. That is, an increase in the amount of a hormone in the body feeds back to stop or decrease further production of that hormone. For example, the hormone thyroxine controls the rate of cellular respiration. When the body needs energy, the thyroid gland releases thyroxine into the blood to increase cellular respiration. The thyroid is controlled by the pituitary gland, which is controlled by the hypothalamus. Increased levels of thyroxine in the blood inhibit signals from the hypothalamus and pituitary to the thyroid, and thyroid activity slows.

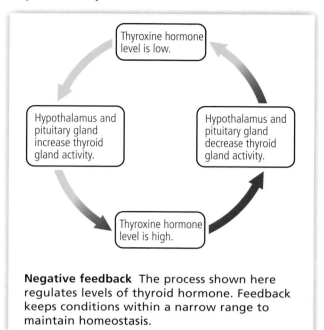

Negative feedback The process shown here regulates levels of thyroid hormone. Feedback keeps conditions within a narrow range to maintain homeostasis.

POSITIVE FEEDBACK

Positive feedback mechanisms do not maintain homeostasis. Rather, they produce a response that continues to increase. When you cut yourself, the damaged tissue releases a chemical that causes production of a clotting factor. This clotting factor signals the production of other chemical reactions that cause threadlike proteins called fibrin to form. Fibrin causes the blood to clot, filling the injured area.

BALANCED AND UNBALANCED HORMONE ACTION

In the body, the action of one hormone is often balanced by the action of another hormone. For example, one hormone may increase the level of glucose in the blood; the other hormone may decrease the glucose level. Because the levels of the two hormones are balanced, homeostasis is maintained. Hormones regulate critical functions in the body, so too little or too much of any hormone can cause serious disease.

The Reproductive System

The reproductive system allows adults to produce offspring. Males and females have different reproductive systems, but both have the same function—to make specialized cells that combine to produce a new individual. These cells contain half the genetic information that an organism needs to form, develop, and grow. Both male and female systems are under the control of hormones, which signal the growth of reproductive organs and the development of sexual characteristics, such as facial hair in males and breasts in women.

MALE REPRODUCTIVE SYSTEM

Males produce sperm cells inside long, coiled tubes inside two testes. Sperm cells have a head and a tail. The head contains the genetic material.

The tail allows the sperm to move. Sperm travel from the testes through several structures. As they travel, they mix with nutrient-rich fluids to form a fluid called **semen.** A drop of semen contains millions of sperm cells. Sperm production is controlled by a hormone released by the testes.

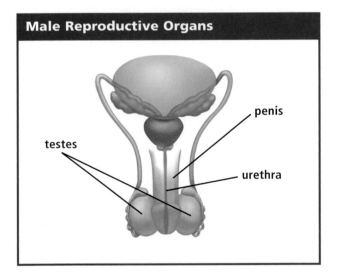

Male Reproductive Organs

penis

testes

urethra

FEMALE REPRODUCTIVE SYSTEM

The female reproductive system produces eggs in two ovaries. It also protects and nourishes the offspring until birth. Each ovary contains thousands of immature egg cells. About every 28 days, the pituitary gland releases a hormone that stimulates an egg to develop and grow. The ovaries then produce hormones that prepare the uterus to receive the egg.

Menstruation After an egg matures, it is released at a signal from another hormone. The egg moves from the ovary into a fallopian tube. If the egg is not fertilized by a sperm cell within 24 hours, both the egg and the lining of the uterus break down and leave the body through a canal called the vagina. This flow of blood and tissue, called **menstruation,** lasts about five days.

Fertilization An egg may be fertilized by a sperm as it passes through the fallopian tube. The fertilized egg moves into the uterus and attaches to its thick lining. Here, the fertilized egg will grow and develop into a fetus.

During sexual intercourse, millions of sperm cells leave the male's body through the urethra, a tube that runs through the penis. The sperm cells enter the female's body through the vagina, travel through the uterus, and continue to the fallopian tubes. If a sperm cell joins with an egg cell in a fallopian tube, **fertilization** occurs. Chemical changes immediately prevent other sperm from entering the egg. The genetic material from the sperm and egg combine.

Implantation The fertilized egg moves from the fallopian tube to the uterus. While it moves, it divides into two cells, then four cells, then eight. A ball of cells, called an **embryo,** forms. The embryo attaches itself to the thick, spongy lining of the uterus in a process called implantation.

Pregnancy The nine months of pregnancy can be divided into three periods, called trimesters. In the first trimester, the embryo grows rapidly. The cells become specialized and form tissues and organs. Both the embryo and the uterus contribute cells to a new organ called the placenta. The placenta has blood vessels from the mother's circulatory system and the embryo's. The embryo's vessels are inside a tube called the umbilical cord. Oxygen and nutrients pass from the mother to the placenta and from the placenta to the growing embryo.

After the eighth week of pregnancy, the developing embryo is called a **fetus.** Major organ systems, a skeleton, and facial features form during the second trimester. In the last twelve weeks of pregnancy, the fetus grows and completes development.

Birth At the end of pregnancy, the fetus is ready to be born. The first stage of birth, **labor,** begins with muscular contractions of the uterus. At first the contractions happen about every half hour. When they happen about every 2 minutes, the fetus is ready to be born. The second stage of birth is **delivery.** With each contraction, the opening to the uterus expands until it is wide enough for the fetus to pass through. During delivery, the fetus is pushed out of the uterus, through the vagina, and out of the body. The fetus is still connected to the mother by the umbilical cord. Within minutes after delivery, the placenta separates from the uterine wall and is delivered. When the umbilical cord is cut, the fetus becomes a separate human.

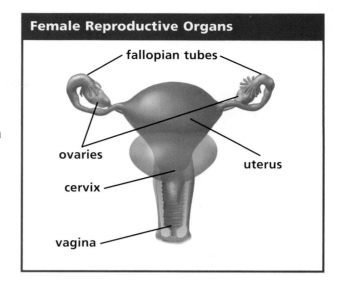

Female Reproductive Organs

fallopian tubes

ovaries

uterus

cervix

vagina

How a Light Microscope Works

Microscopes are used to see objects that are too small to see well with the naked eye. An ordinary light microscope works by combining convex lenses. A lens is a piece of glass or plastic shaped in such a way as to bend light. A convex lens has a bend similar to the curve of a sphere. It is thicker at its center than around the edges.

The object being viewed is mounted on a slide and placed on the stage of the microscope. The lens closer to the object is called the objective. This lens focuses an enlarged image of the object inside the microscope. The other microscope lens—the one you look through—is called the eyepiece. You use this lens to look at the image formed by the objective. Like a magnifying glass, the eyepiece lens forms an enlarged image of the first image.

Very small objects do not reflect much light. Most microscopes use a lamp or a mirror to shine more light on the object.

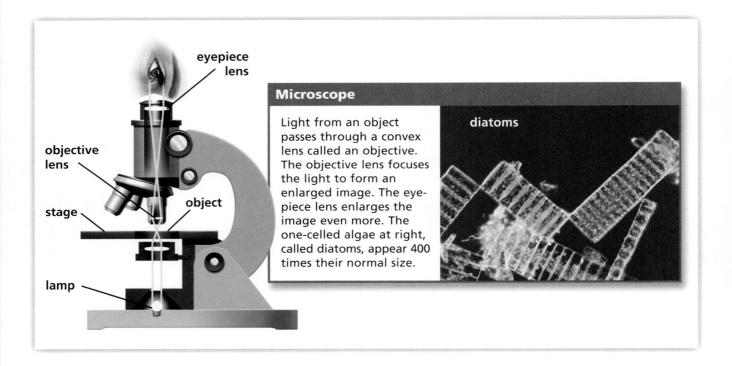

eyepiece lens

objective lens

stage

object

lamp

Microscope

Light from an object passes through a convex lens called an objective. The objective lens focuses the light to form an enlarged image. The eyepiece lens enlarges the image even more. The one-celled algae at right, called diatoms, appear 400 times their normal size.

diatoms

You will notice that many of the photographs of microscopic images included in this book have a magnification factor, for example 400✕. This is the power of magnification of the **microscope.**

California Physical Map

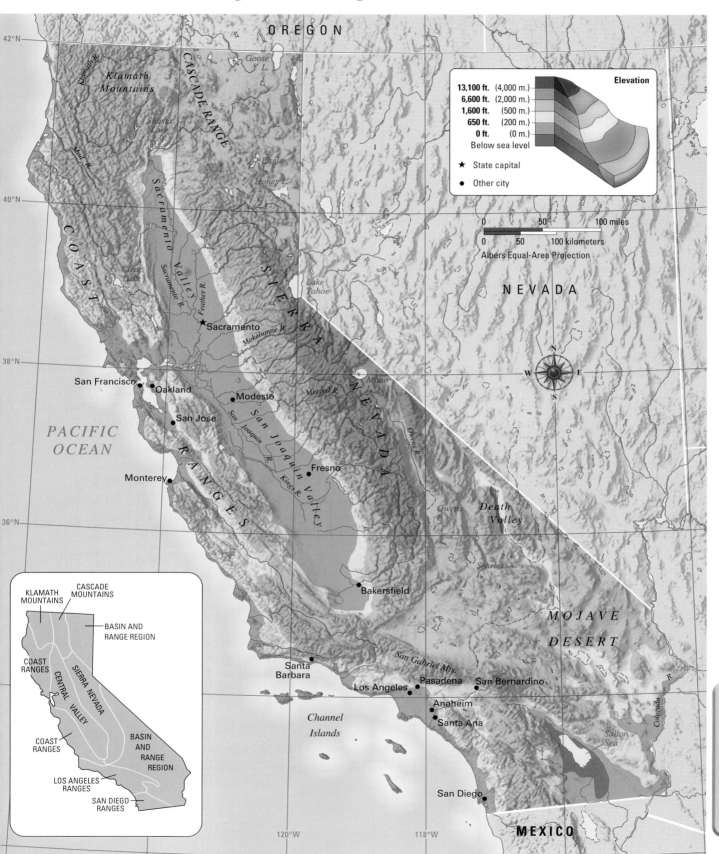

OREGON

42°N

Klamath R.

Klamath Mountains

CASCADE RANGE

Goose L.

Shasta Lake

Mad R.

Eagle L.

Honey L.

Sacramento Valley

40°N

Sacramento R.

Feather R.

Clear Lake

SIERRA

Lake Tahoe

NEVADA

Elevation

13,100 ft.	(4,000 m.)
6,600 ft.	(2,000 m.)
1,600 ft.	(500 m.)
650 ft.	(200 m.)
0 ft.	(0 m.)

Below sea level

★ State capital

● Other city

0   50   100 miles
0   50   100 kilometers
Albers Equal-Area Projection

COAST

★ Sacramento

Mokelumne R.

N

W   E

S

San Francisco ● ● Oakland

38°N

Modesto ●

Merced R.

Mono L.

San Jose ●

San Joaquin R.

San Joaquin Valley

NEVADA

PACIFIC OCEAN

RANGES

Fresno ●

Kings R.

Owens R.

36°N

Monterey ●

Owens L.

Death Valley

Searles L.

KLAMATH MOUNTAINS
CASCADE MOUNTAINS
BASIN AND RANGE REGION
COAST RANGES
SIERRA NEVADA
CENTRAL VALLEY
COAST RANGES
BASIN AND RANGE REGION
LOS ANGELES RANGES
SAN DIEGO RANGES

Bakersfield ●

M O J A V E

D E S E R T

Santa Barbara ●

San Gabriel Mts.

Los Angeles ● Pasadena ● San Bernardino ●

Channel Islands

Anaheim ●
Santa Ana ●

Colorado R.

Salton Sea

San Diego ●

MEXICO

120°W   118°W

Glossary

A

absolute age
The actual age in years of an event or object. (p. 156)

    edad absoluta La edad real en años de un evento u objeto.

absorb
To take in. When a medium absorbs light, the light ceases to exist and the medium gains the energy that was carried by the light. (p. 455)

    absorber Tomar, captar. Cuando un medio absorbe luz, la luz cesa de existir y el medio se beneficia de la energía que era llevada por la luz.

active transport
The process of using energy to move materials through a membrane. (p. 60)

    transporte activo El proceso de usar energía para mover sustancias a través de una membrana.

adaptation
An inherited trait that makes a species able to survive and reproduce in a particular environment. (p. 196)

    adaptación Cualquier rasgo heredado que permite a una especie sobrevivir o reproducirse en un medioambiente.

allele (uh-LEEL)
One form of a gene for a specific trait or gene product. (p. 103)

    alelo Una de las varias formas de un gen para un rasgo específico o un producto del gen.

ancestor
A distant or early form of an organism from which later forms descend. (p. 211)

    ancestro Una forma distante o temprana de un organismo a partir de la cual descienden formas posteriores.

angle of incidence
The angle from the normal at which light comes in to a surface. (p. 496)

    ángulo de incidencia La forma del ángulo en el cual surge la luz a la superficie.

angle of reflection
The angle from the normal of light after bouncing. (p. 496)

    ángulo de reflexión El ángulo de donde rebota lo normal de la luz.

aperture
An opening, such as one that limits the amount of light from each part of an object. (p. 514)

    apertura Una apertura como una que limite la cantidad de luz de cada parte de un objeto.

appendicular skeleton (AP-uhn-DIHK-yuh-luhr)
The bones of the skeleton that function to allow movement, such as arm and leg bones. (p. 350)

    esqueleto apendicular Los huesos del esqueleto cuya función es permitir el movimiento, como los huesos del brazo y los huesos de la pierna.

artery
A blood vessel with strong walls that carries blood away from the heart. (p. 394)

    arteria Un vaso sanguíneo con paredes fuertes que lleva la sangre del corazón hacia otras partes del cuerpo.

asexual reproduction
The process by which a single organism produces offspring that have the same genetic material. (p. 88)

    reproducción asexual El proceso mediante el cual un solo organismo produce crías que tienen el mismo material genético.

atmosphere (AT-muh-SFEER)
The outer layer of gases of a large body in space, such as a planet or star; the mixture of gases that surrounds the solid Earth; one of the four parts of the Earth system. (p. CA19)

    atmósfera La capa externa de gases de un gran cuerpo que se encuentra en el espacio, como un planeta o una estrella; la mezcla de gases que rodea la Tierra sólida; una de las cuatro partes del sistema terrestre.

atom
The smallest particle of an element that has the chemical properties of that element. (p. CA17)

    átomo La partícula más pequeña de un elemento que tiene las propiedades químicas de ese elemento.

axial skeleton
The central part of the skeleton, which includes the skull, the spinal column, and the ribs. (p. 350)

esqueleto axial La parte central del esqueleto que incluye el cráneo, la columna vertebral y las costillas.

B

bacteria (bak-TEER-ee-uh)
A large group of one-celled organisms that sometimes cause disease. Bacteria is a plural word; the singular is bacterium. (p. 14)

bacterias Un grupo grande de organismos unicelulares que algunas veces causan enfermedades.

binary fission
A form of asexual reproduction by which some single-celled organisms reproduce. The genetic material is copied, and one cell divides into two independent cells that are each a copy of the original cell. Prokaryotes such as bacteria reproduce by binary fission. (p. 89)

fisión binaria Una forma asexual de reproducción mediante la cual algunos organismos unicelulares se reproducen. El material genético se copia y una célula se divide en dos células independientes las cuales son copias de la célula original. Los organismos procariotas, tales como las bacterias, se reproducen mediante fisión binaria.

binomial nomenclature
(by-NOH-mee-uhl NOH-muhn-KLAY-chuhr)
The two-part naming system used to identify species. The first part of the name is the genus, and the second part of the name is the species. (p. 233)

nomenclatura biológica El sistema de denominación de dos partes que se usa para identificar a las especies. La primera parte del nombre es el género y la segunda parte del nombre es la especie.

biodiversity
The number and variety of living things found on Earth or within an ecosystem. (p. CA15)

biodiversidad La cantidad y variedad de organismos vivos que se encuentran en la Tierra o dentro de un ecosistema.

biosphere (BY-uh-SFEER)
All living organisms on Earth in the air, on the land, and in the waters; one of the four parts of the Earth system. (p. CA19)

biosfera Todos los organismos vivos de la Tierra, en el aire, en la tierra y en las aguas; una de las cuatro partes del sistema de la Tierra.

C

capillary
A narrow blood vessel that connects arteries with veins. (p. 397)

capilar Un vaso sanguíneo angosto que conecta a las arterias con las venas.

carbohydrate (KAHR-boh-HY-drayt)
A type of molecule made up of subunits of sugars and used for energy and structure. (p. 42)

carbohidrato Un tipo de molécula compuesta de unidades de azúcares y usada como fuente de energía y como material estructural.

cardiac muscle
The involuntary muscle that makes up the heart. (p. 358)

músculo cardíaco El músculo involuntario del que está hecho el corazón.

cartilage
A type of connective tissue that is tough but flexible. (p. 353)

cartílago Un tipo de tejido conectivo que es fuerte y flexible.

cell
The smallest unit that is able to perform the basic functions of life. (p. CA13)

célula La unidad más pequeña capaz de realizar las funciones básicas de la vida.

cell cycle
The normal sequence of growth, maintenance, and division in a cell. (p. 80)

ciclo celular La secuencia normal de crecimiento, mantenimiento y división en una célula.

cell membrane
The outer boundary of the cytoplasm, a layer that controls what enters or leaves the cell; a protective covering enclosing an entire cell. (p. 20)

membrana celular El límite exterior del citoplasma, una capa que controla lo que entra y sale de la célula, una cubierta protectora que encierra una célula entera.

cell theory
Theory that every living thing is made of one or more cells; cells carry out the functions needed to support life; and cells come from other living cells. (p. 13)

teoría celular La teoría de que todo ser viviente está hecho de una o más células; las células ejercen las funciones necesarias para sostener la vida; las células vienen de otras células vivas.

cell wall
A protective outer covering that lies just outside the cell membrane of plant cells. (p. 21)

pared celular Una cubierta exterior protectora que se encuentra justo fuera de la membrana celular de las células vegetales.

cellular respiration
A process in which cells use oxygen to release energy stored in sugars. (p. 50)

respiración celular Un proceso en el cual las células usan oxígeno para liberar energía almacenada en las azúcares.

chemical energy
Energy that is stored in the chemical composition of matter. The amount of chemical energy in a substance depends on the types and arrangement of its atoms. When wood or gasoline burns, chemical energy produces heat. The energy used by the cells in your body comes from chemical energy in the foods you eat. (p. 47)

energía química Energía almacenada en la composición química de la materia. La cantidad de energía química en una sustancia depende de los tipos y la disposición de sus átomos. Cuando se quema madera o gasolina, la energía química produce calor. La energía usada por las células en tu cuerpo proviene de la energía química en los alimentos que comes.

chemical reaction
The process by which chemical changes occur. In a chemical reaction, atoms are rearranged, and chemical bonds are broken and formed. (p. 42)

reacción química El proceso mediante el cual ocurren cambios químicos. En una reacción química, se reacomodan átomos y se rompen y se forman enlaces químicos.

chlorophyll (KLAWR-uh-fihl)
A light-absorbing chemical, a pigment, that traps the energy in sunlight and converts it to chemical energy. Found in chloroplasts of plant cells and the cells of other photosynthetic organisms. (p. 48)

clorofila Una sustancia química que absorbe luz, un pigmento, que atrapa la energía de la luz solar y la convierte a energía química. Se encuentra en los cloroplastos de células vegetales y en las células de otros organismos fotosintéticos.

chloroplast (KLAWR-uh-PLAST)
An organelle in a plant cell that contains chlorophyll, a chemical that uses the energy from sunlight to make sugar. (p. 23)

cloroplasto Un organelo en una célula vegetal que contiene clorofila, una sustancia química que usa la energía de la luz solar para producir azúcar.

chromosome
The physical structure in a cell that contains the cell's genetic material. (p. 75)

cromosoma Una estructura corporal en la célula que contiene el material genético de la célula.

circulatory system
The group of organs, consisting of the heart and blood vessels, that circulates blood through the body. (p. 393)

sistema circulatorio El grupo de órganos, que consiste del corazón y los vasos sanguíneos, que hace circular la sangre por el cuerpo.

cladogram
A branching diagram of relationships among organisms; it is based on characteristics that are passed down from common ancestors. (p. 243)

cladograma Un diagrama de ramificación entre organismos; se basa en las características heredadas de antepasados comunes.

classification
The systematic grouping of different types of organisms by their shared characteristics. (p. 232)

clasificación La agrupación sistemática de diferentes tipos de organismos en base a las características que comparten.

compound
A substance made up of two or more different types of atoms bonded together.

compuesto Una sustancia formada por dos o más diferentes tipos de átomos enlazados.

cone cell
Cone-shaped cells in the retina that allow the eye to detect colors. (p. 477)

célula cónica Células en la retina en forma de cono que permiten al ojo detectar colores.

converge
To come together. (p. 497)

converger Reunirse

cornea (KAWR-nee-uh)
A transparent membrane that covers the front of the eye. (p. 518)

córnea Una membrana transparente que cubre el ojo.

cycle
n. A series of events or actions that repeat themselves regularly; a physical and/or chemical process in which one material continually changes locations and/or forms. Examples include the water cycle, the carbon cycle, and the rock cycle.

v. To move through a repeating series of events or actions.

ciclo Una serie de eventos o acciones que se repiten regularmente; un proceso físico y/o químico en el cual un material cambia continuamente de lugar y/o forma. Ejemplos: el ciclo del agua, el ciclo del carbono y el ciclo de las rocas.

cytokinesis (SY-toh-kuh-NEE-sihs)
The division of a parent cell's cytoplasm following mitosis. (p. 81)

citocinesis La división del citoplasma de la célula madre después de la mitosis.

cytoplasm (SY-tuh-PLAZ-uhm)
A thick, gelatin-like material contained within the cell membrane. Most of the work of the cell is carried out in the cytoplasm. (p. 20)

citoplasma Un material espeso, parecido a la gelatina, contenido dentro de la membrana celular. La mayor parte del trabajo de la célula se realiza en el citoplasma.

D

data
Information gathered by observation or experimentation that can be used in calculating or reasoning. *Data* is a plural word; the singular is *datum*.

datos Información reunida mediante observación o experimentación y que se puede usar para calcular o para razonar.

decibel dB
The unit used to measure the loudness of a sound wave. (p. 442)

decibel La unidad que se usa para medir el volumen de una onda sonora.

density
A property of matter representing the mass per unit volume.

densidad Una propiedad de la materia que representa la masa por unidad de volumen.

derived characteristic
A trait that has changed from its ancestral condition through evolution. (p. 244)

características derivadas Una característica que ha cambiado desde su condición ancestral a través de la evolución.

dichotomous key (dy-KAHT-uh-muhs)
An identification tool that gives a series of choices, each with only two possibilities. (p. 231)

clave dicótoma Una herramienta de identificación que ofrece una serie de opciones, cada una con sólo dos posibilidades.

diffuse
To cause to go in many different directions. (p. 469)

difuso Hacer que vaya en muchas direcciones diferentes.

diffusion (dih-FYOO-zhuhn)
The tendency of a substance to move from an area of higher concentration to an area of lower concentration. (p. 56)

difusión La tendencia de una sustancia a moverse de un área de mayor concentración a un área de menor concentración.

diverge
To move apart. (p. 497)

desviarse Moverse por separado.

DNA
The genetic material found in all living cells that contains the information needed for an organism to grow, maintain itself, and reproduce. Deoxyribonucleic acid (dee-AHK-see-RY-boh-noo-KLEE-ihk). (p. 74)

ADN El material genético que se encuentra en todas las células vivas y que contiene la información necesaria para que un organismo crezca, se mantenga a sí mismo y se reproduzca. Ácido desoxiribunucleico.

domain
One of three divisions in a classification system based on different types of cells. The six kingdoms of living things are grouped into three domains: Archaea, Bacteria, and Eukarya. (p. 249)

dominio Una de las tres divisiones en un sistema de clasificación basado en los diferentes tipos de células. Los seis reinos de los organismos vivos esta agrupados en tres dominios: Archaea, Bacteria y Eukarya.

dominant
A term that describes the allele that determines the phenotype of an individual organism when two different copies are present in the genotype. (p. 107)

dominante Un término que describe al alelo que determina el fenotipo de un organismo cuando están presentes dos copias diferentes en el genotipo.

E

eardrum
A thin, tightly stretched membrane that separates the outer ear from the middle ear. (p. 436)

tambor del oído, tímpano Una delgada membrana, apretadamente estirada, que separa el oído exterior del oído medio.

egg

A female reproductive cell (gamete) that forms in the female reproductive organs and has just a single copy of the genetic material of the parent. (p. 118)

óvulo Una célula reproductiva femenina (gameto) que se forma en los órganos reproductivos de una hembra y tiene una sola copia del material genético de la madre.

electromagnetic spectrum EM spectrum

The range of all electromagnetic frequencies, including the following types (from lowest to highest frequency): radio waves, microwaves, infrared light, visible light, ultraviolet light, x-rays, and gamma rays. (p. 455)

espectro electromagnético La escala de todas las frecuencias electromagnéticas, incluyendo los siguientes tipos (de la frecuencia más baja a la más alta): ondas de radio, microondas, luz infrarroja, luz visible, luz ultravioleta, rayos X y rayos gamma.

electromagnetic wave EM wave

A type of wave, such as a light wave or radio wave, that does not require a material medium to travel; a disturbance that transfers energy through a field. (p. 453)

onda electromagnética Un tipo de onda, como una onda luminosa o de radio, que no requiere un medio material para propagarse; una perturbación que transfiere energía a través de un campo.

element

A substance that cannot be broken down into a simpler substance by ordinary chemical changes. An element consists of atoms of only one type. (p. CA17)

elemento Una sustancia que no puede descomponerse en otra sustancia más simple por medio de cambios químicos normales. Un elemento consta de átomos de un solo tipo.

embryo (EHM-bree-OH)

A multicellular organism, plant or animal, in its earliest stages of development. (p. 325)

embrión Una planta o un animal en su estado mas temprano de desarrollo.

emigration

In population studies, the movement of individuals out of an ecosystem. (p. 204)

emigración En estudios poblacionales, el movimiento de individuos fuera de un ecosistema.

emit

To give off. (p. 463)

emitir Transmitir

endoskeleton

An internal support system typically made of bone, cartilage, ligament, and tendon tissues. It is a distinguishing characteristic of vertebrate animals. (p. 289)

endoesqueleto Un sistema de soporte interno, típicamente constituido de hueso, cartílago, ligamentos y tendones. Es una característica distintiva de los animales vertebrados.

energy

The ability to do work or to cause a change. For example, the energy of a moving bowling ball knocks over pins; energy from food allows animals to move and to grow; and energy from the Sun heats Earth's surface and atmosphere, which causes air to move. (pp. CA17, CA19)

energía La capacidad para trabajar o causar un cambio. Por ejemplo, la energía de una bola de boliche en movimiento tumba los pinos; la energía proveniente de su alimento permite a los animales moverse y crecer; la energía del Sol calienta la superficie y la atmósfera de la Tierra, lo que ocasiona que el aire se mueva.

environment

Everything that surrounds a living thing. An environment is made up of both living and nonliving factors. (p. CA15)

medio ambiente Todo lo que rodea a un organismo vivo. Un medio ambiente está compuesto de factores vivos y factores sin vida.

environmental factors

Conditions that affect survival, such as the food supply, predators, and disease. (p. 196)

factores medioambientales Condiciones que afectan la supervivencia, tales como el suministro de comida, predatores y enfermedades.

eukaryotic cell (yoo-KAR-ee-AHT-ihk)

A cell in which the genetic material is enclosed within a nucleus, surrounded by its own membrane. (p. 20)

célula eucariota Una célula en la cual el material genético esta dentro de un núcleo, rodeado por su propia membrana.

evolution

The process through which species change over time; can refer to the changes in a particular population or to the formation and extinction of species over the course of Earth's history. (p. 191)

evolución El proceso mediante el cual las especies cambian con el tiempo; puede referirse a cambios en una población en particular o a la formación y extinción de especies en el curso de la historia de la Tierra.

exoskeleton

The strong, flexible outer covering of some invertebrate animals, such as arthropods. (p. 288)

exoesqueleto La cubierta exterior fuerte y flexible de algunos animales invertebrados, como los artrópodos.

experiment

An organized procedure to study something under controlled conditions. (p. CA22)

experimento Un procedimiento organizado para estudiar algo bajo condiciones controladas.

extinction

The permanent disappearance of a species. (p. 189)

extinción La desaparición permanente de una especie.

F

fermentation

A chemical process by which cells release energy from sugar when no oxygen is present. (p. 52)

fermentación Un proceso químico mediante el cual las células liberan energía del azúcar cuando no hay oxígeno presente.

fertilization

Part of the process of sexual reproduction in which a male reproductive cell and a female reproductive cell combine to make a new cell that can develop into a new organism. (pp. 118, 317)

fertilización El proceso mediante el cual una célula reproductiva masculina y una célula reproductiva femenina se combinan para formar una nueva célula que puede convertirse en un organismo nuevo.

fetus

The developing human embryo from eight weeks to birth. (p. 338)

feto El embrión humano en desarrollo de las ocho semanas al nacimiento.

fiber optics

Technology that uses transparent fibers to transmit light. This technology is often used in communications. (p. 516)

fibra óptica Tecnología que utiliza fibras transparentes para transmitir luz. Esta tecnología es utilizada frecuentemente en las comunicaciones.

field

An area around an object where the object can apply a force—such as gravitational force, magnetic force, or electrical force—on another object without touching it.

campo Un área alrededor de un objeto donde el objeto puede aplicar una fuerza, como fuerza gravitacional, fuerza magnética o fuerza eléctrica, sobre otro objeto sin tocarlo.

fluid

A substance that can flow easily, such as a gas or a liquid. (p. 387)

fluido Una sustancia que fluye fácilmente, como por ejemplo un gas o un líquido.

focal length

The distance from the center of a lens to its focal point. (p. 504)

distancia focal La distancia desde el centro de un lente hasta su punto focal.

focal point

The point at which parallel light rays come together after reflection from a mirror or refraction by a lens; the point at which parallel light rays appear to diverge from after reflection by a mirror or refraction by a lens. (p. 498)

punto focal El punto en el cual se unen los rayos paralelos de luz después de ser reflejados por un espejo o refractados por un lente; el punto en el cual los rayos paralelos de luz parecen desviarse después de ser reflejados por un espejo o refractados por un lente.

force

A push or a pull; something that changes the motion of an object. (p. 364)

fuerza Un empuje o un jalón; algo que cambia el movimiento de un objeto.

fossil

A trace or the remains of a once-living thing from long ago.

fósil Rastro o los restos de un ser viviente que vivió hace mucho años.

frequency

The number of cycles per unit time; can be measured by the number of waves that pass a fixed point in a given amount of time, usually one second. (p. 428)

frecuencia El número de ciclos por unidad de tiempo; puede ser medido por el número de ondas que pasan por un punto fijo en un determinado tiempo, usualmente un segundo.

GLOSSARY

friction
A force that resists the motion between two surfaces in contact. (p. CA17)

> **fricción** Una fuerza que resiste el movimiento entre dos superficies en contacto.

fruit
The ripened ovary of a flowering plant that contains the seeds. (p. 329)

> **fruta** El ovario maduro de una planta floreciente que contiene las semillas.

fulcrum
A fixed point around which a lever rotates. (p. 372)

> **fulcro** Un punto fijo alrededor del cual gira una palanca.

G

gamete
A sperm or egg cell, containing half the usual number of chromosomes of an organism (one chromosome from each pair), which is found only in the reproductive organs of an organism. (pp. 118, 317)

> **gameto** Un óvulo o un espermatozoide, que contiene la mitad del número usual de cromosomas de un organismo (un cromosoma de cada par), que se encuentra sólo en los órganos reproductivos de un organismo.

gene
The basic unit of heredity that consists of a segment of DNA on a chromosome. (p. 102)

> **gen** La unidad básica de herencia que consiste en un segmento de ADN en un cromosoma.

genetic material
The nucleic acid DNA that is present in all living cells and contains the information needed for a cell's growth, maintenance, and reproduction.

> **material genético** El ácido nucleico ADN, que esta presente en todas las células vivas y que contiene la información necesaria para el crecimiento, el mantenimiento y la reproducción celular.

genetic variation
Differences in DNA in a population. (p. 196)

> **variación genética** Diferencias de ADN en la población.

genotype (JEHN-uh-TYP)
The genetic makeup of an organism; all the alleles that an organism has. (p. 106)

> **genotipo** La estructura genética de un organismo; todos los alelos que tiene un organismo.

genus
The first part of a binomial name that groups together closely related species. The genus Felis includes all species of small cats. (p. 233)

> **género** La primera parte de un nombre biológico que agrupa a especies muy relacionadas entre sí. El género Felis incluye a todas las especies de gatos pequeños.

geologic time scale
The summary of Earth's history, divided into intervals of time defined by major events or changes on Earth. (p. 163)

> **escala de tiempo geológico** El resumen de la historia de la Tierra, dividido en intervalos de tiempo definidos por los principales eventos o cambios en la Tierra.

geosphere (JEE-uh-SFEER)
All the features on Earth's surface—continents, islands, and seafloor—and everything below the surface—the inner and outer core and the mantle; one of the four parts of the Earth system. (p. CA19)

> **geosfera** Todas las características de la superficie de la Tierra, es decir, continentes, islas y el fondo marino, y de todo bajo la superficie, es decir, el núcleo externo e interno y el manto; una de las cuatro partes del sistema de la Tierra.

gland
A group of specialized cells that produces a specific substance, such as a hormone. (p. 298)

> **glándula** Un grupo de células especializadas que produce una sustancia específica, como una hormona.

glucose
A sugar molecule that is a major energy source for most cells, produced by the process of photosynthesis. (p. 47)

> **glucosa** Una molécula de azúcar que es la principal fuente de energía para la mayoría de las células, producida mediante el proceso de fotosíntesis.

gravity
The force that objects exert on each other because of their mass. (p. CA17)

> **gravedad** La fuerza que los objetos ejercen entre sí debido a su masa.

H

half-life
The length of time it takes for half of the nuclei in a sample of a radioactive element to change from an unstable form into another form. (p. 156)

> **vida media** El tiempo que tarda en cambiar la mitad de los núcleos de una muestra de un elemento radioactivo, de una forma inestable a otra.

heredity

The passing of genes from parents to offspring; the genes are expressed in the traits of the offspring. (p. 102)

herencia La transferencia de genes de los progenitores a la crías; los genes se expresan en los rasgos de las crías.

hertz Hz

The unit used to measure frequency. One hertz is equal to one complete cycle per second. (p. 428)

hertzio La unidad usada para medir frecuencia. Un hercio es igual a un ciclo completo por segundo.

hibernation

A sleeplike state in which certain animals spend the winter. Hibernation reduces an animal's need for food and helps protect it from cold. (p. 275)

hibernación Un estado parecido al de sueño en el cual ciertos animales pasan el invierno. La hibernación reduce la necesidad de alimento de un animal y le ayuda a protegerse del frío.

homeostasis (HOH-mee-oh-STAY-sihs)

A condition needed for health and functioning in which an organism or cell maintains a relatively stable internal environment. (p. 295)

homeostasis Una condición necesaria para la salud y el funcionamiento en la cual un organismo o una célula mantiene un medio ambiente estable e interna.

hormone

A chemical that is made in one organ, travels through the blood, and affects target cells. (p. 297)

hormona Una sustancia química que se produce en un órgano y viaja por la sangre, afectando a las células en blanco de tiro.

hydrosphere (HY-druh-SFEER)

All water on Earth—in the atmosphere and in the oceans, lakes, glaciers, rivers, streams, and underground reservoirs; one of the four parts of the Earth system. (p. CA19)

hidrosfera Toda el agua de la Tierra: en la atmósfera y en los océanos, lagos, glaciares, ríos, arroyos y depósitos subterráneos; una de las cuatro partes del sistema de la Tierra.

hypothesis

A tentative explanation for an observation or phenomenon. A hypothesis is used to make testable predictions. (p. CA22)

hipótesis Una explicación provisional de una observación o de un fenómeno. Una hipótesis se usa para hacer predicciones que se pueden probar.

I

ice core

A cylindrical sample that shows the layers of snow and ice that have built up over the years. (p. 175)

núcleo de hielo Una muestra cilíndrica que presenta las capas de nieve y hielo que se han acumulado con los años.

igneous rock (IHG-nee-uhs)

Rock that forms as molten rock cools and becomes solid.

roca ígnea Roca que se forma al enfriarse la roca fundida y hacerse sólida.

image

A picture of an object formed by light. (p. 497)

imagen Retrato de un objeto formado por rayos de luz.

immigration

In population studies, the movement of an organism into a range inhabited by individuals of the same species. (p. 203)

inmigración En estudios poblacionales, el movimiento de un organismo hacia un territorio habitado por individuos de la misma especie.

index fossil

A fossil of an organism that was common, lived in many areas, and existed only during a certain span of time. Index fossils are used to help determine the age of rock layers. (p. 155)

fósil indicador Un fósil de un organismo que era común, vivió en muchas áreas y existió sólo durante cierto período de tiempo. Los fósiles indicadores se usan para ayudar a determinar la edad de las capas de roca.

inner ear

The innermost part of the ear; it includes the semicircular canals and the cochlea. (p. 437)

oído interno La parte interior del oído. Incluye canales semicirculares y la cóclea.

input force

The force exerted on a machine; it enables the machine to do work. (p. 373)

fuerza de la entrada La presión aplicada a una máquina; ayuda la máquina a funcionar para hacer el trabajo.

interaction

The condition of acting or having an influence upon something. Living things in an ecosystem interact with both the living and nonliving parts of their environment. (p. CA15)

interacción La condición de actuar o influir sobre algo. Los organismos vivos en un ecosistema interactúan con las partes vivas y las partes sin vida de su medio ambiente.

interphase

The period in the cell cycle in which a cell grows, maintains itself, and prepares for division. (p. 81)

interfase El período en el ciclo celular en el cual una célula crece, se mantiene y se prepara para la división.

invertebrate

An animal that has no backbone. (p. 253)

invertebrado Un animal que no tiene columna vertebral.

J, K

joint

A place where two bones in the skeletal system meet. (p. 353)

articulación Un lugar donde se encuentran dos huesos en el sistema esquelético.

L

law

In science, a rule or principle describing a physical relationship that always works in the same way under the same conditions. The law of conservation of energy is an example.

ley En las ciencias, una regla o un principio que describe una relación física que siempre funciona de la misma manera bajo las mismas condiciones. La ley de la conservación de la energía es un ejemplo.

law of conservation of energy

A law stating that no matter how energy is transferred or transformed, it continues to exist in one form or another. (p. CA17)

ley de la conservación de la energía Una ley que establece que no importa cómo se transfiere o transforma la energía, toda la energía sigue presente en alguna forma u otra.

lens

A transparent optical tool that refracts light. (p. 503)

lente Una herramienta óptica transparente que refracta la luz.

lever

A solid bar that rotates, or turns, around a fixed point (fulcrum); one of the six simple machines. (p. 372)

palanca Una barra sólida que da vueltas o gira alrededor de un punto fijo (el fulcro); una de las seis máquinas simples.

limiting factor

A factor or condition that prevents the continuing growth of a population in an ecosystem. (p. 204)

factor limitante Un factor o una condición que impide el crecimiento continuo de una población en un ecosistema.

lipid

A type of molecule made up of subunits of fatty acids. Lipids are found in the fats, oils, and waxes used for structure and to store energy. (p. 43)

lípido Un tipo de molécula compuesta de unidades de ácidos grasos. Los lípidos se encuentran en las grasas, los aceites y las ceras usadas como materiales estructurales y para almacenar energía.

M

mass

A measure of how much matter an object is made of.

masa Una medida de la cantidad de materia de la que está compuesto un objeto.

mass extinction

One of several periods in Earth's history when large numbers of species became extinct at nearly the same time. (p. 189)

extinción masiva Uno de varios períodos en la historia de la Tierra cuando grandes números de especies se extinguieron casi al mismo tiempo.

matter

Anything that has mass and volume. Matter exists ordinarily as a solid, a liquid, or a gas. (p. CA19)

materia Todo lo que tiene masa y volumen. Generalmente la materia existe como sólido, líquido o gas.

mechanical advantage
The number of times a machine multiplies the input force; output force divided by input force. (p. 374)

> **ventaja mecánica** El número de veces que una máquina multiplica la fuerza de entrada; la fuerza de salida dividida por la fuerza de entrada.

medium
A substance through which a wave moves. (p. 424)

> **medio** Una sustancia a través de la cual se mueve una onda.

meiosis (my-OH-sihs)
Process in which the nucleus of a cell divides in the production of haploid (*n*) cells, such as egg cells and sperm cells. Meiosis is a part of sexual reproduction and occurs only in reproductive cells. (p. 119)

> **meiosis** El proceso en el cual el núcleo de una célula se divide en la producción de células haploides, tales como óvulos y espermatozoides. La meiosis es una parte de la reproducción sexual y ocurre sólo en células reproductivas.

menstruation
A period of about five days during which blood and tissue exit the body through the vagina. (p. 334)

> **menstruación** Un período de aproximadamente cinco días durante el cual salen del cuerpo sangre y tejido por la vagina.

metamorphic rock (MEHT-uh-MAWR-fihk)
Rock formed as heat or pressure causes existing rock to change in structure, texture, or mineral composition.

> **roca metamórfica** Roca formada cuando el calor o la presión ocasionan que la roca existente cambie de estructura, textura o composición mineral.

microscope
An instrument that uses glass lenses to magnify an object. (p. 12)

> **microscopio** Un instrumento que usa lentes de vidrio para magnificar un objeto.

middle ear
The middle part of the ear; it includes three bones in an air-filled chamber and is connected to the throat by the eustachian tube. (p. 437)

> **oído medio** La parte media de oído; incluye tres huesos en una cavidad llena de aire y está conectada a la garganta por medio de la trompa de Eustaquio.

mitochondria (MY-tuh-KAWN-dree-uh)
Organelles that release energy by using oxygen to break down sugars. (p. 23)

> **mitocondrias** Organelos que liberan energía usando oxígeno para romper los azúcares.

mitosis
The phase in the cell cycle during which the nucleus divides. (p. 81)

> **mitosis** La fase en el ciclo celular durante la cual se divide el núcleo.

molecule
A group of atoms that are held together by covalent bonds so that they move as a single unit.

> **molécula** Un grupo de átomos que están unidos mediante enlaces covalentes de tal manera que se mueven como una sola unidad.

mucus
A fluid produced by epithelial tissues in several parts of the body; it forms a protective coating. (p. 403)

> **mucosidad** Un fluido producido por los tejidos epiteliales en varias partes del cuerpo; forma una capa protectora.

multicellular
A term used to describe an organism that is made up of many cells. (p. 11)

> **multicelular** Un término usado para describir a un organismo que esta formado por muchas células.

muscular system
The muscles of the body that, together with the skeletal system, function to produce movement. (p. 357)

> **sistema muscular** Los músculos del cuerpo que, junto con el sistema óseo, sirven para producir movimiento.

N

natural selection
The process through which members of a species that are best suited to their environment survive and reproduce at a higher rate than other members of the species. (p. 195)

> **selección natural** El proceso mediante el cual los miembros de una especie que están mejor adecuados a su medio ambiente sobreviven y se reproducen a una tasa más alta que otros miembros de la especie.

niche (nihch)
The role a living thing plays in its habitat. A plant is a food producer, whereas an insect both consumes food as well as provides food for other consumers.

> **nicho** El papel que juega un organismo vivo en su hábitat. Una planta es un productor de alimento mientras que un insecto consume alimento y a la vez sirve de alimento a otros consumidores.

nucleic acid (noo-KLEE-ihk)

A type of molecule, made up of subunits of nucleotides, that is part of the genetic material of a cell and is needed to make proteins. DNA and RNA are nucleic acids. (p. 43)

ácido nucleico Un tipo de molécula, compuesto de unidades de nucleótidos, que es parte del material genético de una célula y se necesita para producir proteínas. El ADN y el ARN son ácidos nucleicos.

nucleus (NOO-klee-uhs)

The structure in a eukaryotic cell that contains the genetic material a cell needs to reproduce and function. (p. 20)

núcleo La estructura en una célula eucariota que contiene el material genético que la célula necesita para reproducirse y funcionar.

optics (AHP-tihks)

The study of light, vision, and related technology. (p. 495)

óptica El estudio de la luz, la visión y la tecnología relacionada a ellas.

organ

A structure that is made up of different tissues working together to perform a particular function. (pp. 30, 272)

órgano Una estructura compuesta de diferentes tejidos que trabajan juntos para realizar una función determinada.

organelle (AWR-guh-NEHL)

A structure in a cell that is enclosed by a membrane and that performs a particular function. (p. 20)

organelo Una estructura en una célula, envuelta en una membrana, que realiza una función determinada.

organism

An individual living thing, made up of one or many cells. (p. CA13)

organismo Un ser, compuesto de una o muchas células.

organ system

A group of organs that together perform a function. (p. 272)

sistema de órganos Un grupo de órganos que juntos realizan una función.

original remains

A fossil that is the actual body or body parts of an organism. (p. 174)

restos originales Un fósil que es en realidad el cuerpo o partes del cuerpo de un organismo.

osmosis (ahz-MOH-sihs)

The diffusion of water through a membrane. (p. 59)

osmosis La difusión de agua a través de una membrana.

outer ear

The outermost part of the ear; it includes the part of the ear on the outside of the skull and the ear canal. (p. 436)

oído externo La parte exterior del oído; incluye la parte que está fuera del cráneo y el canal del oído.

output force

The force that a machine exerts on an object. (p. 373)

fuerza de salida La fuerza que emplea la máquina en un objeto.

ovule

A structure in a female reproductive system that holds an immature egg cell. (p. 327)

óvulo Una estructura en el sistema reproductivo femenino que lleva la célula inmadura del huevo.

P, Q

passive transport

The movement of materials through a membrane without any input of energy. (p. 58)

transporte pasivo El movimiento de sustancias a través de una membrana sin aporte de energía.

phenotype

The observable characteristics or traits of an organism. (p. 106)

fenotipo Las características o rasgos visibles de un organismo.

photosynthesis (FOH-toh-SIHN-thih-sihs)

The process by which green plants and other producers use simple compounds and energy from light to make sugar, an energy-rich compound. (p. 48)

fotosíntesis El proceso mediante el cual las plantas verdes y otros productores usan compuestos simples y energía de la luz para producir azúcares, compuestos ricos en energía.

pitch

The quality of highness or lowness of a sound. Pitch is associated with the frequency of a sound wave—the higher the frequency, the higher the pitch. (p. 432)

tono La cualidad de un sonido de ser alto o bajo. El tono está asociado con la frecuencia de una onda sonora: entre más alta sea la frecuencia, más alto es el tono.

placenta

An organ that transports materials between a pregnant female mammal and the offspring developing inside her body. (p. 337)

   placenta Un órgano que transporta sustancias entre un mamífero hembra preñado y la cría que se está desarrollando dentro de su cuerpo.

pollen

Tiny multicellular grains that contain the undeveloped sperm cells of a plant. (p. 325)

   polen Los diminutos granos multicelulares que contienen las células espermáticas sin desarrollar de una planta.

population

A group of organisms of the same species that live in the same area. For example, a desert will have populations of different species of lizards and cactus plants. (p. 196)

   población Un grupo de organismos de la misma especie que viven en la misma área. Por ejemplo, un desierto tendrá poblaciones de distintas especies de lagartijas y de cactus.

pressure

A measure of how much force is acting on a certain area; how concentrated a force is. Pressure is equal to the force divided by area. (p. 388)

   presión Una medida de cuánta fuerza actúa sobre cierta área; el nivel de concentración de la fuerza. La presión es igual a la fuerza dividida entre el área.

probability

The likelihood or chance that a specific outcome will occur out of a total number of outcomes. (p. 112)

   probabilidad La posibilidad de que ocurra un resultado específico en un número total de resultados.

prokaryotic cell (proh-KAR-ee-AWT-ihk)

A type of cell that lacks a nucleus and other organelles. Its DNA is in a single chromosome. (p. 20)

   célula procariota Una célula que carece de núcleo y otros organelos. Su ADN se encuentra en una sola cromosoma.

protein

One of many types of molecules made up of chains of amino acid subunits. Proteins control the chemical activity of a cell and support growth and repair. (p. 43)

   proteína Uno de muchos tipos de moléculas formadas por cadenas de aminoácidos. Las proteínas controlan la actividad química de una célula y sustentan el crecimiento y la reparación.

Punnett square

A chart used to show all the ways alleles from two parents can combine and be passed to offspring; used to predict all genotypes that are possible. (p. 110)

   cuadro de Punnet Una tabla que se usa para mostrar todas las formas en que los alelos de los progenitores pueden combinarse y pasarse a las crías; se usa para predecir todos los genotipos que son posibles.

pupil

The circular opening in the iris of the eye that controls how much light enters the eye. (p. 519)

   pupila La apertura circular en el iris del ojo que controla cuánta luz entra al ojo.

R

radiation (RAY-dee-AY-shuhn)

Energy that travels across distances in the form of electromagnetic waves. (p. 455)

   radiación Energía que viaja a través de la distancia en forma de ondas electromagnéticas.

recessive

A term that describes an allele that is not expressed when combined with a dominant form of the gene. (p. 107)

   recesivo Un término que describe un alelo que no se expresa cuando se combina con una forma dominante del gen.

reflect

To bounce or bounce off; a surface may reflect light; light may reflect after it strikes a surface. (p. 468)

   reflejar Rebotar o rebotar de; una superficie puede rebotar la luz; la luz puede rebotar después de golpear una superficie.

refract

To change direction (of light) due to a change in speed; the surface between two mediums refracts light; light refracts as it encounters a change in medium. (p. 471)

   refractar Cambio de dirección (de la luz) debido a cambio de velocidad; la superficie entre dos medios refracta la luz; la luz se refracta al encontrar cambios en el medio.

regeneration

In some organisms, the process by which certain cells produce new tissue growth at the site of a wound or lost limb; also a form of asexual reproduction. (p. 90)

   regeneración En algunos organismos, el proceso mediante el cual ciertas células producen crecimiento de tejido nuevo en el sitio de una herida o de una extremidad perdida; también un tipo de reproducción asexual.

relative age
The age of an event or object in relation to other events or objects. (p. 151)

edad relativa La edad de un evento u objeto en relación a otros eventos u objetos.

replication
The process by which DNA is copied before it condenses into chromosomes. Replication takes place before a cell divides. (p. 128)

replicación El proceso mediante el cual el ADN se copia antes de condensarse en los cromosomas. La replicación se realiza antes de que una célula se divida.

retina (REHT-uhn-uh)
A light-sensitive tissue that lines the inside of the eye. (p. 476)

retina Un tejido, sensible a la luz, que forra la parte interna del ojo.

RNA
A molecule that carries genetic information from DNA to a ribosome, where the genetic information is used to bring together amino acids to form a protein. Ribonucleic acid (RY-boh-noo-KLEE-ihk). (p. 137)

ARN Una molécula que lleva información genética del ADN al ribosoma, donde la información genética se usa para unir aminoácidos para formar una proteína. Ácido ribonucleico.

rock cycle
The set of natural, repeating processes that form, change, break down, and re-form rocks. (p. 152)

ciclo de las rocas La serie de procesos naturales y repetitivos que forman, cambian, descomponen y vuelven a formar rocas.

rod cell
Long, thin cells located in the retina that let the eye detect dim light; also called rods. (p. 477)

bastoncillo Células largas localizadas en la retina que permiten que el ojo detecte luz baja; también llamadas barras.

root system
The system in a plant that anchors the plant and generally provides for the exchange of materials with soil. (p. 280)

sistema de raíz El sistema en una planta que la ancla y generalmente suple el intercambio de materiales con terreno.

S

sedimentary rock (sehd-uh-MEHN-tuh-ree)
Rock formed as pieces of older rocks and other loose materials get pressed or cemented together or as dissolved minerals re-form and build up in layers.

roca sedimentaria Roca que se forma cuando los pedazos de rocas más viejas y otros materiales sueltos son presionados o cementados o cuando los minerales disueltos vuelven a formarse y se acumulan en capas.

seed
A plant embryo that is enclosed in a protective coating and has its own source of nutrients. (p. 325)

semilla El embrión de una planta que esta dentro de una cubierta protectora y que tiene su propia fuente de nutrientes.

semicircular canals
Fluid-filled chambers in the inner ear that help sense position and motion. (p. 404)

canales semicirculares Compartimientos de fluido en el oído interno que ayuda en la sensación de posición y movimiento.

sexual reproduction
A type of reproduction in which male and female reproductive cells combine to form offspring with genetic material from both cells. (p. 102)

reproducción sexual Un tipo de reproducción en el cual se combinan las células reproductivas femeninas y masculinas para formar una cría con material genético de ambas células.

shoot system
The system in a plant that includes structures for photosynthesis, support, storage, and the exchange of materials with the atmosphere; includes stems and leaves. (p. 281)

sistema de lanzamiento El sistema en una planta que incluye estructuras para fotosíntesis, apoyo, almacenaje y el intercambio de materias con la atmósfera; incluye pedúnculos y hojas.

simple machine
One of the basic machines on which all other mechanical machines are based. The six simple machines are the lever, inclined plane, wheel and axle, pulley, wedge, and screw. (p. 367)

máquina simple Una de las máquinas básicas sobre las cuales están basadas todas las demás máquinas mecánicas. Las seis máquinas simples son la palanca, el plano inclinado, la rueda y eje, la polea, la cuña y el tornillo.

GLOSSARY

skeletal muscle

A voluntary muscle that attaches to the skeleton. (p. 358)

músculo esquelético Un músculo voluntario que está sujeto al esqueleto.

skeletal system

The framework of bones that supports the body, protects internal organs, and anchors all the body's movement. (p. 349)

sistema óseo El armazón de huesos que sostiene al cuerpo, protege a los órganos internos y sirve de ancla para todo el movimiento del cuerpo.

smooth muscle

Muscle that performs involuntary movement and is found inside certain organs, such as the stomach. (p. 358)

músculo liso Músculos que realizan movimiento involuntario y se encuentran dentro de ciertos órganos, como el estómago.

sound

A pressure wave that is produced by a vibrating object and travels through matter. (p. 423)

sonido Un tipo de onda que es producida por un objeto que vibra y que viaja a través de la materia.

specialization

The specific organization of a cell and its structure that allows it to perform a specific function. (p. 28)

especialización La organización específica de una célula y de su estructura que le permite realizar una función específica.

speciation

The evolution of a new species from an existing species. (p. 198)

especiación La evolución de una nueva especie a partir de una especie existente.

species

A group of living things that are so closely related that they can breed with one another and produce offspring that can breed as well. (p. CA15)

especie Un grupo de organismos que están tan estrechamente relacionados que pueden aparearse entre sí y producir crías que también pueden aparearse.

sperm

A male reproductive cell (gamete) that forms in the male reproductive organs and has just a single copy of the genetic material of the parent. (p. 118)

espermatozoide Una célula reproductiva masculina (gameto) que se forma en los órganos reproductivos de un macho y tiene una sola copia del material genético del progenitor.

stomata

Openings in a plant's dermal tissue that control the exchange of water vapor, oxygen, and carbon dioxide with the atmosphere. (p. 278)

stomate Aperturas en los tejidos dermales de una planta, que controlan el intercambio de vapor de aguaoxígeno y dióxido de carbono con la atmósfera.

system

A group of objects or phenomena that interact. A system can be as simple as a rope, a pulley, and a mass. It also can be as complex as the interaction of energy and matter in the four parts of the Earth system.

sistema Un grupo de objetos o fenómenos que interactúan. Un sistema puede ser algo tan sencillo como una cuerda, una polea y una masa. También puede ser algo tan complejo como la interacción de la energía y la materia en las cuatro partes del sistema de la Tierra.

T

taxonomy

The science of classifying and naming organisms. (p. 232)

taxonomía La ciencia de clasificar y ponerle nombre a los organismos.

technology

The use of scientific knowledge to solve problems or engineer new products, tools, or processes.

tecnología El uso de conocimientos científicos para resolver problemas o para diseñar nuevos productos, herramientas o procesos.

theory

In science, a set of widely accepted explanations of observations and phenomena. A theory is a well-tested explanation that is consistent with all available evidence. (p. 211)

teoría En las ciencias, un conjunto de explicaciones de observaciones y fenómenos que es ampliamente aceptado. Una teoría es una explicación bien probada que es consecuente con la evidencia disponible.

tissue

A group of similar cells that are organized to do a specific job. (pp. 29, 272)

tejido Un grupo de células parecidas que juntas realizan una función específica en un organismo.

trait

1. A characteristic of an individual, such as a particular eye color; traits can be inherited or acquired.
2. Any type of feature that can be used to tell two species apart, such as size or bone structure.

rasgo 1. Característica de un individuo, tal como el color de los ojos; rasgos pueden ser heredados o adquiridos.
2. Cualquier característica que puede usarse para diferenciar a dos especies, como el tamaño o la estructura ósea.

transmit

To let pass through. (p. 469)

transmitir Dejar pasar a través.

U

umbilical cord

A long tube in a pregnant female mammal that connects the developing offspring to the placenta. (p. 338)

cordón umbilical Un largo tubo en un mamífero femenino que conecta a la cría en desarrollo a la placenta.

unicellular

A term used to describe an organism that is made up of a single cell. (p. 11)

unicelular Un término usado para describir a un organismo que está compuesto de una sola célula.

uniformitarianism

(YOO-nuh-FAWR-mih-TAIR-ee-uh-NIHZ-uhm)
A theory that processes shaping Earth today, such as erosion and deposition, also shaped Earth in the past, and that these processes cause large changes over geologic time. (p. 161)

uniformismo Una teoría que afirma que los procesos que le dan forma a la Tierra hoy en día, como la erosión y la sedimentación, también le dieron forma a la Tierra en el pasado; además, afirma que estos procesos ocasionan grandes cambios en tiempo geológico.

V

variable

Any factor that can change in a controlled experiment, observation, or model.

variable Cualquier factor que puede cambiar en un experimento controlado, en una observación o en un modelo.

vascular system (VAS-kyuh-lur)

Long tubelike tissues in plants through which water and nutrients move from one part of the plant to another. (p. 278)

sistema vascular Tejidos largos en forma de tubo en las plantas a través de los cuales se mueven agua y nutrientes de una parte de la planta a otra.

vegetative propagation

A form of asexual reproduction in plants, in which offspring are produced from non-reproductive tissues such as leaves, stems, and roots. (p. 323)

propagación vegetativa Una forma de reproducción asexual en las plantas, en la cual las crías son producidas de tejidos no productivos tales como hojas, y raíces.

vein

A blood vessel that carries blood back to the heart. (p. 394)

vena Un vaso sanguíneo que lleva la sangre de regreso al corazón.

vertebrate

An animal with an internal backbone. (p. 253)

vertebrado Un animal que tiene columna vertebral interna.

vestigial organ (veh-STIHJ-ee-uhl)

A physical structure that was fully developed and functional in an earlier group of organisms but is reduced and unused in later species. (p. 212)

órgano vestigial Una estructura física que fue completamente desarrollada y funcional en un grupo anterior de organismos pero que está reducido y en desuso en especies posteriores.

volume

An amount of three-dimensional space, often used to describe the space that an object takes up.

volumen Una cantidad de espacio tridimensional; a menudo se usa este término para describir el espacio que ocupa un objeto.

W, X, Y

wave
A disturbance that transfers energy from one place to another without requiring matter to move the entire distance. (p. 423)

> **onda** Una perturbación que transfiere energía de un lugar a otro sin que sea necesario que la materia se mueva toda la distancia.

wavelength
The distance from one wave crest to the next crest; the distance from any part of one wave to the identical part of the next wave. (p. 428)

> **longitud de onda** La distancia de una cresta de onda a la siguiente cresta; la distancia de cualquier parte de una onda a la parte idéntica de la siguiente onda.

Z

zygote
A fertilized egg formed by the union of an egg cell and a sperm cell; a zygote can develop into a mature individual. (p. 317)

> **cigoto** Un huevo fertilizado formado por la unión de la célula de un huevo y una célula de esperma; una cigota se puede desarrollar hasta convertirse en un individuo maduro.

Index

Page numbers for definitions are printed in **boldface** type.
Page numbers for illustrations, maps, and charts are printed in *italics.*

A

AbioCor heart, CA24, *CA24*, CA25
absolute age, **156,** 156, 158, 178
absolute dating, *157,* 158, 163, 176, 178, 224
absorb, **455**
absorption of light, 469, 472, 484, 495
   color perception and, 480, *480*
   by eye, 475, 476–477, *476, 477*
accuracy, **R22,** *R22*
acid, 33
acoustical engineers, 444
acoustics, 444
acquired traits, 101–102, 192
action forces, 366
active transport, 59–63, **60,** *60, 61,* 66
activity. *See* exercise.
adaptations, **CA15,** 195, **196,** 218, *218,* 320
   change in behavior, 194, *194,* 275
   change in color, *195, 198,* 275, *275*
   change in physiology, 60, 208, 275, 278
   change in structure, 193–194, *193, 194,* 195, *195,*
      197, 244, 277, 278, 282–283, *282, 283,* 288–289
   Chapter Investigation, 200–201, *200, 201*
   derived characteristics, 244
   for protection, *282,* 283, 289
   reproductive success and, 314–320, *314, 315, 317,*
      318, 319, 322–327, *323, 324,* 325, *325, 326, 327,*
      328, 329
adaptive traits
   evolution and, 196, *197*
   extinction and, 206–208
additive system, 478–479, *478,* 481
adenine (A), 215
   in DNA, 126–127, *126,* 128, 130–131, *132*
   in RNA, 130–131, *130, 132*
Adirondack Mountains, *162*
adolescence, 362
adrenal glands, 298, *299*
adrenaline, 297, 298, *299*
aerial roots, 283, *283*
Aerofoam, 491
Age of Mammals, 167
aging, 4, 76, 78, 298
agriculture
   genetic modification and, 140
   Medfly control, 321, *321*
   Mendel's experiment, 99, 104–105, *105,* 139, *139*
   selective breeding, 138, *138,* 195, *195*
AIDS, 408
air, CA19
   as fluid, 391, 409, *409*
   refraction of light and, 471, *471*
   sound waves and, 405, 424, *424,* 427, *427*

speed of light in, 502
   transmission of light, 469
air pressure, 388–389, *404,* 405
alcohol, 52, 53
alcoholic fermentation, 52–53
algae, 89, 187, 189, 211
Alhazen, Ali, 489
alleles, *102,* **103,** *103,* 105, 134, *134*
   dominant and recessive, 107, *107,* 110–112, *111,*
      113, 114
   genotype and phenotype, 106, *106*
   patterns of inheritance of, 110–112, *111, 113,*
      114–116, *115, 116,* 124, *124*
altitude, 409
Alvaro, Pascual-Leone, 266
amber, original remains in, 174, *174*
American chestnut trees, 205
amino acids, 43, *43,* 134
   assembly of, 126, 127, *127,* 129–131, *132,* 133. *See*
   also proteins.
ammonia, 186
ammonite fossils, *181*
amniotic fluid, 408
amoebas, 314
amphibians, 189, 253, 285, 313, 317
amplitude, 458, *458*
amplitude modulation, 458, *458*
AM radio, 458, *458*
analysis, critical, **R8**
anaphase
   of mitosis, *81,* 82, *83, 94, 97*
   I and II of meiosis, 120, *121*
ancestors, **211**
   branching diagrams of, 242–245, *242, 243, 244, 245*
   DNA similarities, 215–216, *216*
   similarities in development, 214, *214*
   similarities in structure, 212, *213*
angiosperms, 327, *327,* 342. *See also* flowering plants.
angle of incidence, 488, **496,** *496,* 500, *500,* 502,
   502, 516
angle of reflection, 488, **496,** *496,* 500, *500*
angular movement, 354, *354*
animal cells, 18, *24, 30, 52,* 252, 253, 285. *See also*
   eukaryotic cells.
   active transport and, 59–63
   basic processes in, 47, *47,* 50, *51,* 52–54, *52, 54*
   diffusion in, 57–59, *58*
   fluid pressure in, 402, *403*
   life cycle of, 80–82, *81, 83,* 84–85, *85*
   organelles of, 21, *21, 22,* 23–24, *23,* 50
   osmosis and, 59
   specialization of, 28
Animalia (kingdom), *236,* 248, 249, 250, **251,** 253,
   253, 258
animals, 37, 274. *See also* organ systems.

INDEX

diagrams, *445. See also* branching diagrams; Punnett square.
    interpretation of, 97, 181, *242,* 261, *305,* 383, *383,* 487, *487,* 527, *527*
    labeling, 242, *242, 243,* 247, *247*
    ray models, 471, *471,* 473, *473,* 479–480, 483, 495, 500
dialysis, 301, *301*
diaphragm, *388,* 389
diastolic pressure, 413
diatoms, *513*
dichotomous key, *230,* **231**
differentiation. *See* specialized cells.
diffraction fringes, 490, *490*
diffraction grating, 476, *476*
diffuse, **469**
diffuse reflection, 472, *473,* 484, 496
diffusion, **56,** 56–59, *57,* 64–65, *64,* 66, *66*
    of light, 469, *469,* 470, *470,* 472
    photographers' use of, 517, *517*
digestion, 273, 286, 287, *299*
digestive system, 253, 273, 294, 394, 407, R82–R83
    function of, 290, 297
    hibernation and, 275
    liver and, 297
    muscles in, 358
    organs of, 297
digital cameras, 515, *515*
digital imaging, 309, *309*
dinosaurs
    era of dominance of, *165,* 166
    extinction of, 146, 147, 167, 190, 208
    fossil evidence of, 171, 222, *222,* 224, *224*
    Mesosaurus, 162
    speed of, 177, *177*
    theropod, 176, *176*
diploid cells, 118–120, *118,* 122, *122,* 123, *123*
Diptera, *236*
direction of forces, 373, *373,* 378
    pulleys and, 368–369, *368*
disease
    bacteria causing, 14, 90–91, 300–301
    and homeostasis, 300–301
    sexually transmitted, 408
diabetes, 301
    genetic, 141
    genetic variation and, 316, *316*
    of heart, CA24
    high blood pressure, 413
    immune system and, 43, 300, *300*
    kidney failure, 301, *301*
    as limiting factor, 205, 207, *207,* 218
    natural selection and, 196, *197*
    studies of, 309
distance, 367, 368, 378
distribution of organisms. *See* geography, species distribution and.
diverge, **497,** *497,* 498, *498,* 503, *503,* 504, *505*
diverging lenses, 503, *503,* 506, *506,* 507, *507. See also* concave lenses.
    contact lenses, 522, *522*
diversity, sexual reproduction and, 92
DNA (deoxyribonucleic acid), CA23, 43–44, **74,** 75, 94, *94. See also* chromosomes; genes.
    analysis of, *457*

    in asexual reproduction, 314, 316
    bromodeoxyuridine (BrdU) and, 79
    cell division and, 75, *75,* 81, *81,* 82, *83,* 85
    classification of organisms by, 239, 241, *241,* 242, 256
    in conjugation, 319
    control of development, 3–5, *3, 4–5,* 214
    damage from radiation, 321, 460
    disease and, 141
    in eukaryotes, 252
    as evidence of evolution, 215–216, *216*
    fertilization and, 337
    as fingerprint, 138, 140, 141, *141*
    fossil classification and, 225
    function of, 125, *126*
    genes and, 102, *102*
    Hox genes, 3–5, *3, 4–5*
    Human Genome Project and, 138, 141, *141*
    identification of organisms, 229
    information passed from parents to offspring, 102–107, *106, 107,* 111–112, *111,* 125, 126, 140
    information passed from parent to offspring, 216
    location of, 75, *75, 126*
    mapping of, 138, 141, *141*
    meiosis and, 98, 119–120, *120, 121,* 315
    in mitochondria, 118
    mitosis and, *81,* 82, *83, 94, 97, 120*
    models of, 32, *32,* 74, *74*
    modification of, 92, 140, *140,* 141, *141*
    molecular structure of, 126–127, *126,* 140, *140*
    protein production by, 98, 134
    replication of, 81, 128–129, *128, 129,* 314
    self-fertilization and, 319
    in sexual reproduction, 317, 319, 320
    similarities in different species, 215–216, *216,* 217
    structure of, 74–75, *74, 75,* 102
    testing in criminal cases, 138, 140
    transcription, 130, *130*
    triplet code, 126–127, *127*
    variations in organisms and, 196, *197*
    x-ray images of, 32, 140, *140,* 461
DNA fingerprints, 138, 140, 141, *141*
dolphins, 418, *418*
domains, **249,** 249
    Archaea, 27
    Bacteria, 27
    Eukarya, 27, 28
dominant alleles, **107,** *107,* 110–112, *111, 113,* 114, 124, 134
Donald, Ian, 308
donor cells, 317, 319, *319*
double-pan balance, R19, *R19*
drawing conclusions, R35
drought, 205
dry fruits, 329
dyes, 46, *46*
dystrophin, 126

E

ear canal, 436, *436,* 440
eardrum, *404,* 405, **436,** *436,* 440, 443
earplugs, 443

F

INDEX

INDEX

INDEX

M

INDEX

INDEX

U

INDEX

Acknowledgments

Photography

Cover © SeaPics.com; **i** © SeaPics.com; **iii** *top to bottom left* Photograph of James Trefil by Evan Cantwell; Photograph of Rita Ann Calvo by Joseph Calvo; Photograph of Linda Carnin by Amilcar Cifuentes; Photograph of Sam Miller by Samuel Miller; *top to bottom right* Photograph of Kenneth Cutler by Kenneth A. Cutler; Photograph of Donald Steely by Marni Stamm; Photograph of Vicky Vachon by Redfern; **v** *left top to bottom* © William M. Bruce; © Jack Castro; Courtesy of Dr. Bernice Filerman; © Mark Handwerker; Courtesy of Sandy Steinburg; **viii** © Kent Foster Photographs/Bruce Coleman, Inc.; **x** © Louis Psihoyos/psihoyos.com; **xii** © Harald Sund/Getty Images; **xiv** © Chip Simons/Getty Images; **xx** Photograph by Frank Siteman; **xxi** *left* Photograph by Sharon Hoogstraten, *right* Photograph by Frank Siteman; **CA1** Photograph by Frank Siteman; **CA11–CA12** © Mark Hamblin/Age Fotostock America Inc.; **CA13–CA14** © Nick Vedros & Assoc./Getty Images; **CA15–CA16** © Jack Affleck/SuperStock; **CA17–CA18** © Tim Fitzharris/Masterfile; **CA19** *bottom right* © Shin Yoshino/Minden Pictures; **CA19** *bottom left* © Michael Gadomski/Animals Animals; **CA20** © Laif Elleringmann/Aurora Photos; **CA21** © Pascal Goetgheluck/Science Photo Library/Photo Researchers, Inc.; **CA22** Sinsheimer Labs/University of California, Santa Cruz; **CA22** *top right* © James King-Holmes/Science Photo Library/Photo Researchers, Inc.; **CA22** *left* © David Parker/Science Photo Library/Photo Researchers, Inc.; **CA23–CA24** *bottom* John Lair, Jewish Hospital, University of Louisville; **CA24** *top* © Brand X Pictures/Alamy; *bottom* AbioMed.

Unit 1

Divider © Dr. Gopal Murti/Photo Researchers, Inc.; **1** © Dr. Gopal Murti/Photo Researchers, Inc.; **2–3** © Mark Smith/Photo Researchers, Inc.; **4** *bottom* © Chedd-Angier Production Company; **5** *top* © Inga Spence/Visuals Unlimited; *bottom* © Carolina Biological/Visuals Unlimited; **6–7** © Biophoto Associates/Photo Researchers, Inc.; **7** Photograph by Frank Siteman; **9** © Nicola Tree/Alamy Images; **10** © Heintges/Premium Stock/PictureQuest; **11** *inset* © Science VU/Visuals Unlimited; *bottom* © David Stone/RAINBOW/PictureQuest; **12** *left* © American Registry of Photography; *right* Library of Congress; **13** *right inset* © Greg Theiman; *bottom* © Tom Walker/Visuals Unlimited, Inc.; **14** © Will & Demi McIntyre/Corbis; **16** *bottom left* Photograph by Ken O'Donoghue; **16** *top* © Science VU/Visuals Unlimited; *center* Photograph by Frank Siteman; *bottom* Photograph by Ken O'Donoghue; **18** *inset* © Dr. Gary Gaugler/Visuals Unlimited, Inc.; Photograph by Ken O'Donoghue; **19** *top* © Eye of Science/Photo Researchers, Inc.; *bottom* © Eye of Science/Photo Researchers, Inc.; **20** *left* © Eric Grave/Photo Reseachers, Inc.; *right* © CNRI/Photo Reseachers, Inc.; **21** *top* Photograph by Ken O'Donoghue; *bottom left* © Biophoto Associates/Science Source/Photo Researchers, Inc.; *bottom right* © Dennis Kunkel/Phototake; **23** © Dr. Martha Powell/Visuals Unlimited, Inc.; **24** *top* © Dr. Henry Aldrich/Visuals Unlimited, Inc.; *bottom* © Biophoto Associates/Photo Researchers, Inc.; **25** *top* © Dr. Gary Gaugler/Visuals Unlimited, Inc.; *bottom* © Dr. Tony Brain and David Parker/Photo Reseachers, Inc.; **26** Photograph by Ken O'Donoghue; **27** *inset* © Alfred Pasieka/Photo Researchers, Inc.; © Ralph White/Corbis; **28** © Stan Flegler/Visuals Unlimited, Inc.; **29** *left* © Ted Whittenkraus/Visuals Unlimited, Inc.; *center* © Gustav Verderber/Visuals Unlimited, Inc.; *right* © Dwight R. Kuhn; **30** *left* © Eric and David Hosking/Corbis; *right* © Frans Lanting/Minden Pictures; **31** Photograph by Ken O'Donoghue; **32** *background* © Ken Eward/BioGrafx/Photo Researchers, Inc.; *bottom* © A. Barrington Brown/Photo Researchers, Inc.; **33** *background* © NOAA Restoration Center & Damage Assessment and Restoration Program; *left* Photo by Philip Bond. Courtesy, Katrina Edwards; *right* Photo by Brett Baker; **34** *top left* © David Stone/RAINBOW/PictureQuest; *top right* © Science VU/Visuals Unlimited; *center left* © CNRI/Photo Reseachers, Inc.; *bottom* © Frans Lanting/Minden Pictures; **35** © Dr. Martha Powell/Visuals Unlimited, Inc.; **36** © Tom Walker/Visuals Unlimited, Inc.; *right inset* © Greg Theiman; **38–39** © Kent Foster Photographs/Bruce Coleman, Inc.; **42** *top* © Corbis/Royalty Free; **42, 43**; **44** *left* © Alfred Pasieka/Photo Researchers, Inc.; *right* Photograph by Ken O'Donoghue; **46** *background left* © Andrew Syred/Photo Researchers, Inc.; *center* © Andrew Syred/Photo Researchers, Inc.; *center right* © Dr. Jeremy Burgess/Photo Researchers, Inc.; *bottom left* © Anna Clopet/Corbis **47** *right* © David Young-Wolff/PhotoEdit; *top inset* © John Durham/Photo Researchers, Inc.; *bottom inset* © Innerspace Imaging/Photo Researchers, Inc.; **48** © Dr. Jeremy Burgess/Photo Researchers; **49** *top center* © Biophoto Associates/Science Source/Photo Researchers, Inc.; **51** *top left* © Dr. Gopal Murti/Photo

ACKNOWLEDGMENTS

Researchers, Inc.; *top right* © Biophoto Associates/Science Source/Photo Researchers, Inc.; **54** © Bob Daemmrich Photo, Inc.; **55** © Roger Ressmeyer/Corbis; **59** *top left* © Marilyn Schaller/Photo Researchers, Inc.; *top right* © Marilyn Schaller/Photo Researchers, Inc.; **60** © Fred Bavendam/Peter Arnold, Inc.; **62** Photograph by Frank Siteman; **64** *top* © Corbis/Royalty Free; *bottom* Photograph by Ken O'Donoghue; **66** *bottom right* © Fred Bavendam/Peter Arnold, Inc.; **70–71** © CNRI/Photo Researchers, Inc.; **71** Photograph by Frank Siteman; **73** Photograph by Ken O'Donoghue; **74** © Will & Deni McIntyre/Photo Researchers, Inc.; **76** Photograph by Frank Siteman; **77** *left inset* © Alexis Rosenfeld/Photo Researchers, Inc.; *right inset* © David Hughes/Bruce Coleman, Inc.; *bottom* © Rudiger Lehnen/Photo Researchers, Inc.; **79** *left* © Nancy Kedersha/UCLA/Photo Researchers, Inc.; *right* Denise Applewhite; **80** *top left* © IFA/eStock Photo/PictureQuest; *top right* © IFA/eStock Photo/PictureQuest; *bottom left* © IFA/eStock Photo/PictureQuest; *bottom right* © IFA/eStock Photo/PictureQuest; **83** © Ed Reschke; **84** Photograph by Ken O'Donoghue; **85** *left* © Dr. Gopal Murti/Photo Researchers, Inc.; *right* © Carolina Biological/Visuals Unlimited; **86** *top left* © Michael Newman/PhotoEdit, Inc.; *top right* Photograph by Ken O'Donoghue; *center* © Science VU/Visuals Unlimited; *bottom left* Photograph by Ken O'Donoghue; *bottom right* © Custom Medical Stock Photo; **88** © M.I. Walker/Photo Researchers, Inc.; **89** *top* © Biophoto Associates/Photo Researchers, Inc.; *bottom* © CNRI/Photo Researchers, Inc.; **90** © David B. Fleetham/Visuals Unlimited; **91** *top* © Cytographics/Visuals Unlimited; *bottom* Photograph by Ken O'Donoghue; **93** © Collection CNRI/Phototake; **94** *top* © Will & Deni McIntyre/Photo Researchers, Inc.; **98–99** © Norbert Rosing/National Geographic Image Collection; **99** *top right* © Photodisc/Getty Images; **101** © Florence Delva/Getty Images; **103** *left* © CNRI/Photo Researchers, Inc.; *inset* © Biophoto Associates/Photo Researchers, Inc.; **106** © Mary Kate Denny/PhotoEdit; **107** © Ken Weingart/Corbis; **108** *top* © Johnny Johnson/Animals Animals; *bottom* Photograph by Ken O'Donoghue; **109, 110** Photograph by Ken O'Donoghue; **113** *background* © Ludovic Maisant/Corbis; *bottom right* © Jane Burton/Bruce Coleman, Inc.; **113**; **113** Illustration by Mick Posen/Wildlife Art Ltd.; **116** *left* © Robert Dowling/Corbis; **119** *top, bottom* © Pascal Goetgheluck/Photo Researchers, Inc.; **123** © David M. Phillips/Photo Researchers, Inc.; **125** Photograph by Ken O'Donoghue; **138** *top left* Library of Congress, Prints and Photographs Division; *top right* Courtesy of The Royal Society of London; *bottom* Courtesy of Professor John Doebley, Genetics Department, University of Wisconsin; **139** *top left* Library and Archives of the Royal Botanical Gardens, Kew; *top center* Drawing by Edward Strasburger; *top right* © Oliver Meckes/Photo Researchers, Inc.; *center left* © Margaret Stones; *bottom* © Vic Small; **140** *top right* © Dr. Gopal Murti/Photo Researchers, Inc.; *top left* Reproduced from *The Journal of Experimental Medicine*, 1944, vol. 79, 158–159, by copyright permission of the Rockefeller University Press; *center left* © Omikron/Photo Researchers, Inc.; *bottom left* © Lennart Nilson/Albert Bonniers Forlag AB; **141** *top left* © David Parker/Photo Researchers, Inc.; *top right* © emeagwali.com; *center* Courtesy of The Whitehead Institute/MIT Center for Genome Research; *bottom* Courtesy of the USC-Keck School of Medicine and Ashanti DeSilva.

Unit 2
Divider © Martin Siepman/Age Fotostock America Inc.; **143** © Martin Siepman/Age Fotostock America Inc.; **144–145** © Alfredo Maiquez/Lonely Planet Images; **145** *left* © Donald Windsor; *bottom* Reprinted with permission from *Timing the Radiations of Leaf Beetles: Hispines on Gingers from Latest Cretaceous to Recent* Peter Wilf and Conrad C. Labandeira, SCIENCE V. 289:291–294 (2000). © 2000 AAAS.; **146** *top left, top right* NASA/Johnson Space Center/Earth Sciences and Image Analysis; *bottom* © The Chedd-Angier Production Company; **147** © The Natural History Museum, London; © Dr. Jin Fan; **148–149** © Louis Psihoyos/psihoyos.com; **149** Photograph by Sharon Hoogstraten; **151** © Digital Vision; **153** *center left* © Andrew J. Martinez/Photo Researchers, Inc.; *center right* © Arthur R. Hill/Visuals Unlimited; **154** *top* © 1993 Tom Bean; *bottom right* © Asa C. Thoresen/Photo Researchers, Inc.; *bottom left* © Dr. Morley Read/Photo Researchers, Inc.; **155** *top* © Sinclair Stammers/Photo Researchers, Inc.; *bottom* Photograph by Sharon Hoogstraten; **157** *background* © G. Brad Lewis/Getty Images; **159** *left* © Jonathan Blair/Corbis; *inset* AP/Wide World Photos; **161** *top left, top right* © John Marshall Photography; *top center* © Wayne Lawler/Photo Researchers, Inc.; **162** *top* © Sime s.a.s./eStock Photography/PictureQuest; **164** *left* Mural by Peter Sawyer © National Museum of Natural History, Smithsonian Institution, Washington, D.C.; *right* Exhibit Museum of Natural History, The University of Michigan, Ann Arbor, Michigan; **165** *left* © Ludek Pesek/Photo Researchers, Inc.; *right* © David Peevers/Lonely Planet Images; **167** © Sisse Brimberg/National Geographic Image Collection; **168** *top* © Jonathan Blair/Corbis; *bottom* Photograph by Sharon Hoogstraten; **170** Photograph by Sharon Hoogstraten; **171** *top* © Mark A. Schneider/Photo Researchers, Inc.; **171** *bottom* © Sinclair Stammers/

Photo Researchers, Inc.; **172** © 2001 Tom Bean; **173** *background* © Images Ideas, Inc./PictureQuest; *top left* © Dorling Kindersley; *top right* © John Elk III; *center right* © Kaj R. Svensson/Photo Researchers, Inc.; *bottom right* © Francesc Muntada/Corbis; **174** *left* Courtesy, Latreille-Cerpolex; **174** *center* © Alfred Pasteka/Photo Researchers, Inc.; *right* © Dominique Braud/ Animals Animals/Earth Scenes; **175** *top* © B & C Alexander; *bottom* © Doug Wilson/Corbis; **176** Courtesy, American Museum of Natural History; **177** © Chris Butler/Photo Researchers, Inc.; *inset* © Robert Dowling/Corbis; **178** *top* © Asa C. Thoresen/Photo Researchers, Inc.; **185** Photograph by Frank Siteman; **186** © Georgette Douwma/Nature Picture Library; **187** Photograph by Frank Siteman; **188** *left* © Dr. Jeremy Burgess/Photo Researchers, Inc.; **189** *bottom left* © Lynette Cook/Photo Researchers, Inc.; **190** *left, right* © D. Van Ravenswaay/Photo Researchers, Inc.; **191** *left* Photograph by Ken O'Donoghue; *right* © Corbis-Royalty Free; **192–193** *background* © Ralph Lee Hopkins/Lonely Planet Images; **192** *top* © The Granger Collection, New York; *bottom* © The Natural History Museum, London; **193** *top* © Volker Steger/Photo Researchers, Inc.; *center left* © Theo Allots/Visuals Unlimited; *center right* © Zig Leszczynski/Animals Animals; **194** *insets* Illustration by Peter Scott/Wildlife Art Ltd.; *background* © Ralph Lee Hopkins/Lonely Planet Images; **194** *top left* © Tui de Roy/Bruce Coleman, Inc.; *top right* © Tui De Roy/Minden Pictures; *bottom left* © Richard I'Anson/Lonely Planet Images; *bottom right* © Tui de Roy/Bruce Coleman, Inc.; **195** *left* © Larry Allan/Bruce Coleman, Inc.; *center* © Larry Allan/Bruce Coleman, Inc.; *right* © Hans Reinhard/Bruce Coleman, Inc.; **197** *background* © Paul Souders/Accent Alaska; *top left inset* © Bruce Coleman, Inc.; **198** *top* © Hans Reinhard/Bruce Coleman, Inc.; *center* © Jane Burton/Bruce Coleman, Inc.; *bottom* © Jane Burton/Bruce Coleman, Inc.; **199** © David Lyons/Alamy Images; **200** *top* © DigitalVision/PictureQuest; **201** *top left* Photograph by Frank Siteman; *center left* © Corbis-Royalty Free; *middle* © Frans Lemmens/Getty Images; *center right* © Arthur Morris/Corbis; **202** © David M. Phillips/Photo Researchers, Inc.; **203** © COLOR-PIC/Animals Animals-Earth Scenes; **204** © Stephen J. Krasemann/DRK Photo; **205** *top* © Peter Lewis/Alamy Images; *bottom* © ML Sinibaldi/Corbis; **207** © Michael Nichols/National Geographic Images/Getty Images; **209** *left* © Ron Garrison/Zoological Society of San Diego; **210** © culliganphoto/Alamy Images; **211** *left* © Mark A. Schneider/Photo Researchers, Inc.; **213** *background* © Corbis-Royalty Free; **214** *bottom left, bottom center* © Photodisc/Getty Images; *bottom right* © Mark Smith/Photo Researchers, Inc.; **215** Photograph by Frank Siteman; **216** © Photodisc/Getty Images; **217** © Mary Evans Picture Library; **218** *left center* © Tui de Roy/Bruce Coleman, Inc.; *bottom left* © Mark A. Schneider/Photo Researchers, Inc.; **220** © Jane Burton/Bruce Coleman, Inc.; **222** *bottom right* © Visuals Unlimited; *bottom left, top right* The Natural History Museum Picture Library, London; **223** *top left* American Museum of Natural History Library; *bottom right* © O. Louis Mazzatenta/National Geographic Image Collection; *center* © Peter Scoones/Photo Researchers, Inc.; *top right* © Geoff Bryant/Photo Researchers, Inc.; **224** *top left* © Science/Visuals Unlimited; *top right* © Kevin O. Mooney/Odyssey/ Chicago; *center right* © Ira Block/National Geographic Image Collection; *bottom left* © James King-Holmes/Photo Researchers, Inc.; **225** *top left* © John Reader/Science Photo Library; *bottom left* © David Parker/Photo Researchers, Inc; *top right* © Dr. Jin Fan; **226–227** © Burke/Triolo/Artville: Bugs and Insects; **227** Photograph by Frank Siteman; **229** *top* © Photodisc/Getty Images; *bottom* Photograph by Frank Siteman; **230** *background* © Photodisc/Getty Images; *top right* Robert Della-Piana/photolibrary /PictureQuest; **232** *top left* © Len Rue, Jr./Bruce Coleman, Inc.; *bottom left* © Tom McHugh/Photo Researchers. Inc.; *bottom center* © Renee Lynn/Photo Researchers, Inc.; *bottom right* © Frans Lanting/ Minden Pictures; **233** Photograph by Ken O'Donoghue; **234** *left* © Joe McDonald/Visuals Unlimited; *right* © Photodisc/Getty Images; **235** *background* © Visuals Unlimited; *foreground* © John Mitchell/ Photo Researchers, Inc.; **236** *left* © S.J. Krasemann/Photo Researchers, Inc.; *right* © David I. Roberts/ Photo Researchers, Inc.; **237** *left* © Kennan Ward/Corbis; *right* © Frans Lanting/Minden Pictures; **238** *top* © Robert Pickett/Corbis; *bottom* © U.S. Fish & Wildlife Service; **239** *background* © E.R. Degginger/ Photo Researchers, Inc.; *top left, center* © Dave Fleetham/Tom Stack & Associates; *bottom left* © Norbert Wu; *right* © Bill Kamin/Visuals Unlimited; **240** *left* © D. Ditchburn/Visuals Unlimited; *right* © M.H. Sharp/Photo Researchers, Inc.; **241** *background* © Corbis-Royalty Free; *top left* © Fritz Polking/ POLKI/Bruce Coleman, Inc.; *top right* © Tom Brakefield/Bruce Coleman, Inc.; *bottom left* © G.C. Kelley/Photo Researchers, Inc.; *bottom right* © Tom McHugh/Photo Researchers, Inc.; **242** *left* © Tom McHugh/Photo Researchers, Inc.; *center left* © Tom Brakefield/Bruce Coleman, Inc.; *center right* © G.C. Kelley/Photo Researchers, Inc.; *right* © Fritz Polking/POLKI/Bruce Coleman, Inc.; **244** © Jeff Foott/PictureQuest; **246** © Louis Psihoyos/Corbis; **248** © Ken Lucas/Visuals Unlimited; **249** *left* © CNRI/ Photo Researchers, Inc.; *center* © Wolfgang Baumeister/Photo Researchers, Inc.; *right* © Biophoto Associates/Photo Researchers, Inc.; **250** *background* © NASA/Corbis; *top right* © Corbis-Royalty Free;

second from top right © Sharna Balfour/Gallo Images/Corbis; *third from top right* © Eric Grave/Photo Researchers, Inc.; *fifth from top right* © Eye of Science/Photo Researchers, Inc.; *fifth from top right* © Rico & Ruiz/Nature Picture Library; *bottom* © Dr. Jeremy Burgess/Photo Researchers, Inc.; **252** *left* © Steve Solum/Bruce Coleman, Inc.; *center* © Hal Horwitz/Corbis; *right* © Nick Garbutt/Nature Picture Library; **253** *left* © M. & C. Photography/Peter Arnold, Inc.; *center* © Jim Zuckerman/Corbis; *right* © Masa Ushioda/Bruce Coleman, Inc.; **254** Photograph by Frank Siteman; **255** *top* © Jeff Foott/Bruce Coleman, Inc.; *bottom left* © Cordelia Molloy/Photo Researchers, Inc.; *bottom right* © Mark Taylor, Warren Photographic/Bruce Coleman, Inc.; **256** *top* © Gary Gaugler/Visuals Unlimited; *bottom* © Dr. M. Rohde, GBF/Photo Researchers, Inc.; **257** © Jane Burton/Bruce Coleman, Inc.; **258** © Mark A. Schneider/ Photo Researchers, Inc.

Unit 3
Divider © Ronnie Kaufman/Corbis; **263** © Ronnie Kaufman/Corbis; © Dr. N.S. Kapany; **268–269** © Harald Sund/Getty Images; **269** *left* © Steven Frame/Stock Boston Inc./PictureQuest; *right* © Rod Planck/Photo Researchers, Inc.; **271** AP/Wide World Photos; **272** Photograph by Frank Siteman; **273** © Joe McDonald/Bruce Coleman, Inc.; **274** *top* © D. Suzio/Photo Researchers, Inc.; *bottom* © D. Suzio/Photo Researchers, Inc.; **275** *top* © Jim Merli/Visuals Unlimited; *bottom* © Jim Merli/Visuals Unlimited; **276** *background* © Hulton-Deutsch Collection/Corbis; *inset* © Underwood & Underwood/Corbis; **277** Photograph by Ken O'Donoghue; **278** *top, bottom* © Dr. Jeremy Burgess/ Photo Researchers, Inc.; **279** © Andrew Syred/Photo Researchers, Inc.; **281** *top* © Peter Dean/Grant Heilman Photography; *inset* © Pascal Goetgheluck/Photo Researchers, Inc.; *bottom* © Ed Webber/ Visuals Unlimited; **282** *top* © Craig K. Lorenz/Photo Researchers, Inc.; *bottom* © Gary W. Carter/Visuals Unlimited; **283** © Carlyn Iverson/Photo Researchers, Inc.; **284** *left* © Patricia Agre/Photo Researchers, Inc.; *inset* © Martin B. Withers; Frank Lane Picture Agency/Corbis; **286** *top* © Joe McDonald/Bruce Coleman, Inc.; *bottom* © Dwight R. Kuhn; **287** © J. Sneesby/B. Wilkins/Getty Images; **288** *top* © Arthur Morris/Visuals Unlimited; *bottom* © Steve Wolper/DRK Photo; **289** © Corbis/Royalty Free; **290** *top* © Brandon Cole; *bottom* © Ron Austing/Photo Researchers, Inc.; **291** © Konrad Wothe/Minden Pictures; **292** © Robert Holmes/Corbis; **294** © SuperStock; **295** Photograph by Frank Siteman; **296** © Norbert Schaefer/Corbis; **297** *top* © Ronnie Kaufman/Corbis; *bottom* © Kwame Zikomo/SuperStock; **298** © ISM/Phototake; **300** *top* © Mary Kate Denny/PhotoEdit; *bottom* © Eddy Gray/Photo Researchers, Inc.; **301** © BSIP/Phototake; **306** *top* © Hulton Archive/Getty Images, *bottom* © Simon Fraser/Photo Researchers, Inc.; **307** *top* © Bettmann/Corbis, *center* © Underwood & Underwood/Corbis, *bottom* © George Bernard/Photo Researchers, Inc.; **308** *top left* © Collection CNRI/Phototake, *top right* © Geoff Tompkinson/ Photo Researchers, Inc., *bottom* © Josh Sher/Photo Researchers, Inc.; **309** *top left* © Simon Fraser/Photo Researchers, Inc., *top right* © Dr. N.S. Kapany; *bottom* © GJLP/Photo Researchers, Inc.; **310–311** © Comstock Images/Alamy Images; **311** © Photospin; **313** © Carmela Leszczynski/Animals Animals/Earth Scenes; **314** *top* © David Scharf/Photo Researchers, Inc.; *bottom* © Dr. Gopal Murti/ Photo Researchers, Inc.; **315** *top* © Tom Adams/Visuals Unlimited; *bottom* © Sinclair Stammers/Photo Researchers, Inc.; **316** © H. Reinhard/zefa/Corbis; **317** © Jose B. Ruiz/naturepl.com; **318** *top* © David Dixon/Ardea London Limited; *bottom* Photograph by Frank Siteman; **319** *top* © Adrian Davies/ naturepl.com; *bottom* © David Scharf/Photo Researchers, Inc.; **320** © Anthony Mercieca/Animals Animals/Earth Scenes; **321** © Ed Young/Alamy Images; *inset* © USDA/Nature Source/Photo Researchers, Inc.; **323** *top* © Evan Sklar/Getty Images; *center* © Nigel Cattlin/Alamy Images; *bottom* © Wally Eberhart/Visuals Unlimited; **324** © Dwight R. Kuhn; **325** *top* © Sylvester Allred/Fundamental Photographs; *inset* © Dwight R. Kuhn; *bottom* © Dwight R. Kuhn; **326** © Scott Barrow/International Stock Photo; **327** © Ed Reschke; **328** *background* © John Marshall; *left* © George D. Lepp/Corbis; *center* © Sergio Piumatti; *right* © Gary Braasch/Corbis; **330** *top* © Michael J. Doolittle/Image Works, Inc.; *right* © James A. Sugar/Corbis; **331** Photograph by Frank Siteman; **334** © Biophoto Associates/ Photo Researchers, Inc.; **339** *left* © Dr. Yorgos Nikas/Photo Researchers, Inc.; *right* © Yoav Levy/ Phototake; **340** © David Degnan/Corbis; **341** *left* © Christopher Brown/Stock Boston, Inc./PictureQuest; *right* © Nissim Men/Photonica; **346–347** © Chris Hamilton/Corbis; **347** *top* Photograph by Frank Siteman; *center right* Photograph by Ken O'Donoghue; **349** *center* Photograph by Frank Siteman; **351** © PhotoDisc/Getty Images; **352** © Prof. P. Motta/Dept. of Anatomy/University La Sapienza, Rome/Photo Researchers, Inc.; **353** *top* © Zephyr/Photo Researchers, Inc.; *bottom* Photograph by Frank Siteman; **354** © D. Roberts/Photo Researchers, Inc.; **355** © Stammers/Thompson/Photo Researchers, Inc.; **356** Photograph by Frank Siteman; **357** © Kevin R. Morris/Corbis; **359** *background* © Mary Kate Denny/PhotoEdit; *insets*, *top* © Martin Rotker/Phototake; *left* © Triarch/Visuals Unlimited;

bottom © Eric Grave/Phototake; **360** AP/Wide World Photos; **362** © Jeff Greenberg/PhotoEdit; **363** © Corbis/Royalty Free; **364** Photograph by Sharon Hoogstraten; **365** © Dennis Kunkel/Phototake; **366** *top, bottom* © Jane Faircloth/Transparencies, Inc.; **368** © Tom Stewart/Corbis; **369** © Stock Connection Distribution/Alamy Images; **370** AP/Wide World Photos; **372** © Geoff Dann/DK Images; **373** © David Young-Wolff/PhotoEdit; **375** © Srdjan Mihic/Diomedia/Alamy Images; **377** © Visions of America, LLC/Alamy Images; **378** © MedioImages Fresca Collection/Alamy Images; **384–385** © Professors P.M. Motta & S. Correr/Photo Researchers, Inc.; **385** Photograph by Ken O'Donoghue; **387** © Richard Folwell/Photo Researchers, Inc.; **388** *left* © Michael Newman/PhotoEdit; **389** Photograph by Ken O'Donoghue; **391** © Akhil Bakshi/Alamy Images; **392** © David R. Frazier Photolibrary, Inc./Alamy Images; **395** *inset* © Dr. Gladden Willis/Visuals Unlimited; *right* © Myrleen Ferguson Cate/PhotoEdit; **396** © Corbis/Royalty Free; **397** *top* © Susumu Nishinaga/Photo Researchers, Inc.; *bottom* © Custom Medical Stock Photo; **400** *top left* © Mauro Fermariello/Photo Researchers, Inc.; **402** © Royalty-Free/Getty Images-Photodisc Green; **403** *top* © Custom Medical Stock Photo; *center* © James Cavallini/Photo Researchers, Inc.; *bottom* © age fotostock/SuperStock; **406** *left* © Huy Nguyen/ Dallas Morning News/Corbis; **407** *inset* © Custom Medical Stock Photo; © Ty Allison/Getty Images; **408** © Custom Medical Stock Photo; **409** *left* © Wade Eakle/Lonely Planet Images; *right* Photo by Mark Udall, courtesy of Chinook Medical Gear, Inc.; **410** © Akhil Bakshi/Alamy Images.

Unit 4

Divider © Scott Tysick/Masterfile; **415** © Scott Tysick/Masterfile; **416–417** © Paul Kuroda/SuperStock; **417** *top* © Powerstock/SuperStock; *bottom* © B. Benoit/Photo Researchers, Inc.; **418** *top* © Stephen Frink/Corbis; *bottom* © The Chedd-Angier Production Company; **419** © George Stetten, M.D., Ph.D; **420–421** © Chip Simons/Getty Images; **421, 423, 426** Photograph by Sharon Hoogstraten; **427** © Jeff Rotman/Getty Images; **430** © Stockbyte Platinum/Alamy Images; **431** *left* © eStock Photo/Alamy Images; *right* © GDT/Getty Images; **432** Photograph by Sharon Hoogstraten; **434** *left top to bottom* © Will Crocker/Getty Images; © Dorling Kindersley; © Photodisc/Getty Images; © Dorling Kindersley © Photodisc/Getty Images; © Stephen Dalton/Animals Animals; © Steve Bloom/Getty Images; *top right* © Don Smetzer/Getty Images; *bottom right* Brian Gordon Green/National Geographic Image Collection; **435** Photograph by Sharon Hoogstraten; **437** © CNIR/Photo Researchers, Inc.; **438** © Corbis; **440** © Tom Main/Getty Images; **441** © Anatomical Travelogue/Photo Researchers, Inc.; **443** *top* © Yehoash Raphael, Kresge Hearing Research Institute, The University of Michigan; *bottom* © Yehoash Raphael, Kresge Hearing Research Institute, The University of Michigan; **444** *left* © Roger Ressmeyer/Corbis; *right* Symphony Center, Home of the Chicago Symphony Orchestra; **445** © Chris Shinn/Getty Images; **446** *bottom* © Anatomical Travelogue/Photo Researchers, Inc.; **448** © Photodisc/Getty Images; **450–451** © Alan Kearney/Getty Images; **451** *top* Photograph by Ken O'Donoghue; *bottom* NASA/ The EIT Consortium; **453** Photograph by Sharon Hoogstraten; **455** © Yoav Levy/Phototake; **456** *left* © China Tourism Press/Getty Images; *center* © David Nunek/Photo Researchers, Inc.; *right* © Dr. Arthur Tucker/Photo Researchers, Inc.; **457** *left* © Jeremy Woodhouse/Getty Images; *center left* © Sinclair Stammers/Photo Researchers, Inc.; *center right* © Hugh Turvey/Photo Researchers, Inc.; *right* © Alfred Pasieka/Photo Researchers; **459** © Dr. Arthur Tucker/Photo Researchers, Inc.; **468** *left, right* © Thomas Eisner, Cornell University; **469** © Martin Spinks; **470** *background* NASA/JHU/AUI/R. Giacconi et al.; *top* Palomar Observatory/Caltech/SAO; *center* NASA/MSFC/SAO; *bottom* NASA/CXC/SAO; **471** *top* © API/Alamy Images; *center right* © Robert F. Sisson/National Geographic Image Collection; **472** © Volker Steger/Photo Researchers, Inc.; **473** Photograph by Sharon Hoogstraten; **474** *background* © Eye of Science/Photo Researchers, Inc.; *left* © Adam Hart-Davis/Photo Researchers, Inc.; *right* © David Parker/Photo Researchers, Inc.; **475** © Traffic Technologies; **476** Photograph by Sharon Hoogstraten; **477** © Jeff Greenberg/Visuals Unlimited; **478** © Raymond Gehman/Corbis; **479** © Jeremy Woodhouse/PhotoDisc Green; **480** © Laura Dwight/Corbis; **483** © Age Fotostock/SuperStock; **484** © David A. Hardy/Photo Researchers, Inc.; **485** © Eye of Science/Photo Researchers, Inc.; **486** © Bill Beatty/Visuals Unlimited; **487** © Jeff Greenberg/Visuals Unlimited; **488** © Dorling Kindersley; **490** *top left* © Michael Newman/PhotoEdit; *bottom left, bottom right* Photograph by Sharon Hoogstraten; **491** *top left, center right* Photograph by Sharon Hoogstraten; © Bettmann/Corbis; **492–493** © Tom Raymond/Getty Images; **493** *top* Photograph by Sharon Hoogstraten; *bottom* © Philippe Plaily/Photo Researchers, Inc.; **495** © Laura Dwight/Corbis; **497** © Marc Hill/Apex News and Pictures/Alamy Images; **499** Photograph by Sharon Hoogstraten; **500** © Peter McBride/Aurora; **501** Photograph by Sharon Hoogstraten; **502** © Richard H. Johnston/Getty Images; **505** © Kim Heacox/Getty Images; **506** © T. R. Thorp/Corbis; **506** © Niall McOnnegal/Alamy Images; **508** *top* © Ruddy Gold/Age Fotostock America,

Inc.; *bottom* Photograph by Sharon Hoogstraten; **509** *left top center* Photograph by Sharon Hoogstraten; **509** Photograph by Sharon Hoogstraten; **510** © Cameron/Corbis; **511** Photograph by Sharon Hoogstraten; **513** *top right* © Andrew Syred/Photo Researchers, Inc.; *center left* NASA/Lunar and Planetary Institute; *bottom right* NASA; **514** © Bettmann/Corbis; **515** *left* Use of Canon Powershot S45 courtesy of Canon USA; **516** *top* © Tom Stewart/Corbis; *bottom* © Photodisc/Getty Images; **517** *top left* © Photodisc/Getty Images; **517** *right* © PhotoFlex.com; **517** *bottom left* © Michael Goldman/Photis/PictureQuest; **518** *center* ©1994 CMCD; **522** © Argentum/Photo Researchers, Inc.; **523** *left* © Roger Ressmeyer/Corbis; **523** *right* © Roger Ressmeyer/Corbis; **524** © Marc Hill/Apex News and Pictures/Alamy Images.

Illustrations and Maps

Accurate Art, Inc. **181**
Ampersand Design Group **517**
Argosy **426**
Richard Bonson/Wildlife Art Ltd. **180**
Eric Chadwick **486, 489**
Steve Cowden **442, 466**
Patrick Gnan/Deborah Wolf, Ltd. **57, 235**
Garry Hincks **153, 166**
Keith Kasnot **49, 51, 52**
George Kelvin **15, 17, 19**
Miriam Kirkman-Oh/KO Studios **127, 132, 279, 302**
Debbie Maisels **3, 22, 30, 34, 58, 60, 61, 126, 273, 289, 292, 293, 302, 304, 326, 328, 352, 358, 360, 484, R79, R88**
Mapquest.com, Inc. **162, 163, 166, 192–193**
Janos Marffy **157**
Linda Nye **333, 335, 336, 337, 339, 396, 398, 410, 412, R92**
Steve Oh/KO Studios **83, 96, 118, 120, 121, 126, 127, 128, 130, 134, R87, R90**
Laurie O'Keefe **214, 218**
Mick Posen/Wildlife Art Ltd. **78, 105, 111, 113, 134, 197, 230, 260**
Peter Scott/Wildlife Art Ltd. **194**
Dan Stuckenschneider **368, 374, 375, 459, 467, 473, 474, 481, 513, 515**
Bart Vallecoccia **299, 333, 351, 388, 395, 404, 406, 433, 436, 446, 515, 518, 524, R81, R82, R85**
Rob Wood/Wood Ronsaville Harlin **180**